Stanley Gibb

CATALOGU

of

King George VI

POSTAGE STAMPS

2001 Edition

Stanley Gibbons
London and Ringwood

By Appointment to Her Majesty The Queen
Stanley Gibbons Ltd, London
Philatelists

Published by **Stanley Gibbons Ltd**
Editorial, Publications Sales Offices and Distribution Centre:
5 Parkside, Christchurch Road, Ringwood,
Hants BH24 3SH.

2001 (7th edition) (extracted from 2001 edition
Part 1 (*British Commonwealth*) *Stamp Catalogue*
in two volumes)

ISBN:0-85259-503-4

Item No. 2884(01)

Text assembled by Black Bear Press Limited, Cambridge
Made and Printed in Great Britain by The Alden Press, Oxford

By Popular Demand

The revival of the *King George VI Catalogue* in 1997 proved to be very popular with collectors and it is now likely to be a regular feature of the Stanley Gibbons Publications programme.

This edition has been extracted from the two volumes of the *Part 1 (British Commonwealth) Catalogue*, 2001 edition, and reformatted into a handy, smaller page size. Countries appear under the names in use during the King George VI period rather than those current today.

There was much correspondence following the last edition concerning the stamps selected for the catalogue, in particular those non-portrait stamps issued before 1936 which continued in use for a considerable period during the new reign. These suggestions have been carefully studied and a number of additional issues have been incorporated into the listing. Printings of King George VI stamps which appear after 1952 are, of course, also included.

Readers are reminded that Stanley Gibbons Publications also publish a printed King George VI album in either fast-bound or loose-leaf styles. There are also two companion catalogues, the *Empire* series, which provide a further extraction from the *Part 1* covering issues between 1840 and 1936.

For those seeking an era in which to specialise somewhere between the Victorian classics and today's new issues, the stamps of King George VI form a fascinating study, spanning years during which there were both important political and philatelic developments. Stamps from this reign are already in considerable demand, and I hope that this new edition will encourage their collection still further.

David J. Aggersberg

Stanley Gibbons Holdings Plc

STANLEY GIBBONS LIMITED, STANLEY GIBBONS AUCTIONS
399 Strand, London WC2R 0LX
Auction Room and Specialist Stamp Departments. Open Monday–Friday, 9.30 a.m. to 5 p.m.
Shop. Open Monday–Friday 8.30 a.m. to 6 p.m. and Saturday 9.30 a.m. to 5.30 p.m.
Telephone 020 7836 8444,
Fax 020 7836 7342, E-mail: enquiries@stanleygibbons.co.uk,
Internet: www.stanleygibbons.com for all departments

STANLEY GIBBONS PUBLICATIONS
5 Parkside, Christchurch Road, Ringwood, Hants BH24 3SH
Telephone +44 (0) 1425 472363 (24 hour answerphone service), Fax +44 (0) 1425 470247,
E-mail info@stanleygibbons.co.uk
Publications Showroom (at above address). Open Monday–Friday 9 a.m. to 3 p.m.
Publications Mail Order. FREEPHONE 0800 611622. Monday-Friday 8.30 a.m to 5 p.m,

Stanley Gibbons Publications has overseas licensees and distributors for Australia, Austria, Belgium, Canada, Denmark, Finland, France, Germany, Hong Kong, Israel, Italy, Japan, Luxembourg, Netherlands, New Zealand, Norway, Singapore, South Africa, Sweden, Switzerland, West Indies and Caribbean. Please contact the Ringwood address for details.

FRASER'S
(a division of Stanley Gibbons Ltd)
399 Strand, London WC2R 0LX
Autographs, photographs, letters and documents
Telephone 020 7836 8444, Fax 020 7836 7342, E-mail: info@frasersautographs.co.uk,
Internet: www.frasersautographs.com
Monday–Friday 9 a.m. to 5.30 p.m. and Saturday 10 a.m. to 4 p.m.

Specialist Philatelic Society

King George VI Collectors Society. Secretary: Mr F. R. Lockyer, OBE, 98 Albany, Manor Road, Bournemouth, Dorset BH1 3EW

Contents

General Philatelic Information

and Guidelines to the Scope of the Part 1
(British Commonwealth) Catalogue
from which this listing is taken

The notes which follow seek to reflect current practice in compiling the Part 1 (British Commonwealth) Catalogue.

It scarcely needs emphasising that the *Stanley Gibbons Stamp Catalogue* has a very long history and that the vast quantity of information it contains has been carefully built up by successive generations through the work of countless individuals. Philately itself is never static and the Catalogue has evolved and developed during this long time-span. Thus, while these notes are important for today's criteria, they may be less precise the further back in the listings one travels. They are not intended to inaugurate some unwanted series of piecemeal alterations in a widely respected work, but it does seem to us useful that Catalogue users know as exactly as possible the policies currently in operation.

PRICES

The prices quoted in this Catalogue are the estimated selling prices of Stanley Gibbons Ltd at the time of publication. They are, *unless it is specifically stated otherwise*, for examples in fine condition for the issue concerned. Superb examples are worth more; those of a lower quality considerably less.

All prices are subject to change without prior notice and Stanley Gibbons Ltd may from time to time offer stamps below catalogue price. Individual low value stamps sold at 399, Strand are liable to an additional handling charge. Purchasers of new issues are asked to note that the prices charged for them contain an element for the service rendered and so may exceed the prices shown when the stamps are subsequently catalogued. Postage and handling charges are extra.

No guarantee is given to supply all stamps priced, since it is not possible to keep every catalogued item in stock. Commemorative issues may, at times, only be available in complete sets and not as individual values.

Quotation of prices. The prices in the left-hand column are for unused stamps and those in the right-hand column are for used.

A dagger (†) denotes that the item listed does not exist in that condition and a blank, or dash, that it exists, or may exist, but no market price is known.

Prices are expressed in pounds and pence sterling. One pound comprises 100 pence (£1 = 100p).

The method of notation is as follows: pence in numerals (e.g. 10 denotes ten pence); pound and pence, up to £100, in numerals (e.g. 4·25 denotes four pounds and twenty-five pence); prices above £100 expressed in whole pounds with the "£" sign shown.

Unused stamps. Prices for unused stamps are for examples in unmounted mint condition.

Some stamps from the King George VI period are often difficult to find in unmounted mint condition. In such instances we would expect that collectors would need to pay a high proportion of the price quoted to obtain mounted mint examples. Generally speaking lightly mounted mint stamps from this reign, issued before 1945, are in considerable demand.

Used stamps. The used prices are normally for stamps postally used but may be for stamps cancelled-to-order where this practice exists.

A pen-cancellation on early issues can sometimes correctly denote postal use. Instances are individually noted in the Catalogue in explanation of the used price given.

Prices quoted for bisects on cover or on large piece are for those dated during the period officially authorised.

Stamps not sold unused to the public (e.g. some official stamps) are priced used only.

The use of "unified" designs, that is stamps inscribed for both postal and fiscal purposes, results in a number of stamps of very high face value. In some instances these may not have been primarily intended for postal purposes, but if they are so inscribed we include them. We only price such items used, however, where there is evidence of normal postal usage.

Minimum price. The minimum catalogue price quoted is 10p. For individual stamps prices between 10p. and 50p. are provided as a guide for catalogue users. The lowest price *charged* for individual stamps purchased from Stanley Gibbons Ltd is 50p.

Set prices. Set prices are generally for one of each value, excluding shades and varieties, but including major colour changes. Where there are alternative shades, etc., the cheapest is usually included. The number of stamps in the set is always stated for clarity. The mint prices for sets containing *se-tenant* pieces are based on the prices quoted for such combinations, and not on those for the individual stamps.

Varieties. Where plate or cylinder varieties are priced in a used condition the price quoted is for a fine used example with the cancellation well clear of the listed flaw.

Specimen stamps. The pricing of these items is explained under that heading.

Stamp booklets. Prices are for complete assembled booklets in fine condition with those issued before 1945 showing normal wear and tear. Incomplete booklets and those which have been "exploded" will, in general, be worth less than the figure quoted.

Repricing. Collectors will be aware that the market factors of supply and demand directly influence the prices quoted in this Catalogue. Whatever the scarcity of a particular stamp, if there is no one in the market who wishes to buy it it cannot be expected to achieve a high price. Conversely, the same item actively sought by numerous potential buyers may cause the price to rise.

All the prices in this Catalogue are examined during the preparation of each new edition by expert staff of Stanley Gibbons and repriced as necessary. They take many factors into account, including supply and demand, and are in close touch with the international stamp market and the auction world.

GUARANTEE

All stamps are guaranteed genuine originals in the following terms:

If not as described, and returned by the purchaser, we undertake to refund the price paid to us in the original transaction. If any stamp is certified as genuine by the Expert Committee of the Royal Philatelic Society, London, or by B.P.A. Expertising Ltd, the purchaser shall not be entitled to make any claim against us for any error, omission or mistake in such certificate.

Consumers' statutory rights are not affected by the above guarantee.

The recognised Expert Committees in this country are those of the Royal Philatelic Society, 41 Devonshire Place, London W1N 1PE, and B.P.A. Expertising Ltd, P.O. Box 137, Leatherhead, Surrey KT22 0RG. They do not undertake valuations under any circumstances and fees are payable for their services.

THE CATALOGUE IN GENERAL

Contents. The Catalogue is confined to adhesive postage stamps, including miniature sheets. For particular categories the rules are:

(*a*) Revenue (fiscal) stamps or telegraph stamps

are listed only where they have been expressly authorised for postal duty.

(*b*) Stamps issued only precancelled are included, but normally issued stamps available additionally with precancel have no separate precancel listing unless the face value is changed.

(*c*) Stamps prepared for use but not issued, hitherto accorded full listing, are nowadays footnoted with a price (where possible).

(*d*) Bisects (trisects, etc.) are only listed where such usage was officially authorised.

(*e*) Stamps issued only on first day covers or in presentation packs and not available separately are not listed but may be priced in a footnote.

(*f*) New printings are only included in this Catalogue where they show a major philatelic variety, such as a change in shade, watermark or paper. Stamps which exist with or without imprint dates are listed separately; changes in imprint dates are mentioned in footnotes.

(*g*) Official and unofficial reprints are dealt with by footnote.

(*h*) Stamps from imperforate printings of modern issues which also occur perforated are covered by footnotes, but are listed where widely available for postal use.

Exclusions. The following are excluded: (*a*) non-postal revenue or fiscal stamps; (*b*) postage stamps used fiscally; (*c*) local carriage labels and private local issues; (*d*) telegraph stamps; (*e*) bogus or phantom stamps; (*f*) railway or airline letter fee stamps, bus or road transport company labels; (*g*) cut-outs; (*h*) all types of non-postal labels and souvenirs; (*i*) documentary labels for the postal service, e.g. registration, recorded delivery, airmail etiquettes, etc.; (*j*) privately applied embellishments to official issues and privately commissioned items generally; (*k*) stamps for training postal officers.

Full listing. "Full listing" confers our recognition and implies allotting a catalogue number and (wherever possible) a price quotation.

In judging status for inclusion in the catalogue broad considerations are applied to stamps. They must be issued by a legitimate postal authority, recognised by the government concerned, and must be adhesives valid for proper postal use in the class of service for which they are inscribed. Stamps, with the exception of such categories as postage dues and officials, must be available to the general public, at face value, in reasonable quantities without any artificial restrictions being imposed on their distribution.

For errors and varieties the criterion is legitimate (albeit inadvertent) sale through a postal administration in the normal course of business. Details of provenance are always important; printers' waste and deliberately manufactured material are excluded.

Certificates. In assessing unlisted items due weight is given to Certificates from recognised Expert Committees and, where appropriate, we will usually ask to see them.

Date of issue. Where local issue dates differ from dates of release by agencies, "date of issue" is the local date. Fortuitous stray usage before the offically intended date is disregarded in listing.

Catalogue numbers. Stamps of each country are catalogued chronologically by date of issue. Subsidiary classes are placed at the end of the country, as separate lists, with a distinguishing letter prefix to the catalogue number, e.g. D for postage due, O for official and E for express delivery stamps.

The catalogue number appears in the extreme left column. The boldface Type numbers in the next column are merely cross-references to illustrations. Catalogue numbers in the *Gibbons Stamp Monthly* Supplement are provisional only and may need to be altered when the lists are consolidated. For the numbering of miniature sheets and sheetlets *see* section below.

Once published in the Catalogue, numbers are changed as little as possible; really serious renumbering is reserved for the occasions when a complete country or an entire issue is being rewritten. The edition first affected includes cross-reference tables of old and new numbers.

Our catalogue numbers are universally recognised in specifying stamps and as a hallmark of status.

Illustrations. Stamps are illustrated at three-quarters linear size. Stamps not illustrated are the same size and format as the value shown, unless otherwise indicated. Stamps issued only as miniature sheets have the stamp alone illustrated but sheet size is also quoted. Overprints, surcharges, watermarks and postmarks are normally actual size. Illustrations of varieties are often enlarged to show the detail. Stamp booklet covers are illustrated half-size, unless otherwise indicated.

Designers. Designers' names are quoted where known, though space precludes naming every individual concerned in the production of a set. In particular, photographers supplying material are usually named only where they also make an active contribution in the design stage; posed photographs of reigning monarchs are, however, an exception to this rule.

CONTACTING THE CATALOGUE EDITOR

The editor is always interested in hearing from people who have new information which will improve or correct the Catalogue. As a general rule he must see and examine the actual stamps before they can be considered for listing; photographs or photocopies are insufficient evidence.

Submissions should be made in writing to the Catalogue Editor, Stanley Gibbons Publications at the Ringwood office. The cost of return postage for items submitted is appreciated, and this should include the registration fee if required.

Where information is solicited purely for the benefit of the enquirer, the editor cannot undertake to reply if the answer is already contained in these published notes or if return postage is omitted. Written communications are greatly preferred to enquiries by telephone and the editor regrets that he or his staff cannot see personal callers without a prior appointment being made. Correspondence may be subject to delay during the production period of each new edition.

The editor welcomes close contact with study circles and is interested, too, in finding reliable local correspondents who will verify and supplement official information in countries where this is deficient.

> We regret we do not give opinions as to the genuineness of stamps, nor do we identify stamps or number them by our Catalogue.

TECHNICAL MATTERS

The meanings of the technical terms used in the catalogue will be found in our *Philatelic Terms Illustrated (new edition in preparation)*.

References below to "more specialised" listings are to be taken to indicate, as appropriate, the Stanley Gibbons *Great Britain Specialised Catalogue* in 5 volumes or the *Great Britain Concise Catalogue*.

1. Printing

Printing errors. Errors in printing are of major interest to the Catalogue. Authenticated items meriting consideration would include: background, centre or frame inverted or omitted; centre or subject transposed; error of colour; error or omission of value; double prints and impressions; printed both sides; and so on. Designs *tête-bêche*, whether intentionally or by accident, are listable. *Se-tenant* arrangements of stamps are recognised in the listings or footnotes. Gutter pairs (a pair of stamps separated by blank margin) are not included in this volume. Colours only partially omitted are not listed. Stamps with embossing omitted and (for Commonwealth countries) stamps printed on the gummed side are reserved for our more specialised listings.

Printing varieties. Listing is accorded to major changes in the printing base which lead to completely new types. In recess-printing this could be a design re-engraved; in photogravure or photolithography a screen altered in whole or in part. It can also encompass flat-bed and rotary printing if the results are readily distinguishable.

To be considered at all, varieties must be constant.

Early stamps, produced by primitive methods, were prone to numerous imperfections: the lists reflect this, recognising re-entries, retouches, broken frames, misshapen letters, and so on. Printing technology has, however, radically improved over the years, during which time photogravure and lithography have become predominant. Varieties nowadays are more in the nature of flaws and these, being too specialised for this general catalogue, are almost always outside the scope. The development of our range of specialised catalogues allows us now to list those items which have philatelic significance in their appropriate volume.

In no catalogue, however, do we list such items as: dry prints, kiss prints, doctor-blade flaws, colour shifts or registration flaws (unless they lead to the complete omission of a colour from an individual stamp), lithographic ring flaws, and so on. Neither do we recognise fortuitous happenings like paper creases or confetti flaws.

Overprints (and surcharges). Overprints of different types qualify for separate listing. These include overprints in different colours; overprints from different printing processes such as litho and typo; overprints in totally different typefaces, etc. Major errors in machine-printed overprints are important and listable. They include: overprint inverted or omitted; overprint double (treble, etc.); overprint diagonal; overprint double, one inverted; pairs with one overprint omitted, e.g. from a radical shift to an adjoining stamp; error of colour; error of type fount; letters inverted or omitted, etc. If the overprint is handstamped, few of these would qualify and a distinction is drawn. We continue, however, to list pairs of stamps where one has a handstamped overprint and the other has not.

Varieties occurring in overprints will often take the form of broken letters, slight differences in spacing, rising spaces, etc. Only the most important would be considered for footnote mention.

Sheet positions. If space permits we quote sheet positions of listed varieties and authenticated data is solicited for this purpose.

2. Paper

All stamps listed are deemed to be on "ordinary" paper of the wove type and white in colour; only departures from this are normally mentioned.

Types. Where classification so requires we distinguish such other types of paper as, for example, vertically and horizontally laid; wove and laid bâtonné; card(board); carton; cartridge;

glazed; granite; native; pelure; porous; quadrillé; ribbed; rice; and silk thread.

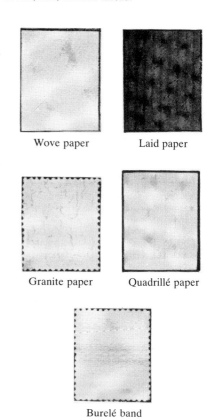

Wove paper   Laid paper

Granite paper   Quadrillé paper

Burelé band

The various makeshifts for normal paper are listed as appropriate. The varieties of double paper and joined paper are recognised. The security device of a printed burelé band on the back of a stamp, as in early Queensland, qualifies for listing.

Descriptive terms. The fact that a paper is handmade (and thus probably of uneven thickness) is mentioned where necessary. Such descriptive terms as "hard" and "soft"; "smooth" and 'rough"; "thick", "medium" and "thin" are applied where there is philatelic merit in classifying papers. We do not, for example, even in more specialised listings, classify paper thicknesses in the Wilding and Machin definitives of Great Britain. Weight standards for the paper apply to complete reels only, so that differences on individual stamps are acceptable to the printer provided the reel conforms overall.

Coloured, very white and toned papers. A coloured paper is one that is coloured right through (front and back of the stamp). In the Catalogue the colour of the paper is given in *italics*, thus:

black/*rose* = black design on rose paper.

Papers have been made specially white in recent years by, for example, a very heavy coating of chalk. We do not classify shades of whiteness of paper as distinct varieties. There does exist, however, a type of paper from early days called toned. This is off-white, often brownish or buffish, but it cannot be assigned any definite colour. A toning effect brought on by climate, incorrect storage or gum staining is disregarded here, as this was not the state of the paper when issued.

"Ordinary" and "Chalk-surfaced" papers. The availability of many postage stamps for revenue purposes made necessary some safeguard against the illegitimate re-use of stamps with removable cancellations. This was at first secured by using fugitive inks and later by printing on chalk-surfaced paper, both of which made it difficult to remove any form of obliteration without also damaging the stamp design.

This catalogue lists these chalk-surfaced paper varieties from their introduction in 1905. Where no indication is given, the paper is "ordinary".

Our chalk-surfaced paper is specifically one which shows a black mark when touched with a silver wire. The paper used during the Second World War for high values, as in Bermuda, the Leeward Islands, etc., was thinly coated with some kind of surfacing which does not react to silver and is therefore regarded (and listed) as "ordinary". Stamps on chalk-surfaced paper can easily lose this coating through immersion in water.

Another paper introduced during the War as a substitute for chalk-surfaced is rather thick, very white and glossy and shows little or no watermark, nor does it show a black line when touched with silver. In the Bahamas high values this paper might be mistaken for the chalk-surfaced (which is thinner and poorer-looking) but for the silver test.

Some modern coated papers show little or no reaction to the silver test and, therefore, cannot be classed as chalk-surfaced.

Green and yellow papers. Issues of the First World War and immediate postwar period occur on green and yellow papers and these are given separate Catalogue listing. The original coloured papers (coloured throughout) gave way to surface-coloured papers, the stamps having "white backs"; other stamps show one colour on the front and a different one at the back. Because of the numerous variations a grouping of colours is adopted as follows:

YELLOW PAPERS

(1) The original *yellow* paper (throughout), usually bright in colour. The gum is often sparse, of harsh consistency and dull-looking.

(2) The *white backs.*

(3) A bright *lemon* paper. The colour must have a pronounced greenish tinge, different from the "yellow" in (1). As a rule, the gum on stamps using this lemon paper is plentiful, smooth and shiny, and the watermark shows distinctly. Care is needed with stamps printed in green on yellow paper (1) as it may appear that the paper is this lemon.

(4) An *orange-buff* paper. The colour must have a distinct brownish tinge. It is not to be confused with a muddy yellow (1) nor the misleading appearance (on the surface) of stamps printed in red on yellow paper where an engraved plate has been insufficiently wiped.

(5) A *pale yellow* paper that has a creamy tone to the yellow.

GREEN PAPERS

(6) The original "green" paper, varying considerably through shades of *blue-green* and *yellow-green*, the front and back sometimes differing.

(7) The *white backs.*

(8) A paper blue-green on the surface with *pale olive* back. The back must be markedly paler than the front and this and the pronounced olive tinge to the back distinguish it from (6).

(9) Paper with a vivid green surface, commonly called *emerald-green*; it has the olive back of (8).

(10) Paper with *emerald-green* both back and front.

3. Perforation and Rouletting

Perforation gauge. The gauge of a perforation is the number of holes in a length of 2 cm. For correct classification the size of the holes (large or small) may need to be distinguished; in a few cases the actual number of holes on each edge of the stamp needs to be quoted.

Measurement. The Gibbons *Instanta* gauge is the standard for measuring perforations. The stamp is viewed against a dark background with the transparent gauge put on top of it. Though the gauge measures to decimal accuracy, perforations read from it are generally quoted in the Catalogue to the nearest half. For example:

Just over perf $12\frac{3}{4}$ to just under $13\frac{1}{4}$ = perf 13
Perf $13\frac{1}{4}$ exactly, rounded up   = perf $13\frac{1}{2}$
Just over perf $13\frac{1}{4}$ to just under $13\frac{3}{4}$ = perf $13\frac{1}{2}$
Perf $13\frac{3}{4}$ exactly, rounded up   = perf 14

However, where classification depends on it, actual quarter-perforations are quoted.

Notation. Where no perforation is quoted for an issue it is imperforate. Perforations are usually abbreviated (and spoken) as follows, though sometimes they may be spelled out for clarity. This notation for rectangular stamps (the majority) applies to diamond shapes if "top" is read as the edge to the top right.

P 14: perforated alike on all sides (read: "perf 14").

P 14 × 15: the first figure refers to top and bottom, the second to left and right sides (read: "perf 14 by 15"). This is a compound perforation. For an upright triangular stamp the first figure refers to the two sloping sides and second to the base. In inverted triangulars the base is first and the second figure refers to the sloping sides.

P 14–15: perforation measuring anything between 14 and 15: the holes are irregularly spaced, thus the gauge may vary along a single line or even along a single edge of the stamp (read: "perf 14 to 15").

P 14 *irregular*: perforated 14 from a worn perforator, giving badly aligned holes irregularly spaced (read: "irregular perf 14").

P comp(*ound*) 14 × 15: two gauges in use but not necessarily on opposite sides of the stamp. It could be one side in one gauge and three in the other; or two adjacent sides with the same gauge. (Read: "perf compound of 14 and 15".) For three gauges or more, abbreviated as "*P* 14, 14½, 15 *or compound*" for example.

P 14, 14½: perforated approximately 14¼ (read: "perf 14 or 14½"). It does *not* mean two stamps, one perf 14 and the other perf 14½. This obsolescent notation is gradually being replaced in the Catalogue.

Imperf: imperforate (not perforated).

Imperf × *P* 14: imperforate at top and bottom and perf 14 at sides.

Perf × imperf

P 14 × *imperf*: perf 14 at top and bottom and imperforate at sides.

Such headings as "*P* 13 × 14 (*vert*) and *P* 14 × 13 (*horiz*)" indicate which perforations apply to which stamp format—vertical or horizontal.

Some stamps are additionally perforated so that a label or tab is detachable; others have been perforated suitably for use as two halves. Listings are normally for whole stamps, unless stated otherwise.

Other terms. Perforation almost always gives circular holes; where other shapes have been used they are specified, e.g. square holes; lozenge perf. Interrupted perfs are brought about by the omission of pins at regular intervals. Perforations merely simulated by being printed as part of the design are of course ignored. With few exceptions, privately applied perforations are not listed.

In the nineteenth century perforations are often described as clean cut (clean, sharply incised holes), intermediate or rough (rough holes, imperfectly cut, often the result of blunt pins).

Perforation errors and varieties. Authenticated errors, where a stamp normally perforated is accidentally issued imperforate, are listed provided no traces of perforation (blind holes or indentations) remain. They must be provided as pairs, both stamps wholly imperforate, and are only priced in that form.

Stamps imperforate between stamp and sheet margin are not listed in this catalogue, but such errors on Great Britain stamps will be found in the *Great Britain Specialised Catalogue*.

Pairs described as "imperforate between" have the line of perforations between the two stamps omitted.

Imperf between (*horiz pair*): a horizontal pair of stamps with perfs all around the edges but none between the stamps.

Imperf between (*vert pair*): a vertical pair of stamps with perfs all around the edges but none between the stamps

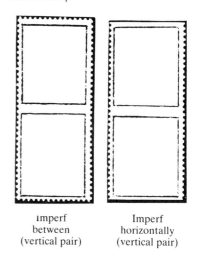

| ımperf between (vertical pair) | Imperf horizontally (vertical pair) |

Where several of the rows have escaped perforation the resulting varieties are listable. Thus:

Imperf vert (*horiz pair*): a horizontal pair of stamps perforated top and bottom; all three vertical directions are imperf—the two outer edges and between the stamps.

Imperf horiz (*vert pair*): a vertical pair perforated at left and right edges; all three horizontal directions are imperf—the top, bottom and between the stamps.

Straight edges. Large sheets cut up before issue to post offices can cause stamps with straight edges, i.e. imperf on one side or on two sides at right angles. They are not usually listable in this condition and are worth less than corresponding stamps properly perforated all round. This does not, however, apply to certain stamps, mainly from coils and booklets, where straight edges on various sides are the manufacturing norm affecting every stamp. The listings and notes make clear which sides are correctly imperf.

Malfunction. Varieties of double, misplaced or partial perforation caused by error or machine malfunction are not listable, neither are freaks, such as perforations placed diagonally from paper folds, nor missing holes caused by broken pins.

Centering. Well-centred stamps have designs surrounded by equal opposite margins. Where this condition affects the price the fact is stated.

Types of perforating. Where necessary for classification, perforation types are distinguished. These include:

Line perforation from one line of pins punching single rows of holes at a time.

Comb perforation from pins disposed across the sheet in comb formation, punching out holes at three sides of the stamp a row at a time.

Harrow perforation applied to a whole pane or sheet at one stroke.

Rotary perforation from toothed wheels operating across a sheet, then crosswise.

Sewing-machine perforation. The resultant condition, clean-cut or rough, is distinguished where required.

Pin-perforation is the commonly applied term for pin-roulette in which, instead of being punched out, round holes are pricked by sharp-pointed pins and no paper is removed.

Mixed perforation occurs when stamps with defective perforations are re-perforated in a different gauge.

Punctured stamps. Perforation holes can be punched into the face of the stamp. Patterns of small holes, often in the shape of initial letters, are privately applied devices against pilferage. These "perfins" are outside the scope except for Australia, Canada, Cape of Good Hope, Papua and Sudan where they were used as official stamps by the national administration. Identification devices, when officially inspired, are listed or noted; they can be shapes, of letters or words formed from holes, sometimes converting one class of stamp into another.

Rouletting. In rouletting the paper is cut, for ease of separation, but none is removed. The gauge is measured, when needed, as for perforations. Traditional French terms descriptive of the type of cut are often used and types include:

Arc roulette (percé en arc). Cuts are minute, spaced arcs, each roughly a semicircle.

Cross roulette (percé en croix). Cuts are tiny diagonal crosses.

Line roulette (percé en ligne or *en ligne droite).* Short straight cuts parallel to the frame of the stamp. The commonest basic roulette. Where not further described, "roulette" means this type.

Rouletted in colour or *coloured roulette (percé en lignes colorées* or *en lignes de couleur).* Cuts with coloured edges, arising from notched rule inked simultaneously with the printing plate.

Saw-tooth roulette (percé en scie). Cuts applied zigzag fashion to resemble the teeth of a saw.

Serpentine roulette (percé en serpentin). Cuts as sharply wavy lines.

Zigzag roulette (percé en zigzags). Short straight cuts at angles in alternate directions, producing sharp points on separation. U.S. usage favours "serrate(d) roulette" for this type.

Pin-roulette (originally *percé en points* and now *perforés trous d'epingle*) is commonly called pin-perforation in English.

4. Gum

All stamps listed are assumed to have gum of some kind; if they were issued without gum this is stated. Original gum (o.g.) means that which was present on the stamp as issued to the public. Deleterious climates and the presence of certain chemicals can cause gum to crack and, with early stamps, even make the paper deteriorate. Unscrupulous fakers are adept in removing it and regumming the stamp to meet the unreasoning demand often made for "full o.g." in cases where such a thing is virtually impossible.

5. Watermarks

Stamps are on unwatermarked paper except where the heading to the set says otherwise.

Detection. Watermarks are detected for Catalogue description by one of four methods: (1) holding stamps to the light; (2) laying stamps face down on a dark background; (3) adding a few drops of petroleum ether 40/60 to the stamp laid face down in a watermark tray; (4) by use of the Morley-Bright Detector, or other equipment, which work by revealing the thinning of the paper at the watermark (Note that petroleum ether is highly inflammable in use and can damage photogravure stamps.)

Listable types. Stamps occurring on both watermarked and unwatermarked papers are different types and both receive full listing.

Single watermarks (devices occurring once on every stamp) can be modified in size and shape as between different issues; the types are noted but not usually separately listed. Fortuitous absence of watermark from a single stamp or its gross displacement would not be listable.

To overcome registration difficulties the device may be repeated at close intervals (a *multiple watermark*), single stamps thus showing parts of several devices. Similarly, a large *sheet watermark* (or *all-over watermark*) covering numerous stamps can be used. We give informative notes and illustrations for them. The designs may be such that numbers of stamps in the sheet automatically lack watermark: this is not a listable variety. Multiple and all-over watermarks sometimes undergo modifications, but if the various types are difficult to distinguish from single stamps notes are given but not separate listings.

Papermakers' watermarks are noted where known but not listed separately, since most stamps in the sheet will lack them. Sheet watermarks which are nothing more than officially adopted papermakers' watermarks are, however, given normal listing.

Marginal watermarks, falling outside the pane of stamps, are ignored except where misplacement caused the adjoining row to be affected, in which case they are footnoted.

AS DESCRIBED (Read through front of stamp)		AS SEEN DURING WATERMARK DETECTION (Stamp face down and back examined)
GvR	Normal	ᖆvᗡ
ᖆ∧ᗡ	Inverted	ᗡ∧ᖆ
ᖆvᗡ	Reversed	GvR
ᗡ∧ᖆ	Reversed and inverted	ᖆ∧ᗡ
Gvᗡᖆvᗡ	Sideways	ᖆvᗡᗡvᖆ
ᗡvᖆᗡvᖆ	Sideways inverted	Gvᖆᖆvᗡ

Watermark errors and varieties. Watermark errors are recognised as of major importance. They comprise stamps intended to be on unwatermarked paper but issued watermarked by mistake, or stamps printed on paper with the wrong watermark. Varieties showing letters omitted from the watermark are also included, but broken or deformed bits on the dandy roll are not.

Watermark positions. The diagram shows how watermark position is described in the Catalogue. Paper has a side intended for printing and watermarks are usually impressed so that they read normally when looked through from that printed side. However, since philatelists customarily detect watermarks by looking at the back of the stamp the watermark diagram also makes clear what is actually seen.

Illustrations in the Catalogue are of watermarks in normal positions (from the front of the stamps) and are actual size where possible.

Differences in watermark position are collectable as distinct varieties. This Catalogue now lists inverted, sideways inverted and reversed watermark varieties on Commonwealth stamps issued after 1936 *except* where the watermark position is completely haphazard.

Great Britain inverted and sideways inverted watermarks can be found in the *Great Britain Specialised Catalogue* and the *Great Britain Concise Catalogue*.

Where a watermark comes indiscriminately in various positions our policy is to cover this by a general note: we do not give separate listings because the watermark position in these circumstances has no particular philatelic importance.

Standard types of watermark. Some watermarks have been used generally for various British possessions rather than exclusively for a single colony. To avoid repetition the Catalogue classifies 17 general types, as under, with references in the headings throughout the listings being given either in words or in the form "W w **14**" (meaning "watermark type w **14**"). In those cases where watermark illustrations appear in the listings, the respective reference reads, for example, W **153**, thus indicating that the watermark will be found in the normal sequence of illustrations as (type) **153**.

Multiple watermarks began in 1904 with w **8**, *Multiple Crown CA*, changed from 1921 to w **9**, *Multiple Crown Script CA*. On stamps of ordinary size portions of two or three watermarks appear and on the large-sized stamps a greater number can be observed. The change to letters in script character with w **9** was accompanied by a Crown of distinctly different shape.

It seems likely that there were at least two dandy rolls for each Crown Agents watermark in use at any one time with a reserve roll being employed when the normal one was withdrawn for maintenance or repair.

w 8	**w 9**
Multiple Crown CA	Multiple Crown Script CA

Both the Mult Crown CA and the Mult Script CA types exist with one or other of the letters omitted from individual impressions. It is possible that most of these occur from the reserve rolls as they have only been found on certain issues. The MCA watermark experienced such problems during the early 1920s and the Script over a longer period from the early 1940s until 1951.

During the 1920s damage must also have occurred on one of the Crowns as a substituted Crown has been found on certain issues. This is smaller than the normal and consists of an oval base joined to two upright ovals with a circle positioned between their upper ends. The upper line of the Crown's base is omitted, as are the left and right-hand circles at the top and also the cross over the centre circle.

Substituted Crown

The *Multiple Crown Script CA* watermark, w **9**, is known with two errors recurring among the 1950–52 printings of several territories. In the first a crown has fallen away from the dandy-roll that impresses the watermark into the paper pulp. It gives w **9a**, *Crown missing*, but this omission has been found in both "Crown only" (*illustrated*) and "Crown CA" rows. The resulting faulty paper was used for Seychelles, Johore and the postage due stamps of nine colonies.

When the omission was noticed a second mishap occurred, which was to insert a wrong crown in the space, giving w **9b**, *St. Edward's Crown*. This produced varieties in Bahamas, St. Kitts-Nevis and Singapore and the incorrect crown likewise occurs in "Crown only" and "Crown CA" rows.

w **9a**: Error, Crown missing

w **9b**: Error, St. Edward's Crown

6. Colours

Stamps in two or three colours have these named in order of appearance, from the centre moving outwards. Four colours or more are usually listed as multicoloured.

In compound colour names the second is the predominant one, thus:

orange-red = a red tending towards orange;

red-orange = an orange containing more red than usual.

Standard colours used. The 200 colours most used for stamp identification are given in the Stanley Gibbons Stamp Colour Key. The Catalogue has used the Stamp Colour Key as standard for describing new issues for some years. The names are also introduced as lists are rewritten, though exceptions are made for those early issues where traditional names have become universally established.

Determining colours. When comparing actual stamps with colour samples in the Stamp Colour Key, view in a good north daylight (or its best substitute: fluorescent "colour-matching" light). Sunshine is not recommended. Choose a solid portion of the stamp design; if available, marginal markings such as solid bars of colour or colour check dots are helpful. Shading lines in the design can be misleading as they appear lighter than solid colour. Postmarked portions of a stamp appear darker than normal. If more than one colour is present, mask off the extraneous ones as the eye tends to mix them.

Errors of colour. Major colour errors in stamps or overprints which qualify for listing are: wrong colours; one colour inverted in relation to the rest; albinos (colourless impressions), where these have Expert Committee certificates; colours completely omitted, but only on unused stamps (if found on used stamps the information is footnoted) and with good credentials, missing colours being frequently faked.

Colours only partially omitted are not recognised. Colour shifts, however spectacular, are not listed.

Shades. Shades in philately refer to variations in the intensity of a colour or the presence of differing amounts of other colours. They are particularly significant when they can be linked to specific printings. In general, shades need to be quite marked to fall within the scope of this Catalogue; it does not favour nowadays listing the often numerous shades of a stamp, but chooses a single applicable colour name which will indicate particular groups of outstanding shades. Furthermore, the listings refer to colours as issued: they may deteriorate into something different through the passage of time.

Modern colour printing by lithography is prone to marked differences of shade, even within a single run, and variations can occur within the same sheet. Such shades are not listed.

Aniline colours. An aniline colour meant originally one derived from coal-tar; it now refers more widely to colour of a particular brightness suffused on the surface of a stamp and showing through clearly on the back.

Colours of overprints and surcharges. All overprints and surcharges are in black unless stated otherwise in the heading or after the description of the stamp.

7. Specimen Stamps

Originally, stamps overprinted SPECIMEN were circulated to postmasters or kept in official records, but after the establishment of the Universal Postal Union supplies were sent to Berne for distribution to the postal administrations of member countries.

During the period 1884 to 1928 most of the stamps of British Crown Colonies required for this purpose were overprinted SPECIMEN in various shapes and sizes by their printers from typeset formes. Some locally produced provisionals were handstamped locally, as were sets prepared for presentation. From 1928 stamps were punched with holes forming the word SPECIMEN, each firm of printers using a different machine or machines.

From 1948 the stamps supplied for U.P.U. distribution were no longer punctured.

Stamps of some other Commonwealth territories were overprinted or handstamped locally, while stamps of Great Britain and those overprinted for use in overseas postal agencies (mostly of the higher denominations) bore SPECIMEN overprints and handstamps applied by the Inland Revenue or the Post Office.

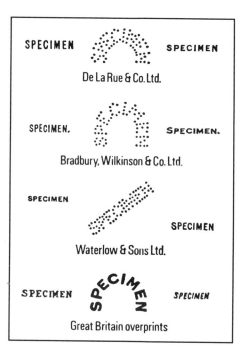

De La Rue & Co. Ltd.

Bradbury, Wilkinson & Co. Ltd.

Waterlow & Sons Ltd.

Great Britain overprints

Some of the commoner types of overprints or punctures are illustrated here. Collectors are warned that dangerous forgeries of the punctured type exist.

The *Part 1 (British Commonwealth) Catalogue* records those Specimen overprints or perforations intended for distribution by the U.P.U. to member countries. In addition the Specimen overprints of Australia and its dependent territories, which were sold to collectors by the Post Office, are also included.

All other Specimens are outside the scope of this volume.

Specimens are not quoted in Great Britain as they are fully listed in the Stanley Gibbons *Great Britain Specialised Catalogue*.

In specifying type of specimen for individual high-value stamps, "H/S" means handstamped, "Optd" is overprinted and "Perf" is punctured.

Some sets occur mixed, e.g. "Optd/Perf". If unspecified, the type is apparent from the date or it is the same as for the lower values quoted as a set.

Prices. Prices for stamps up to £1 are quoted in sets; higher values are priced singly after the colours, thus "(S. £20)". Where specimens exist in more than one type the price quoted is for the cheapest. Specimen stamps have rarely survived even as pairs; these and strips of three, four or five are worth considerably more than singles.

8. Coil Stamps

Stamps issued only in coil form are given full listing. If stamps are issued in both sheets and coils the coil stamps are listed separately only where there is some feature (e.g. perforation or watermark sideways) by which singles can be distinguished. Coil strips containing different stamps *se-tenant* are also listed.

Coil join pairs are too random and too easily faked to permit of listing; similarly ignored are coil stamps which have accidentally suffered an extra row of perforations from the claw mechanism in a malfunctioning vending machine.

9. Stamp Booklets

Stamp booklets (with the exception of those from Great Britain, for which see the current edition of the *Great Britain Concise Catalogue*) are now listed in this catalogue.

Single stamps from booklets are listed if they are distinguishable in some way (such as watermark or perforation) from similar sheet stamps.

Booklet panes are listed where they contain stamps of different denominations *se-tenant*, where stamp-size labels are included, or where such panes are otherwise identifiable. Booklet panes are placed in the listing under the lowest denomination present.

Particular perforations (straight edges) are covered by appropriate notes.

10. Forgeries and Fakes

Forgeries. Where space permits, notes are considered if they can give a concise description that will permit unequivocal detection of a forgery. Generalised warnings, lacking detail, are not nowadays inserted, since their value to the collector is problematic.

Fakes. Unwitting fakes are numerous, particularly "new shades" which are colour changelings brought about by exposure to sunlight, soaking in water contaminated with dyes from adherent paper, contact with oil and dirt from a pocketbook, and so on. Fraudulent operators, in addition, can offer to arrange: removal of hinge marks; repairs of thins on white or coloured papers; replacement of missing margins or perforations; reperforating in true or false gauges; removal of fiscal cancellations; rejoining of severed pairs, strips and blocks; and (a major hazard) regumming. Collectors can only be urged to purchase from reputable sources and to insist upon Expert Committee certification where there is any kind of doubt.

The Catalogue can consider footnotes about fakes where these are specific enough to assist in detection.

ABBREVIATIONS

Printers

A.B.N. Co	American Bank Note Co, New York.
A. & M. Ashton-	Alden & Mowbray Ltd, Oxford.
Potter	Ashton-Potter Ltd, Toronto.
Aspioti-Elka (Aspiotis)	Aspioti-Elka, Greece.
B.A.B.N.	British American Bank Note Co, Ottawa.
B.D.T.	B.D.T. International Security Printing Ltd, Dublin, Ireland.
B.W.	Bradbury Wilkinson & Co, Ltd.
Cartor	Cartor S.A., L'Aigle, France
C.B.N.	Canadian Bank Note Co, Ottawa.
Continental B.N. Co	Continental Bank Note Co.
Courvoisier	Imprimerie Courvoisier S.A., La-Chaux-de-Fonds, Switzerland.
D.L.R.	De La Rue & Co, Ltd, London, and (from 1961) Bogota, Colombia.
Edila	Editions de l'Aubetin, S.A.
Enschedé	Joh. Enschedé en Zonen, Haarlem, Netherlands.
Format	Format International Security Printers, Ltd, London.
Harrison	Harrison & Sons, Ltd, London
Heraclio Fournier	Heraclio Fournier S.A., Vitoria, Spain.
J.W.	John Waddington Security Print Ltd., Leeds
P.B.	Perkins Bacon Ltd, London.
Questa	Questa Colour Security Printers, Ltd., London
Ueberreuter	Ueberreuter (incorporating Bruder Rosenbaum), Korneuburg, Austria.
Walsall	Walsall Security Printers, Ltd.
Waterlow	Waterlow & Sons, Ltd, London.

General Abbreviations

Alph	Alphabet
Anniv	Anniversary
Comp	Compound (perforation)
Des	Designer; designed
Diag	Diagonal; diagonally
Eng	Engraver; engraved
F.C.	Fiscal Cancellation
H/S	Handstamped
Horiz	Horizontal; horizontally
Imp, Imperf	Imperforate
Inscr	Inscribed
L	Left
Litho	Lithographed
mm	Millimetres
MS	Miniature sheet
N.Y.	New York
Opt(d)	Overprint(ed)
P or P-c	Pen-cancelled
P, Pf or Perf	Perforated
Photo	Photogravure
Pl	Plate
Pr	Pair
Ptd	Printed
Ptg	Printing
R	Right
R.	Row
Recess	Recess-printed
Roto	Rotogravure
Roul	Rouletted
S	Specimen (overprint)
Surch	Surcharge(d)
T.C.	Telegraph Cancellation
T	Type
Typo	Typographed
Un	Unused
Us	Used
Vert	Vertical; vertically
W or wmk	Watermark
Wmk s	Watermark sideways

($\dagger$)=Does not exist.

($-$) (or blank price column)=Exists, or may exist, but no market price is known.

/ between colours means "on" and the colour following is that of the paper on which the stamp is printed.

Colour of Overprints and Surcharges

(B.) = blue, (Blk.) = black, (Br.) = brown, (C.) = carmine, (G.) = green, (Mag.) = magenta, (Mve.) = mauve, (Ol.) = olive, (O.) = orange, (P.) = purple, (Pk.) = pink, (R.)=red, (Sil.) = silver, (V.) = violet, (Vm.) or (Verm.) = vermilion, (W.) = white, (Y.) = yellow.

Arabic Numerals

As in the case of European figures, the details of the Arabic numerals vary in different stamp designs, but they should be readily recognised with the aid of this illustration.

·	١	٢	٣	٤	٥	٦	٧	٨	٩
0	1	2	3	4	5	6	7	8	9

Colours of Stamps

Bl (blue); blk (black); brn (brown); car, carm (carmine); choc (chocolate); clar (claret); emer (emerald); grn (green); ind (indigo); mag (magenta); mar (maroon); mult (multicoloured); mve (mauve); ol (olive); orge (orange); pk (pink); pur (purple); scar (scarlet); sep (sepia); turq (turquoise); ultram (ultramarine); verm (vermilion); vio (violet); yell (yellow).

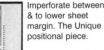

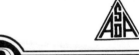

Great Britain

12 pence (d) = 1 shilling
20 shillings = 1 pound

PRINTERS. The following stamps were printed in photogravure by Harrison and Sons, *unless otherwise stated.*

126 King George VI and Queen Elizabeth

(Des E. Dulac)

1937 (13 May). *Coronation. W* **127.** *P* 15 × 14.

461	**126**	1½d. maroon	.. .. ..	50	40

127	**128**	

129	**130**

King George VI and National Emblems

(Des T **128/9**, E. Dulac (head) and E. Gill (frames). T **130,** E. Dulac
(whole stamp))

1937–47. *W* **127.** *P* 15 × 14.

462	**128**	½d. green (10.5.37)	10	25
		a. Wmk sideways (1.38) ..	50	50
		ab. Booklet pane of 4 (6.40) ..	35·00	
463		1d. scarlet (10.5.37) ..	10	25
		a. Wmk sideways (2.38) ..	16·00	9·00
		ab. Booklet pane of 4 (6.40) ..	80·00	
464		1½d. red-brown (30.7.37) ..	20	25
		a. Wmk sideways (2.38) ..	1·00	1·25
		b. Booklet pane. Four stamps plus two printed labels (8.37) ..	55·00	
		c. Imperf three sides (pair) ..		
465		2d. orange (31.1.38) ..	75	50
		a. Wmk sideways (2.38) ..	70·00	35·00
		b. Bisected (on cover) ..	†	28·00
466		2½d. ultramarine (10.5.37) ..	25	15
		a. Wmk sideways (6.40) ..	60·00	28·00
		b. *Tête-bêche* (horiz pair) ..		
467		3d. violet (31.1.38) ..	3·25	1·00
468	**129**	4d. grey-green (21.11.38) ..	60	60
		a. Imperf (pair) ..	£2000	
		b. Imperf three sides (horiz pair) ..	£2500	
469		5d. brown (21.11.38) ..	2·50	75
		a. Imperf (pair) ..	£2500	
		b. Imperf three sides (horiz pair) ..	£2000	
470		6d. purple (30.1.39)	1·25	60

471	**130**	7d. emerald-green (27.2.39) ..	3·25	60
		a. Imperf three sides (horiz pair) ..	£2000	
472		8d. bright carmine (27.2.39) ..	3·50	70
473		9d. deep olive-green (1.5.39) ..	5·50	80
474		10d. turquoise-blue (1.5.39)	5·00	80
		aa. Imperf (pair)	£3500	
474a		11d. plum (29.12.47) ..	2·00	2·00
475		1s. bistre-brown (1.5.39) ..	5·75	75
462/75	.. .. ..	*Set of* 15	30·00	8·75

For later printings of the lower values in apparently lighter shades and different colours, see Nos. 485/90 and 503/8.

No. 465b was authorised for use in Guernsey. See notes on War Occupation Issues.

Nos. 468b and 469b are perforated at foot only and each occurs in the same sheet as Nos. 468a and 469a.

No. 471a is also perforated at foot only, but occurs on the top row of a sheet.

131 King George VI	**132** King George VI

133

(Des E. Dulac (T **131**) and Hon. G. R. Bellew (T **132**). Eng J. A. C. Harrison. Recess Waterlow)

1939–48. *W* **133.** *P* 14.

476	**131**	2s. 6d. brown (4.9.39)	38·00	7·00
476a		2s. 6d. yellow-green (9.3.42)	7·00	1·50
477		5s. red (21.8.39)	14·00	2·00
478	**132**	10s. dark blue (30.10.39)	£180	21·00
478a		10s. ultramarine (30.11.42) ..	30·00	6·00
478b		£1 brown (1.10.48)	10·00	24·00
476/8b	.. ..	*Set of* 6	£250	55·00

134 Queen Victoria and King George VI.

(Des H. L. Palmer)

1940 (6 May). *Centenary of First Adhesive Postage Stamps. W* **127.**
P 14½ × 14.

479	**134**	½d. green	.. ..	30	30
480		1d. scarlet	.. .. ..	1·00	50
481		1½d. red-brown	.. .. ..	50	50
482		2d. orange	.. .. ..	50	50
		a. Bisected (on cover)	.. ..	†	16·00
483		2½d. ultramarine	.. ..	2·25	1·00
484		3d. violet	.. .. ..	3·00	3·25
479/84		.. ..	*Set of* 6	6·50	5·25

No. 482a was authorised for use in Guernsey. See notes on War Occupation Issues.

1941–42. *Head as Nos. 462/7, but lighter background. W* **127.**
P 15 × 14.

485	**128**	½d. pale green (1.9.41)	.. ..	30	30
		a. Tête-bêche (horiz pair)	.. ..	£3000	
		b. Imperf (pair)	.. ..	£1750	
486		1d. pale scarlet (11.8.41)	.. ..	30	30
		a. Wmk sideways (10.42)	.. ..	4·00	6·00
		b. Imperf (pair)	.. ..	£2500	
		c. Imperf three sides (horiz pair)	..	£2500	
487	**128**	1½d. pale red-brown (28.9.42)	..	1·00	70
488		2d. pale orange (6.10.41)	..	75	75
		a. Wmk sideways (6.42)	..	28·00	19·00
		b. Tête-bêche (horiz pair)	..	£2500	
		c. Imperf (pair)	.. ..	£2000	
		d. Imperf pane*	.. ..	£4500	
489		2½d. light ultramarine (21.7.41)	..	30	30
		a. Wmk sideways (8.42)	..	15·00	12·00
		b. Tête-bêche (horiz pair)	..	£2500	
		c. Imperf (pair)	.. ..	£2500	
		d. Imperf pane*	.. ..	£3500	
		e. Imperf three sides (horiz pair)	..	£3500	
490		3d. pale violet (3.11.41)	.. ..	2·00	1·00
485/90		.. ..	*Set of* 6	4·25	3·00

The *tête-bêche* varieties are from defectively made-up stamp booklets.

Nos. 486c and 489e are perforated at foot only and occur in the same sheets as Nos. 486b and 489c.

*BOOKLET ERRORS. Those listed as "imperf panes" show one row of perforations either at the top or at the bottom of the pane of 6.

WATERMARK VARIETIES. Please note that *inverted watermarks* are outside the scope of this listing but are fully listed in the *Great Britain Specialised* and *Great Britain Concise* Catalogues.

135

136 Symbols of Peace and Reconstruction

(Des H. L. Palmer (T **135**) and R. Stone (T **136**))

1946 (11 June). *Victory. W* **127.** *P* 15 × 14.

491	**135**	2½d. ultramarine	.. .. ..	30	30
492	**136**	3d. violet	.. .. ..	30	30

NEW INFORMATION

The editor is always interested to correspond with people who have new information that will improve or correct the Catalogue.

137   **138** King George VI
                          and Queen Elizabeth

(Des G. Knipe and Joan Hassall from photographs by Dorothy Wilding)

1948 (26 Apr). *Royal Silver Wedding. W* **127.** *P* 15 × 14 (2½d.) *or* 14 × 15 (£1).

493	**137**	2½d. ultramarine	.. .. ..	30	30
494	**138**	£1 blue	.. .. ..	38·00	38·00

1948 (10 May). Stamps of 1d. and 2½d. showing seaweed-gathering were on sale at eight Head Post Offices in Great Britain, but were primarily for use in the Channel Islands and are listed there (see after Great Britain Postal Fiscals).

139 Globe and Laurel Wreath

140 "Speed"

141 Olympic Symbol

142 Winged Victory

(Des P. Metcalfe (T **139**), A. Games (T **140**), S. D. Scott (T **141**) and E. Dulac (T **142**))

1948 (29 July). *Olympic Games. W* **127.** *P* 15 × 14.

495	**139**	2½d. ultramarine	.. ..	30	30
496	**140**	3d. violet	.. ..	30	30
497	**141**	6d. bright purple	.. ..	60	30
498	**142**	1s. brown	.. ..	1·25	1·50
495/8		.. ..	*Set of* 4	2·00	2·00

143 Two Hemispheres

144 U.P.U. Monument, Berne

145 Goddess Concordia, Globe and Points of Compass

146 Posthorn and Globe

(Des Mary Adshead (T **143**), P. Metcalfe (T **144**), H. Fleury (T **145**) and Hon. G. R. Bellew (T **146**))

1949 (10 Oct). *75th Anniv of Universal Postal Union.* W **127**. P 15 × 14.

499	143	2½d. ultramarine	..	..	..	30	30
500	144	3d. violet	..	..	..	30	40
501	145	6d. bright purple	..	..	..	60	75
502	146	1s. brown	..	..	..	1·25	1·50
499/502	..	..	..	..	*Set of* 4	2·00	2·75

1950–52. *4d. as Nos. 468 and others as Nos. 485/9, but colours changed.* W **127**. P 15 × 14.

503	128	½d. pale orange (3.5.51)	..	30	30
		a. Imperf (pair)	..		
		b. *Tête-bêche* (horiz pair)	..	£3000	
		c. Imperf pane*	..	£4000	
504		1d. light ultramarine (3.5.51)	..	50	50
		a. Wmk sideways (5.51)	..	1·00	1·25
		b. Imperf (pair)	..	£2000	
		c. Imperf three sides (horiz pair)	..	£1600	
		d. Booklet pane. Three stamps plus three printed labels (3.52)	..	18·00	
		e. Ditto. Partial *tête-bêche* pane	..	£2750	
505		1½d. pale green (3.5.51)	..	50	60
		a. Wmk sideways (9.51)	..	3·00	5·00
506		2d. pale red-brown (3.5.51)	..	50	40
		a. Wmk sideways (5.51)	..	1·75	2·00
		b. *Tête-bêche* (horiz pair)	..	£3000	
		c. Imperf three sides (horiz pair)	..	£1500	
507		2½d. pale scarlet (3.5.51)	..	50	40
		a. Wmk sideways (5.51)	..	1·75	1·75
		b. *Tête-bêche* (horiz pair)	..		
508	129	4d. light ultramarine (2.10.50)	..	2·50	1·75
		a. Double impression	..	†	£5000
503/8	..	..	*Set of* 6	4·25	3·25

No. 504c is perforated at foot only and occurs in the same sheet as No. 504b.
No. 506c is also perforated at foot only.

*BOOKLET ERRORS. Those listed as "imperf panes" show one row of perforations either at the top or at the bottom of the pane of 6.

147 H.M.S. *Victory*

148 White Cliffs of Dover

149 St. George and the Dragon

150 Royal Coat of Arms

(Des Mary Adshead (T **147/8**), P. Metcalfe (T **149/50**). Recess Waterlow)

1951 (3 May). W **133**. P 11 × 12.

509	147	2s. 6d. yellow-green	..	..	..	6·00	1·00
510	148	5s. red	..	..	..	32·00	1·50
511	149	10s. ultramarine	..	..	..	21·00	8·50
512	150	£1 brown	..	..	..	32·00	20·00
509/12	..	..	..	..	*Set of* 4	80·00	25·00

151 "Commerce and Prosperity"

152 Festival Symbol

(Des E. Dulac (T **151**), A. Games (T **152**))

1951 (3 May). *Festival of Britain.* W **127**. P 15 × 14.

513	151	2½d. scarlet	..	..	..	30	30
514	152	4d. ultramarine	..	..	..	50	55

STAMP BOOKLETS

For a full listing of Great Britain stamp booklets see the *Great Britain Concise Catalogue* published each Spring.

POSTAGE DUE STAMPS

PERFORATIONS. All postage due stamps are perf 14×15.

D 1   D 2

(Des G. Eve. Typo Harrison)

1937–38. W **127** (G VI R) *sideways.*

D27	D 1	½d. emerald (5.38)	..	..	9·00	5·00
D28		1d. carmine (5.38)	..	..	3·00	75
D29		2d. agate (5.38)	..	..	2·50	75
D30		3d. violet (12.37)	..	..	12·00	1·00
D31		4d. dull grey-green (9.37)	..	..	65·00	12·00
D32		5d. yellow-brown (11.38)	..	..	14·00	2·00
D33		1s. deep blue (10.37)	..	..	60·00	2·00
D34	D 2	2s. 6d. purple/*yellow* (9.38)	..	..	60·00	2·50
D27/34	..	..	..	*Set of 8*	£200	23·00

The 2d. is known bisected in June 1951 (Boreham Wood, Harpenden and St. Albans) and on 30 October 1954 (Harpenden).

DATES OF ISSUE. The dates for Nos. D35/9 are those on which stamps were first issued by the Supplies Department to postmasters.

1951–52. *Colours changed and new value* (1½d.). W **127** (G VI R) *sideways.*

D35	D 1	½d. orange (18.9.51)	..	..	1·00	3·00
D36		1d. violet-blue (6.6.51)	..	..	1·50	1·50
D37		1½d. green (11.2.52)	..	..	1·75	3·00
D38		4d. blue (14.8.51)	..	..	30·00	12·00
D39		1s. ochre (6.12.51)	..	..	35·00	14·00
D35/9	..	..	..	*Set of 5*	60·00	30·00

The 1d. is known bisected (Dorking, 1952, and Camberley, 6 April 1954).

CHANNEL ISLANDS
GENERAL ISSUE

C 1 Gathering Vraic

C 2 Islanders gathering Vraic

(Des J. R. R. Stobie (1d.) or from drawing by E. Blampied (2½d.). Photo Harrison)

1948 (10 May). *Third Anniv of Liberation.* W **127** *of Great Britain.* *P* 15 × 14.

C1	C 1	1d. scarlet	..	..	..	30	30
C2	C 2	2½d. ultramarine	..	..	..	30	30

GUERNSEY
WAR OCCUPATION ISSUES

Stamps issued under British authority during the German Occupation

BISECTS. On 24 December 1940 authority was given, by Post Office notice, that prepayment of penny postage could be effected by using half a British 2d. stamp, diagonally bisected. Such stamps were first used on 27 December 1940.

The 2d. stamps generally available were those of the Postal Centenary issue, 1940 (S.G. 482) and the first colour of the King George VI issue (S.G. 465). These are listed under Nos. 482a and 465b. A number of the 2d. King George V, 1912–22, and of the King George V photogravure stamp (S.G. 442) which were in the hands of philatelists, were also bisected and used.

1

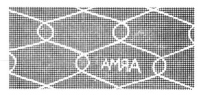

1a Loops (*half actual size*)

(Des E. W. Vaudin. Typo Guernsey Press Co Ltd)

1941–44. *Rouletted. (a) White paper. No wmk.*

1	1	½d. light green (7.4.41)	..	..	3·25	2·50
		a. Emerald-green (6.41)	..	..	4·25	2·50
		b. Bluish green (11.41)	..	..	45·00	20·00
		c. Bright green (2.42)	..	..	28·00	11·00
		d. Dull green (9.42)	..	..	4·25	3·25
		e. Olive-green (2.43)	..	..	32·00	20·00
		f. Pale yellowish green (7.43 and later)				
		(shades)	..	..	3·25	2·75
		g. Imperf (pair)	..	..	£200	
		h. Imperf between (horiz pair)	..	£700	
		i. Imperf between (vert pair)	..	£800	
2		1d. scarlet (18.2.41)	..	..	2·75	1·50
		a. Pale vermilion (7.43) (etc.)	..	2·75	1·50
		b. Carmine (1943)	..	..	3·00	3·00
		c. Imperf (pair)	..	..	£150	75·00
		d. Imperf between (horiz pair)	..	£700	
		da. Imperf vert (centre stamp of horiz strip of 3)	..	..	..	
		e. Imperf between (vert pair)	..	£800	
		f. Printed double (scarlet shade)	..	£100	
3		2½d. ultramarine (12.4.44)	..	..	4·50	4·50
		a. Pale ultramarine (7.44)	..	4·50	4·50
		b. Imperf (pair)	..	..	£500	
		c. Imperf between (horiz pair)	..	£1000	

(*b*) *Bluish French bank-note paper. W 1a (sideways)*

4	1	½d. bright green (11.3.42)	..	..	21·00	22·00
5		1d. scarlet (9.4.42)	..	..	12·00	24·00

The dates given for the shades of Nos. 1/3 are the months in which they were printed as indicated on the printer's imprints. Others are issue dates.

MINIMUM PRICE

The minimum price quote is 10p which represents a handling charge rather than a basis for valuing common stamps. For further notes about prices see introductory pages.

JERSEY

WAR OCCUPATION ISSUES

Stamps issued under British authority during the German Occupation

1

(Des Major N. V. L. Rybot. Typo *Jersey Evening Post*, St. Helier)

1941–43. *White paper* (*thin to thick*). *No wmk. P* 11.

1	**1**	½d. bright green (29.1.42)	..	..	4·00	3·25
		a. Imperf between (vert pair)	..	..	£800	
		b. Imperf between (horiz pair)	..	..	£700	
		c. Imperf (pair)	..	..	£250	
		d. On greyish paper (1.43)	..	..	5·00	5·75
2		1d. scarlet (1.4.41)	..	..	4·25	3·25
		a. Imperf between (vert pair)	..	..	£800	
		b. Imperf between (horiz pair)	..	..	£700	
		c. Imperf (pair)	..	..	£275	
		d. On chalk-surfaced paper	..	..	40·00	38·00
		e. On greyish paper (1.43)	..	..	5·00	5·75

2 Old Jersey Farm

3 Portelet Bay

4 Corbière Lighthouse

5 Elizabeth Castle

6 Mont Orgueil Castle   **7** Gathering Vraic (seaweed)

(Des E. Blampied. Eng H. Cortot. Typo French Govt Works, Paris)

1943–44. *No wmk. P* 13½.

3	**2**	½d. green (1 June)	..	..	..	8·00	7·25
		a. Rough, grey paper (6.10.43)	..	8·50	8·50
4	**3**	1d. scarlet (1 June)	..	..	2·25	1·00
		a. On newsprint (28.2.44)	..	..	2·50	2·00
5	**4**	1½d. brown (8 June)	..	..	4·00	4·00
6	**5**	2d. orange-yellow (8 June)	..	..	5·25	4·00
7	**6**	2½d. blue (29 June)	..	..	2·00	1·75
		a. On newsprint (25.2.44)	..	1·50	2·25
		ba. Thin paper*	..	..	£200	
8	**7**	3d. violet (29 June)	..	..	1·50	3·75
3/8		..	..	..	*Set of* 6	20·00	20·00

*On No. 7ba the design shows clearly through the back of the stamp.

Aden

1937. 12 pies = 1 anna; 16 annas = 1 rupee
1951. 100 cents = 1 shilling

CROWN COLONY

1 Dhow

3 Aidrus Mosque, Crater

(Recess D.L.R.)

1937 (1 Apr). *Wmk Mult Script CA sideways. P* 13 × 12.

1	1	½ a. yellow-green	3·75	1·40
2		9 p. deep green	3·75	1·60
3		1 a. sepia	3·75	70
4		2 a. scarlet	3·75	2·00
5		2½ a. bright blue	3·50	80
6		3 a. carmine	9·00	6·50
7		3½ a. grey-blue	7·50	2·00
8		8 a. pale purple	20·00	5·50
9		1 r. brown	29·00	6·00
10		2 r. yellow	48·00	16·00
11		5 r. deep purple	90·00	65·00
12		10 r. olive-green	£225	£275
1/12		*Set of* 12	£400	£350
1/12 Perf "Specimen"		*Set of* 12	£300	

1937 (12 May). *Coronation. As Nos.* 95/7 *of Antigua, but ptd by D.L.R. P* 14.

13	1 a. sepia	65	80
14	2½ a. light blue	75	1·40
15	3½ a. grey-blue	1·00	2·50
13/15	*Set of* 3	2·25	4·25
13/15 Perf "Specimen"	*Set of* 3	70·00	

(Recess Waterlow)

1939 (19 Jan)–**48**. *Horiz designs as T* **3**. *Wmk Mult Script CA. P* 12½.

16	½ a. yellowish green	50	60
	a. Bluish green (9.48)	2·00	3·50
17	¾ a. red-brown	1·25	1·25
18	1 a. pale blue	20	30
19	1½ a. scarlet	55	60
20	2 a. sepia	20	25
21	2½ a. deep ultramarine	40	30
22	3 a. sepia and carmine	60	25
23	8 a. red-orange	55	40
23*a*	14 a. sepia and light blue (15.1.45)	2·25	1·00
24	1 r. emerald-green	2·25	2·00
25	2 r. deep blue and magenta	4·75	2·25
26	5 r. red-brown and olive-green	11·00	8·00
27	10 r. sepia and violet	29·00	11·00
16/27	*Set of* 13	48·00	25·00
16/27 Perf "Specimen"	*Set of* 13	£180	

Designs:—½ a., 2 a., Type **3**; ¾ a., 5 r. Adenese Camel Corps; 1 a., 2 r. The Harbour; 1½ a., 1 r. Adenese Dhow; 2½ a., 8 a. Mukalla; 3 a., 14 a., 10 r. "Capture of Aden, 1839" (Capt. Rundle).

1946 (15 Oct). *Victory. As Nos.* 110/11 *of Antigua.*

28	1½ a. carmine	15	1·00
29	2½ a. blue	15	30
	w. Wmk inverted	£400	
28/9 Perf "Specimen"	*Set of* 2	50·00	

1949 (7 Jan). *Royal Silver Wedding. As Nos.* 112/13 *of Antigua.*

30	1½ a. scarlet (*p* 14×15)	40	80
31	10 r. mauve (*p* 11½×11)	27·00	30·00

1949 (10 Oct). *75th Anniv of U.P.U. As Nos.* 114/17 *of Antigua, surch with new values by Waterlow.*

32	2½ a. on 20 c. ultramarine	75	1·50
33	3 a. on 30 c. carmine-red	1·75	1·50
34	8 a. on 50 c. orange	1·60	1·50
35	1 r. on 1 s. blue	2·10	2·75
32/5	*Set of* 4	5·75	6·50

(New Currency. 100 cents = 1 shilling)

5
CENTS

(12)

1951 (1 Oct). *Nos.* 18 *and* 20/7 *surch with new values, in cents or shillings, as T* **12**, *or in one line between bars* (30 *c.*) *by Waterlow.*

36	5 c. on 1 a. pale blue	15	40
37	10 c. on 2 a. sepia	15	45
38	15 c. on 2½ a. deep ultramarine	20	1·25
	a. Surch double	£600	
39	20 c. on 3 a. sepia and carmine	30	40
40	30 c. on 8 a. red-orange (R.)	30	65
41	50 c. on 8 a. red-orange	30	35
42	70 c. on 14 a. sepia and light blue	1·75	1·50
43	1 s. on 1 r. emerald-green	35	30
44	2 s. on 2 r. deep blue and magenta	7·50	2·75
	a. Surch albino	£375	
45	5 s. on 5 r. red-brown and olive-green	16·00	8·50
46	10 s. on 10 r. sepia and violet	24·00	11·00
36/46	*Set of* 11	45·00	24·00

ADEN PROTECTORATE STATES

KATHIRI STATE OF SEIYUN

1 Sultan of Seiyun

2 Seiyun

(Recess D.L.R.)

1942 (July–Oct). *Designs as T* **1**/**2**. *Wmk Mult Script CA. T* **1**, *perf* 14; *others, perf* 12 × 13 (*vert*) *or* 13 × 12 (*horiz*).

1	½ a. blue-green	20	50
2	¾ a. brown	30	65
3	1 a. blue	60	50
4	1½ a. carmine	60	60
5	2 a. sepia	30	70
6	2½ a. blue	90	1·00
7	3 a. sepia and carmine	1·50	2·00
8	8 a. red	75	50
9	1 r. green	2·50	75
10	2 r. blue and purple	7·00	10·00
11	5 r. brown and green	20·00	14·00
1/11	*Set of* 11	30·00	28·00
1/11 Perf "Specimen"	*Set of* 11	£140	

Designs:—½ to 1 a. Type **1**. *Vert as T* **2**—2 a. Tarim; 2½ a. Mosque, Seiyun; 1 r. South Gate, Tarim; 5 r. Mosque entrance, Tarim. *Horiz as T* **2**—3 a. Fortress, Tarim; 8 a. Mosque, Seiyun; 2 r. A Kathiri house.

VICTORY

ISSUE

8TH JUNE 1946

(10)

1946 (15 Oct). *Victory. No. 4 optd with T 10, and No. 6 optd similarly but in four lines, by De La Rue.*

12	1½ a. carmine ..	..	..	..	..	10	65
13	2½ a. blue (R.) ..	..	..	..	..	10	10
	a. Opt inverted	..	..	..	..	£400	
12/13	Perf "Specimen"	..	*Set of* 2			55·00	

No. 13 is known with overprint double but the second impression is almost coincident with the first.

1949 (17 Jan). *Royal Silver Wedding. As Nos. 112/13 of Antigua.*

14	1½ a. scarlet	..	..	..	..	30	2·00
15	5 r. green	..	..	..	..	14·00	9·00

1949 (10 Oct). *75th Anniv of U.P.U. As Nos. 114/17 of Antigua, surch with new values by Waterlow.*

16	2½ a. on 20 c. ultramarine	..	..	..	25	50	
17	3 a. on 30 c. carmine-red	..	..	..	1·00	65	
18	8 a. on 50 c. orange	..	..	..	40	75	
19	1 r. on 1 s. blue	..	..	..	60	90	
16/19	..	..	..	..	*Set of* 4	2·00	2·50

5 CTS **50 CENTS** **5/-**

(11) (12) (13)

1951 (1 Oct). *Currency changed. Nos. 3 and 5/11 surch as T 11 (5 c.), 12 (10 c. ("CTS"), 15 c. ("CTS"), 20 c. and 50 c.) or 13 (1s. to 5s.), by Waterlow.*

20	5 c. on 1 a. blue (R.) ..	..	..	..	15	30	
21	10 c. on 2 a. sepia	..	..	..	30	30	
22	15 c. on 2½ a. blue	..	..	..	15	40	
23	20 c. on 3 a. sepia and carmine	..	..	20	80	
24	50 c. on 8 a. red	..	..	..	20	30	
25	1 s. on 1 r. green	..	..	..	20	80	
26	2 s. on 2 r. blue and purple ..	..	..	2·75	16·00	
27	5 s. on 5 r. brown and green ..	..	16·00	32·00	
20/27	..	..	..	..	*Set of* 8	18·00	45·00

QU'AITI STATE OF SHIHR AND MUKALLA

1 Sultan of Shihr
and Mukalla

2 Mukalla Harbour

VICTORY

ISSUE

8TH JUNE

1946

(10)

(Recess D.L.R.)

1942 (July)–**46**. *Wmk Mult Script CA. Designs as T 1 (½ to 1 a.) or T 2 (others). P 14 (½ to 1 a.), 12 × 13 (1½, 2, 3 a. and 1 r.) or 13 × 12 (others).*

1	½ a. blue-green	..	..	..	60	40	
	a. Olive-green (12.46)	..	..	24·00	35·00	
2	¾ a. brown	..	..	..	70	30	
3	1 a. blue	..	..	..	80	90	
4	1½ a. carmine	..	..	..	90	50	
5	2 a. sepia ..	..	..	..	1·25	1·00	
6	2½ a. blue	..	..	..	40	30	
7	3 a. sepia and carmine	..	..	80	60	
8	8 a. red	..	..	..	50	40	
9	1 r. green ..	..	..	..	2·75	2·00	
	a. "A" of "CA" missing from wmk	..	†	
10	2 r. blue and purple	..	..	11·00	8·00	
11	5 r. brown and green	..	..	14·00	11·00	
1/11	..	..	..	*Set of* 11	30·00	23·00
1/11	Perf "Specimen"	..	*Set of* 11	£140	

Designs: *Vert*—2 a. Gateway of Shihr; 3 a. Outpost of Mukalla; 1 r. Du'an. *Horiz*—2½ a. Shibam; 8 a. 'Einat; 2 r. Mosque in Hureidha; 5 r. Meshhed.

1946 (15 Oct). *Victory. No. 4 optd. with T 10 and No. 6 optd similarly, but in three lines, by De La Rue.*

12	1½ a. carmine ..	..	..	..	10	65	
13	2½ a. blue (R.) ..	..	..	..	10	10	
12/13	Perf "Specimen"	..	..	*Set of* 2	55·00	

1949 (17 Jan). *Royal Silver Wedding. As Nos. 112/13 of Antigua.*

14	1½ a. scarlet	..	..	..	50	2·25	
15	5 r. green	..	..	..	15·00	9·00	

1949 (10 Oct). *75th Anniv of U.P.U. As Nos. 114/17 of Antigua, surch with new values by Waterlow.*

16	2½ a. on 20 c. ultramarine	..	..	20	20	
17	3 a. on 30 c. carmine-red	..	..	1·10	50	
18	8 a. on 50 c. orange	..	..	..	55	60	
19	1 r. on 1s. blue	..	..	..	60	50	
	a. Surch omitted	..	..	£1200	
16/19	..	..	..	*Set of* 4	2·25	1·60

1951 (1 Oct). *Currency changed. Surch with new values in cents or shillings as T 11 (5 c.), 12 (10 c. ("CTS"), 15 c., 20 c. and 50 c.) or 13 (1 s. to 5 s.) of Seiyun, by Waterlow.*

20	5 c. on 1 a. blue (R.) ..	..	..	..	15	15	
21	10 c. on 2 a. sepia	..	..	..	15	15	
22	15 c. on 2½ a. blue	..	..	..	15	15	
23	20 c. on 3 a. sepia and carmine	..	..	30	30	
	a. Surch double, one albino..	..	£170	
24	50 c. on 8 a. red	..	..	..	30	60	
25	1 s. on 1 r. green	..	..	..	1·00	30	
26	2 s. on 2 r. blue and purple ..	..	..	7·00	10·00	
27	5 s. on 5 r. brown and green ..	..	10·00	15·00	
20/27	..	..	..	..	*Set of* 8	17·00	24·00

Antigua

1937. 12 pence (d) = 1 shilling; 20 shillings = 1 pound
1951. 100 cents = 1 West Indian dollar

CROWN COLONY

14 King George VI and
Queen Elizabeth

(Des D.L.R.. Recess B.W.)

1937 (12 May). *Coronation. Wmk Mult Script CA. P* 11×11½.
95	**14**	1d. carmine	..	..	..	..	50	80
96		1½d. yellow-brown		..	..	60	90
97		2½d. blue	..	..	..	1·25	1·60
95/7		..	..	..	*Set of* 3	2·10	3·00
95/7 Perf "Specimen"		..	..	*Set of* 3	50·00	

15 English Harbour   **16** Nelson's Dockyard

(Recess Waterlow)

1938 (15 Nov)–**51.** *T* **15, 16** *and similar designs. Wmk Mult Script CA. P* 12½.
98	**15**	½d. green	..	..	..	30	1·00
99	**16**	1d. scarlet	..	..	..	2·75	1·75
		a. Red (8.42 and 11.47)	..	..	3·50	2·00
100		1½d. chocolate-brown	..	..	5·50	60
		a. Dull reddish brown (12.43)	..	2·25	1·25
		b. Lake-brown (7.49)	..	26·00	13·00
101	**15**	2d. grey	..	..	..	50	50
		a. Slate-grey (6.51)	..	..	6·00	4·50
102	**16**	2½d. deep ultramarine	..	..	70	80
103	–	3d. orange	..	..	..	60	80
104	–	6d. violet	..	..	..	2·00	90
105	–	1s. black and brown	..	..	3·00	1·10
		a. Black and red-brown (7.49)	..	30·00	9·50
		ab. Frame ptd double, once albino	..	£2750	
106	–	2s. 6d. brown-purple	..	..	42·00	8·50
		a. Maroon (8.42)	..	..	22·00	8·50
107	–	5s. olive-green	..	..	14·00	7·00
108	**16**	10s. magenta (1.4.48)	..	..	16·00	25·00
109	–	£1 slate-green (1.4.48)	..	25·00	35·00
98/109		..	..	*Set of* 12	75·00	70·00
98/109 Perf "Specimen"		..	*Set of* 12	£180	

Designs: *Horiz*—3d., 2s. 6d., £1 Fort James. *Vert*—6d., 1s., 5s. St. John's Harbour.

17 Houses of Parliament,
London

(Des and recess D.L.R.)

1946 (1 Nov). *Victory. Wmk Mult Script CA. P* 13½×14.
110	**17**	1½d. brown	..	..	..	15	10
111		3d. red-orange	..	..	..	15	30
110/111 Perf "Specimen"		..	..	*Set of* 2	50·00	

18   **19**
King George VI and Queen Elizabeth

(Des and photo Waterlow (T **18**). Design recess; name typo B.W. (T **19**))

1949 (3 Jan). *Royal Silver Wedding. Wmk Mult Script CA.*
112	**18**	2½d. ultramarine (*p* 14×15)	..	..	40	1·00
113	**19**	5s. grey-olive (*p* 11½×11)	..	..	8·50	6·00

20 Hermes, Globe and
Forms of Transport

21 Hemispheres, Jet-
powered Vickers Viking
Airliner and Steamer

22 Hermes and Globe   **23** U.P.U. Monument

(Recess Waterlow (T **20, 23**). Designs recess, name typo B.W. (T **21/2**))

1949 (10 Oct). *75th Anniv of Universal Postal Union. Wmk Mult Script CA.*
114	**20**	2½d. ultramarine (*p* 13½–14)	..	..	40	50
115	**21**	3d. orange (*p* 11 × 11½)	..	..	1·50	1·75
116	**22**	6d. purple (*p* 11 × 11½)	..	..	45	1·25
117	**23**	1s. red-brown (*p* 13½–14)	..	..	45	75
114/17		..	..	..	*Set of* 4	2·50	3·75

(New Currency. 100 cents = 1 West Indian,
later Eastern Caribbean, dollar)

24 Arms of University   **25** Princess Alice

(Recess Waterlow)

1951 (16 Feb). *Inauguration of B.W.I. University College. Wmk Mult Script CA. P* 14×14½.

118	24	3 c. black and brown	..	..	45	50
119	25	12 c. black and violet	..	..	65	80

Ascension

12 pence (d) = 1 shilling; 20 shillings = 1 pound

DEPENDENCY OF ST. HELENA

1937 (19 May). *Coronation. As Nos. 95/7 of Antigua, but printed by D.L.R. P* 14.

35	1d. green				50	70
36	2d. orange				1·00	40
37	3d. bright blue				1·00	50
35/7				Set of 3	2·25	1·40
35/7 Perf "Specimen"			Set of 3	£130	

10 The Pier

Long centre bar to "E" in
"GEORGETOWN" (R. 2/3)

"Davit" flaw (R. 5/1) (all
ptgs of 1½d. and 2s. 6d.)

(Recess D.L.R.)

1938 (12 May)–**53.** *Horiz designs as King George V issue, but modified and with portrait of King George VI as in T* **10**. *Wmk Mult Script CA. P* 13½.

38	**3**	½d. black and violet			3·50	1·25
		a. Long centre bar to E			£110	
		b. Perf 13. *Black and bluish violet*				
		(17.5.44)			70	1·75
		ba. Long centre bar to E		50·00		

39	–	1d. black and green			40·00	7·50
39a	–	1d. black and yellow-orange (8.7.40)		14·00	9·00
		b. Perf 13 (5.42)			45	60
		c. Perf 14 (17.2.49)			70	16·00
39d	–	1d. black and green, *p* 13 (1.6.49)		60	50
40	**10**	1½d. black and vermilion		4·00	1·40
		a. Davit flaw			£170	
		b. Perf 13 (17.5.44)			85	80
		ba. Davit flaw			85·00	
		c. Perf 14 (17.2.49)			2·25	13·00
		ca. Davit flaw			£120	
40d		1½d. black and rose-carmine, *p* 14 (1.6.49)	55	80
		da. Davit flaw			80·00	
		db. *Black and carmine*			7·00	5·00
		dba. Davit flaw			£200	
		e. Perf 13 (25.2.53)			45	6·50
		ea. Davit flaw			75·00	
41	–	2d. black and red-orange			3·75	1·00
		a. Perf 13 (17.5.44)			80	40
		b. Perf 14 (17.2.49)			2·25	35·00
41c	–	2d. black and scarlet, *p* 14 (1.6.49)		1·00	85
42	–	3d. black and ultramarine			£100	26·00
42a	–	3d. black and grey (8.7.40)		17·00	90
		b. Perf 13 (17.5.44)			70	80
42c	–	4d. black and ultramarine (8.7.40)		15·00	3·25
		d. Perf 13 (17.5.44)			4·50	3·00
43	–	6d. black and blue			9·00	1·50
		a. Perf 13 (17.5.44)			9·00	5·00
44	**3**	1s. black and sepia			16·00	1·50
		a. Perf 13 (17.5.44)			4·75	2·00
45	**10**	2s. 6d. black and deep carmine		42·00	9·50
		a. Frame printed double, once albino £2750		
		b. Davit flaw			£600	£250
		c. Perf 13 (17.5.44)			35·00	32·00
		ca. Davit flaw			£500	
46	–	5s. black and yellow-brown			£110	8·50
		a. Perf 13 (17.5.44)			48·00	27·00
47	–	10s. black and bright purple		£110	42·00
		a. Perf 13 (17.5.44)			55·00	55·00
38/47a				Set of 16	£275	90·00
38/47 Perf "Specimen"			Set of 13	£475	

Designs: *Horiz*—1d. (Nos. 39/c), 2d., 4d. Green Mountain; 1d. (No. 39d), 6d., 10s. Three Sisters; 3d., 5s. Long Beach.

1946 (21 Oct). *Victory. As Nos.* 110/11 *of Antigua.*

48	2d. red-orange				40	50
49	4d. blue				40	30
48/9 Perf "Specimen"			Set of 2	£140	

1948 (20 Oct). *Royal Silver Wedding. As Nos.* 112/13 *of Antigua.*

50	3d. black				50	30
51	10s. bright purple			45·00	40·00

1949 (10 Oct). *75th Anniv of Universal Postal Union. As Nos.* 114/17 *of Antigua.*

52	3d. carmine				1·40	1·25
53	6d. deep blue				3·50	1·25
54	6d. olive				3·75	2·75
55	1s. blue-black				3·75	1·50
52/5				Set of 4	11·00	6·00

Australia

12 pence (d) = 1 shilling; 20 shillings = 1 pound

DOMINION

15

22 Hermes

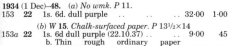

34 Laughing Kookaburra   **35** Platypus   **36** Superb Lyrebird

38 Queen Elizabeth   **39** King George VI

(Des F. D. Manley. Eng E. Broad and F. D. Manley. Recess John Ash until April 1940; W. C. G. McCracken thereafter)

1934 (1 Dec)–**48.** (*a*) *No wmk. P* 11.

153	**22**	1s. 6d. dull purple	..	..	.. 32·00	1·00

    (*b*) *W* **15.** *Chalk-surfaced paper. P* 13½×14

153*a*	**22**	1s. 6d dull purple (22.10.37) ..	..	9·00	45
		b. Thin rough ordinary paper (12.2.48) ..	..	..	.. 3·00	1·25

40 King George VI and Queen Elizabeth

27 Wallaroo   **28**   Queen Elizabeth   **28***a*

29   **30** King George VI   **30***a*

31 King George VI   **32** Koala   **33** Merino Ram

Dies of 3d.:

Die I   Die Ia   Die II

Die I. The letters "TA" of "POSTAGE" at right are joined by a white flaw; the outline of the chin consists of separate strokes.

No. 168*a* is a preliminary printing made with unsuitable ink and may be detected by the absence of finer details; the King's face appears whitish and the wattles are blank. The greater part of this printing was distributed to the Press with advance notices of the issue.

Die Ia. As Die I, but "T" and "A" have been clearly separated by individual retouches made on the plates.

Die II. A completely new die. "T" and "A" are separate and a continuous line has been added to the chin. The outline of the cheek extends to about 1 mm above the lobe of the King's right ear.

Die III. Differs from Dies I and II in the King's left eyebrow which is shaded downwards from left to right instead of from right to left.

NEW INFORMATION

The editor is always interested to correspond with people who have new information that will improve or correct the Catalogue.

12　Australia

Line to Kangaroo's ear (Rt pane R. 6/8)

Medal flaw
(Right pane R. 2/5)

(Des R. A. Harrison (T **28/30**), F. D. Manley (T **27, 31/6**), H. Barr
(T **38/9**), H. Barr and F. D. Manley (T **40**). Eng F. D. Manley
and T. C Duffell (T **34**), T. C Duffell (revised lettering for
T **28a, 30a**), F. D. Manley (others). All recess with John Ash,
W. C. G. McCracken or "By Authority ..." imprints)

1937–49. W **15** (*sideways on* 5d., 9d., 5s. *and* 10s.). *Chalk-
surfaced paper* (3d. (No. 168), 5s., 10s., £1).

(a) P 13½ × 14 (*vert designs*) *or* 14 × 13½ (*horiz*)
164	27	½d. orange (3.10.38)		.. 2·50	45
165	28	1d. emerald-green (10.5.37)	..	.. 40	10
166	29	1½d. maroon (20.4.38)		.. 9·00	3·00
167	30	2d. scarlet (10.5.37)		.. 40	10
168	31	3d. blue (Die I) (2.8.37)		.. 60·00	9·50
		a. "White wattles" (from 1st ptg)	..	£120	70·00
		b. Die Ia	..	.. £140	6·50
		c. Die II (3.38)		.. 60·00	3·50
		ca. *Bright blue* (*ordinary thin paper*)			
		(20.12.38)		.. 60·00	2·50
170	32	4d. green (1.2.38)		.. 14·00	85
171	33	5d. purple (1.12.38)		.. 2·00	60
172	34	6d. purple-brown (2.8.37)		.. 23·00	90
173	35	9d. chocolate (1.9.38)		.. 5·00	90
174	36	1s. grey-green (2.8.37)		.. 48·00	2·25
175	31	1s. 4d. pale magenta (3.10.38)		.. 1·50	1·50
		a. *Deep magenta* (1943)		.. 3·25	2·00

(b) P 13½
176	38	5s. claret (1.4.38)		.. 14·00	1·25
		a. Thin rough ordinary paper (4.2.48)		.. 4·00	2·00
177	39	10s. dull purple (1.4.38) (Optd S. £30)	38·00	12·00
		a. Thin rough ordinary paper (11.48)		.. 42·00	29·00
178	40	£1 bl-slate (1.11.38) (Optd S. £400)	65·00	30·00
		a. Thin rough ordinary paper (4.4.49)		.. 65·00	60·00
164/78				Set of 14 £250	48·00

(c) P 15×14 (*vert designs*) *or* 14×15 (*horiz*) (1d. *and* 2d. *redrawn
with background evenly shaded and lettering strengthened*)
179	27	½d. orange (28.1.42)		.. 55	10
		a. Line to kangaroo's ear		.. 12·00	
		b. Coil pair (1942)		.. 15·00	17·00
		ba. Coil block of four (1943)		.. £250	
180	28a	1d. emerald-green (1.8.38)	..	.. 2·50	10
181		1d. maroon (10.12.41)		.. 1·25	10
		a. Coil pair (1942)		.. 12·00	16·00
182	29	1½d. maroon (21.11.41)		.. 4·00	7·50
183		1½d. emerald-green (10.12.41)		.. 1·00	70
184	30a	2d. scarlet (11.7.38)		.. 2·75	10
		a. Coil pair (10.41)		.. £325	£375
		b. Medal flaw		.. £100	
		w. Wmk inverted (*from booklets*)	.. 4·00	50
185		2d. bright purple (10.12.41)		.. 50	80
		a. Coil pair (1942)		.. 42·00	48·00
		b. Medal flaw		.. 40·00	
		w. Wmk inverted (*from coils*)	.. 80·00	24·00

186	31	3d. bright blue (Die III) (11.40)	.. 45·00	2·25
187		3d. purple-brown (Die III) (10.12.41)	30	10
188	32	4d. green (10.42)	..	.. 1·00	10
		w. Wmk inverted	..	.. †	£650
189	33	5d. purple (17.12.45)	..	.. 45	1·50
190	34	6d. red-brown (6.42)	..	.. 2·00	10
		a. *Purple-brown* (1944)	..	.. 1·75	10
191	35	9d. chocolate (12.9.43)	..	.. 1·00	20
192	36	1s. grey-green (29.3.41)	..	.. 1·00	10
		w. Wmk inverted	..	.. £650	£375
179/92				Set of 14 55·00	11·00

For unwmkd issue, see Nos. 228/30d.

Thin paper. Nos. 176a, 177a, 178a. In these varieties the
watermark is more clearly visible on the back and the design is
much less sharp. On early printings of No. 176a the paper
appears tinted.

SPECIAL COIL PERFORATION. This special perforation of
large and small holes on the narrow sides of the stamps was
introduced after 1939 for stamps issued in coils and was
intended to facilitate separation. Where they exist they are
listed as "Coil pairs".

The following with "special coil" perforation were placed on
sale in *sheets*: Nos. 179, 205, 222a (1952), 228, 230, 237, 262
(1953), 309, 311, and 314. These are listed as "Coil blocks of
four".

Coils with "normal" perforations also exist for Nos. 180 and
184.

41 "Governor Phillip at
Sydney Cove" (J. Alcott)

"Tail" flaw (Left pane
R. 7/1. Later retouched)

(Des and eng E. Broad and F. D. Manley. Recess J. Ash)

1937 (1 Oct). 150*th Anniv of Foundation of New South Wales*
W **15**. *P* 13½ × 14.
193	41	2d. scarlet	..	.. 2·25	15
		a. "Tail" flaw	..	.. £250	60·00
194		3d. bright blue	..	.. 6·00	2·25
195		9d. purple	..	.. 16·00	10·00
193/5	..			Set of 3 22·00	11·00

42 A.I.F. and Nurse

(Des and eng F. D. Manley from drawing by Virgil Reilly. Recess W. C. G. McCracken)

1940 (15 July). *Australian Imperial Forces.* W **15** (*sideways*). P 14 × 13½.

196	42	1d. green	.. .. ..	1·75	1·25
197		2d. scarlet	.. .. ..	1·75	50
198		3d. blue ..	.. .. ..	12·00	7·50
199		6d. brown-purple	.. ..	22·00	13·00
196/9		.. .. ..	*Set of* 4	35·00	20·00

(43) 　　　　(44)　　　　(45)

(Opts designed by F. D. Manley)

1941 (10 Dec). *Nos.* 184, 186 *and* 171 *surch with* T **43/5**.

200	40b	2½d. on 2d. scarlet (V.)	.. ..	60	40
		a. Pair, one without surcharge	..	£3750	
		b. Medal flaw	.. ..	95·00	
201	31	3½d. on 3d. bright blue (Y. on Black)	75	1·50
202	33	5½d. on 5d. purple (V.)	..	3·50	4·00
200/2		.. .. ..	*Set of* 3	4·25	5·50

Nos 200/2 were prepared in connection with the imposition of a ½d. "war tax" increase on most postage rates.

One sheet of the 2½d. on 2d. was discovered showing the surcharge omitted on R.1/4 and R.1/5.

46　Queen Elizabeth　**46a**　　　**47** King George VI

48 King George VI 　　**49** King George VI　　**50** Emu

(Des F. D. Manley. Eng F. D. Manley and T. C. Duffell (T **46**/a) or F. D. Manley (others))

1942–50. *Recess.* W **15**. P 15 × 14.

203	46	1d. brown-purple (2.1.43) ..	..	50	10
		a. Coil pair (1944)	..	18·00	23·00
204	46a	1½d. green (1.12.42) ..	..	40	10
205	47	2d. bright purple (4.12.44) ..	..	55	60
		b. Coil pair (1.49)	..	90·00	95·00
		ba. Coil block of four (5.50)	..	£850	
206	48	2½d. scarlet (7.1.42) ..	..	30	10
		a. Imperf (pair)*	..	£2750	
		w. Wmk inverted (*from booklets*) ..	3·75	30
207	49	3½d. bright blue (3.42)	..	40	20
		a. Deep blue	..	50	20
208	50	5½d. slate-blue (12.2.42)	..	65	10
203/8		.. .. ..	*Set of* 6	2·50	80

*No. 206a comes in horizontal pair with the right-hand stamp completely imperforate and the left-hand stamp imperforate at right only.

Coils with normal perforations exist for 1d.

For stamps as Nos. 204/5 but without watermark see Nos. 229/30.

NEW INFORMATION

The editor is always interested to correspond with people who have new information that will improve or correct the Catalogue.

The following items are understood to have been the subject of unauthorised leakages from the Commonwealth Note and Stamp Printing Branch and are therefore not listed by us.

It is certain that none of this material was distributed to post offices for issue to the public.

Imperforate all round. 1d. Princess Elizabeth; 1½d. Queen; 2½d. King; 4d. Koala; 6d. Kookaburra; 9d. Platypus; 1s. Lyrebird (small) (also imperf three sides); 1s. 6d. Air Mail (Type 22); 2½d. Mitchell; 2½d. Newcastle (also imperf three sides or imperf vertically).

Also 2½d. Peace, unwatermarked; 2½d. King, *tête-bêche*; 3½d. Newcastle, in dull ultramarine; 2½d. King on "toned" paper.

52 Duke and Duchess of Gloucester

(Des F. D. Manley. Eng F. D. Manley and T. C. Duffell. Recess)

1945 (19 Feb). *Arrival of Duke and Duchess of Gloucester in Australia.* W **15**. P 14½.

209	52	2½d. lake	.. .. ..	10	10
210		3½d. ultramarine	.. ..	15	55
211		5½d. indigo ..	.. .. ..	20	55
209/11		.. .. ..	*Set of* 3	40	1·10

A 　　　　　　B

1945 (24 Dec). *Kangaroo type, as No.* 134, *but re-engraved as* B. W **15**. P 12.

212	1	2s. maroon	.. .. ..	3·50	4·25
		w. Wmk inverted	.. ..		† £1300

No. 134 has two background lines between the value circle and "TWO SHILLINGS"; No. 212 has only one line in this position. There are also differences in the shape of the letters.

53 Star and Wreath 　　56 Sir Thomas Mitchell and Queensland

(Des F. D. Manley (2½d.), F. D. Manley and G. Lissenden (3½d.), G. Lissenden (5½d.). Eng F. D. Manley. Recess)

1946 (18 Feb). *Victory Commemoration. T* **53** *and similar designs.* W **15** (*sideways on* 5½d.). P 14½.

213		2½d. scarlet	.. .. ..	10	10
214		3½d. blue	.. .. ..	25	75
215		5½d. green	.. .. ..	30	50
213/15		.. ..	*Set of* 3	60	1·25

Designs: *Horiz*—3½d. Flag and dove. *Vert*—5½d. Angel.

For these designs re-issued in 1995 with face values in decimal currency see Nos. 1542/4.

(Des F. D. Manley. Eng F. D. Manley and T. C. Duffell. Recess)

1946 (14 Oct). *Centenary of Mitchell's Exploration of Central Queensland.* W **15**. P 14½.

216	56	2½d. scarlet	.. .. ..	10	10
217		3½d. blue ..	.. .. ..	35	80
218		1s. grey-olive	.. .. ..	35	30
216/18		.. ..	*Set of* 3	70	1·10

57 Lt. John   **58** Steel Foundry   **59** Coal Carrier Cranes
Shortland R.N.

(Des and eng G. Lissenden (5½d.), F. D. Manley (others).
Recess)

1947 (8 Sept). *150th Anniv of City of Newcastle, New South Wales.* W **15** *(sideways on* 3½d.). *P* 14½ *or* 15×14 *(2½d.).*
219   **57**   2½d. lake   10   10
220   **58**   3½d. blue   40   65
221   **59**   5½d. green   40   45
219/21   ..   ..   *Set of* 3   80   1·10

60 Queen Elizabeth II when Princess

(Des R. A. Harrison. Eng. F. D. Manley. Recess)

1947 (20 Nov)–**52.** *Marriage of Princess Elizabeth. P* 14×15.

(*a*) W **15** *(sideways)*
222   **60**   1d. purple   15   10

(*b*) *No wmk*
222a   **60**   1d. purple (8.48)   10   10
     b. Coil pair (1.50)   ..   ..   2·25   4·50
     c. Coil block of four (9.52)   ..   4·50

61 Hereford Bull   **61a** Hermes and Globe

62 Aboriginal Art   **62a** Commonwealth
Coat of Arms

(Des G. Sellheim (T **62**), F. D. Manley (others). Eng G. Lissenden
(T **62**), F. D. Manley (1s. 3d., 1s. 6d., 5s.), F. D. Manley and R.
J. Becker (10s., £1, £2). Recess)

1948 (16 Feb)–**56.** (*a*) W **15** *(sideways). P* 14½
223   **61**   1s. 3d. brown-purple   ..   1·75   95
223a   **61a**   1s. 6d. blackish brown (1.9.49)   ..   90   10
224   **62**   2s. chocolate   ..   ..   2·00   10

(*b*) W **15.** *P* 14½×13½
224a   **62a**   5s. claret (11.4.49)   ..   ..   2·75   20
     ab. Thin paper (1951)   ..   ..   27·00   11·00
224b   10s. purple (3.10.49)   ..   ..   14·00   70
224c   £1 blue (28.11.49)   ..   ..   30·00   3·50
224d   £2 green (16.1.50)   ..   ..   95·00   14·00
224b/d Optd "Specimen"   ..   *Set of* 3   £140

(*c*) *No wmk. P* 14½
224e   **61a**   1s. 6d. blackish brown (2.12.56)   ..   13·00   1·50
224f   **62**   2s. chocolate (27.6.56)   ..   13·00   60
223/4f   ..   ..   ..   *Set of* 9   £150   19·00

No. 224ab is an emergency printing on white Harrison paper
instead of the toned paper used for No. 224a.

No. 224b exists with watermark inverted and overprinted
"SPECIMEN".

63 William J.   **64** F. von Mueller   **65** Boy Scout
Farrer

(Des and eng F. D. Manley. Recess)

1948 (12 July). *William J. Farrer (wheat research) Commemoration.* W **15.** *P* 15×14.
225   **63**   2½d. scarlet   10   10

(Des and eng F. D. Manley. Recess)

1948 (13 Sept). *Sir Ferdinand von Mueller (botanist) Commemoration.* W **15.** *P* 15×14.
226   **64**   2½d. lake   10   10

(Des and eng F. D. Manley. Recess)

1948 (15 Nov). *Pan-Pacific Scout Jamboree, Wonga Park.* W **15** *(sideways). P* 14 × 15.
227   **65**   2½d. lake   10   10
See also No. 254.

Sky retouch (normally unshaded near hill) (Rt pane
R. 6/8) (No. 228a retouched in 1951)

"Green mist" retouch. A
large area to the left of
the bird's feathers is
recut (upper plate left
pane R. 9/3)

1948–56. *No wmk. P* 15×14 *or* 14×15 (9*d.*).

228	27	½d. orange (15.9.49)	..	..	20	10
		a. Line to kangaroo's ear		..	9·00	
		b. Sky retouch	..	..	21·00	
		c. Coil pair (1950)	..	..	75	2·25
		ca. Line to kangaroo's ear		..	32·00	
		cb. Sky retouch (in pair)	..		£110	
		d. Coil block of four (1953)		..	£250	
229	46*a*	1½d. green (17.8.49)	..	..	1·25	85
230	47	2d. bright purple (20.12.48)		..	80	80
		aa. Coil pair	..	..	3·00	5·50
230*a*	32	4d. green (18.8.56)	..	..	2·00	80
230*b*	34	6d. purple-brown (18.8.56)		..	4·75	70
230*c*	35	9d. chocolate (13.12.56)	..	..	22·00	2·75
230*d*	36	1s. grey green (13.12.56)	..	..	4·00	90
		da. "Green mist" retouch	..	..	£650	
228/30*d*	..			*Set of* 7	32·00	6·00

66 "Henry Lawson"
(Sir Lionel Lindsay)

67 Mounted Postman
and Convair CV 240
Aircraft

(Des F. D. Manley. Eng. E. R. M. Jones. Recess)

1949 (17 June). *Henry Lawson (poet) Commemoration. P* 15×14.

231	66	2½d. maroon	..	..	15	10

(Des Sir Daryl Lindsay and F. D. Manley. Eng F. D. Manley. Recess)

1949 (10 Oct). *75th Anniv of Founding of U.P.U. P* 15 × 14.

232	67	3½d. ultramarine	..	..	30	40

68 John, Lord
Forrest of
Bunbury

69 Queen
Elizabeth

70 King
George VI

(Des and eng F. D. Manley. Recess)

1949 (28 Nov). *John, Lord Forrest of Bunbury (explorer and politician) Commemoration. W* 15. *P* 15×14.

233	68	2½d. lake	..	..	15	10

(Des and eng F. D. Manley. Recess)

1950 (12 Apr)–52. *P* 15×14. (*a*) *W* 15

234	70	2½d. scarlet (12.4.50)	..	..	10	10
235		3d. scarlet (28.2.51)	..	..	15	10
		aa. Coil pair (4.51)	..	..	17·00	20·00

(*b*) *No wmk*

236	69	1½d. green (19.6.50)	..	..	15	10
237		2d. yellow-green (28.3.51)	..	..	15	10
		a. Coil pair	..	..	5·00	7·50
		b. Coil block of four (11.52)	..	..	10·00	
237*c*	70	2½d. purple-brown (23.5.51)	..	..	15	15
237*d*		3d. grey-green (14.11.51)	..	..	15	10
		da. Coil pair (12.51)	..	..	24·00	30·00
234/7*d*	..			*Set of* 6	80	40

On 14 October 1951 No. 235 was placed on sale in sheets of 144 originally intended for use in stamp booklets. These sheets contain 3 panes of 48 (16×3) with horizontal gutter margin between.

71 Aborigine

72
73
Reproductions of First Stamps of New
South Wales and Victoria

(Des and eng F. D. Manley. Recess)

1950 (14 Aug). *W* 15. *P* 15×14.

238	71	8½d. brown	..	..	15	45

For T **71** in a larger size, see Nos. 253/*b*.

(Des and eng G. Lissenden (T **72**), E. R. M. Jones (T **73**). Recess)

1950 (27 Sept). *Centenary of First Adhesive Postage Stamps in Australia. P* 15×14.

239	72	2½d. maroon	..	..	20	10
		a. Horiz pair. Nos. 239/40	..	..	40	55
240	73	2½d. maroon	..	..	20	10

Nos. 239/40 were printed alternately in vertical columns throughout the sheet.

74 Sir Edmund
Barton

75 Sir Henry
Parkes

76 "Opening First Federal
Parliament" (T. Roberts)

77 Federal Parliament House,
Canberra

(Des and eng F. D. Manley. Recess)

1951 (1 May). *50th Anniv of Commonwealth of Australia. P* 15×14.

241	74	3d. lake	..		30	10
		a. Horiz pair. Nos. 241/2	..	..	1·75	2·25
242	75	3d. lake	..	..	30	10
243	76	5½d. blue	..	..	20	2·00
244	77	1s. 6d. purple-brown	..	..	35	50
241/4	..			*Set of* 4	2·00	2·50

Nos. 241/2 are printed alternately in vertical columns throughout the sheet.

78
E. H. Hargraves

79
C. J. Latrobe

(Des and eng F. D. Manley. Recess)

1951 (2 July). *Centenaries of Discovery of Gold in Australia and of Responsible Government in Victoria. P* 15×14.

245	78	3d. maroon	..	..	30	10
		a. Horiz pair. Nos. 245/6	..	..	70	95
246	79	3d. maroon	..	..	30	10

Nos. 245/6 were printed alternately in vertical columns throughout the sheet.

80	81	82	B 1

King George VI

(Des E. R. M. Jones (7½d.), F. D. Manley (others). Eng. F. D. Manley. Recess)

1951–52. W 15 (sideways on 1s. 0½d.). P 14½ (1s. 0½d.) or 15×14 (others).

247	80	3½d. brown-purple (28.11.51)	..	..	10	10
		a. Imperf between (horiz pair)		.. £5500		
248		4½d. scarlet (20.5.52)	..	..	15	70
249		6½d. brown (20.2.52)	..	..	15	60
250		6½d. emerald-green (9.4.52)	..	..	10	15
251	81	7½d. blue (31.10.51)	..	..	15	45
		a. Imperf three sides (vert pr)		.. £7500		
252	82	1s. 0½d. indigo (19.3.52)	..	..	35	30
247/52		..	..	Set of 6	90	2·00

No. 251a occurs on the left-hand vertical row of one sheet.

(Des F. D. Manley. Eng E. R. M. Jones. Recess)

1952 (19 Mar)–**65.** P 14½. (a) W 15 (sideways*)

253	2s. 6d. deep brown	..	..	1·50	35
	aw. Wmk Crown to left of C of A	..	†	£700	

(b) No wmk

253b	2s. 6d. deep brown (30.1.57)	..	..	5·00	55
	ba. Sepia (10.65)	..	..	12·00	12·00

Design:—2s. 6d. As T **71** but larger (21×25½ mm).

*The normal sideways watermark on No. 253 shows Crown to right of C of A, as seen from the back of the stamp.

No. 253ba was an emergency printing and can easily be distinguished from No. 253b as it is on white Harrison paper, No. 253b being on toned paper.

(Des and eng F. D. Manley. Recess)

1952 (19 Nov). Pan-Pacific Scout Jamboree, Greystanes. As T **65**, but inscr "1952–53". W **15** (sideways). P 14 × 15.

254	3½d. brown-lake	..	..	..	10	10

STAMP BOOKLETS

All booklets to 1949 were stapled.

1938 (Dec). Black on green cover with Commonwealth Savings Bank advertisement on front cover inscr "WHEREVER THERE IS A MONEY ORDER POST OFFICE". Postal rates on interleaves.

SB27	2s. booklet containing twelve 2d. (No. 184 or 184w) in blocks of 6	..	..	£350
	a. With waxed interleaves. Postal rates on back cover	..	..	£450
	b. Black on buff cover ..	..	..	£400

1942 (Aug). Black on buff cover, size 73×47½ mm. Postal rates on interleaves.

SB28	2s. 6d. booklet containing twelve 2½d. (No. 206 or 206w) in blocks of 6, upright within the booklet	..	..	£110
	a. With waxed interleaves. Postal rates on back cover	..	..	£200

1949 (Sept). Black on buff cover, size 79½×42½ mm including figure of Hermes.

SB29	2s. 6d. booklet containing twelve 2½d. (No. 206) in blocks of 6, sideways within the booklet	80·00

All booklets from 1952 were stitched and stapled booklets of this period are remakes of defective stitched booklets with new covers.

1952 (24 June). Vermilion and deep blue on green cover a Type B **1**.

SB30	3s. 6d. booklet containing twelve 3½d. (No. 247) in blocks of 6	..	..	..	17·00
	a. With waxed interleaves	..	..	..	90·00

POSTAGE DUE STAMPS

D 8	D 9

A	B	C

The differences are found in the middle of the "D"

D	E

Type E. Larger "1" with only three background lines above hyphen more upright.

(Frame recess. Value typo J. Ash)

1938 (May–Aug). W **15**. P 14½×14.

D112	D 8	½d. carmine and green (A) (Aug)	..	3·75	2·50
D113		1d. carmine and green (A)	..	10·00	60
D114		2d. carmine and green (A)	..	10·00	1·25
D115		3d. carmine and green (B) (Aug)	..	30·00	13·00
D116		4d. carmine and green (A) (Aug)	..	12·00	60
D117		6d. carmine and green (A) (Aug)	..	70·00	42·00
D118		1s. carmine and green (D) (Aug)	..	50·00	12·00
D112/18		..	..	Set of 7	£170	65·00

Shades exist

1946–57. Redrawn as Type C and E (1s). W **15**. P 14½×14.

D119	D 9	½d. carmine and green (9.56)	..	85	3·00
D120		1d. carmine and green (1.11.47)	..	1·25	80
D121		2d. carmine and green (9.46)	..	4·50	1·25
D122		3d. carmine and green (25.9.46)	..	6·00	1·25
D123		4d. carmine and green (30.7.52)	..	9·00	1·75
D124		5d. carmine and green (16.12.48)	..	12·00	3·00
D125		6d. carmine and green (9.47)	..	11·00	1·75
D126		7d. carmine and green (26.8.53)	..	4·25	8·50
D127		8d. carmine and green (24.4.57)	..	10·00	25·00
D128		1s. carmine and green (9.47)	..	18·00	1·60
D119/28		..	..	Set of 10	65·00	42·00

There are many shades in this issue.

BRITISH COMMONWEALTH OCCUPATION FORCE (JAPAN)

Nos. J1/7 were used by the Australian forces occupying Japan after the Second World War. Initially their military post offices supplied unoverprinted Australian stamps, but it was decided to introduce the overprinted issue to prevent currency speculation.

B.C.O.F.	B.C.O.F.	
JAPAN	JAPAN	
1946	1946	
(1)	(2)	

1946

Wrong fount "6"
(left pane R. 9/4)

AN AN

Normal   Narrow "N"
(right pane R. 1/8)

1946 (11 Oct)–**48.** *Stamps of Australia optd as T* **1** (1*d.,* 3*d.*) *or T* **2** (*others*) *at Hiroshima Printing Co, Japan.*

J1	27	¹/₂d. orange (No. 179)	..	..	3·00	4·50
		a. Wrong fount "6"	..	..	65·00	75·00
		b. Narrow "N" ..	..	..	65·00	75·00
		c. Stop after "JAPAN" (right pane R.5/5)		65·00	75·00
J2	46	1d. brown-purple (No. 203)	..		2·50	1·75
		a. Blue-black overprint	..	..	55·00	95·00
J3	31	3d. purple-brown (No. 187)	..		2·00	2·00
		a. Opt double ..	..	..		£500
J4	34	6d. purple-brown (No. 189*a*) (8.5.47)		15·00	9·00
		a. Wrong fount "6"	..	..	£180	£130
		b. Stop after "JAPAN" (right pane R. 5/5)		£180	£130
		c. Narrow "N" ..	..	..	£180	£130
J5	36	1s. grey-green (No. 191) (8.5.47)		15·00	11·00
		a. Wrong fount "6"	..	..	£190	£150
		b. Stop after "JAPAN" (right pane R. 5/5)		£190	£150
		c. Narrow "N" ..	..	..	£190	£150
J6	1	2s. maroon (No. 212) (8.5.47)	..		42·00	45·00
J7	38	5s. claret (No. 176) (8.5.47)	..		£120	£120
		a. Thin rough paper (No. 176*a*) (1948)		£120	£140
J1/7		..	..	*Set of* 7	£180	£180

The ¹/₂d., 1d. and 3d. values were first issued on 11 October 1946, and withdrawn two days later, but were re-issued together with the other values on 8 May 1947.

The following values with T **2** in the colours given were from proof sheets which, however, were used for ¹/₂d. (red), 1d. (red or black) and 3d. (gold, red or black). (*Prices for black opts* £100, *each, and for red or gold from* £300 *each, all un*)

The use of B.C.O.F. stamps ceased on 12 February 1949.

NAURU
AUSTRALIAN MANDATE

4 *Century* (freighter)	**6**

(Des R. A. Harrison. Eng T. S. Harrison. Recess Note Printing Branch of the Treasury, Melbourne and from 1926 by the Commonwealth Bank of Australia)

1924–48. *No wmk. P* 11.

A. *Rough surfaced, greyish paper* (1924–34).

26A	4	¹/₂d. chestnut	..	..	..	1·50	2·75
27A		1d. green	..	..	..	3·25	2·75
28A		1¹/₂d. scarlet	..	..	..	4·00	4·00
29A		2d. orange	..	..	..	4·00	11·00

30A	4	2¹/₂d. slate-blue	..	..	5·50	19·00
		c. *Greenish blue* (1934)	..	..	5·50	14·00
31A		3d. pale blue ..	..	..	3·00	13·00
32A		4d. olive-green	..	..	7·00	16·00
33A		5d. brown	..	..	3·75	6·50
34A		6d. dull violet	..	..	4·25	12·00
35A		9d. olive-brown	..	..	9·00	19·00
36A		1s. brown-lake	..	..	6·00	13·00
37A		2s. 6d. grey-green	..	..	27·00	45·00
38A		5s. claret ..	..	..	50·00	90·00
39A		10s. yellow ..	..	..	£110	£150
26A/39A		..	..	*Set of* 14	£200	£350

B. *Shiny surfaced, white paper* (1937–48)

26B	4	¹/₂d. chestnut ..	..	..	8·00	13·00
		c. Perf 14 (1947)	..	..	1·40	9·50
27B		1d. green	..	..	2·50	3·00
28B		1¹/₂d. scarlet	..	..	90	1·50
29B		2d. orange ..	..	..	1·75	8·00
30*d*B		2¹/₂d. dull blue (1948) ..	..	2·00	4·00
		da. Imperf between (vert pair)	..	£4500	£4500
		db. Imperf between (horiz pair)	..	£4500	£4500
31*c*B		3d. greenish grey (1947)	..	2·75	10·00
32B		4d. olive-green	..	..	4·25	12·00
33B		5d. brown	..	..	3·50	4·00
34B		6d. dull violet	..	..	3·25	4·50
35B		9d. olive-brown	..	..	7·50	20·00
36B		1s. brown-lake	..	..	5·50	2·75
37B		2s. 6d. grey-green	..	..	25·00	35·00
38B		5s. claret	..	..	35·00	50·00
39B		10s. yellow ..	..	..	£100	£130
26B/39B		..	..	*Set of* 14	£170	£250

(Recess John Ash, Melbourne)

1937 (10 May). *Coronation. P* 11.

44	6	1¹/₂d. scarlet	..	..	45	1·25
45		2d. orange	..	..	45	1·75
46		2¹/₂d. blue ..	..	..	45	60
47		1s. purple	..	..	65	90
44/7		..	..	*Set of* 4	1·75	4·00

Japanese forces invaded Nauru on 26 August 1942 and virtually all the inhabitants were removed to Truk in the Caroline Islands.

The Australian army liberated Nauru on 13 September 1945. After an initial period without stamps Australian issues were supplied during October 1945 and were used from Nauru until further supplies of Nos. 26/39 became available. The deportees did not return until early in 1946.

NEW GUINEA
AUSTRALIAN MANDATE

16 Bulolo Goldfields	**18**

(Recess John Ash, Melbourne)

1937 (18 May). *Coronation. P* 11.

208	18	2d. scarlet	..	..	50	30
209		3d. blue	..	..	50	55
210		5d. green	..	..	50	55
		a. Re-entry (design completely duplicated) (Pl 2a R. 5/2)		55·00	80·00
211		1s. purple	..	..	50	35
208/11		..	..	*Set of* 4	1·75	1·60

(Recess John Ash, Melbourne)

1939 (1 Mar). *Air. Inscr* "AIR MAIL POSTAGE" *at foot. P* 11.

212	16	¹/₂d. orange	..	..	3·00	3·00
213		1d. green	..	..	3·25	4·00
214		1¹/₂d. claret	..	..	3·25	7·50

215	**16**	2d. vermilion	..	..	..	7·50	3·50
216		3d. blue ..	..	..	..	9·50	18·00
217		4d. yellow-olive..	..	..	..	10·00	8·00
218		5d. deep green ..	..	..	..	8·00	2·75
219		6d. bistre-brown	..	..	..	19·00	15·00
220		9d. violet	..	..	..	19·00	20·00
221		1s. pale blue-green	..	..	..	19·00	18·00
222		2s. dull lake	..	..	..	50·00	48·00
223		5s. olive-brown ..	..	..	..	£120	95·00
224		10s. pink ..	..	..	..	£325	£225
225		£1 olive-green ..	..	..	..	£100	£110
212/25		..	..	..	Set of 14	£600	£500

Civil Administration in New Guinea was suspended in 1942, following the Japanese invasion.

Various New Guinea stamps exist overprinted with an anchor and three Japanese characters in a style similar to the Japanese Naval Control Area overprints found on the stamps of Netherlands Indies. These overprints on New Guinea are bogus. Two different versions are known, one produced in Japan during 1947 and the other in Australia during the late 1980s.

On resumption, after the Japanese defeat in 1945, Australian stamps were used until the appearance of the issue for the combined territories of Papua & New Guinea.

NORFOLK ISLAND

1 Ball Bay

(Recess Note Ptg Branch, Commonwealth Bank)

1947 (10 June)–**59.** *Toned paper. P* 14.

1	**1**	¹/₂d. orange	..	..	..	85	60
		a. White paper (11.56)	..	..	1·10	4·50
2		1d. bright violet	..	..	..	50	60
		a. White paper (8.57)	..	..	5·00	14·00
3		1¹/₂d. emerald-green	..	..	50	70
		a. White paper (11.56)	..	..	7·50	20·00
4		2d. reddish violet	..	..	..	55	40
		a. White paper (11.56)	..	..	90·00	£130
5		2¹/₂d. scarlet	..	..	..	80	30
6		3d. chestnut	..	..	..	70	70
6a		3d. emerald-green (*white paper*) (6.7.59)	16·00	7·00
7		4d. claret	..	..	..	1·25	40
8		5¹/₂d. indigo	..	..	..	70	30
9		6d. purple-brown	..	..	..	70	30
10		9d. magenta	..	..	..	1·25	40
11		1s. grey-green ..	..	..	..	70	40
12		2s. yellow-bistre	..	..	..	1·00	1·00
12a		2s. deep blue (*white paper*) (6.7.59)	..	24·00	7·50
1/12a		..		Set of 14	45·00	18·00

Stamps as Type **1**, some in different colours, perforated 11 were prepared in 1940, but never issued. Examples exist from sheets stolen prior to the destruction of these stocks.

PAPUA

35   36 Port Moresby

(Recess J. Ash)

1937 (14 May). *Coronation. P* 11.

154	**35**	1d. green	..	..	..	55	15
155		2d. scarlet	..	..	..	55	50
156		3d. blue ..	..	..	..	55	55
157		5d. purple	..	..	..	55	1·25
154/7	..	..	..	..	Set of 4	2·00	2·40

Some covers franked with these stamps and posted on 2 June 1937 were postmarked 2 April 1937 in error.

(Recess J. Ash)

1938 (6 Sept). *Air. 50th Anniv of Declaration of British Possession. P* 11.

158	**36**	2d. rose-red	..	..	..	3·75	2·25
159		3d. bright blue ..	..	..	3·75	2·25
160		5d. green	..	..	..	3·75	3·25
161		8d. brown-lake ..	..	..	11·00	14·00
162		1s. mauve	..	..	..	30·00	15·00
158/62		..	..	..	Set of 5	48·00	32·00

37 Natives poling Rafts

(Recess J. Ash)

1939 (6 Sept). *Air. P* 11.

163	**37**	2d. rose-red	..	..	..	3·50	3·75
164		3d. bright blue ..	..	..	3·50	6·50
165		5d. green	..	..	..	3·75	1·50
166		8d. brown-lake ..	..	..	10·00	2·50
167		1s. mauve	..	..	..	13·00	6·00

(Recess W. C. G. McCracken)

1941 (2 Jan). *Air. P* 11¹/₂.

168	**37**	1s. 6d. olive-green	..	..	35·00	32·00
163/168		..	..	..	Set of 6	60·00	45·00

Civil Administration, in Papua, was suspended in 1942; on resumption, after the Japanese defeat in 1945. Australian stamps were used until the appearance of the issue of the combined territories of Papua & New Guinea.

Bahamas

12 pence (d) = 1 shilling; 20 shillings = 1 pound

CROWN COLONY

18

(Recess B.W.)

1931 (14 July)–**46.** *Wmk Mult Script CA. P* 12.
131	18	2s. slate-purple and deep ultramarine	..	20·00	25·00
		a. *Slate-purple and indigo* (9.42)	..	65·00	38·00
		b. *Brownish black and indigo* (13.4.43)	6·50	2·75
		c. *Brownish black and steel-blue* (6.44)	10·00	1·25
132		3s. slate-purple and myrtle-green	..	28·00	26·00
		a. *Brownish black and green* (13.4.43)	7·00	2·00
		b. *Brownish blk & myrtle-grn* (1.10.46)	6·00	2·50
131/2		Perf "Specimen"	..	..	*Set of 2* 70·00

Most of the stamps from the September 1942 printing (No. 131a and further stocks of the 3s. similar to No. 132) were used for the 1942 "LANDFALL" overprints

1937 (12 May). *Coronation. As Nos. 95/7 of Antigua, but printed by D.L.R. P* 14.
146		½d. green	..	..	..	15	15
147		1½d. yellow-brown	..	..	..	30	75
148		2½d. bright blue	..	..	..	50	75
146/8	..	..	..	..	*Set of 3*	85	1·50
146/8		Perf "Specimen"	..	..	*Set of 3* 60·00

20 King George VI

Accent flaw (right pane
R. 1/5) (1938 ptg only)

Short "T" in "TWO"
(right pane R. 3/6)
(Retouched on No. 152c,
although bottom of letter
is still pointed)

(Typo D.L.R.)

1938 (11 Mar)–**52.** *Wmk Mult Script CA. Chalk-surfaced paper*
(1s. *to* £1). *P* 14.
149	20	½d. green	..	..	..	15	90
		a. Elongated "E"	..	..	..	45·00
		b. Accent flaw	..	..	..	75·00
		c. *Bluish green* (11.9.42)	..	..	1·75	1·25
		ca. Elongated "E"	..	..	..	95·00
		d. *Myrtle-green* (11.12.46)	..	..	5·50	5·00
		da. Elongated "E"	..	..	..	£180

149e	20	½d. brown-purple (18.2.52)	..	..	90	2·50
		ea. Error. Crown missing	..	..	£5500
		eb. Error. St. Edward's Crown	..	£2250
		ec. Elongated "E"	..	..	85·00
150		1d. carmine	..	..	..	8·50	4·75
150a		1d. olive-grey (17.9.41)	..	..	3·25	3·25
		ab. *Pale slate* (11.9.42)	..	..	50	60
151		1½d. red-brown (19.4.38)	...	..	1·25	1·00
		a. *Pale red-brown* (19.4.48)	..	4·25	2·25
152		2d. pale slate (19.4.38)	..	..	18·00	6·00
		a. Short "T"	..	..	..	£475
152b		2d. scarlet (17.9.41)	..	..	75	55
		ba. Short "T"	..	..	..	85·00
		bb. "TWO PENCE" printed double	..	† £5000
		bc. *Dull rose-red* (19.4.48)	..	2·75	2·75
152c		2d. green (1.5.51)	..	..	1·00	80
153		2½d. ultramarine	..	..	3·25	2·00
153a		2½d. violet (1.7.43)	..	..	1·25	70
		ab. "2½ PENNY" printed double	..	£2750
154		3d. violet (19.4.38)	..	..	16·00	4·00
154a		3d. blue (4.43)	..	..	60	90
		ab. *Bright ultramarine* (19.4.48)	..	4·00	4·00
154b		3d. scarlet (1.2.52)	..	..	50	3·00
154c		10d. yellow-orange (18.11.46)	..	2·00	20
155		1s. grey-black and carmine (*thick paper*) (15.9.38)	..	..	16·00	5·50
		a. *Brownish grey and scarlet* (4.42)	£275	55·00
		b. *Ordinary paper. Black and carmine* (9.42)	..	17·00	6·50
		c. *Ordinary paper. Grey-black and bright crimson* (6.3.44)	..	9·00	65
		d. *Pale brownish grey and crimson* (19.4.48)	..	..	9·50	1·00
156		5s. lilac & blue (*thick paper*) (19.4.38)	£170	£100
		a. *Reddish lilac and blue* (4.42)	..	£1200	£400
		b. *Ordinary paper. Purple & bl* (9.42)	27·00	15·00
		c. *Ordinary paper. Dull mauve and deep blue* (11.46)	..	75·00	35·00
		d. *Brown-purple & dp brt bl* (19.4.48)	30·00	9·00
		e. *Red-purple & dp bright blue* (8.51)	23·00	12·00
157	20	£1 deep grey-green and black (*thick paper*) (15.9.38)	..	..	£250	£140
		a. *Ordinary paper. Blue-green and black* (13.4.43)	..	60·00	45·00
		b. *Ordinary paper. Grey-green and black* (3.44)	..	..	95·00	65·00
149/57a	..	..	..	*Set of 17*	£130	70·00
149/57		Perf "Specimen"	..	..	*Set of 14*	£425

Nos. 149/50a exist in coils, constructed from normal sheets.

No. 149eb occurs on a row in the watermark in which the crowns and letters "CA" alternate.

The thick chalk-surfaced paper, used for the initial printing of the 1s., 5s. and £1, was usually toned and had streaky gum. The April 1942 printing for the 1s. and 5s., which was mostly used for the "LANDFALL" overprints, was on thin, white chalk-surfaced paper with clear gum. Printings of the three values between September 1942 and November 1946 were on a thick, smooth, opaque ordinary paper.

21 Sea Garden, Nassau

22 Fort Charlotte

23 Greater Flamingos in Flight

3d.

(24)

(Recess Waterlow)

1938 (1 July). *Wmk Mult Script CA. P* 12½.

158	**21**	4d. light blue and red-orange	..	1·00	90
159	**22**	6d. olive-green and light blue	..	60	90
160	**23**	8d. ultramarine and scarlet	..	6·00	2·00
158/60			Set of 3	7·00	3·50
158/60 Perf "Specimen"		..	Set of 3	£100	

1940 (28 Nov). *No.* 153 *surcharged with T* 24 *by* The Nassau Guardian.

161	**20**	3d. on 2½d. blue ..	..	..	90	60

1 4 9 2 LANDFALL OF COLUMBUS 1 9 4 2

(25)

"RENCE" flaw (Right pane R. 9/3. Later corrected so that it does not occur on No. 154a)

1942 (12 Oct). *450th Anniv of Landing of Columbus in New World. Optd as T* 25 *by* The Nassau Guardian.

162	**20**	½d. bluish green	..	..	30	60
		a. Elongated "E"	..	..	40·00	
		b. Opt double	..	..	£1000	
163		1d. pale rose	..	..	30	60
164		1½d. red-brown ..	..	..	40	60
165		2d. scarlet	..	..	30	65
		a. Short "T" ..	..	..	70·00	
166		2½d. ultramarine	..	..	30	65
167		3d. ultramarine	..	..	30	65
		a. "RENCE" flaw	..	..	95·00	
168	**21**	4d. light blue and red-orange ..		40	90
		a. "COIUMBUS" (R. 5/2)	..	£650	£650
169	**22**	6d. olive-green and light blue	..	40	1·75
		a. "COIUMBUS" (R. 5/2)	..	£650	£700
170	**23**	8d. ultramarine and scarlet	..	90	70
		a. "COIUMBUS" (R. 5/2)	..	£4750	£2250
171	**20**	1s. brownish grey and scarlet	..	4·50	3·50
		a. Ordinary paper. *Black and carmine*	4·50	4·00
		b. Ordinary paper. *Grey-black and bright crimson*	..	9·00	6·00
172	**18**	2s. slate-purple and indigo	..	8·00	10·00
		a. Brownish black and indigo	..	8·00	10·00
		b. Brownish black and steel-blue	..	22·00	22·00
		c. Stop after "COLUMBUS" (R. 2/12)	£3000	
173		3s. slate-purple and myrtle-green	..	6·50	
		a. Brownish black and green	..	40·00	32·00
		b. Stop after "COLUMBUS" (R. 2/12)	£2000	

174	**20**	5s. reddish lilac and blue	..	..	30·00	15·00
		a. Ordinary paper. *Purple and blue*	..	18·00	14·00
175		£1 deep grey-green & blk (*thick paper*)	65·00	50·00
		a. Ordinary paper. *Grey-green & black*	30·00	25·00
162/75		..	..	Set of 14	60·00	60·00
162/75 Perf "Specimen"		..	Set of 14	£400	

These stamps replaced the definitive series for a period of six months. Initially stocks of existing printings were used, but when further supplies were required for overprinting a number of new printings were produced, some of which, including the new colour of the 3d., did not appear without overprint until much later.

1946 (11 Nov). *Victory. As Nos.* 110/11 *of Antigua.*

176		1½d. brown	..	..	..	10	40
177		3d. blue ..	..	..	..	10	40
176/7 Perf "Specimen"		..	..	Set of 2	55·00	

26 Infant Welfare Clinic

(Recess C.B.N.)

1948 (11 Oct). *Tercentenary of Settlement of Island of Eleuthera. T* 26 *and similar horiz designs. P* 12.

178		½d. orange	..	..	..	30	90
179		1d. sage-green	..	..	..	30	35
180		1½d. yellow	..	..	..	30	80
181		2d. scarlet	..	..	..	30	40
182		2½d. brown-lake	..	..	..	45	75
183		3d. ultramarine	..	..	..	85	85
184		4d. black	..	..	..	60	70
185		6d. emerald-green ..	..	..	1·75	80
186		8d. violet	..	..	..	60	70
187		10d. carmine ..	..	..	..	60	35
188		1s. sepia	..	..	..	1·00	50
189		2s. magenta	..	..	..	4·00	8·50
190		3s. blue	..	..	..	8·00	8·50
191		5s. mauve	..	..	..	8·50	4·50
192		10s. grey	..	..	..	9·50	9·00
193		£1 vermilion	..	..	..	11·00	14·00
178/93		..	..	Set of 16	40·00	45·00

Designs:—1d. Agriculture (combine harvester); 1½d. Sisal; 2d. Straw work; 2½d. Dairy farm; 3d. Fishing fleet; 4d. Island settlement; 6d. Tuna fishing; 8d. Paradise Beach; 10d. Modern hotels; 1s. Yacht racing; 2s. Water sports (skiing); 3s. Shipbuilding; 5s. Transportation; 10s. Salt production; £1, Parliament Buildings.

1948 (1 Dec). *Royal Silver Wedding. As Nos.* 112/13 *of Antigua.*

194		1½d. red-brown	..	..	20	25
195		£1 slate-green	..	..	32·00	32·00

1949 (10 Oct). *75th Anniv of Universal Postal Union. As Nos.* 114/17 *of Antigua.*

196		2½d. violet	..	..	..	35	40
197		3d. deep blue ..	..	..	2·25	2·25
198		6d. greenish blue	..	..	55	2·25
199		1s. carmine	..	..	..	55	75
196/9 ..		..	..	Set of 4	3·25	5·00

STAMP BOOKLETS

1938. *Black on pink cover with map and* "BAHAMAS ISLES OF JUNE" *on reverse. Stapled.*

SB1	2s. booklet containing twelve 1d. (No. 150) in blocks of 6 and eight 1½d. (No. 151) in folded block of 8	..	..	..	£5000

Bahrain

12 pies = 1 anna; 16 annas = 1 rupee

INDIAN AND SUBSEQUENTLY BRITISH POSTAL ADMINISTRATION

BAHRAIN
(1)

BAHRAIN
(2)

Stamps of India overprinted with T 1 or T 2 (rupee values)

1938–41. *King George VI.*

20	91	3 p. slate (5.38)	..	8·00	3·25
21		½ a. red-brown (5.38)	..	4·25	10
22		9 p. green (5.38)	..	3·50	3·75
23		1 a. carmine (5.38)	..	2·75	10
24	92	2 a. vermilion (1939)	..	6·50	1·50
26	–	3 a. yellow-green (1941)	..	10·00	5·00
27	–	3 a. 6 p. bright blue (7.38)	..	4·25	3·00
28	–	4 a. brown (1941)	..	£120	65·00
30	–	8 a. slate-violet (1940)	..	£140	35·00
31	–	12 a. lake (1940)	..	£100	45·00
32	93	1 r. grey and red-brown (1940)	..	2·75	1·75
33		2 r. purple and brown (1940)	..	13·00	2·75
34		5 r. green and blue (1940)	..	15·00	13·00
35		10 r. purple and claret (1941)	..	65·00	30·00
36		15 r. brown and green (1941)	..	48·00	48·00
		w. Wmk inverted	..	48·00	48·00
37		25 r. slate-violet and purple (1941)	..	95·00	85·00
20/37			*Set of 16*	£550	£300

1942–45. *King George VI on white background.*

38	100a	3 p. slate	..	1·75	60
39		½ a. purple	..	4·00	90
40		9 p. green	..	12·00	12·00
41		1 a. carmine	..	3·50	50
42	101	1 a. 3 p. bistre	..	8·00	14·00
43		1½ a. dull violet	..	4·75	4·25
44		2 a. vermilion	..	4·50	1·50
45		3 a. bright violet	..	15·00	4·00
46		3½ a. bright blue	..	3·50	13·00
47	102	4 a. brown	..	2·00	1·50
48		6 a. turquoise-green	..	9·50	9·00
49		8 a. slate-violet	..	3·25	2·50
50		12 a. lake	..	5·50	4·00
38/50			*Set of 13*	70·00	60·00

Stamps of Great Britain surcharged

For similar surcharges without the name of the country, see BRITISH POSTAL AGENCIES IN EASTERN ARABIA.

BAHRAIN

BAHRAIN

I ANNA
(3)

5 RUPEES
(4)

1948 (1 Apr)–49. *Surch as T 3, 4 (2 r. and 5 r.) or similar surch with bars at foot (10 r.).*

51	128	½ a. on ½d. pale green	..	40	85
52		1 a. on 1d. pale scarlet	..	40	1·25
53		1½ a. on 1½d. pale red-brown	..	40	1·25
54		2 a. on 2d. pale orange	..	40	20
55		2½ a. on 2½d. light ultramarine	..	50	1·25
56		3 a. on 3d. pale violet	..	40	10
57	129	6 a. on 6d. purple	..	40	10
58	130	1 r. on 1s. bistre-brown	..	1·25	10
59	131	2 r. on 2s. 6d. yellow-green	..	5·00	4·50
60		5 r. on 5s. red	..	5·50	4·50
60a	132	10 r. on 10s. ultramarine (4.7.49)	..	60·00	42·00
51/60a			*Set of 11*	65·00	50·00

BAHRAIN 2½ ANNAS
(5)

BAHRAIN 15 RUPEES
(6)

1948 (26 Apr). *Silver Wedding, surch as T 5 or 6.*

61	137	2½ a. on 2½d. ultramarine	..	1·00	30
62	138	15 r. on £1 blue	..	40·00	48·00

1948 (29 July). *Olympic Games, surch as T 5, but in one line (6 a.) or two lines (others); the 1 r. also has a square of dots as T 7.*

63	139	2½ a. on 2½d. ultramarine	..	55	1·25
		a. Surch double	..	£800	£1400
64	140	3 a. on 3d. violet	..	55	2·00
65	141	6 a. on 6d. bright purple	..	1·50	2·50
66	142	1 r. on 1s. brown	..	1·50	2·50
63/6			*Set of 4*	3·75	7·50

Fourteen used examples of No. 63a are known, of which twelve were postmarked at Experimental P.O. K-121 (Muharraq), one at F.P.O. 756 (Shaibah) and one apparently cancelled-to-order at Bahrain on 10 October 1949.

BAHRAIN 3 ANNAS

(7)

1949 (10 Oct). *75th Anniv of U.P.U., surch as T 7, in one line (2½ a.) or in two lines (others).*

67	143	2½ a. on 2½d. ultramarine	..	55	2·25
68	144	3 a. on 3d. violet	..	85	2·75
69	145	6 a. on 6d. bright purple	..	75	3·00
70	146	1 r. on 1s. brown	..	1·60	2·00
67/70			*Set of 4*	3·25	9·00

BAHRAIN

BAHRAIN

2 RUPEES
(7a)

2 RUPEES
Type II

BAHRAIN

Extra bar (R. 6/1)

Three Types of 2 r.:

Type I. As Type 7a showing "2" level with "RUPEES" and "BAHRAIN" sharp.

Type II. "2" raised. "BAHRAIN" worn. 15 mm between "BAHRAIN" and "2 RUPEES".

Type III. As Type II, but 16 mm between "BAHRAIN" and "2 RUPEES". Value is set more to the left of "BAHRAIN".

1950 (2 Oct)–55. *Surch as T 3 or 7a (rupee values).*

71	128	½ a. on ½d. pale orange (3.5.51)	..	1·00	1·25
72		1 a. on 1d. light ultramarine (3.5.51)		2·00	10
73		1½ a. on 1½d. pale green (3.5.51)	..	2·00	9·50
74		2 a. on 2d. pale red-brown (3.5.51)	..	80	30
75		2½ a. on 2½d. pale scarlet (3.5.51)	..	2·00	9·50
76	129	4 a. on 4d. light ultramarine	..	2·00	1·50
77	147	2 r. on 2s. 6d. yellow-green (3.5.51)	..	21·00	6·00
		a. Surch Type II (1953)	..	65·00	32·00
		b. Surch Type III (1955)	..	£700	80·00
		ba. "I" inverted and raised (R.2/1)		£2500	£600
78	148	5 r. on 5s. red (3.5.51)	..	13·00	3·75
		a. Extra bar	..	£250	
79	149	10 r. on 10s. ultramarine (3.5.51)	..	26·00	7·00
71/79			*Set of 9*	60·00	32·00

Barbados

1937. 12 pence (d) = 1 shilling; 20 shillings = 1 pound
1950. 100 cents = 1 West Indian dollar

CROWN COLONY

1937 (14 May). *Coronation. As Nos. 95/7 of Antigua, but printed by D.L.R. P* 14.

245	1d. scarlet			30	15
246	1½d. yellow-brown			40	60
247	2½d. bright blue			70	45
245/7			Set of 3	1·25	1·10
245/7 Perf "Specimen"			Set of 3	50·00	

21 Badge of the Colony

Recut line (R. 10/6)

Extra frame line (R. 11/9)

Mark on central ornament (R. 1/3, 2/3, 3/3)

Vertical line over horse's head (R. 4/10) (corrected on Dec 1947 ptg)

"Flying mane" (R. 4/1) (corrected on Dec 1947 ptg)

Curved line at top right (R. 7/8)

Cracked plate (extends to top right ornament) (R. 6/10))

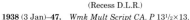

(Recess D.L.R.)

1938 (3 Jan)–**47**. *Wmk Mult Script CA. P* 13½×13.

248	21	½d. green		6·00	15
		a. Recut line		£110	
		b. Perf 14 (8.42)		70·00	1·25
		ba. Recut line		£300	
248c		½d. yellow-bistre (16.10.42)		15	30
		ca. "A" of "CA" missing from wmk		£1100	
		cb. Recut line		16·00	
249		1d. scarlet (1941)		£275	4·00
		a. Perf 14 (3.1.38)		16·00	10
249b		1d. blue-green (1943)		2·50	80
		c. Perf 14 (16.10.42)		15	10
		ca. "A" of "CA" missing from wmk		£1100	
250		1½d. orange		15	40
		a. "A" of "CA" missing from wmk		£1100	
		b. Perf 14 (11.41)		4·75	65
250c		2d. claret (3.6.41)		40	2·00
		ca. Extra frame line		28·00	
250d		2d. carmine (20.9.43)		15	60
		da. Extra frame line		17·00	
		e. Perf 14 (11.9.44)		15	1·40
		ea. Extra frame line		17·00	
251		2½d. ultramarine		50	40
		a. Mark on central ornament		32·00	
		b. *Blue* (17.2.44)		1·10	4·25
		ba. "A" of "CA" missing from wmk		£1000	
		bb. Mark on central ornament		42·00	
252		3d. brown		20	1·90
		a. Vertical line over horse's head		75·00	
		b. Perf 14 (4.41)		20	55
		ba. Vertical line over horse's head		75·00	
252c		3d. blue (1.4.47)		20	1·50
		ca. Vertical line over horse's head		75·00	
253		4d. black		20	10
		a. Flying mane		80·00	
		b. Curved line at top right		70·00	
		c. Cracked plate		70·00	
		d. Perf 14 (11.9.44)		20	3·50
		da. Flying mane		80·00	
		db. Curved line at top right		70·00	
		dc. Cracked plate		70·00	
254		6d. violet		80	10
254a		8d. magenta (9.12.46)		55	2·00
255		1s. olive-green		16·00	2·50
		a. *Deep brown-olive* (19.11.45)		1·00	10
256		2s. 6d. purple		6·50	1·50
256a		5s. indigo (3.6.41)		3·25	5·50
		ab. "A" of "CA" missing from wmk		£1300	
248/56a			Set of 16	32·00	13·00
248/56a Perf "Specimen"			Set of 16	£190	

No. 249a was perforated by two machines, one gauging 13.8×14.1 (1938), the other 14.1 (1939).

Nos. 248/c and 249/c exist in coils constructed from normal sheets.

22 Kings Charles I, George VI, Assembly Chamber and Mace

(Recess D.L.R.)

1939 (27 June). *Tercentenary of General Assembly. Wmk Mult Script CA. P* 13½ × 14.

257	**22**	½d. green	..	..	..	.. 2·25	30
258		1d. scarlet	..	..	..	.. 2·25	30
259		1½d. orange	..	..	..	.. 2·25	60
260		2½d. bright ultramarine	..	..	.. 2·25	3·75
261		3d. brown	..	..	..	.. 2·25	2·25
257/61		..	..	..	*Set of* 5	10·00	6·50
257/61 Perf "Specimen"		..	..	*Set of* 5	£140

Two flags on tug
(R. 5/2)

1946 (18 Sept). *Victory. As Nos. 110/11 of Antigua.*

262	1½d. red-orange	..	..	..	..	15	15
	a. Two flags on tug	.	..	..	.. 20·00	
263	3d. brown	..	..	..	..	15	15
262/3 Perf "Specimen"		..	..	*Set of* 2	48·00

ONE
PENNY
(23)

NY PEN

Short "Y" (R. 6/2)   Broken "E" (R. 7/4 and
11/4)

(Surch by Barbados Advocate Co)

1947 (21 Apr). *Surch with T* **23**. (*a*) *P* 14.

264	**21**	1d. on 2d. carmine (No. 250e)	..	.. 1·25	2·25
		a. Extra frame line	..	..	.. 50·00
		b. Short "Y"	..	..	.. 50·00
		c. Broken "E"	..	..	.. 26·00

(*b*) *P* 13½×13

264d	**21**	1d. on 2d. carmine (No. 250d)	..	4·50	5·00
		da. Extra frame line	..	..	£150
		db. Short "Y"	..	..	.. £150
		dc. Broken "E"	..	..	.. 90·00

The relationship of the two words in the surcharge differs on each position of the sheet.

1948 (24 Nov). *Royal Silver Wedding. As Nos. 112/13 of Antigua.*

265	1½d. orange	..	..	..	..	30	10
266	5s. indigo	..	..	..	.. 10·00	6·50

1949 (10 Oct). *75th Anniv of Universal Postal Union. As Nos. 114/17 of Antigua.*

267	1½d. red-orange	..	..	..	30	35
268	3d. deep blue	..	..	..	.. 1·50	1·50
269	4d. grey	..	..	..	..	35	2·00
270	1s. olive	..	..	..	..	35	60
267/70		..	..	..	*Set of* 4	2·25	4·00

MINIMUM PRICE

The minimum price quote is 10p which represents
a handling charge rather than a basis for valuing
common stamps. For further notes about prices
see introductory pages.

(**New Currency. 100 cents = 1 West Indian, later
Barbados, dollar**)

24 Dover Fort   **27** Statue of Nelson

(Recess B.W.)

1950 (1 May). *T* **24**, **27** *and similar designs. Wmk Mult Script CA. P* 11 × 11½ (*horiz*), 13½ (*vert*).

271	1 c. indigo	..	..	..	..	15	2·00
272	2 c. emerald-green	..	..	..	15	2·00
273	3 c. reddish brown and blue-green	..	.. 1·00	2·25
274	4 c. carmine	..	..	..	..	15	40
275	6 c. light blue	..	..	..	15	2·00
276	8 c. bright blue and purple-brown	..	.. 1·00	2·00
277	12 c. greenish blue and brown-olive ..		..	90	1·00
278	24 c. scarlet and black	..	..	..	90	40
279	48 c. violet	..	..	..	.. 8·00	6·00
280	60 c. green and claret	..	..	.. 7·00	8·50
281	$1.20, carmine and olive-green	..	.. 8·50	3·75
282	$2.40, black	..	..	..	.. 15·00	14·00
271/282		..	..	*Set of* 12	38·00	40·00

Designs: *Horiz*—2 c. Sugar cane breeding; 3 c. Public buildings; 6 c. Casting net; 8 c. *Frances W. Smith* (schooner); 12 c. Four-winged Flyingfish; 24 c. Old Main Guard Garrison; 60 c. Careenage; $2.40, Seal of Barbados. *Vert*—48 c. St. Michael's Cathedral; $1.20, Map of Barbados and wireless mast.

1951 (16 Feb). *Inauguration of B.W.I. University College. As Nos. 118/19 of Antigua.*

283	3 c. brown and blue-green	..	..	..	30	30
284	12 c. blue-green and brown-olive	..	..	55	1·40

36 King George VI and Stamp of 1852

(Recess Waterlow)

1952 (15 Apr). *Barbados Stamp Centenary. Wmk Mult Script CA. P* 13½.

285	**36**	3 c. green and slate-green	..	..	15	40
286		4 c. blue and carmine	..	..	15	1·00
287		12 c. slate-green and bright green	..	15	1·00
288		24 c. red-brown and brownish black	..	15	55
285/8	..	..	..	..	*Set of* 4	55	2·75

STAMP BOOKLETS

1938 (3 Jan). *Black on light blue cover. Advocate Co. Ltd. advertisement on front. Stapled.*

SB7	2s. booklet containing ½d. and 1d. (Nos. 248, 249a) each in block of 10 and 1½d. (No. 250) in block of 6	.. ..	.. £1300

POSTAGE DUE STAMPS

(Typo D.L.R.)

1934 (2 Jan)–**47**. *Wmk Mult Script CA. P* 14.

D1	D 1	¹/₂d. green (10.2.35)	..	..	1·25	7·00
D2		1d. black	..	..	1·25	1·25
		a. Bisected (¹/₂d.) (on cover)	..		† £800
D3		3d. carmine (13.3.47) ..		..	20·00	18·00
D1/3		..	..	..	*Set of 3* 20·00	24·00
D1/3 Perf "Specimen"		..	..	*Set of 3* 65·00

The bisected 1d. was officially authorised for use between March 1934 and February 1935. Some specimens had the value "¹/₂d." written across the half stamp in red or black ink (*Price on cover* £900).

(Typo D.L.R.)

1950 (8 Dec)–**53**. *Values in cents. Wmk Mult Script CA. Ordinary paper. P* 14.

D4	D 1	1 c. green	..	..	..	3·75	18·00
		a. Chalk-surfaced paper. *Deep green*				
		(29.11.51) ..	..	..	30	3·00
		ab. Error. Crown missing, W **9**a	..	£300
		ac. Error. St. Edward's Crown, W **9**b	£160

D5	D 1	2 c. black	..	..	..	7·00	10·00
		a. Chalk-surfaced paper (20.1.53)	..	60	5·00
		ac. Error. St. Edward's Crown, W **9**b	£300
D6		6 c. carmine	..	..	..	16·00	17·00
		a. Chalk-surfaced paper (20.1.53)	..	1·00	8·50
		ab. Error. Crown missing, W **9**a	..	£170
		ac. Error. St. Edward's Crown, W **9**b	£130
D4/6		..	..	..	*Set of 3* 24·00	40·00
D4a/6a		..	..	..	*Set of 3* 1·75	15·00

The 1 c. has no dot below "c".

Basutoland

12 pence (d) = 1 shilling; 20 shillings = 1 pound

CROWN COLONY

1937 (12 May). *Coronation. As Nos. 95/7 of Antigua, but ptd by D.L.R. P* 14.

15	1d. scarlet	..	..	..	35	50
16	2d. bright purple	..	..	..	50	85
17	3d. bright blue	..	..	..	60	85
15/17 ..	..	..	..	Set of 3	1·25	2·00
15/17 Perf "Specimen"		..	..	Set of 3	55·00	

2 King George VI,   Tower flaw (R. 2/4)
Nile Crocodile
and Mountains

(Recess Waterlow)

1938 (1 Apr). *Wmk Mult Script CA. P* 12½.

18	**2**	½d. green	..	..	..	30	1·00
19		1d. scarlet	..	..	..	50	60
		a. Tower flaw ..	..	..	..	80·00	
20		1½d. light blue	..	..	..	40	50
21		2d. bright purple	..	..	..	30	60
22		3d. bright blue ..	..	..	..	30	90
23		4d. grey ..	..	..	..	1·50	3·25
24		6d. orange-yellow	..	..	..	50	85
25		1s. red-orange ..	..	..	..	50	90
26		2s. 6d. sepia	..	..	..	8·00	7·50
27		5s. violet	..	..	..	22·00	9·00
28		10s. olive-green ..	..	..	..	22·00	17·00
18/28 ..		..	..	..	Set of 11	50·00	38·00
18/28 Perf "Specimen"			..	..	Set of 11	£190	

Basutoland
(3)

1945 (3 Dec). *Victory. Stamps of South Africa, optd with T* **3**, *inscr alternately in English and Afrikaans.*

					Un. pair	Used pair	Used single
29	**55**	1d. brown and carmine	..	..	40	40	10
30	**56**	2d. slate-blue and violet	..	..	40	40	10
31	**57**	3d. deep blue and blue	..	..	40	70	15
29/31		..	..	Set of 3	1·10	1·40	30

4 King George VI   **5** King George VI and Queen
Elizabeth

6 Queen Elizabeth II as Princess, and Princess Margaret

7 The Royal Family

(Recess Waterlow)

1947 (17 Feb). *Royal Visit. Wmk Mult Script CA. P* 12½.

32	**4**	1d. scarlet	..	..	..	10	10
33	**5**	2d. green	..	..	..	10	10
34	**6**	3d. ultramarine	..	..	..	10	10
35	**7**	1s. mauve	..	..	..	15	10
32/5 ..		..	..	..	Set of 4	40	30
32/5 Perf "Specimen"			..	..	Set of 4	80·00	

1948 (1 Dec). *Royal Silver Wedding. As Nos.* 112/13 *of Antigua.*

36	1½d. ultramarine	..	..	..	20	10
37	10s. grey-olive	..	..	..	30·00	27·00

1949 (10 Oct). *75th Anniv of Universal Postal Union. As Nos.* 114/17 *of Antigua.*

38	1½d. blue	..	..	..	30	60
39	3d. deep blue ..	..	..	..	1·75	1·75
40	6d. orange	..	..	..	1·50	1·75
41	1s. red-brown	..	..	..	1·00	90
38/41	..	..	..	Set of 4	4·00	4·50

POSTAGE DUE STAMPS

D 1   Normal   Large "d."
(R. 9/6, 10/6)

(Typo D.L.R.)

1933 (1 Dec)–**52**. *Wmk Mult Script CA. Ordinary paper. P* 14.

D1	D **1**	1d. carmine	..	..	..	1·75	7·00
		a. *Scarlet* (1938)	..	..	32·00	40·00	
		b. Chalk-surfaced paper. *Deep carmine* (24.10.51) ..	..	..	65	1·75	
		ba. Error. Crown missing, W9a	..	£110			
		bb. Error. St. Edward's Crown, W9b	..	65·00			
D2		2d. violet	..	..	..	7·50	14·00
		a. Chalk-surfaced paper (6.11.52)	..	30	7·00		
		ab. Error. Crown missing, W9a	..	£120			
		ac. Error. St. Edward's Crown, W9a	..	65·00			
		ad. Large "d"	..	..	..	5·50	
D1/2 Perf "Specimen"			..	..	Set of 2	42·00	

Bechuanaland Protectorate

12 pence (d) = 1 shilling; 20 shillings = 1 pound

PROTECTORATE

1937 (12 May). *Coronation. As Nos. 95/7 of Antigua, but printed by D.L.R. P 14.*

115	1d. scarlet			45	40
116	2d. yellow-brown			60	1·00
117	3d. bright blue			60	1·25
115/17			Set of 3	1·50	2·40
115/17 Perf "Specimen"			Set of 3	55·00	

23 King George VI,
Baobab Tree and
Cattle drinking

(Recess Waterlow)

1938 (1 Apr)–**52**. *Wmk Mult Script CA. P 12½.*

118	**23**	½d. green		2·00	2·25
		a. *Light yellowish green* (1941)		5·00	6·00
		b. *Yellowish green* (4.43)		3·50	3·50
		c. *Deep green* (4.49)		2·50	6·00
119		1d. scarlet		60	50
120		1½d. dull blue		8·50	2·00
		a. *Light blue* (4.43)		60	1·00
121		2d. chocolate-brown		60	50
122		3d. deep ultramarine		60	2·00
123		4d. orange		1·75	3·00
124		6d. reddish purple		4·00	3·00
		a. *Purple* (1944)		3·50	2·50
125		1s. black and brown-olive		3·50	3·00
		a. *Grey-black and olive-green* (21.5.52)	13·00	15·00
126		2s.6d. black and scarlet		14·00	12·00
127		5s. black and deep ultramarine		30·00	12·00
		a. *Grey-black & dp ultramarine* (10.46)	65·00	35·00
128		10s. black and red-brown		14·00	18·00
118/28			Set of 11	65·00	50·00
118/28 Perf "Specimen"		Set of 11	£170	

Bechuanaland

(24)

24a King George VI and
Queen Elizabeth

1945 (3 Dec). *Victory. Stamps of South Africa optd with T **24**. Inscr alternately in English and Afrikaans.*

			Un. pair	Used pair	Used single
129	**55**	1d. brown and carmine	50	55	10
130	**56**	2d. slate-blue and violet	50	1·00	10
131	**57**	3d. deep blue and blue	50	1·00	10
		a. Opt omitted (in vert pair with normal)		£6500	
129/31			Set of 3	1·40	2·25	25

No. 131a comes from a sheet on which the overprint was displaced downwards so that it is omitted from stamps in the top row and shown on the sheet margin at foot.

(Recess Waterlow)

1947 (17 Feb). *Royal Visit. T **24**a and similar designs. Wmk Mult Script CA. P 12½.*

132	1d. scarlet			10	10
133	2d. green			10	10
134	3d. ultramarine			10	10
135	1s. mauve			10	10
132/5			Set of 4	35	30
132/5 Perf "Specimen"		Set of 4	80·00	

Designs: *Vert*—1d. King George VI. *Horiz*—3d. Princess Elizabeth and Princess Margaret; 1s. The Royal Family.

1948 (1 Dec). *Royal Silver Wedding. As Nos. 112/13 of Antigua.*

136	1½d. ultramarine			30	10
137	10s. black			27·00	35·00

1949 (10 Oct). *75th Anniv of Universal Postal Union. As Nos. 114/17 of Antigua.*

138	1½d. blue			45	75
139	3d. deep blue			1·25	2·00
140	6d. magenta			90	1·00
141	1s. olive			95	1·00
138/41			Set of 4	3·25	4·25

POSTAGE DUE STAMPS

D 3

Normal

Large "d"
(R. 9/6, 10/6)

Serif on "d" (R.1/6)

(Typo D.L.R.)

1932 (12 Dec)–**58**. *Wmk Mult Script CA. Ordinary paper. P 14.*

D4	D **3**	½d. sage-green		6·00	32·00
D5		1d. carmine		6·50	9·00
		a. Chalk-surfaced paper (27.11.58)	1·00	13·00
D6		2d. violet		9·00	38·00
		a. Large "d"		90·00	
		b. Chalk-surfaced paper (27.11.58)	15·00	18·00
		ba. Large "d"		24·00	
		bb. Serif on "d"		30·00	
D4/6b			Set of 3	7·75	55·00
D4/6 Perf "Specimen"		Set of 3	65·00	

No. D6a first occurred on the 1947 printing.

Bermuda

12 pence (d) = 1 shilling; 20 shillings = 1 pound

1937 (14 May). *Coronation. As Nos. 95/7 of Antigua, but printed by D.L.R. P* 14.

107	1d. scarlet	..	..	..	..	50	50
108	1½d. yellow-brown	..	..	..	..	60	1·50
109	2½d. bright blue	..	..	..	..	70	1·50
107/9	..	..	..	..	*Set of 3*	1·60	3·25
107/9 Perf "Specimen"	..	..		*Set of 3*	£110		

114*b* **28**	7½d. black, blue & brt grn (*a*) (18.12.41)	6·50	2·00
	c. Black, blue & yellow-grn (*a*) (3.43)	4·50	2·25
115 **26***a*	1s. green (*a*) (*b*)	2·00	50
	a. Bluish green (*b*) (20.6.52)	6·50	6·00

Perforations. Two different perforating machines were used on the various printings of these stamps: (*a*) the original 11.9 line perforation; (*b*) 11.9 × 11.75 comb perforation, introduced in July 1950. These perforations occur as indicated above.

22 *Lucie* (yacht)

26 Ships in Hamilton Harbour

29 King George VI

26*a* Grape Bay, Paget Parish

27 St. David's Lighthouse

Shading omitted from top right scroll (R. 1/1. March 1943 ptgs of 2s. and £1)

Lower right scroll with broken tail (R. 2/10. Line perforated printings only)

28 White-tailed Tropic Bird, Arms of Bermuda and Native Flower

(Des Miss Higginbotham (T **28**). Recess B.W.)

1938 (20 Jan)–**52.** *T* **22** *and T* **26** *to* **28.** *Wmk Mult Script CA. P* 12.

110	**26**	1d. black and red (*a*) (*b*)		65	20
111		1½d. deep blue and purple-brown (*a*) (*b*)		6·00	1·50
		a. Blue and brown (*a*) (3.43)	..	5·50	2·50
		b. Lt blue & purple-brn (*b*) (9.45)		2·25	35
		ba. "A" of "CA" missing from wmk	..		
112	**22**	2d. light blue and sepia (*a*)	..	45·00	8·50
112*a*		2d. ultramarine and scarlet (*a*) (*b*)			
		(8.11.40)	..	1·50	80
113	**26***a*	2½d. light and deep blue (*a*)	..	11·00	1·25
113*a*		2½d. lt blue & sepia-black (*a*) (18.12.41)		3·00	1·50
		b. Pale blue & sepia-black (*a*) (3.43)		2·75	1·25
		c. Bright blue and deep sepia-black			
		(*b*) (23.9.52)	..	5·00	4·00
114	**27**	3d. black and rose-red (*a*)	..	17·00	2·00
114*a*		3d. black & deep blue (*a*) (*b*) (16.7.41)		1·75	40

Broken top right scroll (R. 5/11. Line perforated ptgs only. A retouched state of the flaw is visible in later ptgs up to March 1943)

Broken lower right scroll (R. 5/12. Occurs on printings made between May 1941 and March 1943)

Gash in chin (R.2/5.
Ptgs between May
1941 and March 1943

Missing pearl
(R.5/1, Nov 1945
ptg of 5s. only)

"ER" joined (R. 1/2. Occurs in its complete state on
1938 ptg only. Subsequent ptgs show it incomplete)

Damaged left value tablet
(R. 1/11. Part of 1951 ptg
only)

(Typo D.L.R.)

1938 (20 Jan)–53. *T* **29.** *Wmk Mult Crown CA* (£1) *or Mult
Script CA* (*others*). *Chalk-surfaced paper. P* 14 (*comb*).

116	2s. deep purple and ultramarine/*grey-blue*			£110	10·00

a. *Deep reddish purple and ultram/grey-
blue* (21.11.40)* .. .. .. £275 22·00
b. Perf 14¼ *line. Deep purple and ultram/
grey-blue* (14.11.41)* .. .. £300 85·00
bc. Lower right scroll with broken tail .. £1300 £550
bd. Broken top right scroll £1100 £450
be. Broken lower right scroll £1100 £450
bf. Gash in chin £1200 £500
c. Ordinary paper. *Pur & bl /dp bl* (7.6.42) 7·00 1·50
ce. Broken lower right scroll .. .. £200 80·00
cf. Gash in chin .. .. .. £225 85·00
d. Ordinary paper. *Purple and deep
blue/pale blue* (5.3.43) .. .. 11·00 1·50
db. Shading omitted from top right scroll .. £900 £475
de. Broken lower right scroll £550 £300
df. Gash in chin £600 £325
e. Perf 13. Ordinary paper. *Dull purple
and blue/pale blue* (15.2.50) .. 17·00 14·00
f. Perf 13. Ordinary paper. *Reddish purple
and blue/pale blue* (10.10.50) .. 8·50 14·00
117 2s. 6d. black and red/*grey-blue* .. .. 70·00 8·50
a. Perf 14¼ *line. Black and red/grey-blue*
(21.2.42)* £475 £110
ac. Lower right scroll with broken tail .. £1500 £600
ad. Broken top right scroll £1300 £500
ae. Broken lower right scroll £1300 £500
af. Gash in chin £1400 £550

(117) b. Ordinary paper. *Black and red/pale blue*
(5.3.43) .. .. .. 19·00 6·50
be. Broken lower right scroll .. £450 £200
bf. Gash in chin £475 £225
c. Perf 13. Ordinary paper. *Black and
orange-red/pale blue* (10.10.50) .. 19·00 11·00
d. Perf 13. Ordinary paper. *Black and red/
pale blue* (18.6.52) .. .. 16·00 12·00
118 5s. green and red/*yellow* .. .. £140 26·00
a. *Pale green and red/yellow* (14.3.39)* £300 65·00
b. Perf 14¼ *line. Dull yellow-green and
red/yellow* (5.1.43)* .. .. £225 29·00
bc. Lower right scroll with broken tail .. £950 £375
bd. Broken top right scroll .. £800 £275
be. Broken lower right scroll .. £800 £275
bf. Gash in chin £850 £325
c. Ordinary paper. *Dull yellow-green and
carmine-red/pale yellow* (5.42)* .. £450 95·00
ce. Broken lower right scroll .. £3000 £1000
cf. Gash in chin £3000 £1000
d. Ordinary paper. *Pale bluish green and
carmine-red/pale yellow* (5.3.43) .. £100 50·00
de. Broken lower right scroll .. £750 £425
df. Gash in chin £750 £425
e. Ordinary paper. *Green and red/pale
yellow* (11.45)* .. .. 50·00 20·00
ea. Missing pearl £750
f. Perf 13. Ordinary paper. *Yellow-green
and red/pale yellow* (15.2.50) .. 22·00 18·00
g. Perf 13. *Green and scarlet/yellow
(chalk-surfaced)* (10.10.50) .. 35·00 35·00
119 10s. green and deep lake/*pale emerald* £450 £275
a. *Bluish green and deep red/green* (8.39)* £200 £130
b. Perf 14¼ *line. Ordinary paper. Yellow-
green and carmine/green* (1942)* .. £400 £120
bc. Lower right scroll with broken tail .. £1400 £750
bd. Broken top right scroll .. £1200 £600
be. Broken lower right scroll .. £1200 £600
bf. Gash in chin £1300 £650
c. Ordinary paper. *Yellowish green and
deep carmine-red/green* (5.3.43) .. 80·00 60·00
ce. Broken lower right scroll .. £2250
cf. Gash in chin £2250
d. Ordinary paper. *Deep green and dull
red/green* (emerald back) (11.12.46) .. 85·00 60·00
e. Perf 13. Ordinary paper. *Green and
vermilion/green* (19.9.51) .. 35·00 42·00
f. Perf 13. Ordinary paper. *Green and dull
red/green* (16.4.53) .. .. 35·00 48·00
120 12s. 6d. deep grey and brownish orange .. £475 £425
a. *Grey and brownish orange* (*shades*) .. £180 65·00
b. *Grey and pale orange* (9.11.40)* .. 95·00 50·00
c. Ordinary paper (2.3.44)* .. £100 60·00
ce. Broken lower right scroll .. £1700 £1800
cf. Gash in chin £1700
d. Ordinary paper. *Grey & yell†* (17.9.47)* £600 £475
e. Perf 13. *Grey and pale orange* (*chalk-
surfaced*) (10.10.50) .. .. 95·00 75·00
121 £1 purple and black/*red* £275 £100
a. "ER" joined £650
b. *Pale purple & black/pale red* (13.5.43)* 80·00 60·00
bb. Shading omitted from top right scroll £1600
be. Broken lower right scroll .. £1100 £800
bf. Gash in chin £1100 £800
c. *Dp reddish pur & blk/pale red* (5.3.43)* 70·00 48·00
ce. Broken lower right scroll .. £1100
cf. Gash in chin £1100
d. Perf 13. *Violet & black/scarlet* (7.12.51) 48·00 75·00
da. Damaged left value tablet .. £1500
e. Perf 13. *Brt violet & blk/scar* (10.12.52) £160 £150
110/21d .. .. .. Set of 16 £275 £160
110/21 Perf "Specimen" .. .. Set of 16 £1500

Following extensive damage to their printing works on 29
December 1940 much of De La Rue's work was transferred to
other firms operating under their supervision. It is understood
that Williams Lea & Co produced those new printings ordered
for the Bermuda high value stamps during 1941. The first batch
of these printings showed the emergency use, by Williams Lea,
of a 14¼ line perforating machine (exact gauge 14.15) instead of
the comb perforation (exact gauge 13.9 × 13.8).

Dates marked * are those of earliest known use.

In No. 116c the coloured surfacing of the paper is mottled with
white specks sometimes accompanied by very close horizontal
lines. In Nos. 116d, 117b and 118c/d the surfacing is the same
colour as the back, sometimes applied in widely spaced
horizontal lines giving the appearance of laid paper.

†No. 120d is the so-called "lemon" shade.

**HALF
PENNY**

X   X

(30)   31 Postmaster Perot's Stamp

1940 (20 Dec). *No. 110 surch with T* **30** *by Royal Gazette, Hamilton.*
122 **26** ¹/₂d. on 1d. black and red (*shades*)   ..   40   45
     The spacing between "PENNY" and "X" varies from 12¹/₂ mm to 14 mm.

1946 (6 Nov). *Victory. As Nos. 110/11 of Antigua.*
123   1¹/₂d. brown   15   15
124   3d. blue   15   15
123/4 Perf "Specimen"   ..   *Set of 2*   75·00

1948 (1 Dec). *Royal Silver Wedding. As Nos. 112/13 of Antigua.*
125   1¹/₂d. red-brown   30   50
126   £1 carmine ..   ..   40·00 48·00

(Recess B.W.)

1949 (11 Apr). *Centenary of Postmaster Perot's Stamp. Wmk Mult Script CA. P* 13¹/₂.
127 **31**   2¹/₂d. blue and brown   15   15
128   3d. black and blue   15   15
129   6d. violet and green   15   15
127/9   ..   ..   *Set of 3*   40   40

1949 (10 Oct). *75th Anniv of Universal Postal Union. As Nos. 114/17 of Antigua.*
130   2¹/₂d. blue-black   60   75
131   3d. deep blue ..   ..   ..   1·75   1·25
132   6d. purple   60   75
133   1s. blue-green   60   75
130/3   ..   ..   *Set of 4*   3·25   3·25

STAMP BOOKLETS

1948 (5 Apr–10 May). *Pink (No. SB1), or light blue (No. SB2) covers. Stapled.*
SB1   5s. booklet containing six 1d., 1¹/₂d., 2d., 2¹/₂d. and 3d. (Nos. 110, 111b, 112a, 113b, 114a) in blocks of 6 (10 May) £130
SB2   10s. 6d. booklet containing six 3d. and eighteen 6d. (Nos. 114a, 104) in blocks of 6 with twelve air mail labels £150

POSTAL FISCAL

1937 (1 Feb). *As T* **29** *(portrait of King George V), but inscr* "REVENUE" *at each side. Wmk Mult Script CA. Chalk-surfaced paper. P* 14.
F1   12s. 6d. grey and orange £1000 £1100
     a. Break in scroll (R. 1/12)   ..   £3000
     b. Broken crown and scroll (R. 2/12)   ..   £3000
     c. Breaks in scrolls at right (R. 1/3)   ..   £3000
No. F1 was issued for fiscal purposes towards the end of 1936. Its use as a postage stamp was authorised from 1 February to April 1937. The used price quoted above is for examples postmarked during this period. Later in the same year postmarks with other dates were obtained by favour.

British Forces in Egypt

1000 milliemes = 100 piastres = 1 Egyptian pound

ISSUED BY THE EGYPTIAN POSTAL ADMINISTRATION

A **6** King Fuad I   A **7** King Farouk

(Types A **6**/A **7**. Photo Survey Dept, Cairo)

1936. *W* **48** *of Egypt. P* 13½×14.
A12	A **6**	3 m. green (9.11.36)	..	.. 1·00	90
A13		10 m. carmine (1.3.36)	..	.. 2·50	10
		w. Wmk inverted	..	..	

1939 (16 Dec). *W* **48** *of Egypt. P* 13×13½.
A14	A **7**	3 m. green	..	.. 1·75	3·50
A15		10 m. carmine	..	.. 2·25	10
		w. Wmk inverted	..	..	

These stamps were withdrawn in April 1941 but the concession, without the use of special stamps, continued until October 1951 when the postal agreement was abrogated.

W **48** of Egypt

British Guiana

100 cents = 1 British Guiana dollar

CROWN COLONY

1937 (12 May). *Coronation. As Nos. 95/7 of Antigua, but ptd by D.L.R. P* 14.

305	2 c. yellow-brown	..	..	..	15	10
306	4 c. grey-black	..	..	..	50	30
307	6 c. bright blue	..	..	..	60	1·00
305/7	..	..	..	*Set of* 3	1·10	1·25
305/7 Perf "Specimen"		..	..	*Set of* 3	50·00	

53 South America   **54** Victoria Regia Lilies

(Recess Waterlow)

1938 (1 Feb)–**1952.** *As earlier types but with portrait of King George VI as in T* 53/4. *Wmk Mult Script CA. P* 12½

308	43	1 c. yellow-green	..	..	..	14·00	55
		aa. Green (1944)	..	..	..	30	10
		a. Perf 14 × 13 (1949)	..	..	30	80	
309	–	2 c. slate-violet	..	..	..	60	10
		a. Perf 13 × 14 (28.4.49)	..	..	30	10	
310	53	4 c. scarlet and black	..	..	..	70	30
		a. Imperf horiz (vert pair)	..	.	£12000	£9000	
		b. Perf 13 × 14 (1952)	..	..	45	15	
311	40	6 c. deep ultramarine	..	..	..	40	10
		a. Perf 13 × 14 (24.10.49)	..	..	30	30	
312	–	24 c. blue-green	..	..	..	26·00	10·00
		a. Wmk sideways	..	..	..	1·25	10
313	–	36 c. bright violet (7.3.38)	..	..	2·00	20	
		a. Perf 13 × 14 (13.12.51)	..	..	3·00	30	
314	–	48 c. orange	..	..	..	60	40
		a. Perf 14×13 (8.5.51*)	..	..	1·50	1·25	
315	–	60 c. red-brown	..	..	..	11·00	3·75
316	–	96 c. purple	..	..	..	2·50	2·75
		a. Perf 12½ × 13½ (1944)	..	..	6·00	8·00	
		b. Perf 13 × 14 (8.2.51)	..	..	2·75	6·00	
317	–	$1 bright violet	..	..	..	11·00	35
		a. Perf 14 × 13(1951)	..	..	£300	£400	
318	–	$2 purple (11.6.45)	..	..	4·50	14·00	
		a. Perf 14 × 13 (9.8.50)	..	..	10·00	15·00	
319	54	$3 red-brown (2.7.45)	..	..	27·00	25·00	
		a. Bright red-brown (12.46)	..	..	28·00	28·00	
		b. Perf 14 × 13. *Red-brown* (29.10.52)	..	25·00	45·00		
308a/19		..	..	..	*Set of* 12	55·00	40·00
308/19 Perf "Specimen"		..	..	*Set of* 12	£200		

Designs: *Vert*—2 c., 36 c. Kaieteur Falls; 96 c. Sir Walter Raleigh and his son. *Horiz*—24 c. Sugar cane in punts; 48 c. Forest road; 60 c. Shooting logs over falls; $1 Botanical Gardens; $2 Mount Roraima.
* Earliest known postmark date.

1946 (1 Oct). *Victory. As Nos. 110/11 of Antigua.*

320	3 c. carmine	..	..	..	10	20
321	6 c. blue	..	..	..	30	50
320/1 Perf "Specimen"	..	..	*Set of* 2	48·00		

1948 (20 Dec). *Royal Silver Wedding. As Nos. 112/13 of Antigua, but $3 in recess.*

322	3 c. scarlet	..	..	..	10	40
323	$3 red-brown	..	..	..	12·00	23·00

1949 (10 Oct). *75th Anniv of Universal Postal Union. As Nos. 114/17 of Antigua.*

324	4 c. carmine	..	..	..	30	20
325	6 c. deep blue	..	..	..	90	65
326	12 c. orange	..	..	..	30	45
327	24 c. blue-green	..	..	..	30	60
324/7	..	..	..	*Set of* 4	1·60	1·75

1951 (16 Feb). *University College of B.W.I. As Nos. 118/19 of Antigua.*

328	3 c. black and carmine	..	..	30	30	
329	6 c. black and blue	..	..	..	30	60

STAMP BOOKLETS

1938. *Black on orange cover. Stitched.*
SB7 36 c. booklet containing four 1 c., eight 2 c. and four 4 c. (Nos. 308/10) in blocks of 4   .. £190

1944. *Black on orange cover. Stitched.*
SB8 24 c. booklet containing eight 1 c. and eight 2 c. (Nos. 308/9) in blocks of 4   ..   .. £150

1945–49. *Black on red cover. Stitched.*
SB9 24 c. booklet containing 1 c., 2 c. and 3 c. (Nos. 290, 308, 309), each in block of 4   .. 65·00
   a. Containing Nos. 290, 308aa, 309   .. 65·00
   b. Containing Nos. 290, 308a, 309a   ..
   c. Containing Nos. 290a, 308aa, 309   .. 65·00
   d. Containing Nos. 290b, 308aa, 309   .. 65·00
   e. Containing Nos. 290b, 308aa, 309a   .. 65·00
   f. Containing Nos. 290b, 308a, 309a   .. 65·00

POSTAGE DUE STAMPS

D 1

(Typo D.L.R.)

1940 (Mar)–**55.** *Wmk Mult Script CA. Chalk-surfaced paper* (4 c.). *P* 14.

D1	D 1	1 c. green	..	..	..	3·75	6·50
		a. Chalk-surfaced paper. *Deep green,* (30.4.52)	..	..	1·50	8·50	
		ab. W9*a* (Crown missing)	..	..	£190		
		ac. W9*b* (St. Edward's Crown)	..	..	85·00		
D2		2 c. black	..	..	..	14·00	2·00
		a. Chalk-surfaced paper (30.4.52)	..	1·50	3·50		
		ab. W9*a* (Crown missing)	..	..	£160		
		ac. W9*b* (St. Edward's Crown)	..	75·00			
D3		4 c. bright blue (1.5.52)	..	..	30	8·50	
		a. W9*a* (Crown missing)	..	..	£140		
		b. W9*b* (St. Edward's Crown)	..	75·00			
D4		12 c. scarlet	..	..	..	25·00	4·00
		a. Chalk-surfaced paper (19.7.55)	..	11·00	22·00		
D1a/4a	..	..	..	..	*Set of* 4	13·00	35·00
D1, D2 and D4 Perf "Specimen"	..		*Set of* 3	50·00		

British Honduras

100 cents = 1 British Honduras dollar

CROWN COLONY

1937 (12 May). *Coronation. As Nos. 95/7 of Antigua, but printed by D.L.R. P* 14.

147	3 c. orange	..	..	..	..	30	30
148	4 c. grey-black	..	..	..	..	70	30
149	5 c. bright blue	..	..	..	..	80	1·40
147/9	..	..	..	..	*Set of* 3	1·60	1·75
147/9 Perf "Specimen"		..	..	*Set of* 3	50·00	

24 Maya Figures

25 Chicle Tapping

(Recess B.W.)

1938 (10 Jan)–**47**. *T* **24/5** *and similar designs. Wmk Mult Script CA (sideways on horizontal stamps). P* 11½ × 11 (*horiz designs*) *or* 11 × 11½ (*vert designs*).

150	1 c. bright magenta and green (14.2.38)	..		10	1·50
151	2 c. black and scarlet (14.2.38)	..	..	20	90
	a. Perf 12 (1947)	..	..	1·90	90
152	3 c. purple and brown	..	..	30	70
153	4 c. black and green	..	..	30	70
154	5 c. mauve and dull blue	..	..	75	60
155	10 c. green and reddish brown (14.2.38)	..	75	60
156	15 c. brown and light blue (14.2.38)	..	..	2·00	70
157	25 c. blue and green (14.2.38)..	..	..	2·00	1·25
158	50 c. black and purple (14.2.38)	..	..	11·00	3·00
159	$1 scarlet and olive (28.2.38)	..	..	20·00	10·00
160	$2 deep blue and maroon (28.2.38)..	..	26·00	16·00
161	$5 scarlet and brown (28.2.38)	..	..	26·00	23·00
150/61	..	..	..	*Set of* 12	80·00	55·00
150/61 Perf "Specimen"		..	*Set of* 12	£160	

Designs: *Vert*—3 c. Cohune palm; $1 Court House, Belize. $2 Mahogany felling; $5 Arms of Colony. *Horiz*—4 c. Local products; 5 c. Grapefruit; 10 c. Mahogany logs in river; 15 c. Sergeant's Cay; 25 c. Dorey; 50 c. Chicle industry.

1946 (9 Sept). *Victory. As Nos.* 110/11 *of Antigua.*

162	3 c. brown	..	..	..	..	10	10
163	5 c. blue	..	..	..	..	10	10
162/3 Perf "Specimen"		..	..	*Set of* 2	50·00	

1948 (1 Oct). *Royal Silver Wedding. As Nos.* 112/13 *of Antigua.*

164	4 c. green	..	..	..	..	15	50
165	$5 brown	..	..	..	..	16·00	38·00

36 Island of St George's Cay

37 H.M.S. *Merlin*

(Recess Waterlow)

1949 (10 Jan). *150th Anniv of Battle of St. George's Cay. Wmk Mult Script CA. P* 12½.

166	**36**	1 c. ultramarine and green	..	..	10	50
167		3 c. blue and yellow-brown	..	..	10	1·25
168		4 c. olive and violet	..	..	10	50
169	**37**	5 c. brown and deep blue	..	..	80	20
170		10 c. green and red-brown	..	..	70	30
171		15 c. emerald and ultramarine	..	..	70	30
166/71		..	..	..	*Set of* 6	2·00	2·75

1949 (10 Oct). *75th Anniv of U.P.U. As Nos.* 114/17 *of Antigua.*

172	4 c. blue-green	..	..	..	..	40	30
173	5 c. deep blue..	..	..	..	..	1·50	50
174	10 c. red-brown	..	..	..	..	50	2·25
175	25 c. blue	..	..	..	..	60	50
172/5	..	..	..	..	*Set of* 4	2·75	3·25

1951 (16 Feb). *Inauguration of B.W.I. University College. As Nos.* 118/19 *of Antigua.*

176	3 c. reddish violet and brown	..	..	45	1·25
177	10 c. green and brown..	..	..	..	45	30

POSTAGE DUE STAMPS

D 1

(Typo D.L.R.)

1923–64. *Wmk Mult Script CA. Ordinary paper. P* 14.

D1	D 1	1 c. black	..	..	2·25	13·00
		a. Chalk-surfaced paper (25.9.56)	..	50	17·00
		b. White uncoated paper (9.4.64)	..	14·00	27·00
D2		2 c. black	..	..	..	2·25	7·50
		a. Chalk-surfaced paper (25.9.56)	..	50	17·00
D3		4 c. black	..	..	..	1·25	6·00
		a. Missing top serif on "C" (R. 6/6)	..	12·00	
		b. Chalk-surfaced paper (25.9.56)	..	90	11·00
		ba. Missing top serif on "C" (R. 6/6)	..	11·00	
		w. Wmk inverted	..	..	£150	
D1/3	..	..	..	*Set of* 3	5·25	24·00
D1a/3b	..	..	..	*Set of* 3	17·00	40·00
D1/3 Optd "Specimen"	..	..	*Set of* 3	50·00	

The early ordinary paper printings were yellowish and quite distinct from No. D1b.

British Occupation of Italian Colonies

MIDDLE EAST FORCES

For use in territory occupied by British Forces in Eritrea (1942), Italian Somaliland (from 13 April 1942), Cyrenaica (1943), Tripolitania (1943), and some of the Dodecanese Islands (1945).

PRICES. Our prices for used stamps with "M.E.F." overprints are for specimens with identifiable postmarks of the territories in which they were issued. These stamps were also used in the United Kingdom with official sanction, from the summer of 1950 onwards, and with U.K. postmarks are worth considerably less.

PRINTERS. Considerable research has been undertaken to discover the origins of Nos. M1/10. It is now suggested that Nos. M1/5, previously assigned to Harrison and Sons, were produced by the Army Printing Services, Cairo, and that the smaller printing, Nos. M6/10, previously identified as the work of the Army Printing Services, Cairo, was from an unidentified printer within the Middle East Forces area.

M.E.F. M.E.F.

(M 1)   (M 2)

Opt. 14 mm long. Regular lettering and upright oblong stops.

Opt. 13½ mm long. Regular lettering and square stops.

M.E.F.

(M 2a)

Opt. 13½ mm long. Rough lettering and round stops.

(Illustrations twice actual size)

M.E.F.

Sliced "M"
(R.6/10)

1942 (2 Mar). *Stamps of Great Britain optd.* W 127. *P* 15 × 14.

		(a) With Type M 1			
M 1	128	1d. scarlet (No. 463)	..	60	1·50
		a. Sliced "M"	..	48·00	
M 2		2d. orange (No. 465)	..	30	2·50
		a. Sliced "M"	..	32·00	
M 3		2½d. ultramarine (No. 466)	..	30	45
		a. Sliced "M"	..	32·00	
M 4		3d. violet (No. 467)	..	30	10
		a. Opt double	..	—	£2000
M 5	129	5d. brown	..	30	15
		a. Sliced "M"	..	32·00	

		(b) With Type M 2			
M 6	128	1d. scarlet (No. 463)	..	55·00	12·00
		a. Optd. with Type M 2a	..	45·00	8·50
		b. Nos. M6/a se-tenant vert ..		£200	80·00
M 7		2d. orange (No. 465)	..	65·00	75·00
		a. Optd with Type M 2a	..	55·00	65·00
		b. Nos. M7/a se-tenant vert ..		£275	£200
M 8		2½d. ultramarine (No. 466)	..	35·00	7·00
		a. Optd with Type M 2a	..	32·00	5·50
		b. Nos. M8/a se-tenant vert ..		£160	55·00
M 9		3d. violet (No. 467)	..	95·00	28·00
		a. Optd with Type M 2a	..	85·00	26·00
		b. Nos. M9/a se-tenant vert ..		£375	£140

M10	129	5d. brown	..	..	£375	90·00
		a. Optd with Type M 2a	..	£350	80·00
		b. Nos. M10/a se-tenant vert..		£1200	£600

See note after No. M21.
Nos. M6/10 were issued in panes of 60 (6 × 10), rows 2, 3, and 7 being overprinted with Type M 2 and the other seven rows with Type M 2a.

M.E.F.

(M 3)

Optd 13½ mm long. Regular lettering and upright oblong stops.

(Illustration twice actual size)

1943 (1 Jan)–**1947.** *Stamps of Great Britain optd with Type* M 3 *by Harrison & Sons.* W **127**, *P* 15 × 14 (1d. *to* 1s.); W **133**, *P* 14 *(others).*

M11	128	1d. pale scarlet (No. 486)	..	..	1·50	10
M12		2d. pale orange (No. 488)	..	..	1·50	1·25
M13		2½d. light ultramarine (No. 489)	..	45	10
M14		3d. pale violet (No. 490)	..	..	1·50	10
M15	129	5d. brown	..	..	..	2·25	10
M16		6d. purple	..	..	..	40	10
M17	130	9d. deep olive-green	..	..	85	10
M18		1s. bistre-brown	..	..	50	10
M19	131	2s. 6d. yellow-green	..	..	7·00	1·00
M20		5s. red (1947) ..	..	..	11·00	17·00
M21	132	10s. ultramarine (1947)	..	..	14·00	10·00
M11/21			*Set of* 11	35·00	27·00
M18/21 Optd "Specimen"	..	..	*Set of* 4	£500	

The overprint on No. M15 should not be confused with the other overprints on the 5d. value. It can be distinguished from No. M5 by the ½ mm difference in length; and from No. M10 by the more intense colour, thicker lettering and larger stops.

POSTAGE DUE STAMPS

M.E.F.

(MD 1)

1942. *Postage Due stamps of Great Britain Nos.* D27/30 *and* D33 *optd with Type* MD 1, *in blue-black.*

MD1	D 1	½d. emerald	..	..	..	30	9·50
MD2		1d. carmine	..	..	..	30	1·75
MD3		2d. agate	..	..	..	1·25	1·25
MD4		3d. violet	..	..	..	50	4·25
MD5		1s. deep blue (Optd S. £150)	..	..	3·25	10·00
MD1/5			*Set of* 5	5·00	24·00

CYRENAICA

In June 1949 the British authorities recognised the leader of the Senussi, Amir Mohammed Idris Al-Senussi, as Amir of Cyrenaica with autonomy in internal affairs.

(Currency. 10 millièmes = 1 piastre, 100 piastres = 1 Egyptian pound)

24   Mounted Warrior   25

(Recess Waterlow)

1950 (16 Jan). *P* 12½.

136	**24**	1 m. brown	..	..	..	70	2·00
137		2 m. carmine	..	..	..	90	2·00
138		3 m. orange-yellow	..	..		90	2·00
139		4 m. blue-green	..	..		1·25	2·50
140		5 m. grey-black	..	..		60	70
141		8 m. orange	..	..		75	65
142		10 m. violet	..	..		75	65
143		12 m. scarlet	..	..		75	65
144		20 m. blue	..	..		75	60
145	**25**	50 m. ultramarine and purple-brown	..		2·25	3·00
146		100 m. carmine and black		..		6·00	9·00
147		200 m. violet and deep blue		..		11·00	25·00
148		500 m. orange-yellow and green		..		42·00	65·00
136/148		..	..	..	*Set of 13*	60·00	£100

POSTAGE DUE STAMPS

D 26

(Recess Waterlow)

1950 (16 Jan). *P* 12½

D149	**D 26**	2 m. brown	..	..	..	45·00	95·00
D150		4 m. blue-green	..	..		45·00	95·00
D151		8 m. scarlet	..	..		45·00	95·00
D152		10 m. orange	..	..		45·00	95·00
D153		20 m. orange-yellow	..	..		45·00	95·00
D154		40 m. blue	..	..		45·00	95·00
D155		100 m. grey-brown	..	..		45·00	95·00
D149/155		..	..	..	*Set of 7*	£275	£600

On 24 December 1951 Cyrenaica united with Tripolitania, Fezzan and Ghadames to form the independent Kingdom of Libya, whose issues are listed in Part 13 (*Africa since Independence F–M*) of this catalogue.

ERITREA

From early 1950 examples of Nos. E1/32 exist precancelled in manuscript by a black or blue horizontal line for use by British troops on concession rate mail.

BRITISH MILITARY ADMINISTRATION

(Currency. 100 cents = 1 shilling)

B. M. A.
ERITREA

B. M. A.
ERITREA

10
CENTS

5 SHILLINGS

(E 1)

(E 2)

SH. 50 SH .50

Normal   Misplaced Stop

1948–9. *Stamps of Great Britain surch as Types* E 1 *or* E 2.

E 1	**128**	5 c. on ½d. pale green	..	..		50	65
E 2		10 c. on 1d. pale scarlet	..	..		65	2·00
E 3		20 c. on 2d. pale orange	..	..		45	2·25
E 4		25 c. on 2½d. light ultramarine	..		40	60
E 5		30 c. on 3d. pale violet	..	..		1·25	4·00
E 6	**129**	40 c. on 5d. brown	..	..		30	4·00
E 7		50 c. on 6d. purple	..	..		30	60

E 7a	**130**	65 c. on 8d. bright carmine (1.2.49)		7·00	2·00
E 8		75 c. on 9d. deep olive-green	..		50	75
E 9		1 s. on 1s. bistre-brown	..	..		50	50
E10	**131**	2 s. 50 c. on 2s. 6d. yellow-green		6·50	10·00
		a. Misplaced stop (R. 4/7)	..		85·00	£120
E11		5 s. on 5s. red	..	..		6·50	16·00
E12	**132**	10 s. on 10s. ultramarine	..		20·00	21·00
E1/12	..	..	..	..	*Set of 13*	40·00	55·00

BRITISH ADMINISTRATION

1950 (6 Feb). *As Nos.* E1/12, *but surch* "B.A. ERITREA" *and new values instead of* 'B.M.A.' *etc.*

E13	**128**	5 c. on ½d. pale green	..	..		50	6·00
E14		10 c. on 1d. pale scarlet	..	..		30	2·75
E15		20 c. on 2d. pale orange	..	..		30	70
E16		25 c. on 2½d. light ultramarine	..		30	40
E17		30 c. on 3d. pale violet	..	..		30	1·00
E18	**129**	40 c. on 5d. brown	..	..		40	90
E19		50 c. on 6d. purple	..	..		30	20
E20	**130**	65 c. on 8d. bright carmine	..		40	1·00
E21		75 c. on 9d. deep olive-green		..		30	25
E22		1 s. on 1s. bistre-brown	..		30	15
E23	**131**	2 s. 50 c. on 2s. 6d. yellow-green		3·50	4·50
E24		5 s. on 5s. red	..	..		6·00	9·00
E25	**132**	10 s. on 10s. ultramarine	..		55·00	55·00
E13/25		..	..	..	*Set of 13*	60·00	70·00

1951 (28 May*). *Nos.* 503/4, 506/7 *and* 509/11 *of Great Britain surch* "B.A. ERITREA" *and new values.*

E26	**128**	5 c. on ½d. pale orange	..	..		30	60
E27		10 c. on 1d. light ultramarine	..		30	60
E28		20 c. on 2d. pale red-brown	..		30	30
E29		25 c. on 2½d. pale scarlet	..		30	30
E30	**147**	2 s. 50 c. on 2s. 6d. yellow-green		6·00	18·00
E31	**148**	5 s. on 5s. red	..	..		20·00	18·00
E32		10 s. on 10s. ultramarine	..		20·00	18·00
E26/32		..	..	..	*Set of 7*	42·00	50·00

*This is the local release date. The stamps were placed on sale in London on 3 May.

POSTAGE DUE STAMPS

B. M. A.
ERITREA

10 CENTS

(ED 1)

1948. *Postage Due stamps of Great Britain Nos.* D27/30 *and* D33 *surch as Type* ED 1.

ED1	**D 1**	5 c. on ½d. emerald	..	..		9·50	18·00
ED2		10 c. on 1d. carmine	..	..		8·50	20·00
		a. No stop after "B"	..		£100	
ED3		20 c. on 2d. agate	..	..		7·00	15·00
		a. No stop after "A"	..		60·00	
		b. No stop after "B" (R. 1/9)		£120	
ED4		30 c. on 3d. violet	..	..		8·50	14·00
ED5		1 s. on 1s. deep blue	..	..		16·00	27·00
ED1/5		..	..	..	*Set of 5*	45·00	85·00

1950 (6 Feb). *As Nos.* ED1/5, *but surch* "B.A. ERITREA" *and new values instead of* "B.M.A." *etc.*

ED6	**D 1**	5 c. on ½d. emerald	..	..		11·00	42·00
ED7		10 c. on 1d. carmine	..	..		9·00	15·00
		a. "C" of "CENTS" omitted		£1600	
		ab. "C" omitted and vertical oblong for "E" of "CENTS"	..	£2750	
ED8		20 c. on 2d. agate	..	..		9·50	13·00
ED9		30 c. on 3d. violet	..	..		9·50	13·00
		w. Wmk sideways-inverted*		—	50·00
ED10		1 s. on 1s. deep blue	..		15·00	22·00
		a. Stop after "A" omitted (R. 2/13)		£275	
ED6/10		..	..	..	*Set of 5*	48·00	95·00

No. ED7a, and probably No. ED7ab, occurred on R.7/20, but the error was quickly corrected.

*No. ED9w shows the Crowns pointing to the left, *as seen from the back of the stamp.*

Stamps of Ethiopia were used in Eritrea after 15 September 1952 following federation with Ethiopia.

SOMALIA
BRITISH OCCUPATION

E.A.F.

(S 1. "East Africa Forces")

1943 (15 Jan)–**46**. *Stamps of Great Britain optd with Type* S 1, *in blue.*

S1	128	1d. pale scarlet	.	..	..	60	40
S2		2d. pale orange..		..	..	1·50	1·25
S3		2½d. light ultramarine	..	..	..	30	3·50
S4		3d. pale violet	..	..	..	50	15
S5	129	5d. brown	..	..	..	50	40
S6		6d. purple	..	..	..	30	90
S7	130	9d. deep olive-green	..	..	60	2·25
S8		1s. bistre-brown	..	..	1·25	15
S9	131	2s. 6d. yellow-green (1946)	..	6·00	6·50
S1/9				*Set of* 9	10·50	14·00
S8/9 Optd "Specimen"		..	..	*Set of* 2	£250

The note *re* used prices above Type M 1 of Middle East Forces also applies to the above issue.

BRITISH MILITARY ADMINISTRATION

(Currency. 100 cents = 1 shilling)

1948 (27 May). *Stamps of Great Britain surch* "B.M.A./ SOMALIA" *and new values, as Types* E 1 *and* E 2 *of Eritrea.*

S10	128	5 c. on ½d. pale green	..	..	..	50	1·25
S11		15 c. on 1½d. pale red-brown	..	..	80	13·00
S12		20 c. on 2d. pale orange	..	..	2·00	3·25
S13		25 c. on 2½d. light ultramarine..		1·75	4·00
S14		30 c. on 3d. pale violet	..	..	2·00	9·00
S15	129	40 c. on 5d. brown	..	..	..	40	20
S16		50 c. on 6d. purple	..	..	..	40	2·00
S17	130	75 c. on 9d. deep olive-green	..	2·00	15·00
S18		1 s. on 1s. bistre-brown..	..	..	1·25	20
S19	131	2 s. 6d. on 2s. 6d. yellow-green		3·25	24·00
		a. Misplaced stop (R. 4/7)	..	80·00	£225
S20		5 s. on 5s. red	..	..	8·00	32·00
S10/20		..	..	*Set of* 11	20·00	90·00

For illustration of No. S19a, see previous column above No. E1 of Eritrea.

BRITISH ADMINISTRATION

1950 (2 Jan). *As Nos.* S10/20, *but surch* "B.A./SOMALIA" *and new values, instead of* "B.M.A." *etc.*

S21	128	5 c. on ½d. pale green	..	..	20	2·25
S22		15 c. on 1½d. pale red-brown	..	..	60	14·00
S23		20 c. on 2d. pale orange	..	..	60	5·00
S24		25 c. on 2½d. light ultramarine..		40	6·00
S25		30 c. on 3d. pale violet	..	..	1·00	3·00
S26	129	40 c. on 5d. brown	..	..	55	85
S27		50 c. on 6d. purple	..	..	..	40	1·00
S28	130	75 c. on 9d. deep olive-green	..	1·00	5·50
S29		1 s. on 1s. bistre-brown	..	..	1·00	1·50
S30	131	2 s. 50 c. on 2s. 6d. yellow-green	..	4·00	22·00
S31		5 s. on 5s. red	..	..	..	8·50	27·00
S21/31		..	..	*Set of* 11	16·00	80·00

Somalia reverted to Italian Administration on 1 April 1950 later becoming independent. Later issues will be found listed in Part 8 (*Italy and Switzerland*) of this catalogue.

TRIPOLITANIA
BRITISH MILITARY ADMINISTRATION

(Currency. 100 centesimi = 1 Military Administration lira)

4   **4**

M.A.L. M.A.L.

Normal   Misaligned surcharge (R.8/8, 18/8)

1948 (1 July). *Stamps of Great Britain surch* "B.M.A./TRIPOLI- TANIA" *and new values, as Types* E 1 *and* E 2 *of Eritrea, but expressed in* M(*ilitary*) A(*dministration*) L(*ire*).

T 1	128	1 l. on ½d. pale green	..	..	30	80
T 2		2 l. on 1d. pale scarlet	..	..	20	15
T 3		3 l. on 1½d. pale red-brown	..	20	50
		a. Misaligned surch	..	..	20·00	
T 4		4 l. on 2d. pale orange	..	..	25	50
		a. Misaligned surch	..	..	23·00	
T 5		5 l. on 2½d. light ultramarine	..	30	20
T 6		6 l. on 3d. pale violet	..	..	20	40
T 7	129	10 l. on 5d. brown	..	..	20	15
T 8		12 l. on 6d. purple	..	..	30	20
T 9	130	18 l. on 9d. deep olive-green	..	50	65
T10		24 l. on 1s. bistre-brown..	..	50	65
T11	131	60 l. on 2s. 6d. yellow-green	..	2·00	7·00
T12		120 l. on 5s. red	..	..	11·00	15·00
T13	132	240 l. on 10s. ultramarine	..	19·00	80·00
T1/13		..	..	*Set of* 13	32·00	95·00

BRITISH ADMINISTRATION

1950 (6 Feb). *As Nos.* T1/13, *but surch.* "B.A. TRIPOLITANIA" *and new values, instead of* "B.M.A." *etc.*

T14	128	1 l. on ½d. pale green	..	..	90	10·00
T15		2 l. on 1d. pale scarlet	..	..	1·00	40
T16		3 l. on 1½d. pale red-brown	..	35	11·00
		a. Misaligned surch	..	..	30·00	
T17		4 l. on 2d. pale orange	..	..	25	4·50
		a. Misaligned surch	..	..	23·00	
T18		5 l. on 2½d. light ultramarine	..	25	70
T19		6 l. on 3d. pale violet	..	..	90	3·25
T20	129	10 l. on 5d. brown	..	..	30	4·00
T21		12 l. on 6d. purple	..	..	75	50
T22	130	18 l. on 9d. deep olive-green	..	75	2·50
T23		24 l. on 1s. bistre-brown..	..	75	3·50
T24	131	60 l. on 2s. 6d. yellow-green	..	4·25	12·00
T25		120 l. on 5s. red	..	..	17·00	22·00
T26	132	240 l. on 10s. ultramarine	..	27·00	50·00
T14/26		..	..	*Set of* 13	48·00	£110

1951 (3 May). *Nos.* 503/7 *and* 509/11 *of Great Britain surch* "B.A. TRIPOLITANIA" *and new values.*

T27	128	1 l. on ½d. pale orange..	..	..	20	4·50
T28		2 l. on 1d. light ultramarine	..	20	90
T29		3 l. on 1½d. pale green..	..	..	30	6·50
T30		4 l. on 2d. pale red-brown	..	20	1·25
T31		5 l. on 2½d. pale scarlet	..	30	6·50
T32	147	60 l. on 2s. 6d. yellow-green	..	3·50	19·00
T33	148	120 l. on 5s. red	..	..	7·50	23·00
T34	149	240 l. on 10s. ultramarine	..	30·00	38·00
T27/34		..	..	*Set of* 8	38·00	90·00

POSTAGE DUE STAMPS

1948. *Postage Due stamps of Great Britain Nos.* D27/30 *and* D33 *surch.* "B.M.A./TRIPOLITANIA" *and new values, as Type* ED 1 *of Eritrea, but expressed in* M(*ilitary*) A(*dministration*) L(*ire*).

TD1	D 1	1 l. on ½d. emerald	..	..	4·50	42·00
		a. No stop after "A"	..	..	60·00	
TD2		2 l. on 1d. carmine	..	..	2·50	28·00
		a. No stop after "A"	..	..	42·00	
		b. No stop after "M" (R.1/17)	..	80·00	
TD3		4 l. on 2d. agate	..	..	7·00	26·00
		a. No stop after "A"	..	..	£120	
		b. No stop after "M"	..	..	£150	
TD4		6 l. on 3d. violet	..	..	7·50	20·00
TD5		24 l. on 1s. deep blue	..	..	28·00	£100
TD1/5		..	..	*Set of* 5	45·00	£190

1950 (6 Feb). *As Nos.* TD1/5, *but surch* "B.A. TRIPOLITANIA" *and new values, instead of* "B.M.A." *etc.*

TD 6	D 1	1 l. on ½d. emerald	..	..	11·00	75·00
		a. No stop after "B"	..	..	£110	
TD 7		2 l. on 1d. carmine	..	..	2·50	26·00
		a. No stop after "B"	..	..	65·00	
TD 8		4 l. on 2d. agate	..	..	2·75	29·00
		a. No stop after "B"	..	..	70·00	
TD 9		6 l. on 3d. violet	..	..	17·00	60·00
		a. No stop after "B"	..	..	£170	
		w. Wmk sideways-inverted*	..	50·00	
TD10		24 l. on 1s. deep blue	..	..	42·00	£140
		a. No stop after "A"	..	..	£325	
		b. No stop after "B"	..	..	£325	
TD6/10		..	..	*Set of* 5	65·00	£300

*No. TD9w shows the Crowns pointing to the left, *as seen from the back of the stamp.*

Tripolitania became part of the independent kingdom of Libya on 24 December 1951.

British Postal Agencies in Eastern Arabia

12 pies = 1 anna; 16 annas = 1 rupee

Certain Arab States in Eastern Arabia, whilst remaining independent, had British postal administrations.

Bahrain and Kuwait (from 1948) and Qatar (from 1957) used British stamps overprinted and surcharged in local currency. Abu Dhabi (from 1964) and Trucial States (from 1961 and used only in Dubai) had definitive issues made under the auspices of the British Agencies.

In addition, British stamps were surcharged with value only for use in Muscat and certain other states. They were formerly listed under Muscat as they were first put on sale there, but in view of their more extended use, the list has been transferred here, retaining the same numbering.

The stamps were used in Muscat from 1 April 1948 to 29 April 1966; in Dubai from 1 April 1948 to 6 January 1961; in Qatar: Doha from August 1950, Umm Said from February 1956, to 31 March 1957; and in Abu Dhabi from 30 March 1963 (Das Island from December 1960) to 29 March 1964.

Nos. 21/2 were placed on sale in Kuwait Post Offices in April and May 1951 and from February to November 1953 due to shortages of stamps with "KUWAIT" overprint. Isolated examples of other values can be found commercially used from Bahrain or Kuwait.

(Currency. 12 pies= 1 anna; 16 annas = 1 rupee)

Stamps of Great Britain surcharged

■ ■

I
ANNA
(3)

2 RUPEES
(4)

$1\frac{1}{2}$ $1\frac{1}{2}$

I II

Two types of 1½ a. surcharge:
I. "1" 3¼ mm high and aligns with top of "2" in "½" (Rows 1 to 10).
II. "1" 3½ mm high with foot of figure below top of "2" (Rows 11 to 20).

1948 (1 Apr). *Surch with T 3 (½ a. to 1 r.) or 4 (2 r.).*
16	**128**	½ a. on ½d. pale green	..	2·00	6·50
17		1 a. on 1d. pale scarlet	..	2·00	20
18		1½ a. on 1½d. pale red-brown (I)	..	5·00	1·50
		a. Type II	..	5·00	1·50
		b. Vert pair. Nos. 18/a	..	30·00	
19		2 a. on 2d. pale orange	..	1·50	1·25
20		2½ a. on 2½d. light ultramarine	..	2·50	4·50
21		3 a. on 3d. pale violet ..	..	2·50	10
22	**129**	6 a. on 6d. purple	..	2·50	10

23	**130**	1 r. on 1s. bistre-brown	..	3·00	50
24	**131**	2 r. on 2s. 6d. yellow-green	..	8·00	28·00
16/24		.. ..	*Set of 9*	26·00	38·00

One example of No. 22 is known with the surcharge almost completely omitted from position R. 20/2 in the sheet.

$2\frac{1}{2}$
ANNAS
(5)

15
RUPEES
=
(6)

1948 (26 Apr). *Royal Silver Wedding. Nos. 493/4 surch with T 5 or 6.*
25	**137**	2½ a. on 2½d. ultramarine	..	1·75	1·50
26	**138**	15 r. on £1 blue..	..	23·00	35·00

1948 (29 July). *Olympic Games. Nos. 495/8 surch with new values in "ANNAS" or "1 RUPEE", as T 5/6, but in one line on 2½ a. (vert) or 6 a. and 1 r. (horiz) and grills obliterating former values of all except 2½ a.*
27	**139**	2½ a. on 2½d. ultramarine	..	35	2·00
28	**140**	3 a. on 3d. violet	..	45	2·00
29	**141**	6 a. on 6d. bright purple	..	45	2·00
30	**142**	1 r. on 1s. brown	..	1·25	2·00
		a. Surch double	..	£700	
27/30	..	.. .. ..	*Set of 4*	2·25	7·50

1949 (10 Oct). *75th Anniv of Universal Postal Union. Nos. 499/502 surch with new values in "ANNAS" or "1 RUPEE" as T 3/4, but all in one line, with grills obliterating former values.*
31	**143**	2½ a. on 2½d. ultramarine	..	60	2·50
32	**144**	3 a. on 3d. violet	..	60	2·50
33	**145**	6 a. on 6d. bright purple	..	60	1·75
34	**146**	1 r. on 1s. brown	..	3·00	2·75
31/4	..	.. .. ..	*Set of 4*	4·25	8·50

= 2 RUPEES
(6a)

= 2 RUPEES
(6b)

Type 6a. "2" and "RUPEES" level and in line with lower of the two bars.

Type 6b. "2" raised in relation to "RUPEES" and whole surcharge below the lower bar.

1950 (2 Oct)–55. *Nos. 503/8 surch as T 3 and No. 509 with T 6a.*
35	**128**	½ a. on ½d. pale orange (3.5.51)	..	30	9·00
36		1 a. on 1d. light ultramarine (3.5.51) ..		30	7·50
37		1½ a. on 1½d. pale green (I) (3.5.51)	..	5·00	21·00
		a. Type II	..	5·00	21·00
		b. Vert pair. Nos. 37/a	..	30·00	
38		2 a. on 2d. pale red-brown (3.5.51)	..	30	8·50
39		2½ a. on 2½d. pale scarlet (3.5.51)	..	30	16·00
40	**129**	4 a. on 4d. light ultramarine ..		30	3·00
41	**147**	2 r. on 2s. 6d. yellow-green (3.5.51)	..	23·00	6·50
		a. Surch with Type 6b (1955)	..	£130	65·00
35/41	..	.. .. ..	*Set of 7*	27·00	65·00

British Solomon Islands

12 pence (d) = 1 shilling; 20 shillings = 1 pound

PROTECTORATE

1937 (13 May). *Coronation. As Nos. 95/7 of Antigua.*
P 11×11½.

57	1d. violet	..	..	..	..	..	30	70
58	1½d. carmine		..	..	..	..	30	60
59	3d. blue	..	..	..	..	..	50	50
57/9	..	..	..	..	*Set of* 3	1·00	1·60
57/9 Perf "Specimen"		..	..	*Set of* 3	60·00	

5 Spears and Shield	6 Native Constable and Chief

7 Canoe House	8 Roviana Canoe

(Recess D.L.R. (2d., 3d., 2s. and 2s. 6d.), Waterlow (others))

1939 (1 Feb)–**1951**. *T* 5/8 *and similar designs. Wmk Mult Script CA. P* 13½ (2d., 3d., 2s. *and* 2s. 6d.) *or* 12½ (*others*).

60	½d. blue and blue-green	..	..	15	1·00
61	1d. brown and deep violet		..	30	1·00
62	1½d. blue-green and carmine		..	70	1·25
63	2d. orange-brown and black		..	80	1·50
	a. Perf 12 (7.11.51)	..		30	1·50
64	2½d. magenta and sage-green		..	1·50	1·50
	a. Imperf horiz (vert pair)		..	£8500	
65	3d. black and ultramarine		..	1·00	1·25
	a. Perf 12 (29.11.51)	..		1·50	2·50
66	4½d. green and chocolate	..	..	4·00	13·00
67	6d. deep violet and reddish purple		75	9·50
68	1s. green and black	..	..	1·25	90
69	2s. black and orange	..	..	6·00	5·00
70	2s. 6d. black and violet	..		26·00	4·50
71	5s. emerald-green and scarlet	..		32·00	9·50
72	10s. sage-green and magenta (27.4.42)		5·00	8·50
60/72	..	..	..	*Set of* 13	70·00	45·00
60/72 Perf "Specimen"	..	..	*Set of* 13	£275	

Designs: *Horiz* (as *T* 8)—1½d. Artificial Island, Malaita; 1s. Breadfruit; 5s. Malaita canoe. (As *T* 7)—3d. Roviana canoes; 2s. Tinakula volcano; 2s. 6d. Common Scrub Hen. *Vert* (as *T* 6)—4½d., 10s. Native house, Reef Islands; 6d. Coconut plantation.

1946 (15 Oct). *Victory. As Nos. 110/11 of Antigua.*

73	1½d. carmine	..	..	..	..	15	80
74	3d. blue	..	..	..	..	15	10
73/4 Perf "Specimen"	..	..	*Set of* 2	55·00	

Pocket handkerchief
flaw (R. 1/6)

1949 (14 Mar). *Royal Silver Wedding. As Nos. 112/13 of Antigua.*

75	2d. black	..	..	..	..	50	50
	a. Pocket handkerchief flaw	..	22·00	
76	10s. magenta	..	..	..	13·00	11·00

1949 (10 Oct). *75th Anniv of U.P.U. As Nos. 114/17 of Antigua.*

77	2d. red-brown	..	..	..	..	75	1·00
78	3d. deep blue	..	..	..	..	2·25	1·00
79	5d. deep blue-green	..	..	..	75	1·40
80	1s. blue-black	..	..	..	..	75	1·00
77/80	..	..	..	..	*Set of* 4	4·00	4·00

POSTAGE DUE STAMPS

D 1

(Typo B.W.)

1940 (1 Sept). *Wmk Mult Script CA. P* 12.

D1	D 1	1d. emerald-green	..	..	..	6·50	7·00
D2		2d. scarlet	..	..	..	7·00	7·00
D3		3d. brown	..	..	..	7·00	11·00
D4		4d. blue	..	..	..	11·00	11·00
D5		5d. grey-green	..	..	..	12·00	21·00
D6		6d. purple	..	..	..	12·00	15·00
D7		1s. violet	..	..	..	16·00	26·00
D8		1s. 6d. turquoise-green	..	..	26·00	48·00
D1/8	..	..	..	*Set of* 8	85·00	£130
D1/8 Perf "Specimen"	..	..	*Set of* 8	£150	

Brunei

100 cents = 1 Malayan dollar

PROTECTED STATE

Sultan Ahmed Tajudin Akhazul Khairi Wadin, 1924–1950

PRINTERS. All Brunei stamps from Nos. 60 to 95 were recess-printed by De La Rue.

5 View on Brunei River   7 Native houses, Water Village

Retouch   Normal

RETOUCHES. We list the very distinctive 5 c. Retouch (top left value tablet, 1st row, 8th stamp) but there are others of interest, notably in the clouds.

1924 (Feb)–**37.** *Printed from single plates as Type* II, *except 30 c. and $1 as Type* I. *Wmk Mult Script CA. P* 14.

60	5	1 c. black (9.26)		80	60
61		2 c. brown (3.24)		90	5·50
62		2 c. green (3.33)		60	50
63		3 c. green (3.24)		80	6·00
64		4 c. maroon (3.24)		1·50	75
65		4 c. orange (1929)		1·00	60
66		5 c. orange-yellow* (3.24)		4·25	1·25
		a. "5 c." retouch		£160	£120
67		5 c. grey (1931)		9·50	9·50
		a. "5 c." retouch		£350	£300
68		5 c. chocolate (1933)		8·50	50
		a. "5 c." retouch		£170	50·00
69	7	6 c. intense black** (3.24)		14·00	10·00
		x. Wmk reversed			
70		6 c. scarlet (1931)		3·75	11·00
71	5	8 c. ultramarine (9.27)		6·00	5·00
72		8 c. grey-black (1933)		8·50	55
73		10 c. purple/*yellow* (3.37)		13·00	26·00
74	7	12 c. blue		4·50	9·00
		a. *Pale greenish blue* (1927)		£130	£200
75	5	25 c. slate-purple (1931)		5·50	12·00
76		30 c. purple and orange-yellow (1931)		8·50	16·00
77		50 c. black/*emerald* (1931)		7·00	15·00
78		$1 black and red/*blue* (1931)		24·00	70·00
60/78			Set of 19	£110	£180
60/72, 74/8 Optd/Perf "Specimen"			Set of 18	£350	

*For 5 c. orange, see No. 82. No. 66 is a "Wet" printing and No. 82 a "Dry".

**For 6 c. black, see No. 83. Apart from the difference in shade there is a variation in size, No. 69 being 37¾ mm long and No. 83 39 mm.

The 2 c. orange and 3 c. blue-green in Type **5**, and the 6 c. greenish grey, 8 c. red and 15 c. ultramarine in Type **7** were not issued without the Japanese Occupation overprint although unoverprinted examples exist. It is believed that these 1941 printings were produced and possibly perforated, by other firms in Great Britain following bomb damage to the De La Rue works at the end of 1940 (*Price for set of* 5, £450 *un*).

During the life of this issue De La Rue changed the method of production from a "Wet" to a "Dry" process. Initially the stamps were printed on ungummed paper which was dampened before being put on the press. Once the paper had dried, and contracted in the process, the gum was then applied. "Dry" printings, introduced around 1934, were on pre-gummed paper. The contraction of the "Wet" printings was considerable and usually involves a difference of between 0.5 mm and 1 mm when compared with the larger "Dry" printings. The following stamps occur from both "Wet" and "Dry" versions: 1 c., 2 c. green, 4 c. orange, 5 c. chocolate, 6 c. scarlet, 8 c. grey-black, 10 c. and 25 c.

Stamps of this issue can be found either line or comb perforated.

Brunei was occupied by the Japanese Army in January 1942 and remained under Japanese administration until liberated by the 9th Australian Division in June 1945.

After the cessation of hostilities with the Japanese postal services were re-introduced by the British Military Administration. Post offices under B.M.A. control were opened at Brunei Town and Kuala Belait on 17 December 1945 where B.M.A. overprints on the stamps of NORTH BORNEO and SARAWAK were used until the reappearance of Brunei issues on 2 January 1947.

Redrawn clouds (R. 1/1 of No. 80*ab* only)

1947 (2 Jan)–**51.** *Colours changed and new values. Wmk Mult Script CA. P* 14.

79	5	1 c. chocolate		50	1·75
		a. "A" of "CA" missing from wmk		£1100	
80		2 c. grey		90	2·50
		a. Perf 14½×13½ (25.9.50)		1·50	4·25
		ab. Black (27.6.51)		2·00	6·00
		ac. Redrawn clouds		65·00	
81	7	3 c. green		1·00	4·00
82	5	5 c. orange*		80	1·25
		a. "5 c." retouch		55·00	75·00
		b. Perf 14½×13½ (25.9.50)		4·00	12·00
		c. Ditto "5 c." retouch		£120	£180
83	7	6 c. black*		1·00	3·75
84	5	8 c. scarlet		40	80
		a. Perf 13 (25.1.51)		55	3·50
85		10 c. violet		70	30
		a. Perf 14½×13½ (25.9.50)		2·00	4·75
86		15 c. ultramarine		50	60
87		25 c. deep claret		1·50	80
		a. Perf 14½×13½ (25.1.51)		1·50	7·00
88		30 c. black and orange		1·25	1·00
		a. Perf 14½×13½ (25.1.51)		1·50	11·00
89		50 c. black		2·50	1·00
		a. Perf 13 (25.9.50)		1·75	14·00
90		$1 black and scarlet		5·50	5·00
91		$5 green and red-orange (2.2.48)		16·00	17·00

92	5	$10 black and purple (2.2.48)	..	..	48·00	30·00
79/92		.. .. ..	..	Set of 14	70·00	55·00
79/92 Perf "Specimen"	..	..		Set of 14	£200	

*See also Nos. 66 and 69.

The 1, 2, 3, 5, 6, 10 and 25 c. values utilised the plates of the pre-war issue and were line perforated until the introduction of the 14½×13½ comb machine for some values in 1950–51. The 8, 15, 50 c., $1, $5 and $10 were from new plates with the sheets comb perforated. The 30 c. was initially a pre-war plate, but it is believed that a new plate was introduced in 1951.

8 Sultan Ahmed Tajudin and Water Village

1949 (22 Sept). *Sultan's Silver Jubilee. Wmk Mult Script CA. P 13.*

93	8	8 c. black and carmine ..		..	70	80
94		25 c. purple and red-orange	..	..	70	1·40
95		50 c. black and blue	..	..	70	1·40
93/5	..	.. .. ..	..	Set of 3	1·90	3·25

1949 (10 Oct). *75th Anniv of Universal Postal Union. As Nos. 114/17 of Antigua.*

96	8 c. carmine ..	..	..	..	1·25	1·25
97	15 c. deep blue ..		..	..	3·50	1·50
98	25 c. magenta ..	..	..	..	1·25	1·50
99	50 c. blue-black	..	..	..	1·75	1·25
96/9	.. .. ..	..	..	Set of 4	7·00	5·00

JAPANESE OCCUPATION OF BRUNEI

Japanese forces landed in Northern Borneo on 15 December 1941 and the whole of Brunei had been occupied by 6 January 1942.

Brunei, North Borneo, Sarawak and, after a short period, Labuan, were administered as a single territory by the Japanese. Until September–October 1942, previous stamp issues, without overprint, continued to be used in conjunction with existing postmarks. From the Autumn of 1942 onwards unoverprinted stamps of Japan were made available and examples can be found used from the area for much of the remainder of the War. Japanese Occupation issues for Brunei, North Borneo and Sarawak were equally valid throughout the combined territory but not, in practice, equally available.

(1)

(2)

("Imperial Japanese Government")

("Imperial Japanese Postal Service $3")

1942 (Oct)–**44**. *Stamps of Brunei handstamped with T 1 in violet to blue. Wmk Mult Script CA (except Nos. J18/19, Mult Crown CA). P 14.*

J 1	5	1 c. black	..	..	6·00	23·00
		a. Red opt ..	..	..	50·00	70·00
J 2		2 c. green	..	..	48·00	£100
J 3		2 c. orange (1943)	..	..	3·00	9·00
J 4		3 c. blue-green	..	..	28·00	75·00
		a. Opt omitted (in pair with normal)	£1500			
J 5		4 c. orange	..	..	3·00	13·00
J 6		5 c. chocolate ..	..	..	3·00	13·00
		a. "5 c." retouch	..	..	£150	£375
J 7	7	6 c. greenish grey (p 14×11½) (1944)	50·00	£200		
J 8		6 c. scarlet	..	..	£550	£550
J 9	5	8 c. grey-black	..	..	£650	£850
J10	7	8 c. red	..	..	3·75	12·00
		a. Opt omitted (in pair with normal)	£1100			
J11	5	10 c. purple/*yellow*	..	..	8·50	26·00
J12	7	12 c. blue	..	..	22·00	26·00
		a. Red opt	..	..	£140	£200
J13		15 c. ultramarine (1944)	..	13·00	26·00	
J14	5	25 c. slate-purple	..	..	23·00	50·00
		a. Red opt	..	..	£225	£300
J15		30 c. purple and orange-yellow ..	..	95·00	£180	
J16		50 c. black/*emerald*	..	..	38·00	60·00
		a. Red opt	..	..	£250	
J17		$1 black and red/*blue* (1944)	..	55·00	70·00	
		a. Red opt ..	..	..	—	£550
J18		$5 carmine/*green* (1944)	..	..	£800	£1700
J19		$25 black/*red* (1944) ..	..	..	£850	£1700

The overprint varies in shade from violet to blue, and being handstamped, exists double, double one inverted and treble.

Nos. J3, J7, J10 and J13 were not issued without the overprint.

1944 (11 May). *No. J1 surch with T 2 in orange-red.*

J20	5	$3 on 1 c. black	..	..	£6000	£5500
		a. Surch on No. 60 of Brunei	..	£7000		

Three separate handstamps were used to apply Type 2, one for the top line, one for the bottom and the third for the two central characters.

Burma

12 pies = 1 anna; 16 annas = 1 rupee

BRITISH ADMINISTRATION

From 1 January 1886 Burma was a province of the Indian Empire but was separated from India and came under direct British administration on 1 April 1937.

BURMA
(1)

BURMA
(1a)

1937 (1 Apr). *Stamps of India (King George V inscr* "INDIA POSTAGE") *optd with T* **1** *or* **1a** *(rupee values). W* **69.** *P* 14.

1	3 p. slate	..	..	..	30	10
	w. Wmk inverted	..	..	..	1·00	50
2	½ a. green	..	..	..	60	10
	w. Wmk inverted	..	..	..	1·50	50
3	9 p. deep green	..	..	..	75	10
	w. Wmk inverted	..	..	..	1·00	50
4	1 a. chocolate	..	..	..	40	10
	w. Wmk inverted	..	..	..	1·25	50
5	2 a. vermilion (*small die*)	..	..	40	10
6	2½ a. orange	..	..	..	30	10
	w. Wmk inverted	..	..	..	1·25	50
7	3 a. carmine	..	..	..	75	30
	w. Wmk inverted	..	..	..	2·50	1·00
8	3½ a. deep blue	..	..	..	65	10
	aw. Wmk inverted	..	..	..	1·00	20
	b. *Dull blue*	..	..	..	6·50	6·00
	bw. Wmk inverted	..	..	..	4·25	4·00
9	4 a. sage-green	..	..	..	70	10
	w. Wmk inverted	..	..	..	—	24·00
10	6 a. bistre	..	..	..	60	35
	w. Wmk inverted	..	..	..	—	24·00
11	8 a. reddish purple	..	..	..	1·50	10
12	12 a. claret	..	..	..	2·50	85
	w. Wmk inverted	..	..	..	6·00	1·75
13	1 r. chocolate and green	..	..	16·00	2·25
14	2 r. carmine and orange	..	..	25·00	9·00
	w. Wmk inverted	..	..	..	35·00	13·00
15	5 r. ultramarine and purple	..	..	35·00	15·00
16	10 r. green and scarlet	..	..	70·00	50·00
17	15 r. blue and olive (*wmk inverted*)	..	£225	95·00
18	25 r. orange and blue	..	..	£450	£225
	w. Wmk inverted	..	..	..	£500	£275
1/18	..	..	at	*Set of* 18	£750	£350

The opt is at top on all values except the 3 a.

The 1 a. has been seen used from Yenangyaung on 22 Mar 1937.

2 King George VI and "Chinthes"

3 King George VI and "Nagas"

4 *Karaweik* (royal barge)

8 King George VI and Peacock

10 Elephants' Heads

Extra trees flaw (R. 11/8)

(Des Maung Kyi (2 a. 6 p.), Maung Hline (3 a.), Maung Ohn Pe (3 a. 6 p.) and N. K. D. Naigamwalla (8 a.). Litho Security Ptg Press, Nasik)

1938 (15 Nov)–**40.** *T* **2/4, 8** *and similar designs. W* **10.** *P* 14 (*vert*) *or* 13½×13 (*horiz*).

18a	2	1 p. red-orange (1.8.40)	..	..	3·00	80
19	–	3 p. bright violet	..	..	20	30
20	–	6 p. bright blue	..	..	20	10
21	–	9 p. yellow-green	..	..	1·00	80
22	3	1 a. purple-brown	..	..	20	10
23	–	1½ a. turquoise-green	..	..	20	60
24	–	2 a. carmine	..	..	45	10
25	4	2 a. 6 p. claret	..	..	14·00	90
26	–	3 a. dull violet	..	..	14·00	10
27	–	3 a. 6 p. light blue and blue	..	1·25	3·75
		a. Extra trees flaw	..	..	40·00	
28	3	4 a. greenish blue	..	..	60	10
29	–	8 a. myrtle-green	..	..	5·00	30
30	8	1 r. purple and blue	..	..	7·50	20
31	–	2 r. brown and purple	..	..	16·00	1·75
32	–	5 r. violet and scarlet	..	..	48·00	22·00
33	–	10 r. brown and myrtle	..	..	55·00	45·00
18a/33	..	..	..	*Set of* 16	£150	70·00

Designs: *Horiz* (*as T* **4**)—3 a. Burma teak; 3 a. 6 p. Burma rice; 8 a. River Irrawaddy. *Vert* (*as T* **8**)—5 r., 10 r. King George VI and "Nats".

The 1 a. exists lithographed or typographed, the latter having a "Jubilee" line in the sheet margin.

COMMEMORATION POSTAGE STAMP
6th MAY 1840

(11)

1940 (6 May)   *Centenary of First Adhesive Postage Stamps. No. 25 surch with T 11.*

34	**4**	1 a. on 2 a. 6 p. claret	..	..	..	3·75	1·50

For stamps issued in 1942–45 see under Japanese Occupation.

CHIN HILLS DISTRICT.

This area, in the far north-west of the country, remained in British hands when the Japanese overran Burma in May 1942.

During the period July to December 1942 the local officials were authorised to produce provisional stamps and the letters "OHMS" are known overprinted by typewriter on Nos. 3, 20, 22/4, 28/9 and 31 of Burma or handstamped, in violet, on Nos. 25, 27 and 29. The two types can also occur together or in combination with a handstamped "SERVICE".

From early in 1943 ordinary postage stamps of India were used from the Chin Hills post offices of Falam, Haka, Fort White and Tiddim, this expedient continuing until the fall of Falam to the Japanese on 7 November 1943.

The provisional stamps should only be collected on Official cover where dates and the sender's handwriting can be authenticated.

BRITISH MILITARY ADMINISTRATION

Preparations for the liberation of Burma commenced in February 1943 when the Civil Affairs Service (Burma) (CAS(B)) was set up at Delhi as part of the proposed military administration structure. One of the specific tasks assigned to CAS(B) was the operation of a postal service for the civilian population.

Operations against the Japanese intensified during the second half of 1944. The port of Akyab in the Arakan was reoccupied in January 1945. The 14th Army took Mandalay on 29 March and Rangoon was liberated from the sea on 3 May.

Postal services for the civilian population started in Akyab on 13 April 1945 while post offices in the Magwe Division around Meiktila were operating from 4 March. Mandalay post offices opened on 8 June and those in Rangoon on 16 June, but the full network was only completed in December 1945, just before the military administration was wound-up.

MILY ADMN	**MILY ADMN**
(12)	(13)

1945 (from 11 Apr). *Nos. 18a to 33 optd with T 12 (small stamps) or 13 (others) by Security Printing Press, Nasik.*

35	**2**	1 p. red-orange	..	..	..	10	10
		a. Opt omitted (in pair with normal)		..	£1600		
36		3 p. bright violet	..	..	..	10	40
37		6 p. bright blue	..	..	..	10	30
38		9 p. yellow-green	..	..	..	30	40
39	**3**	1 a. purple-brown (16.6)	..	..	..	10	10
40		1½ a. turquoise-green (16.6)	..	..	10	15
41		2 a. carmine	..	..	..	10	15
42	**4**	2 a. 6 p. claret	..	..	..	2·00	60
43	–	3 a. dull violet	..	..	..	1·50	20
44	–	3 a. 6 p. light blue and blue	..	..	10	70
		a. Extra trees flaw	..	..	15·00		
45	**3**	4 a. greenish blue	..	..	..	10	25
46	–	8 a. myrtle-green	..	..	..	10	50
47	**8**	1 r. purple and blue	..	..	..	40	50
48		2 r. brown and purple	..	..	..	40	1·00
49	–	5 r. violet and scarlet	..	..	40	1·00
50	–	10 r. brown and myrtle	..	..	40	1·00
35/50			..	..	Set of 16	4·75	6·50

Only the typographed version of the 1 a., No. 22, received this overprint.

The exact dates of issue for Nos. 35/50 are difficult to establish.

The initial stock of overprints is known to have reached CAS(B) headquarters, Imphal, at the beginning of April 1945. Postal directives issued on 11 April refer to the use of the overprints in Akyab and in the Magwe Division where surcharged pre-war postal stationery envelopes had previously been in use. The 6 p., 1 a., 1½ a. and 2 a. values were placed on sale at Mandalay on 8 June and the 1 a. and 2 a. at Rangoon on 16 June. It has been suggested that only a limited service had initially been available in Rangoon. All values were on sale by 9 August 1945.

BRITISH CIVIL ADMINISTRATION

1946 (1 Jan).   *As Nos. 19/33, but colours changed.*

51	**2**	3 p. brown	..	..	..	10	1·25
52		6 p. deep violet	..	..	..	10	30
53		9 p. green	..	..	..	15	1·60

54	**3**	1 a. blue	..	..	..	15	20
55		1½ a. orange	..	..	..	15	10
56		2 a. claret	..	..	..	15	40
57	**4**	2 a. 6 p. greenish blue	..	..	2·00	3·50
57a	–	3 a. blue-violet	..	..	6·50	3·00
57b	–	3 a. 6 p. black and ultramarine	..	30	1·50
		ba. Extra trees flaw	..	..	29·00		
58	**3**	4 a. purple	..	..	..	30	30
59	–	8 a. maroon	..	..	..	1·75	2·00
60	**8**	1 r. violet and maroon	..	..	1·00	40
61		2 r. brown and orange	..	..	6·00	2·25
62	–	5 r. green and brown	..	..	6·00	11·00
63	–	10 r. claret and violet	..	..	6·50	17·00
51/63					Set of 15	28·00	40·00

No. 54 was printed in typography only.

14 Burman

(Des A. G. I. McGeogh. Litho Nasik)

1946 (2 May).   *Victory. T 14 and similar vert designs. W 10 (sideways). P 13.*

64		9 p. turquoise-green	..	..	..	20	20
65		1½ a. violet	..	..	..	20	10
66		2 a. carmine	..	..	..	20	10
67		3 a. 6 p. ultramarine	..	..	50	20
64/7					Set of 4	1·00	50

Designs:—1½ a. Burmese woman; 2 a. Chinthe; 3 a. 6 p. Elephant.

INTERIM BURMESE GOVERNMENT

ကြၣ်းဖြတ်	၁းဖြတ်ကြ	တ်ကြၣ်းဖြ
အစိုးရ။	အစိုးရ။	အစိုးရ။
(18 Trans.	18a	18b

"Interim Government")

Type **18a** shows the first character transposed to the end of the top line (R. 6/15).

Type **18b** shows the last two characters transposed to the front of the top line (R. 14/14).

Some sheets of the 3 p. show both errors corrected by a handstamp as Type 18.

1947 (1 Oct).   *Stamps of 1946 optd with T 18 (small stamps) or larger opt (others).*

68	**2**	3 p. brown	..	..	..	70	70
		a. Opt Type 18a	..	..	20·00		
		ab. Corrected by handstamp as Type 18				
		b. Opt Type 18b	..	..	20·00		
		ba. Corrected by handstamp as Type 18				
69		6 p. deep violet	..	..	..	10	30
		a. Opt Type 18a	..	..	11·00		
70		9 p. green	..	..	..	10	30
		a. Opt inverted	..	..	19·00	22·00
71	**3**	1 a. blue	..	..	..	10	30
		a. Vert pair, one with opt omitted	..			
72		1½ a. orange	..	..	..	90	10
73		2 a. claret	..	..	..	30	15
		a. Horiz pair, one with opt omitted	..			
		b. Opt Type 18a	..	..	22·00		
74	**4**	2 a. 6 p. greenish blue	..	..	1·75	95
75	–	3 a. blue-violet	..	..	2·50	1·50
76	–	3 a. 6 p. black and ultramarine	..	45	2·00
		a. Extra trees flaw	..	..	26·00		
77	**3**	4 a. purple	..	..	..	1·75	30
78	–	8 a. maroon	..	..	..	1·75	90

79	8	1 r. violet and maroon	..	..	..	2·75	30
80		2 r. brown and orange				3·75	2·50
81	–	5 r. green and brown				3·75	3·25
82	–	10 r. claret and violet				3·25	3·25
68/82					*Set of* 15	21·00	15·00

The 3 p., 6 p., 2 a., 2 a. 6 p., 3 a. 6 p. and 1 r. are also known with overprint inverted.

OFFICIAL STAMPS

BURMA   **BURMA**

SERVICE   **SERVICE**

(O 1)   (O 1a)

1937 (Apr–June).   *Stamps of India (King George V inscr "INDIA POSTAGE") optd with Type* O 1 *or* O 1a *(rupee values).* W **69**. P 14.

O 1		3 p. slate	..	..	..	1·00	10
		w. Wmk inverted	..	..		—	12·00
O 2		½ a. green				6·00	10
O 3		9 p. deep green	..			3·50	30
O 4		1 a. chocolate	..	..		4·00	10
O 5		2 a. vermilion (*small die*)				7·00	35
		w. Wmk inverted				—	12·00
O 6		2½ a. orange				4·00	1·75
O 7		4 a. sage-green	..	..		4·25	10
O 8		6 a. bistre	..	..		4·00	5·50
O 9		8 a. reddish purple (1.4.37)	..		3·25	80
O10		12 a. claret (1.4.37)	..	..		3·25	3·25
O11		1 r. chocolate and green (1.4.37)	..		20·00	3·75
O12		2 r. carmine and orange	..		45·00	30·00
		w. Wmk inverted	..	..		55·00	38·00
O13		5 r. ultramarine and purple	..		90·00	42·00
O14		10 r. green and scarlet	..		£250	£120
O1/14					*Set of* 14	£400	£180

For the above issue the stamps were either overprinted 'BURMA" and "SERVICE" at one operation or had the two words applied separately. Research has yet to establish if all values exist with both forms of overprinting.

SERVICE   **SERVICE**

(O 2)   (O 3)

1939.   *Nos.* 19/24 *and* 28 *optd with Type* O 2 *(typo) and Nos.* 25 *and* 29/33 *optd with Type* O 3 *(litho).*

O15	2	3 p. bright violet	..	..		15	20
O16		6 p. bright blue	..			15	20
O17		9 p. yellow-green	..	..		5·00	2·50
O18	3	1 a. purple-brown	..			15	15
O19		1½ a. turquoise-green	..			4·50	1·50
O20		2 a. carmine	..	..		1·25	20
O21	4	2 a. 6 p. claret	..	..		25·00	10·00
O22	3	4 a. greenish blue	..			5·50	40
O23	–	8 a. myrtle-green	..			25·00	3·75
O24	8	1 r. purple and blue	..			38·00	5·00
O25		2 r. brown and purple	..			45·00	11·00
O26	–	5 r. violet and scarlet	..		42·00	28·00
O27	–	10 r. brown and myrtle	..		£120	38·00
O15/27					*Set of* 13	£275	90·00

Both versions of the 1 a. value exist with this overprint.

1946.   *British Civil Administration. Nos.* 51/6 *and* 58 *optd with Type* O 2 *(typo) and Nos.* 57 *and* 59/63 *optd with Type* O 3 *(litho).*

O28	2	3 p. brown				90	2·50
O29		6 p. deep violet	..			90	4·00
O30		9 p. green	..	..		20	2·75
O31	3	1 a. blue	..	..	..	20	1·75
O32		1½ a. orange	..	..		20	1·75
O33		2 a. claret	..	..		20	1·75
O34	4	2 a. 6 p. greenish blue	..		1·40	4·50
O35	3	4 a. purple	..	..		20	70
O36	–	8 a. maroon	..	..		1·50	3·00

O37	8	1 r. violet and maroon	..	..	..	60	3·00
O38		2 r. brown and orange	..	..		7·00	35·00
O39	–	5 r. green and brown	..			9·00	40·00
O40	–	10 r. claret and violet	..		17·00	48·00
O28/40					*Set of* 13	35·00	£130

1947.   *Interim Burmese Government. Nos.* O28/40 *optd with T* **18** *(small stamps) or larger opt (others).*

O41	2	3 p. brown	..	..		15	40
O42		6 p. deep violet	..			80	10
O43		9 p. green	..	..		1·40	90
O44	3	1 a. blue	..	..		1·75	80
O45		1½ a. orange	..	..		3·50	30
O46		2 a. claret	..	..		1·75	15
O47	4	2 a. 6 p. greenish blue	..		22·00	8·50
O48	3	4 a. purple	..	..		7·00	40
O49	–	8 a. maroon	..	..		6·50	3·75
O50	8	1 r. violet and maroon	..		14·00	2·25
O51		2 r. brown and orange	..		14·00	18·00
O52	–	5 r. green and brown	..		14·00	19·00
O53	–	10 r. claret and violet	..		14·00	30·00
O41/53					*Set of* 13	90·00	75·00

Later stamp issues will be found listed in Part 21 (*South-East Asia*) of this catalogue.

JAPANESE OCCUPATION OF BURMA

BURMA INDEPENDENCE ARMY ADMINISTRATION

The Burma Independence Army, formed by Aung San in 1941, took control of the Delta area of the Irrawaddy in May 1942. They reopened a postal service in the area and were authorised by the Japanese to overprint local stocks of stamps with the Burmese emblem of a peacock.

Postage and Official stamps with the peacock overprints or hand-stamps were used for ordinary postal purposes with the probable exception of No. J44.

DISTINGUISHING FEATURES. Type 1. Body and head of Peacock always clearly outlined by broad uncoloured band. There are four slightly different sub-types of overprint Type 1.

Type 2. Peacock with slender neck and more delicately detailed tail. Clear spur on leg at right. Heavy fist-shaped blob of ink below and parallel to beak and neck.

Type 4. No basic curve. Each feather separately outlined. Straight, short legs.

Type 5. Much fine detail in wings and tail in clearly printed overprints. Thin, long legs ending in claws which, with the basic arc, enclose clear white spaces in well-printed copies. Blob of colour below beak shows shaded detail and never has the heavy fist-like appearance of this portion in Type 2.

Two sub-types may be distinguished in Type 5, the basic arc of one having a chord of 14–15 mm and the other 12½–13 mm.

Type 6. Similar to Type 5, but with arc deeply curved and reaching nearly to the top of the wings. Single diagonal line parallel to neck below beak.

Collectors are warned against forgeries of these overprints, often in the wrong colours or on the wrong values.

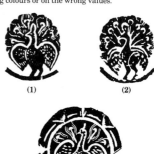

(1)   (2)

(3)

1942 (May). *Stamps of Burma overprinted with the national device of a Peacock.*

I. *Overprinted at Myaungmya*

A. *With Type* **1** *in black*

On Postage Stamps of King George V

J 1		9 p. deep green (No. 3)	..	..	..	£110
J 2		3½ a. deep blue (No. 8)	..	..	..	50·00

On Official Stamp of King George V

J 3		6 a. bistre (No. O8) ..	..	..	..	70·00

On Postage Stamps of King George VI

J 4	2	9 p. yellow-green		..	..	£150
J 5	3	1 a. purple-brown		..	..	£500
J 6		4 a. greenish blue (opt black on red)		..	£160
		a. Triple opt, black on double red		..	£425

On Official Stamps of King George VI

J 7	2	3 p. bright violet	..	..	22·00	75·00
J 8		6 p. bright blue	..	..	15·00	50·00
J 9	3	1 a. purple-brown	..	..	14·00	42·00
J 9a		1½ a. turquoise-green	..	..	£650	
J10		2 a. carmine	..	..	22·00	80·00
J11		4 a. greenish blue	..	..	20·00	65·00

The overprint on No. J6 was apparently first done in red in error, and then corrected in black. Some stamps have the black overprint so accurately superimposed that the red hardly shows. These are rare.

Nos. J5 and J9 exist with the Peacock overprint on both the typographed and the litho printings of the original stamps.

B. *With Types* **2** *or* **3** *(rupee values), in black*

On Postage Stamps of King George VI

J12	2	3 p. bright violet		..	17·00	60·00
J13		6 p. bright blue ..		..	48·00	85·00
J14		9 p. yellow-green		..	17·00	60·00
J15	3	1 a. purple-brown		..	14·00	50·00
J16		2 a. carmine	..	..	17·00	65·00
J17		4 a. greenish blue		..	32·00	85·00
		a. Opt double ..		..		
		b. Opt inverted		..	£550	
		c. Opt double, one inverted		..	£400	
		d. Opt double, both inverted	..		£550	
J18		1 r. purple and blue	..		£250	
J19		2 r. brown and purple	..	..	£150	

The Myaungmya overprints (including No. J44) are usually clearly printed.

(4)	(5)	(6)

Type **5** generally shows the details of the peacock much less clearly and, due to heavy inking, or careless impression, sometimes appears as almost solid colour.

Type **6** was officially applied only to postal stationery. However, the handstamp remained in the possession of a postal official who used it on postage stamps after the war. These stamps are no longer listed.

II. *Handstamped (at Pyapon?) with T* **4**, *in black (so-called experimental type)*

On Postage Stamps of King George VI

J19a	6 p. bright blue ..	..	..	..	£120	
J19b	3	1 a. purple-brown	..	..	95·00	£250
J20		2 a. carmine	..	..	£110	£250
J21		4 a. greenish blue	..	..	£650	£650

Unused specimens of Nos. J20/1 are usually in poor condition.

III. *Overprinted at Henzada with T* **5** *in blue, or blue-black*

On Postage Stamps of King George V

J22		3 p. slate (No. 1)		..	..	3·00	17·00
		a. Opt double	..	..	..	10·00	48·00
J23		9 p. deep green (No. 3)		..	..	21·00	60·00
		a. Opt double	..	..	..	80·00	
J24		2 a. vermilion (No. 5)..		..	..	£100	£180

On Postage Stamps of King George VI

J25	2	1 p. red-orange		..	..	£180	£275
J26		3 p. bright violet	..		..	30·00	75·00
J27		6 p. bright blue	..		..	25·00	50·00
		a. Opt double	..	..	..	£100	£150
		b. Clear opt, on back and front		..	£275	
J28		9 p. yellow-green		..	..	£750	
J29	3	1 a. purple-brown		..	..	9·00	40·00
		a. Opt inverted	..	..	..	£500	
J30		1½ a. turquoise-green		..	..	21·00	65·00
		a. Opt omitted (in pair with normal)		£1500	
J31		2 a. carmine ..	..	..	..	21·00	65·00
		a. Opt double	..	..	..	£500	
J32		4 a. greenish blue		..	..	42·00	95·00
		a. Opt double	..	..	..	£250	
		b. Opt inverted	..	..	..	£950	

On Official Stamps of King George VI

J33	2	3 p. bright violet		..	..	£100	£225
J34		6 p. bright blue ..		..	..	£140	£225
J35	3	1½ a. turquoise-green		..	..	£150	£250
J35a		2 a. carmine	..	..	..	£325	£400
J36		4 a. greenish blue		..	..	£950	

(6a)

("Yon Thon" = "Office use")

V. *Official Stamp of King George VI optd at Myaungmya with Type* **6a** *in black*

J44	7	8 a. myrtle-green		..	..	80·00

No. J44 was probably for official use.

There are two types of T **6a**, one with base of peacock 8 mm long and the other with base about 5 mm long. The neck and other details also vary. The two types are found *se-tenant* in the sheet.

Stocks of the peacock types were withdrawn when the Japanese Directorate-General took control of the postal services in the Delta in August 1942.

JAPANESE ARMY ADMINISTRATION

7	8 Farmer

1942 (1 June). *Impressed by hand. Thick yellowish paper.* P 12 × 11. *No gum.*

J45	7	(1 a.) red ..	..	..	38·00	65·00

This device was the personal seal of Yano Sitza, the Japanese official in charge of the Posts and Telegraphs department of the Japanese Army Administration. It was impressed on paper already perforated by a line machine. Some stamps show part of the papermaker's watermark, either "ABSORBO DUPLICATOR" or "ELEPHANT BRAND", each with an elephant.

Other impressions of this seal on different papers, and showing signs of wear, were not valid for postal purposes.

(Des T. Kato. Typo *Rangoon Gazette* Press)

1942 (15 June). *Value in annas. P* 11 *or* 11 × 11½. *Laid bâtonné paper. No gum.*
J46   **8**   1 a. scarlet   ..   ..   .. 15·00 15·00
Some stamps show part of the papermaker's watermark, either "ELEPHANT BRAND" or "TITAGHUR SUPERFINE", each with an elephant.

(9)   **(10)**

1942 (22 Sept). (*a*) *Nos.* 314/17, 320/2, 325, 327 *and* 396 *of Japan surch as T* **9/10**.
J47   **9**   ¼ a. on 1 s. chestnut (Rice harvesting)   23·00 27·00
    a. Surch inverted   ..   ..   95·00 95·00
    b. Surch double, one inverted   ..   £140
J48   ½ a. on 2 s. bright scarlet (General Nogi) 24·00 28·00
    a. Surch inverted   ..   ..   85·00 90·00
    b. Surch double, one inverted   ..   £140
J49   ¾ a. on 3 s. green (Power station)   ..   50·00 55·00
    a. Surch inverted £110 £110
    b. Surch double, one inverted   ..   —   £160
J50   1 a. on 5 s. claret (Admiral Togo)   ..   40·00 40·00
    a. Surch inverted £150 £150
    b. Surch double, one inverted   ..   £170 £170
    c. Surch omitted (in pair with normal)   —   £200
J51   3 a. on 7 s. green (Diamond Mts)   ..   80·00 90·00
    a. Surch inverted £150
J52   4 a. on 4 s. emerald (Togo)   ..   38·00 40·00
    a. Surch inverted £150
J53   8 a. on 8 s. violet (Meiji Shrine)   ..   £150 £150
    a. Surch inverted £225 £225
    b. Surch double, one inverted   ..   £350
    c. Surch in red £225 £250
    d. Red surch inverted £350
    e. Surch double (black and red)   ..   £550
J54   **10**   1 r. on 10 s. deep carmine (Yomei Gate) 15·00 24·00
    a. Surch inverted   ..   ..   80·00 90·00
    b. Surch double   ..   ..   80·00 £100
    c. Surch double (black and red)   ..   £400
    d. Surch omitted (in pair with normal) £190 £190
    e. Surch   omitted   (in   pair   with
      inverted surch) £300
J55   2 r. on 20 s. ultramarine (Mt Fuji)   ..   45·00 45·00
    a. Surch inverted £110 £110
    b. Surch double, one inverted   ..   £130
    c. Surch omitted (in pair with normal
      black surch) £160 £160
    d. Surch in red   ..   ..   42·00 42·00
    e. Red surch inverted £110 £110
    f. Red surch double £110 £110
    g. Surch omitted (in pair with normal
      red surch) £200 £200
    ga. Surch omitted (in pair with double
      red surch)   ..   ..
    h. Surch double (black and red)   ..   £325
J56   **9**   5 r. on 30 s. turquoise (Torii Shrine)   12·00 27·00
    a. Surch inverted   ..   ..   85·00
    b. Surch double £110
    c. Surch double, one inverted   ..   £150
    d. Surch omitted (in pair with normal
      surch) £180 £180
    e. Surch   omitted   (in   pair   with
      inverted black surch)   ..   £275
    f. Surch in red   ..   ..   23·00 32·00
    fa. Red surch inverted   ..   ..   90·00 90·00
    fb. J56a and J56fa *se-tenant*   ..   £400 £400
    fc. Surch omitted (in pair with normal
      red surch) £180 £180

(*b*) *No.* 386 *of Japan commemorating the fall of Singapore similarly surch*
J56*g*   **9**   4 a. on 4 + 2 s. green and red   ..   £150 £160
    h. Surch omitted (in pair with normal) £500
    ha. Surch   omitted   (in   pair   with
      inverted surch) £550
    i. Surch inverted £350

(New Currency. 100 cents = 1 rupee)

15 C.   **15 C.**   **15 C.**
  (11)   **(12)**   **(13)**

1942 (15 Oct). *Previous issues, with "anna" surcharges obliterated, handstamped with new value in cents, as T* **11** *and* **12** (*No.* J57 *handstamped with new value only*).

(*a*) *On No.* J46
J57   5 c. on 1 a. scarlet   ..   ..   11·00 15·00
    a. Surch omitted (in pair with normal) £1000

(*b*) *On Nos.* J47/53
J58   1 c. on ¼ a. on 1 s. chestnut   ..   40·00 40·00
    a. "1 c." omitted (in pair with normal) .. £500
    b. "¼ a." inverted £250
J59   2 c. on ½ a. on 2 s. bright scarlet   ..   38·00 40·00
J60   3 c. on ¾ a. on 3 s. green   ..   42·00 42·00
    a. Surch in blue £170
J61   5 c. on 1 a. on 5 s. claret   ..   65·00 65·00
J62   10 c. on 3 a. on 7 s. green   ..   £100 95·00
J63   15 c. on 4 a. on 4 s. emerald   ..   29·00 32·00
J64   20 c. on 8 a. on 8 s. violet   ..   £375 £325
    a. Surch on No. J53c (surch in red)   ..   £225 £150
The "anna" surcharges were obliterated by any means available, in some cases by a bar or bars, and in others by the butt of a pencil dipped in ink. In the case of the fractional surcharges, the letter "A" and one figure of the fraction, were sometimes barred out, leaving the remainder of the fraction to represent the new value, e.g. the "1" of "½" deleted to create the 2 c. surcharge or the "4" of "¾" to create the 3 c. surcharge.

1942. *Nos.* 314/17, 320/1 *and* 396 *of Japan surcharged in cents only as T* **13**.
J65   1 c. on 1 s. chestnut (Rice harvesting)   ..   19·00 20·00
    a. Surch inverted £110 £110
J66   2 c. on 2 s. brt scarlet (General Nogi)   ..   38·00 32·00
J67   3 c. on 3 s. green (Power station)   ..   42·00 38·00
    a. Pair, with and without surch   ..   —   £200
    b. Surch inverted £120
    c. Surch in blue   ..   ..   85·00 95·00
    d. Surch in blue inverted   ..   £200 £225
J68   5 c. on 5 s. claret (Admiral Togo)   ..   45·00 42·00
    a. Pair, with and without surch   ..   £250
    b. Surch in violet £130 £150
    ba. Surch inverted   ..   ..   —   £225
J69   10 c. on 7 s. green (Diamond Mts)   ..   55·00 55·00
J70   15 c. on 4 s. emerald (Togo)   ..   14·00 20·00
    a. Surch inverted £120 £130
    b. Pair, with and without surch   ..   —   £190
J71   20 c. on 8 s. violet (Meiji Shrine)   ..   £130 85·00
    a. Surch double £275
Nos. J67c and J68b were issued for use in the Shan States.

BURMESE GOVERNMENT

On 1 November 1942 the Japanese Army Administration handed over the control of the postal department to the Burmese Government. On 1 August 1943 Burma was declared by the Japanese to be independent.

14 Burma State Crest   **15** Farmer

(Des U Tun Tin and Maung Tin from drawing by U Ba Than. Typo Rangoon)

1943 (15 Feb). *P* 11. *No gum.*

J72	14	5 c. scarlet				15·00	19·00
		a. Imperf				16·00	20·00
		ab. Printed on both sides			85·00	

No. J72 was usually sold affixed to envelopes, particularly those with the embossed 1 a. King George VI stamp, which it covered. Unused specimens off cover are not often seen and blocks are rare.

1943. *Typo. No gum. P* 11½.

J73	15	1 c. orange (22 March)			1·40	3·50
		a. *Brown-orange*			70	3·75
J74		2 c. yellow-green (24 March)			60	1·00
		a. "3" for "2" in face value (R.2/10)		£150	
		b. *Blue-green*				7·50	
J75		3 c. light blue (25 March)			1·00	85
		a. On laid paper			18·00	26·00
		b. Imperf between (horiz pair)		—	£250
J76		5 c. carmine (small "c") (17 March)		14·00	9·00
J77		5 c. carmine (large "C")			1·75	3·00
		a. Imperf (pair)			£120	
		b. "G" for "C" (R.2/6)			£170	
J78		10 c. grey-brown (25 March)			3·50	3·50
		a. Imperf (pair)			£120	
		b. Imperf between (horiz pair)		—	£250
J79		15 c. magenta (26 March)			30	90
		a. Imperf between (vert strip of 3)			
		b. On laid paper			6·00	16·00
		c. Inverted "C" in value (R.2/3)		£130	
J80		20 c. grey-lilac (29 March)			30	65
J81		30 c. deep blue-green (29 March)			30	70

The 1 c., 2 c. and 3 c. have large "C" in value as illustrated. The 10 c. and higher values have small "c". Nos. J73/81 had the face values inserted individually into the plate used for No. J46 with the original face value removed. There were a number of printings for each value, often showing differences such as missing stops, various founts of figures or "c", etc., in the value tablets.

The face value error, No. J74a, was later corrected.

Some sheets of No. J75a show a sheet watermark of Britannia seated within a crowned oval spread across fifteen stamps in each sheet. This paper was manufactured by T. Edmonds and the other half of the sheet carried the watermark inscription "FOOLSCAP LEDGER". No stamps have been reported showing letters from this inscription, but a block of 25 is known on laid paper showing a different sheet watermark "HERTFORDSHIRE LEDGER MADE IN ENGLAND". Examples showing parts of these sheet watermarks are rare.

No. J79a shows the horizontal perforations omitted between rows 3/4 and 4/5.

There are marked varieties of shade in this issue.

Normal   Skyline flaw (R. 5/6)

(Des Maung Ba Thit (**16**), Naung Ohn Maung (**17**), and Maung Soi Yi (**18**). Typo State Press, Rangoon)

1943 (1 Aug). *Independence Day.* (*a*) *P* 11.

J82	16	1 c. orange				7·50	13·00
J83	17	3 c. light blue				8·00	14·00
J84	18	5 c. carmine				15·00	8·00
		a. Skyline flaw				65·00	
J82/4					Set of 3	27·00	32·00

(b) Rouletted

J85	16	1 c. orange				1·00	1·50
		b. Perf×roul				95·00	95·00
		c. Imperf (pair)				45·00	55·00
J86	17	3 c. light blue				1·00	1·50
		b. Perf×roul				85·00	85·00
		c. Imperf (pair)				45·00	55·00
J87	18	5 c. carmine				1·00	1·50
		a. Horiz roulette omitted (vert pair)			
		b. Perf×roul				55·00	55·00
		c. Imperf (pair)				45·00	55·00
		d. Skyline flaw				7·00	
J85/7					Set of 3	2·75	4·00

The stamps perf × rouletted may have one, two or three sides perforated.

The rouletted stamps often appear to be roughly perforated owing to failure to make clean cuts. These apparent perforations are very small and quite unlike the large, clean holes of the stamps perforated 11.

A few imperforate sets, mounted on a special card folder and cancelled with the commemorative postmark were presented to officials. These are rare.

19 Burmese Woman   **20** Elephant carrying Log   **21** Watch Tower, Mandalay

(Litho G. Kolff & Co, Batavia)

1943 (1 Oct). *P* 12½.

J88	19	1 c. red-orange				22·00	15·00
J89		2 c. yellow-green				50	2·00
J90		3 c. deep violet				50	2·25
		a. *Bright violet*				80	2·75
J91	20	5 c. carmine				55	60
J92		10 c. blue				85	95
J93		15 c. red-orange				65	2·25
J94		20 c. yellow-green				65	1·75
J95		30 c. olive-brown				65	1·75
J96	21	1 r. red-orange				30	2·00
J97		2 r. bright violet				30	2·25
J88/97					Set of 10	24·00	27·00

16 Soldier carving word "Independence"   **17** Rejoicing Peasant

18 Boy with National Flag

NEW INFORMATION

The editor is always interested to correspond with people who have new information that will improve or correct the Catalogue.

22 Bullock Cart

23 Shan Woman

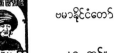

(24 "Burma State" and value)

(Litho G. Kolff & Co, Batavia)

1943 (1 Oct).　*Issue for Shan States. P 12½.*

J 98	**22**	1 c. olive-brown	..	..	.. 24·00	30·00
J 99		2 c. yellow-green			.. 22·00	32·00
J100		3 c. bright violet	..	..	.. 3·00	10·00
J101		5 c. ultramarine	..	..	.. 2·00	5·50
J102	**23**	10 c. blue	..	..	.. 8·50	17·00
J103		20 c. carmine	..	..	.. 22·00	17·00

J104	**23**	30 c. olive-brown	..	..	.. 14·00	32·0(
J98/104		..	..	..	*Set of* 7 85·00	£13(

The Shan States, except for the frontier area around Ken, Tung which was ceded to Thailand, were placed under th administration of the Burmese Government on 24 Decembe 1943, and these stamps were later overprinted as T **24** for us throughout Burma.

1944 (1 Nov).　*Optd as T **24** (the lower characters differ for eac\` value).*

J105	**22**	1 c. olive-brown	..	..	.. 2·50	6·00
J106		2 c. yellow-green	..	..	.. 40	1·75
		a. Opt inverted	..	..	.. £330	£550
J107		3 c. bright violet	..	..	.. 1·50	7·00
J108		5 c. ultramarine	..	..	.. 80	1·00
J109	**23**	10 c. blue	..	..	.. 2·25	2·00
J110		20 c. carmine	..	..	.. 40	1·50
J111		30 c. olive-brown	..	..	.. 40	1·75
J105/11	..	..	..		*Set of* 7 7·50	19·00

The British 14th Army recaptured Mandalay on 29 Marcl 1945 and Rangoon on 3 May.

Canada

100 cents = 1 Canadian dollar

DOMINION

100 King George VI and Queen Elizabeth

1937 (10 May). *Coronation. P* 12.
356 **100** 3 c. carmine 85 30
No. 356 exists imperforate (*Price per pair* £425, *un*).

101 King George VI   **102** Memorial Chamber
Parliament Buildings,
Ottawa

107 Fairchild 45-80 Sekani
Seaplane over *Distributor* on
River Mackenzie

(T **101**. Photograph by Bertram Park)

1937–38. *T* **101/2**, **107** *and similar designs.* (*a*) *Postage.*

(i) *P* 12.
357	**101**	1 c. green (1.4.37)	1·50	10
		a. Booklet pane of 4 + 2 labels (14.4.37)	28·00	
		b. Booklet pane of 6 (18.5.37) ..	3·50	
358		2 c. brown (1.4.37)	1·75	10
		a. Booklet pane of 4 + 2 labels (14.4.37)	55·00	
		b. Booklet pane of 6 (3.5.38) ..	11·00	
359	**101**	3 c. scarlet (1.4.37)	1·75	10
		a. Booklet pane of 4 + 2 labels (14.4.37)	4·25	
360		4 c. yellow (10.5.37)	3·75	1·75
361		5 c. blue (10.5.37)	4·00	10
362		8 c. orange (10.5.37)	3·75	1·75
363	**102**	10 c. rose-carmine (15.6.38) ..	5·00	10
		a. Red	5·00	10
364	–	13 c. blue (15.11.38)	14·00	90
365	–	20 c. red-brown (15.6.38) ..	22·00	50
366	–	50 c. green (15.6.38)	45·00	7·00
367	–	$1 violet (15.6.38)	60·00	8·50
		a. Imperf horiz (vert pair) ..	£2500	
357/67		.. .. *Set of* 11	£150	18·00

Nos. 357/67 exist imperforate (*Prices per pair* 1 c. *to* 8 c. *each* £160, 10 c. *to* 50 c. *each* £200, $1 £300 *un*).

(ii) *Coil stamps. Imperf* × *perf* 8
368	**101**	1 c. green (15.6.37)	3·50	2·25
369		2 c. brown (18.6.37)	3·50	2·50
370		3 c. scarlet (15.4.37)	17·00	75
368/70		.. .. *Set of* 3	22·00	5·00

(*b*) *Air. P* 12
371 **107** 6 c. blue (15.6.38) .. .. .. 11·00 60
Designs: *Horiz* (*as T* **107**)—13 c. Entrance to Halifax Harbour;
20 c. Fort Garry Gate, Winnipeg; 50 c. Entrance, Vancouver
Harbour; $1 Chateau de Ramezay, Montreal.
No. 371 exists imperforate (*Price per pair* £325, *un*).

108 Queen Elizabeth II when   **109** National War
Princess and Princess Margaret   Memorial, Ottawa

110 King George VI and Queen Elizabeth

1939 (15 May). *Royal Visit. P* 12.
372	**108**	1 c. black and green ..	..	1·75	10
373	**109**	2 c. black and brown ..	..	60	50
374	**110**	3 c. black and carmine ..	..	60	10
372/4		.. .. *Set of* 3		2·75	60

Nos. 372/4 exist imperforate (*Price* £300, *un, for each pair*).

111   **112**   **113**
King George VI   King George VI   King George VI in
in Naval uniform   in Military uniform   Air Force uniform

114 Grain Elevator   **116** Parliament
Buildings

117 Ram Tank   121 Air Training Camp

1942 (1 July)–**48.** *War Effort.* T 111/14, 116/17, 121 *and similar designs.* (*a*) *Postage.* (i) *P* 12.

375	111	1 c. green	1·50	10
		a. Booklet pane of 4 + 2 labels (12.9.42)	22·00	
		b. Booklet pane of 6 (24.11.42)	2·50	
376	112	2 c. brown	1·75	10
		a. Booklet pane of 4 + 2 labels (12.9.42)	26·00	
		b. Booklet pane of 6 (6.10.42)	18·00	
377	113	3 c. carmine-lake	1·25	60
		a. Booklet pane of 4 + 2 labels (20.8.42)	4·25	
378		3 c. purple (30.6.43)	90	10
		a. Booklet pane of 4 + 2 labels (28.8.43)	5·50	
		b. Booklet pane of 6 (24.11.47)	11·00	
379	114	4 c. slate	5·50	90
380	112	4 c. carmine-lake (9.4.43)	70	10
		a. Booklet pane of 6 (3.5.43)	3·50	
381	111	5 c. blue	3·00	10
382	–	8 c. red-brown	5·50	75
383	116	10 c. brown	5·50	10
384	117	13 c. dull green	6·50	6·50
385		14 c. dull green (16.4.43)	15·00	90
386	–	20 c. chocolate	14·00	20
387	–	50 c. violet	26·00	2·50
388	–	$1 blue	42·00	5·50
375/88		*Set of* 14	£110	16·00

Nos. 375/88 exist imperforate (*Prices per pair* 1 c. to 8 c. *each* £180, 10 c. to 20 c. *each* £250, 50 c. and $1 *each* £325, *un*).

(ii) *Coil stamps. Imperf* × *perf* 8

389	111	1 c. green (9.2.43)	1·00	1·50
390	112	2 c. brown (24.11.42)	2·25	1·50
391	113	3 c. carmine-lake (23.9.42)	2·00	5·00
392		3 c. purple (19.8.43)	5·50	3·00
393	112	4 c. carmine-lake (13.5.43)	6·00	1·50
389/93		*Set of* 5	15·00	11·00

(iii) *Booklet stamps. Imperf* × *perf* 12 (1.9.43)

394	111	1 c. green	3·00	1·25
		a. Booklet pane of 3	9·00	
395	113	3 c. purple	3·00	1·50
		a. Booklet pane of 3	9·00	
396	112	4 c. carmine-lake	3·00	1·75
		a. Booklet pane of 3	9·00	
394/6		*Set of* 3	8·00	4·00

Nos. 394/6 are from booklets in which the stamps are in strips of three, imperforate at top and bottom and right-hand end.

(iv) *Coil stamps. Imperf* × *perf* 9½

397	111	1 c. green (13.7.48)	3·00	4·00
397a	112	2 c. brown (1.10.48)	7·50	19·00
398	113	3 c. purple (2.7.48)	4·75	6·00
398a	112	4 c. carmine-lake (22.7.48)	7·00	3·50
397/8a		*Set of* 4	20·00	29·00

(*b*) *Air. P* 12

399	121	6 c. blue (1.7.42)	16·00	4·50
400		7 c. blue (16.4.43)	3·00	10

Designs:—*Horiz* (as T 114)—8 c. Farm scene. (*As* T 117)—20 c. Launching of corvette H.M.C.S. *La Malbaie*, Sorel; 50 c. Munitions factory; $1 H.M.S. *Cossack* (destroyer).

Nos. 399/400 exist imperforate (*Price* £400, *un*, *for each pair*).

MINIMUM PRICE

The minimum price quote is 10p which represents a handling charge rather than a basis for valuing common stamps. For further notes about prices see introductory pages.

122 Ontario Farm Scene   129 Alexander Graham Bell and "Fame"

1946 (16 Sept)–**47.** *Peace Re-conversion.* T 122 *and similar horiz designs. P* 12. (*a*) *Postage.*

401		8 c. brown	1·25	1·50
402		10 c. olive-green	1·75	10
403		14 c. sepia	4·00	80
404		20 c. slate	3·00	10
405		50 c. green	17·00	2·25
406		$1 purple	27·00	2·75

(*b*) *Air*

407		7 c. blue	4·00	10
		a. Booklet pane of 4 (24.11.47)	4·00	
401/7		*Set of* 7	50·00	6·50

Designs:—7 c. Canada Geese in flight; 10 c. Great Bear Lake; 14 c. St. Maurice River Power Station; 20 c. Combine Harvester; 50 c. Lumbering in British Columbia; $1 *Abegweit* (train ferry), Prince Edward Is.

1947 (3 Mar). *Birth Centenary of Bell (inventor of telephone). P* 12.

408	129	4 c. blue	15	10

130 "Canadian   131 Queen Elizabeth II
Citizenship".   when Princess

1947 (1 July). *Advent of Canadian Citizenship and Eightieth Anniv of Confederation. P* 12.

409	130	4 c. blue	10	10

(From photograph by Dorothy Wilding)

1948 (16 Feb). *Princess Elizabeth's Marriage. P* 12.

410	131	4 c. blue	10	10

132 Queen Victoria, Parliament   133 Cabot's Ship *Matthew*
Building, Ottawa, and King
George VI

1948 (1 Oct). *One Hundred Years of Responsible Government. P* 12.

411	132	4 c. grey	10	10

1949 (1 Apr). *Entry of Newfoundland into Canadian Confederation. P* 12.

412	133	4 c. green	30	10

134 "Founding of Halifax, 1749" (C. W. Jefferys)

1949 (21 June). *Bicentenary of Halifax, Nova Scotia.* P 12.
413   134   4 c. violet   30   10

135   **136**   **137**

138   King George VI   **139**

(From photographs by Dorothy Wilding)
1949 (15 Nov)–**51.**   (i) *P* 12.
414	135	1 c. green	..	..	10	10
415	136	2 c. sepia	..	..	60	30
415*a*		2 c. olive-green (25.7.51)	..		30	10
416	137	3 c. purple	..	..	30	10
		a. Booklet pane of 4 + 2 labels (12.4.50)		2·25		
417	138	4 c. carmine-lake	..	..	20	10
		a. Booklet pane of 6 (5.5.50)..		27·00		
417*b*		4 c. vermilion (2.6.51)	..		40	10
		ba. Booklet pane of 6	..	6·00		
418	139	5 c. blue	..	..	2·00	10
414/18	..	..	*Set of 7*	3·50		40

(ii) *Imperf × perf* 9½ (*coil stamps*)
419	135	1 c. green (18.5.50)	..	..	1·25	1·00
420	136	2 c. sepia (18.5.50)	..		5·50	5·50
420*a*		2 c. olive-green (9.10.51)	..		1·75	2·00
421	137	3 c. purple (18.5.50)	..		2·25	2·00
422	138	4 c. carmine-lake (20.4.50)	..		14·00	7·50
422*a*		4 c. vermilion (27.11.51)	..		2·00	2·50
419/22*a*	..	..	..	*Set of 6*	24·00	18·00

(iii) *Imperf × perf* 12 (*booklets*)
422*b*	135	1 c. green (18.5.50)	..	..	50	1 75
		ba. Booklet pane of 3	..	1·50		
423	137	3 c. purple (18.5.50)	..		1·25	1·00
		a. Booklet pane of 3 ..		3·75		
423*b*	138	4 c. carmine-lake (18.5.50)	..		15·00	7·00
		ba. Booklet pane of 3	..	45·00		
423*c*		4 c. vermilion (25.10.51)	..		7·00	7·00
		ca. Booklet pane of 3 ..		21·00		
422*b*/3*c*		..	..	*Set of 4*	21·00	15·00

These booklet panes are imperforate at top, bottom and right-hand end.

140 King George VI   **141** Oil Wells in Alberta

(From photograph by Dorothy Wilding)
1950 (19 Jan). *As T* **135/9** *but without* "POSTES POSTAGE", *as T* **140.** (i) *P* 12.
424	1 c. green	..	..	..	..	..	10	50
425	2 c. sepia	..	..	..	..	..	10	1·00
426	3 c. purple	..	..	..	..	..	10	90
427	4 c. carmine-lake	..	..	..	..		10	20
428	5 c. blue	..	..	..	..		30	1·25
424/8	..	..	..	..	..	*Set of 5*	60	3·50

(ii) *Imperf × perf* 9½ (*coil stamps*)
429	1 c. green	..	..	..	..	30	1·00
430	3 c. purple	..	..	..	..	80	1·50

1950 (1 Mar).   *P* 12.
431   141   50 c. green   ..   ..   7·50   1·00

142 Drying Furs   **143** Fisherman

1950 (2 Oct).   *P* 12.
432   142   10 c. brown-purple   ..   ..   ..   1·60   10

1951 (1 Feb).   *P* 12.
433   143 $1 ultramarine   ..   ..   ..   38·00   5·00

144 Sir R. L. Borden   **145** W. L. Mackenzie King

1951 (25 June). *Prime Ministers* (1*st issue*). *P* 12.
434	144	3 c. blue-green	..	..	10	50
435	145	4 c. rose-carmine	..	..	10	10

See also Nos. 444/5, 475/6 and 483/4.

146 Mail Trains, 1851 and 1951   **147** SS. *City of Toronto* and SS. *Prince George*

148 Mail Coach and DC-4M North Star   **149** Reproduction of 3d., 1851

1951 (24 Sept). *Canadian Stamp Centenary. P* 12.
436	146	4 c. black	..	..	..	35	10
437	147	5 c. violet	..	..	..	65	1·75
438	148	7 c. blue ..	..	..	..	35	1·00
439	149	15 c. scarlet	..	..	..	1·10	10
436/9	..	..	..	..	*Set of 4*	2·25	2·75

150 Queen Elizabeth II
when Princess and
Duke of Edinburgh

1951 (26 Oct).   *Royal Visit. P* 12.
440   **150**   4 c. violet   10   10

STAMP BOOKLETS

Booklet Nos. SB28/48 are stapled.

B 3

B 4

1937 (14 Apr)–**38**.   *Blue and white cover. Panes of four* 1 c., 2 c.
and 3 c. (*Nos.* 357a, 358a, 359a) *and* 2 *labels*.
SB28   25 c. booklet. Cover as Type B **3** with English text   85·00
    a. French text (4.1.38)   .. ..   95·00
SB29   25 c. booklet. Cover as Type B **4** with English text
    57 mm wide   .. ..   70·00
    a. English text 63 mm wide .. ..   85·00
    b. French text 57 mm wide (4.1.38) ..   .. 90·00
    ba. French text 63 mm wide £140

1937 (23–27 Apr).   *Red and white cover. Two panes of four* 3 c.
(*No.* 359a) *and* 2 *labels*.
SB30   25 c. booklet. Cover as Type B **3** with English text
    (27 Apr)   .. ..   19·00
    a. French text (23 Apr)   .. ..   30·00
SB31   25 c. booklet. Cover as Type B **4** with English text
    57 mm wide (27 Apr)   .. ..   10·00
    a. English text 63 mm wide ..   .. 35·00
    b. French text 57 mm wide (23 Apr)   .. 13·00
    ba. French text 63 mm wide £130

1937 (18 May)–**38**.   *Green and white cover. Four panes of six*
1 c. (*No.* 357b).
SB32   25 c. booklet. Cover as Type B **3** with English text   30·00
    a. French text (14.10.38)   .. 42·00
SB33   25 c. booklet. Cover as Type B **4** with English text
    57 mm wide   .. ..   17·00
    a. English text 63 mm wide   .. 55·00
    b. French text 57 mm wide (14.10.38) ..   18·00
    ba. French text 63 mm wide £120

1938 (3 May)–**39**.   *Brown and white cover. Two panes of six* 2 c.
(*No.* 358b).
SB34   25 c. booklet. Cover as Type B **3** with English text   40·00
    a. French text (3.3.39)   .. ..   50·00
SB35   25 c. booklet. Cover as Type B **4** with English text
    57 mm wide   .. ..   .. 23·00
    a. English text 63 mm wide   .. ..   60·00
    b. French text 57 mm wide ..   .. 42·00
    ba. French text 63 mm wide ..   .. 85·00

1942 (20–29 Aug)   *Red and white cover. Two panes of four* 3 c.
(*No.* 377a) *and* 2 *labels*.
SB36   25 c. booklet. Cover as Type B **4** with English text   8·50
    a. French text (29 Aug)   .. ..   12·00

1942 (12–14 Sept).   *Violet and white cover. Panes of four* 1 c.,
2 c. *and* 3 c. (*Nos.* 375a, 376a, 377a), *each with* 2 *labels*.
SB37   25 c. booklet. Cover as Type B **4** with English text
    (14 Sept)   .. ..   48·00
    a. French text (12 Sept)   .. ..   90·00

1942 (6 Oct)–**43**.   *Brown and white cover. Two panes of six* 2 c.
(*No.* 376b).
SB38   25 c. booklet. Cover as Type B **4** with English text   42·00
    a. French text (6.4.43)   .. ..   70·00

1942 (24 Nov)–**46**.   *Green and white cover. Four panes of six* 1 c.
(*No.* 375b).
SB39   25 c. booklet. Cover as Type B **4** with English text   11·00
    a. French text (16.2.43)   .. ..   17·00
    b. Bilingual text (8.1.46)   .. ..   20·00

1943 (3 May)–**46**.   *Orange and white cover. One pane of six* 4 c.
(*No.* 380a).
SB40   25 c. booklet. Cover as Type B **4** with English text   4·00
    a. French text (12.5.43)   .. ..   10·00
    b. Bilingual text (8.1.46)   .. ..   13·00

1943 (28 Aug)–**46**.   *Purple and white cover. Two panes of four*
3 c. (*No.* 378a) *and* 2 *labels*.
SB41   25 c. booklet. Cover as Type B **4** with English text   10·00
    a. French text (7.9.43)   .. ..   25·00
    b. Bilingual text (8.1.46)   .. ..   18·00

B 5

1943 (1 Sept)–**46**.   *Black and white cover. Panes of three* 1 c.,
3 c. *and* 4 c. (*Nos.* 394a, 395a, 396a) (3×1).
SB42   25 c. booklet. Cover as Type B **5** with English text   26·00
    a. French text (18.9.43)   .. ..   32·00
    c. Bilingual text (23.1.46)   .. ..   30·00

CANADA – POSTAGE
STAMPS

B 6

1947 (24 Nov).   *Brown on orange cover. Panes of six* 3 c. *and* 4 c.
(3×2) *and two panes of four* 7 c. (2×2) (*Nos.* 378b, 380a, 407a).
SB43   \$1 booklet. Cover as Type B **6** with English text   25·00
    a. French text   .. ..   40·00

1950 (12 Apr–18 May).   *Purple and white cover. Two panes of*
four 3 c. (*No.* 416a) *and* 2 *labels*.
SB44   25 c. booklet. Cover as Type B **4** with English text   5·00
    a. Bilingual text (18 May)   .. ..   5·00

1950 (5–10 May). *Orange and white cover. One pane of six* 4 *c.* (*No.* 417a) (3×2).
SB45 25 c. booklet. Cover as Type B **4** with English text 28·00
    a. Stitched .. .. 60·00
    b. Bilingual text (10 May) .. .. 32·00

1950 (18 May). *Black and white cover. Panes of three* 1 *c.,* 3 *c. and* 4 *c.* (*Nos.* 422ba, 423a, 423ba) (3×1).
SB46 25 c. booklet. Cover as Type B **5** with English text 50·00
    a. Bilingual text .. .. .. 55·00

1951 (2 June). *Orange and white cover. One pane of six* 4 *c.* (*No.* 417ba) (3×2).
SB47 25 c. booklet. Cover as Type B **4** with English text 6·00
    a. Stitched .. .. 12·00
    b. Bilingual text .. .. .. 8·50

1951 (25 Oct)–52. *Black and white cover. Panes of three* 1 *c.,* 3 *c. and* 4 *c.* (*Nos.* 422ba, 423a, 423ca) (3×1).
SB48 25 c. booklet. Cover as Type B **5** with English text 26·00
    a. Bilingual text (9.7.52) .. .. 30·00

SPECIAL DELIVERY STAMPS

Nos. S9/17 were recess-printed by the Canadian Bank Note Co.

S **6** Canadian Coat of Arms

1938–39. *P* 12.
S **9** S **6** 10 c. green (1.4.39) .. .. .. 18·00 3·00
S10 20 c. scarlet (15.6.38) .. .. 40·00 23·00
Nos. S9/10 exist imperforate (*Price* £375, *un, for each pair*).

(S **7**)

1939 (1 Mar). *Surch with Type* S **7.**
S11 S **6** 10 c. on 20 c. scarlet .. .. .. 9·00 8·00

S **8** Coat of Arms and Flags

S **9** Lockheed L.18 Lodestar

1942 (1 July)–**1943.** *War Effort. P* 12. (*a*) *Postage.*
S12 S **8** 10 c. green .. .. 4·50 30
    (*b*) *Air*
S13 S **9** 16 c. ultramarine .. .. .. 5·00 45
S14 17 c. ultramarine (1.4.43) .. .. 4·00 55
Nos. S12/14 exist imperforate (*Prices per un pair* 10 c. £350, 16 c. £400, 17 c. £400)

S **10** Arms of Canada and Peace Symbols

S **11** Canadair DC-4M North Star

1946 (16 Sept–5 Dec). *P* 12. (*a*) *Postage*
S15 S **10** 10 c. green .. .. 2·75 30
    (*b*) *Air.* (i) *Circumflex accent in* "EXPRÊS"
S16 S **11** 17 c. ultramarine .. .. .. 4·50 3·50
    (ii) *Grave accent in* "EXPRÈS"
S17 S **11** 17 c. ultramarine (5.12.46) .. .. 5·00 4·00

POSTAGE DUE STAMPS

D **4**

(Recess Canadian Bank Note Co)
1935–65. *P* 12.
D18 D **4** 1 c. violet (14.10.35) 70 10
D19 2 c. violet (9.9.35) 70 10
D20 3 c. violet (4.65) .. .. .. 3·75 5·00
D21 4 c. violet (2.7.35) .. .. .. 1·50 10
D22 5 c. violet (12.48) .. .. .. 3·00 90
D23 6 c. violet (1957).. .. .. .. 1·50 3·00
D24 10 c. violet (16.9.35) 60 10
D18/24 .. .. *Set of* 7 10·50 8·25
The 1 c., 2 c., 4 c. and 10 c. exist imperforate (*Price* £150 *for each un pair*).

OFFICIAL STAMPS

Stamps perforated "O H M S" were introduced in May 1923 for use by the Receiver General's department in Ottawa and by the Assistant Receiver Generals' offices in provincial cities. From 1 July 1939 this use was extended to all departments of the federal government and such stamps continued to be produced until replaced by the "O.H.M.S." overprinted issue of 1949.

The perforated initials can appear either upright, inverted or sideways on individual stamps. The prices quoted are for the cheapest version. Stamps perforated with Type O **1** are only priced used. Only isolated examples are known mint and these are very rare.

A number of forged examples of the perforated "O.H.M.S." are known, in particular of Type O **1**. Many of these forged perforated initials were applied to stamps which had already been used and this can aid their detection. Genuine examples, postmarked after the perforated initials were applied, often show the cancellation ink bleeding into the holes.

(O 1)
(Five holes in
vertical bars of
"H")

(O 2)
(Four holes in vertical
bars of "H")

1937 (10 May). *Coronation. No. 356 punctured as Type* O 1.
O96 **100** 3 c. carmine .. .. — 40·00

1937–38. *Nos. 357/67, 370 and 371 punctured as Type* O 1.

(a) Postage

O 97	**101**	1 c. green ..	..	..	— 2·50
O 98		2 c. brown ..			— 2·75
O 99		3 c. scarlet ..			— 2·50
O100		4 c. yellow ..			— 8·00
O101		5 c. blue ..			— 6·50
O102		8 c. orange ..			— 13·00
O103	**102**	10 c. rose-carmine ..			— 20·00
		a. Red ..			— 23·00
O104	–	13 c. blue ..			— 28·00
O105	–	20 c. red-brown ..			— 28·00
O106	–	50 c. green ..			— 65·00
O107	–	$1 violet ..			— 95·00
O97/107	..	.. ..	*Set of* 11		£250

(b) Coil stamp

O108 **101** 3 c. scarlet .. .. .. — 65·00

(c) Air

O109 **107** 6 c. blue .. .. .. — 28·00

1939 (15 May). *Royal Visit. Nos. 372/4 punctured as Type* O 1.
O110 **108** 1 c. black and green .. .. .. — 32·00
O111 **109** 2 c. black and brown .. .. — 42·00
O112 **110** 3 c. black and carmine .. .. — 32·00
O110/12 .. .. .. *Set of* 3 — 95·00

1939 (1 July). *Air. No. 274 punctured as Type* O 2.
O113 **59** 5 c. olive-brown .. .. .. 20·00 14·00

1939 (1 July). *Nos. 347/50 and 355 punctured as Type* O 2.

(a) Postage

O114 **94** 10 c. carmine .. .. .. 55·00 38·00
O115 – 13 c. purple .. .. .. 60·00 38·00
O116 – 20 c. olive-green .. .. 75·00 48·00
O117 – 50 c. deep violet .. .. 60·00 38·00

(b) Air

O118 **99** 6 c. red-brown .. .. 50·00 42·00
O114/18 .. .. .. *Set of* 5 £275 £180

1939 (1 July). *Coronation. No. 356 punctured as Type* O 2.
O119 **100** 3 c. carmine .. .. .. 70·00 45·00

1939 (1 July). *Nos. 357/67, 369/70 and 371 punctured as Type*
O 2. *(a) Postage*

O120	**101**	1 c. green ..	..	..	1·50	10
O121		2 c. brown ..			2·25	10
O122		3 c. scarlet ..			2·50	10
O123		4 c. yellow ..			5·00	2·25
O124		5 c. blue ..			3·50	20
O125		8 c. orange ..			13·00	4·25
O126	**102**	10 c. rose-carmine ..			50·00	3·25
		a. Red ..			8·00	30
O127	–	13 c. blue ..			13·00	1·50
O128	–	20 c. red-brown ..			35·00	2·00
O129	–	50 c. green ..			40·00	8·00
O130	–	$1 violet ..			110·00	30·00
O120/30	..	..	*Set of* 11		£200	42·00

(b) Coil stamps

O131 **101** 2 c. brown .. .. .. 70·00 45·00
O132 3 c. scarlet .. .. .. 70·00 45·00

(c) Air

O133 **107** 6 c. blue .. .. .. 3·00 80

1939 (1 July). *Royal Visit. Nos. 372/4 punctured as Type* O 2.
O134 **108** 1 c. black and green .. .. 80·00 38·00
O135 **109** 2 c. black and brown .. 80·00 38·00
O136 **110** 3 c. black and carmine .. 80·00 38·00
O134/6 .. .. *Set of* 3 £225 £100

1942–43. *War Effort. Nos. 375/88 and 399/400 punctured as
Type* O 2. *(a) Postage*

O137	**111**	1 c. green ..	..	..	40	10
O138	**112**	2 c. brown ..		..	50	10
O139	**113**	3 c. carmine-lake ..		..	1·10	40
O140		3 c. purple ..		..	60	10
O141	**114**	4 c. slate ..		..	2·75	75
O142	**112**	4 c. carmine-lake ..		..	55	10
O143	**111**	5 c. blue ..		..	1·25	15
O144	–	8 c. red-brown ..		..	7·50	2·00
O145	**116**	10 c. brown ..		..	4·50	20
O146	**117**	13 c. dull green ..		..	5·50	5·50
O147		14 c. dull green ..		..	9·00	85
O148	–	20 c. chocolate ..		..	12·00	70
O149	–	50 c. violet ..		..	35·00	5·50
O150	–	$1 blue ..		..	90·00	25·00

(b) Air

O151 **121** 6 c. blue .. .. .. 4·00 2·00
O152 7 c. blue .. .. .. 3·25 25
O137/52 .. .. .. *Set of* 16 £160 40·00

1946. *Peace Re-conversion. Nos. 401/7 punctured as Type* O 2.

(a) Postage

O153 **122** 8 c. brown .. .. .. 10·00 3·50
O154 – 10 c. olive-green .. .. 3·25 15
O155 – 14 c. sepia .. .. .. 4·25 65
O156 – 20 c. slate .. .. .. 4·50 50
O157 – 50 c. green .. .. 23·00 5·00
O158 – $1 purple .. .. .. 60·00 15·00

(b) Air

O159 – 7 c. blue .. .. .. 3·00 40
O153/9 .. .. .. *Set of* 7 95·00 23·00

1949. *Nos. 415 and 416 punctured as Type* O 2.
O160 **136** 2 c. sepia 75 75
O161 **137** 3 c. purple 75 75

O.H.M.S.

(O 3)

1949. *Nos. 375/6, 378, 380 and 402/7 optd as Type* O 3 *by
typography.*

(a) Postage

O162	**111**	1 c. green ..	..	1·75	2·00
		a. Missing stop after "S"	..	£150	50·00
O163	**112**	2 c. brown ..	..	12·00	12·00
		a. Missing stop after "S"	..	£150	85·00
O164	**113**	3 c. purple ..	..	1·25	1·10
O165	**112**	4 c. carmine-lake ..	..	2·00	80
O166	–	10 c. olive-green ..	..	3·75	65
		a. Missing stop after "S"	..	80·00	35·00
O167	–	14 c. sepia ..	..	4·50	1·75
		a. Missing stop after "S"	..	£100	48·00
O168	–	20 c. slate ..	..	12·00	60
		a. Missing stop after "S"	..	£140	50·00
O169	–	50 c. green ..	..	£160	£120
		a. Missing stop after "S"	..	£850	£550
O170	–	$1 purple ..	..	45·00	48·00
		a. Missing stop after "S"	..	£1500	

(b) Air

O171 – 7 c. blue .. .. 24·00 7·00
a. Missing stop after "S" .. £130 60·00
O162/71 .. .. .. *Set of* 10 £225 £140

Forgeries exist of this overprint. Genuine examples are
2.3×15 mm and show the tops of all letters aligned, as are the
stops.

Only a few sheets of the $1 showed the variety, No. O170a.

MISSING STOP VARIETIES. These occur on R. 6/2 of the lower left pane (Nos. O162a, O163a and O176a) or R. 10/2 of the lower left pane (O166a, O167a, O168a, O169a, O170a and O171a). No. O176a also occurs on R. 8/8 of the upper left pane in addition to R. 6/2 of the lower left pane.

1949–50. *Nos. 414/15, 416/17, 418 and 431 optd as Type* O 3 *by typography.*

O172	**135**	1 c. green	..	..	..	85	85
O173	**136**	2 c. sepia	..	..	..	1·75	1·60
O174	**137**	3 c. purple	..	..	..	1·00	70
O175	**138**	4 c. carmine-lake	..	..	1·50	15
O176	**139**	5 c. blue (1949)	..	..	2·75	2·00
		a. Missing stop after "S"	..	85·00	38·00
O177	**141**	50 c. green (1950)	..	..	32·00	28·00
O172/7	..	..	..	*Set of* 6	35·00	30·00

G   G   G

(O 4)   (O 5)   (O 6)

Type O **6** differs from Type O **5** in having a thinner appearance and an upward sloping left serif to the lower arm. It results from a new plate introduced in 1961/62. Variations in thickness are known in Type O 4 but these are due to wear and subsequent cleaning of the plate. All are produced by typography. Examples showing the "G" applied by lithography are forgeries.

1950 (2 Oct)–52. *Nos. 402/4, 406/7, 414/18 and 431 optd with Type* O 4 (1 *to* 5 *c.*) *or* O 5 (7 *c. to* $1). (*a*) *Postage*.

O178	**135**	1 c. green	..	..	..	70	10
O179	**136**	2 c. sepia	..	..	..	1·50	1·60
O180		2 c. olive-green (11.51)	..	..	1·75	10
O181	**137**	3 c. purple	..	..	..	1·50	10
O182	**138**	4 c. carmine-lake	..	..	1·50	30
O183		4 c. vermilion (1.5.52)	..	..	1·90	10
O184	**139**	5 c. blue	..	..	..	2·50	30
O185	–	10 c. olive-green	..	..	..	3·00	10
O186	–	14 c. grey	..	..	..	11·00	2·75
O187	–	20 c. slate	..	..	..	16·00	20
O188	**141**	50 c. green	..	..	..	11·00	9·00
O189	–	$1 purple	..	..	..	60·00	60·00
		(*b*) *Air*					
O190	–	7 c. blue	..	..	..	24·00	13·00
O178/90	..	..	..	*Set of* 13	£120	75·00

1950–51. *Nos. 432/3 optd with Type* O 5.

O191	**142**	10 c. brown-purple	..	..	..	2·25	10
		a. Opt omitted in pair with normal	£400	£350
O192	**143**	$1 ultramarine (1.2.51)	..	..	55·00	60·00

OFFICIAL SPECIAL DELIVERY STAMPS

1938–39. *Nos. S9/10 punctured as Type* O 1.

OS7	S **6**	10 c. green	..	..	..	—	38·00
OS8		20 c. scarlet	..	..	..	—	60·00

1939 (1 Mar). *No. S11 punctured as Type* O 1.

OS9	S **6**	10 c. on 20 c. scarlet	..	..	—	60·00

1939 (1 July). *Inscr* "CENTS" *at foot. No. S7 punctured as Type* O 2.

OS10	S **4**	20 c. brown-red	..	..	£150	80·00

1939 (1 July). *No. S8 punctured as Type* O 2.

OS11	S **5**	20 c. scarlet	..	..	..	85·00	38·00

1939 (1 July). *No. S9 punctured as Type* O 2.

OS12	S **6**	10 c. green	..	..	..	7·00	4·50

1939 (1 July). *No. S11 punctured as Type* O 2.

OS13	S **6**	10 c. on 20 c. scarlet	..	..	£100	50·00

1942–43. *Nos. S12/14 punctured as Type* O 2. (*a*) *Postage*

OS14	S **8**	10 c. green	..	..	..	9·00	6·50
		(*b*) *Air*				
OS15	S **9**	16 c. ultramarine	..	..	17·00	13·00
OS16		17 c. ultramarine	..	..	10·00	8·00

1946–47. *Nos. S15/17 punctured as Type* O 2. (*a*) *Postage*

OS17	S **10**	10 c. green	..	..	..	6·50	4·50
		(*b*) *Air*				
OS18	S **11**	17 c. ultramarine (circumflex accent)	26·00	22·00
OS19		17 c. ultramarine (grave accent)	..	55·00	55·00

1950. *No. S15 optd as Type* O 3, *but larger*.

OS20	S **10**	10 c. green	..	..	..	17·00	21·00

1950 (2 Oct). *No. S15 optd as Type* O 4, *but larger*.

OS21	S **10**	10 c. green	..	..	..	26·00	27·00

Cayman Islands

12 pence (d) = 1 shilling; 20 shillings = 1 pound

DEPENDENCY OF JAMAICA

1937 (13 May). *Coronation Issue. As Nos. 95/7 of Antigua.*
P 11×11½.

112	½d. green	..	..	..	30	75
113	1d. carmine	..	..	..	50	20
114	2½d. blue	..	..	..	95	40
112/14	..	..	..	Set of 3	1·60	1·25
112/14 Perf "Specimen"	..	..	Set of 3	75·00	

26 Beach View

27 Dolphin (fish)
(*Coryphaena hippurus*)

(Recess D.L.R. (½d., 2d., 6d., 1s., 10s.), Waterlow (others))

1938 (5 May)–**48**. *T* **26/7** *and similar designs. Wmk Mult Script CA (sideways on ¼d., 1d., 1½d., 2½d., 3d., 2s., 5s.). Various perfs.*

115	26	¼d. red-orange (*p* 12½)	..	40	55
		a. Perf 13½×12½ (16.7.43)	..	10	55
116	27	½d. green (*p* 13×11½)	..	75	55
		a. Perf 14 (16.7.43)	..	1·25	1·40
		ab. "A" of "CA" missing from wmk	.. £1000	
117	–	1d. scarlet (*p* 12½)	..	30	75
118	26	1½d. black (*p* 12½)	..	30	10
119	–	2d. violet (*p* 11½×13)	..	2·25	40
		a. Perf 14 (16.7.43)	..	60	30
120	–	2½d. bright blue (*p* 12½)	..	40	20
120a	–	2½d. orange (*p* 12½) (25.8.47)	..	2·25	50
121	–	3d. orange (*p* 12½)	..	40	15
121a	–	3d. bright blue (*p* 12½) (25.8.47)	..	2·25	30
122	–	6d. olive-green (*p* 11½×13)	..	9·00	4·00
		a. Perf 14 (16.7.43)	..	2·00	1·25
		b. Brownish ol (*p* 11½×13) (8.7.47)	3·00	1·50
123	27	1s. red-brown (*p* 13×11½)	..	5·50	1·50
		a. Perf 14 (16.7.43)	..	4·00	2·00
		ab. "A" of "CA" missing from wmk	.. £1100	
124	26	2s. yellow-green (*shades*) (*p* 12½)	..	48·00	14·00
		a. Deep green (16.7.43)	..	25·00	9·00
125	–	5s. carmine-lake (*p* 12½)	..	32·00	15·00
		a. Crimson (1948)	..	60·00	22·00
126	–	10s. chocolate (*p* 11½×13)	..	23·00	9·00
		a. Perf 14 (16.7.43)	..	21·00	9·00
115/26a	..	..	Set of 14	80·00	35·00
115/26 Perf "Specimen"	..	Set of 14	£275	

Designs: *Horiz* (as *T* **26**)—1d., 3d. Cayman Islands map; 2½d., 5s. *Rembro* (schooner). *Vert* (as *T* **27**)—2d., 6d., 10s. Hawksbill Turtles.

Stop after "1946" (R.2/1)

1946 (26 Aug). *Victory. As Nos. 110/11 of Antigua.*

127	1½d. black	..	..	20	10
128	3d. orange-yellow	..	..	20	10
	a. Stop after "1946"	..	..	16·00	
127/8 Perf "Specimen"	..	Set of 2	65·00	

1948 (29 Nov). *Royal Silver Wedding. As Nos. 112/13 of Antigua.*

129	½d. green	..	..	..	10	10
130	10s. violet-blue	..	..	..	13·00	11·00

1949 (10 Oct). *75th Anniv of Universal Postal Union. As Nos. 114/17 of Antigua.*

131	2½d. orange	..	..	..	30	30
132	3d. deep blue	..	..	..	1·50	1·40
133	6d. olive	..	..	..	60	1·40
134	1s. red-brown	..	..	..	60	30
131/4	..	..	..	Set of 4	2·75	3·00

31 Cat Boat

32 Coconut Grove, Cayman Brac

(Recess B.W.)

1950 (2 Oct). *T* **31/2** *and similar horiz designs. Wmk Mult Script CA. P* 11½ × 11.

135	¼d. bright blue and pale scarlet	..	..	15	60
136	½d. reddish violet and emerald-green	..	15	1·25
137	1d. olive-green and deep blue	..	..	60	75
138	1½d. green and brown	..	..	30	75
139	2d. reddish violet and rose-carmine	..	1·25	60
140	2½d. turquoise and black	..	..	70	60
141	3d. bright green and light blue	..	1·40	1·50
142	6d. red-brown and blue	..	..	2·00	1·25
143	9d. scarlet and grey-green	..	..	4·50	2·00
144	1s. brown and orange	..	..	3·25	2·75
145	2s. violet and reddish purple	..	8·00	9·00
146	5s. olive-green and violet	..	..	13·00	7·00
147	10s. black and scarlet	..	..	15·00	14·00
135/47	..	..	..	Set of 13	45·00	38·00

Designs:—1d. Green Turtle; 1½d. Thatch rope industry; 2d. Cayman seamen; 2½d. Map of Cayman Islands; 3d. Parrotfish; 6d. Bluff, Cayman Brac; 9d. Georgetown harbour; 1s. Turtle in "crawl"; 2s. *Ziroma* (schooner); 5s. Boat-building; 10s. Government Offices, Grand Cayman.

PRICES OF SETS

Set prices are given for many issues, generally those containing three stamps or more. Definitive sets include one of each value or major colour change, but do not cover different perforations, die types or minor shades. Where a choice is possible the set prices are based on the cheapest versions of the stamps included in the listings.

Ceylon

100 cents = 1 rupee

CROWN COLONY

1937 (12 May). *Coronation. As Nos. 95/7 of Antigua.*
P 11×11½.

383	6 c. carmine	..	..	..	..	..	..	65	15
384	9 c. green	..	..	..	..	..	..	2·50	3·25
385	20 c. blue	..	..	..	..	..	..	3·50	3·00
383/5	..	..	..	..	..	*Set of 3*		6·00	5·75
383/5 Perf "Specimen"		..	..	*Set of 3* 65·00					

69 Tapping Rubber

70 Sigiriya (Lion Rock)

71 Ancient Guard-stone,
Anuradhapura

72 King George VI

COCONUT PALMS

Apostrophe flaw (Frame Pl 1A
R.6/6) (ptg of 1 Jan 1943 only)

(Recess B.W. (stamps perf 11 × 11½ or 11½ × 11), D.L.R. (all
others) T **72** typo D.L.R.)

1938–49. *T* **69/72** *and designs as* 1935–36, *but with portrait of
King George VI instead of King George V,* "POSTAGE &
REVENUE" *omitted and some redrawn. Wmk Mult Script CA
(sideways on* 10, 15, 25, 30 c. *and* 1 r.). *Chalk-surfaced paper
(*5 r.). *Various perfs.*

386	69	2 c. blk & carm (p 11½×13) (25.4.38)	10·00	1·75
		a. Perf 13½×13 (1938)	£120	1·75
		b. Perf 13½ (25.4.38) ..	2·00	10
		c. Perf 11×11½ (17.2.44)	65	85
		cw. Wmk inverted	—	£425
		d. Perf 12 (22.4.49)	2·00	3·50

387	60	3 c. black & dp blue-green (p 13×11½)		
		(21.3.38)	10·00	50
		a. Perf 13×13½ (1938)	£250	7·50
		b. Perf 13½ (21.3.38)	3·50	10
		c. Perf 14 (7.41)	£120	95
		d. Perf 11½×11 (14.5.42)	80	10
		da. "A" of "CA" missing from wmk ..	£800	£800
		e. Perf 12 (14.1.46)	65	70
387f		5 c. sage-grn & orge (p 13½) (1.1.43)	30	10
		fa. Apostrophe flaw	48·00	
		g. Perf 12 (1947)	1·25	30
388	–	6 c. black and blue (p 11×11½) (1.1.38)	30	10
389	70	10 c. blk & light bl (p 11½×11) (1.2.38)	2·25	10
		a. Wmk upright (1.6.44) ..	2·50	40
390	–	15 c. grn & red-brn (p 11½×11) (1.1.38)	1·75	10
		a. Wmk upright (23.7.45) ..	2·75	60
391	–	20 c. blk & grey-bl (p 11½×11) (15.1.38)	3·25	10
392	–	25 c. dp bl & choc (p 11½×11) (15.1.38)	4·50	30
		a. Wmk upright (1944)	4·25	10
393	–	30 c. carm & grn (p 11½×11) (1.2.38)	11·00	1·25
		a. Wmk upright (16.4.45) ..	12·00	2·75
394	–	50 c. blk & mve (p 13×11½) (25.4.38) ..	£160	42·00
		a. Perf 13×13½ (1938) ..	£350	2·75
		b. Perf 13½ (25.4.38)	15·00	30
		c. Perf 14 (4.42)	£100	27·00
		d. Perf 11½×11 (14.5.42) ..	4·25	3·00
		e. Perf 12 (14.1.46)	75	20
395	–	1 r. blue-violet & chocolate (p 11½×11)		
		(1.2.38)	15·00	85
		a. Wmk upright (1944)	16·00	2·25
396	71	2 r. black & carm (p 11×11½) (1.2.38)	13·00	2·25
		a. "A" of "CA" missing from wmk ..		
396b		2 r. black & violet (p 11×11½) (15.3.47)	1·75	1·60
397	72	5 r. green and purple (p 14) (1.7.38) ..	38·00	4·25
		a. Ordinary paper. *Green and pale*		
		purple (19.2.43)	13·00	2·25
386/97a (*cheapest*)		.. ..	*Set of 14* 65·00	7·50
386/97 Perf "Specimen"		..	*Set of 14* £300	

Designs: *Vert*—5 c. Coconut Palms; 6 c. Colombo Harbour;
20 c. Plucking tea. *Horiz*—15 c. River scene; 25 c. Temple of the
Tooth, Kandy; 30 c. Ancient irrigation tank; 50 c. Wild
elephants; 1 r. Trincomalee.

3 CENTS
(73)

3 CENTS
(74)

1940–41. *Nos.* 388 *and* 391 *surch.*

398	73	3 c. on 6 c. (10.5.41) ..	..	..	10	10
399	74	3 c. on 20 c. (5.11.40) ..	..	..	2·00	1·50

1946 (10 Dec). *Victory. As Nos.* 110/11 *of Antigua.*

400		6 c. blue	..	..	..	..	..	10	10
401		15 c. brown	..	..	..	..	..	10	40
400/1 Perf "Specimen"		..	..	*Set of 2* 55·00					

STANLEY GIBBONS
STAMP COLLECTING SERIES

Introductory booklets on *How to Start, How to
Identify Stamps* and *Collecting by Theme.* A series
of well illustrated guides at a low price.
Write for details.

75 Parliament Building   **76** Adam's Peak

(Des R. Tenison and M. S. V. Rodrigo. Recess B.W.)

1947 (25 Nov). *Inauguration of New Constitution. T* **75/6** *and similar designs. Wmk Mult Script CA. P* 11 × 12 (*horiz*) *or* 12 × 11 (*vert*).

402	6 c. black and blue	..	..	..	10	15
403	10 c. black, orange and carmine				10	20
404	15 c. green and purple..	..	..	..	10	80
405	25 c. ochre and emerald-green		..		10	20
402/5 ..		..	..	*Set of* 4	35	1·25
402/5 Perf "Specimen"			*Set of* 4	85·00	

Designs: *Horiz*—15 c. Temple of the Tooth. *Vert*—25 c. Anuradhapura.

DOMINION

79 Lion Flag of   **80** D. S. Senanayake
Dominion

81 Lotus Flowers and Sinhalese Letters "Sri"

(Recess (flag typo) B.W.)

1949 (4 Feb–5 Apr). *First Anniv of Independence.* (*a*) *Wmk Mult Script CA* (*sideways on* 4 *c.*). *P* 12½×12 (4 *c.*) *or* 12×12½ (5 *c.*).

406	79	4 c. yellow, carmine and brown	..	10	20
407	80	5 c. brown and green	..	..	10	10

(*b*) *W* **81** (*sideways on* 15 *c.*). *P* 13 × 12½ (15 *c.*) *or* 12 × 12½ (25 *c.*)
(5 April)

408	79	15 c. yellow, carmine and vermilion	..	25	15
409	80	25 c. brown and blue	..	..	15	40
406/9 ..		..	..	*Set of* 4	40	75

The 15 c. is larger, measuring 28 × 12 mm.

82 Globe and Forms of Transport

83   **84**

(Recess D.L.R.)

1949 (10 Oct). *75th Anniv of Universal Postal Union. W* **81**. *P* 13 (25 *c.*) *or* 12 (*others*).

410	82	5 c. brown and bluish green	..	..	75	10
411	83	15 c. black and carmine		..	..	1·40	1·75
412	84	25 c. black and ultramarine	..	..	1·40	1·10
410/12	..	..	..	..	*Set of* 3	3·25	2·50

85 Kandyan   **88** Sigiriya
Dancer   (Lion Rock)

89 Octagon Library, Temple   **90** Ruins at Madirigiriya
of the Tooth

(Recess B.W.)

1950 (4 Feb). *T* **85**, **88/90** *and similar designs. W* **81**. *P* 11 × 11½ (75 *c.*), 11½ × 11 (1 *r.*), 12 × 12½ (*others*).

413	4 c. purple and scarlet	..	..	..	10	10
414	5 c. green	..	..	..	10	10
415	15 c. blue-green and violet	..	..	..	1·50	30
416	30 c. carmine and yellow	..	..	30	40
417	75 c. ultramarine and orange	..	..	3·00	10
418	1 r. deep blue and brown	..	..	..	1·75	30
413/18	..	..	..	*Set of* 6	6·00	95

Designs: *Vert* (*as T* **88**)—5 c. Kiri Vehera, Polonnaruwa; 15 c. Vesak Orchid.

For these values with redrawn inscriptions see Nos. 450/1, 454, 456, 460 and 462.

91 Sambars, Ruhuna   **92** Ancient Guard-   **96** Star Orchid
National Park   stone, Anuradhapura

97 Rubber Plantation   99 Tea Plantation

I. No. 424   II. No. 424a (Dot added)

(Photo Courvoisier)

1951 (1 Aug)–**54.** *T* **91/2, 96/7, 99** *and similar designs. No wmk.*
P 11½.

419	2 c. brown and blue-green (15.5.54) ..	..	10	50
420	3 c. black and slate-violet (15.5.54) ..	..	10	50
421	6 c. brown-black & yellow-green (15.5.54)	..	10	30
422	10 c. green and blue-grey	.. ..	75	65
423	25 c. orange-brown & bright blue (15.3.54)	..	10	20
424	35 c. red and deep green (I) (1.2.52) ..	..	1·50	1·50
	a. Type II (1954) ..	..	5·50	60
425	40 c. deep brown (15.5.54) ..	..	4·50	90
426	50 c. indigo and slate-grey (15.3.54) ..	..	30	10
427	85 c. black and deep blue-green (15.5.54)	..	50	10
428	2 r. blue and deep brown (15.5.54) ..	..	6·50	1·00
429	5 r. brown and orange (15.3.54) ..	..	4·75	1·25
430	10 r. red-brown and buff (15.3.54)	..	32·00	9·00
419/30	.. .. *Set of* 12	45·00	13·50

Designs: *Vert* (*as T* **91**)—6 c. Harvesting rice; 10 c. Coconut trees;
25 c. Sigiriya fresco. (*As T* **99**)—5 r. Bas-relief, Anuradhapura;
10 r. Harvesting rice. *Horiz* (*as T* **97**)—50 c. Outrigger canoe;
(*as T* **99**)—2 r. River Gal Dam.

STAMP BOOKLETS

1937 (Apr–June). *Coronation of King George VI. Black on blue
(No. SB15) or olive-green (No. SB16) covers. Stapled.*
SB15	1 r. 80, booklet containing thirty 6 c. (No. 383) in blocks of 10 and pane of four airmail labels (June)	£750
SB16	2 r. 70, booklet containing thirty 9 c. (No. 384) in blocks of 10 and pane of four airmail labels	£800

1938. *Black on blue (No. SB17) or grey (No. SB18) covers.
Stapled.*
SB17	1 r. 80, booklet containing thirty 6 c. (No. 388) in blocks of 10 and pane of four airmail labels	
SB18	3 r. booklet containing fifteen 20 c. (No. 391) in blocks of 5 or 10 and pane of four airmail labels	£900

1941. *Black on pink cover, with contents amended in
manuscript. Stapled.*
SB19	1 r. 80, booklet containing sixty 3 c. on 6 c. (No. 398) in blocks of 10	
	a. Black on blue cover	.. ..

1951 (5 Dec). *Black on buff cover. Stitched.*
SB20	1 r. booklet containing twenty 5 c. (No. 414) in blocks of four and pane of airmail labels ..	12·00
	a. Containing two blocks of ten 5 c. stamps and no airmail labels	

1952 (21 Jan). *Black on green cover. Stitched.*
SB21	6 r. booklet containing eight 75 c. (No. 417) in blocks of 4 and two panes of four airmail labels	18·00

POSTAL FISCALS

1952 (1 Dec). *As T* **72** *but inscr* "REVENUE" *at sides.
Chalk-surfaced paper.*
F1	10 r. dull green and yellow-orange ..	..	60·00 28·00

This revenue stamp was on sale for postal use from 1 December
1952, until 14 March 1954.

Cyprus

180 piastres = 1 Cyprus pound

CROWN COLONY

1937 (12 May). *Coronation. As Nos. 95/7 of Antigua.*
P 11×11½.

148	¾ pi. grey				60	20
149	1½ pi. carmine				90	80
150	2½ pi. blue				2·00	1·25
148/50				Set of 3	3·25	2·00
148/50 Perf "Specimen"			Set of 3	£100	

35 Vouni Palace    **36** Map of Cyprus

37 Othello's Tower,   **38** King George VI
Famagusta

(Recess Waterlow)

1938 (12 May)–**1951.** *T* **35** *to* **38** *and other designs as 1934, but with portrait of King George VI. Wmk Mult Script CA. P* 12½.

151	**35**	¼ pi. ultramarine and orange-brown		20	20
152	**25**	½ pi. green		30	10
152a	–	½ pi. violet (2.7.51)		1·75	20
153	–	¾ pi. black and violet		14·00	40
154	–	1 pi. orange		50	10
		a. Perf 13½ × 12½ (1944)		£375	27·00
155	–	1½ pi. carmine		5·00	1·50
155a	–	1½ pi. violet (15.3.43)		30	30
155ab	–	1½ pi. green (2.7.51)		2·25	40
155b	–	2 pi. black and carmine (2.2.42)		50	10
		c. Perf 12½ × 13½ (10.44)		2·00	6·00

156	–	2½ pi. ultramarine			18·00	2·50
156a	–	3 pi. ultramarine (2.2.42)			80	15
156b	–	4 pi. ultramarine (2.7.51)			3·00	30
157	**36**	4½ pi. grey			40	10
158	**31**	6 pi. black and blue			65	1·00
159	**37**	9 pi. black and purple			1·75	20
160	–	18 pi. black and olive-green			5·00	85
		a. Black and sage-green (19.8.47)		7·50	1·50
161	–	45 pi. green and black			14·00	2·50
162	**38**	90 pi. mauve and black			20·00	4·75
163		£1 scarlet and indigo			45·00	22·00
151/63				Set of 19	£110	32·00
151/63 Perf "Specimen"			Set of 16	£375	

Designs: *Horiz*—¾ pi., 2 pi. Peristerona Church; 1 pi. Soli Theatre; 1½ pi. Kyrenia Harbour; 2½ pi., 3 pi., 4 pi. Kolossi Castle; 45 pi. Forest scene. *Vert*—18 pi. Buyuk Khan, Nicosia.

1946 (21 Oct). *Victory. As Nos. 110/11 of Antigua.*

164	1½ pi. deep violet					15	10
165	3 pi. blue					15	15
164/5 Perf "Specimen"			Set of 2	90·00	

Extra decoration
(R. 3/5)

1948 (20 Dec). *Royal Silver Wedding. As Nos. 112/13 of Antigua.*

166	1½ pi. violet				50	20
	a. Extra decoration			30·00	
167	£1 indigo			42·00	48·00

1949 (10 Oct). *75th Anniv of Universal Postal Union. As Nos. 114/ 17 of Antigua but inscr "CYPRUS" (recess).*

168	1½ pi. violet				90	70
169	2 pi. carmine-red			2·00	1·50
170	3 pi. deep blue			1·25	1·00
171	9 pi. purple			1·50	1·10
168/71				Set of 4	5·00	3·75

Dominica

1937. 12 pence (d) = 1 shilling; 20 shillings = 1 pound
1949. 100 cents = 1 West Indian dollar

CROWN COLONY

1937 (12 May). *Coronation. As Nos. 95/7 of Antigua.*
P 11×11½.

96	1d. carmine	..	..	 40	10
97	1½d. yellow-brown ..	..	..	.. 40	10
98	2½d. blue ..	..	..	.. 60	1·25
96/8	..	..	..	*Set of 3* 1·25	1·25
96/8 Perf "Specimen"		..	..	*Set of 3* 55·00	

17 Fresh Water Lake

18 Layou River

(Recess Waterlow)

1938 (15 Aug)–47. *T* **17/18** *and similar horiz designs.* Wmk Mult
Script CA. P 12½.

99	**17**	½d. brown and green	..	.. 10	15
100	**18**	1d. grey and scarlet ..	..	.. 20	20
101	–	1½d. green and purple..	..	.. 30	70
102	–	2d. carmine and grey-black ..		.. 50	1·00
103	–	2½d. purple and bright blue ..		.. 4·00	1·75
		a. Purple & bright ultramarine (8.42)		20	1·25
104	**18**	3d. olive-green and brown	..	30	40
104a	–	3½d. ultramarine and purple (15.10.47)		1·75	1·25
105	**17**	6d. emerald-green and violet	..	1·75	1·00
105a		7d. green and yellow-brown (15.10.47)		1·75	1·25
106	–	1s. violet and olive-green	..	2·25	1·00
106a	**18**	2s. slate and purple (15.10.47)	..	4·50	8·00
107	**17**	2s. 6d. black and vermilion ..		.. 12·00	4·75
108	**18**	5s. light blue and purple ..		.. 7·50	8·00
108a	–	10s. black and brown-orange (15.10.47)		12·00	14·00
99/108a		.. ..	*Set of 14*	40·00	38·00

Designs:–1½d., 2½d., 3½d. Picking limes; 2d., 1s., 10s. Boiling
Lake.

21 King George VI

(Photo Harrison)

1940 (15 Apr)–**42**. *Wmk Mult Script CA. Chalk-surfaced
paper. P* 15×14.

109	**21**	¼d. chocolate ..	..	.. 60	15
		a. Ordinary paper (1942)	..	.. 10	10
99/109 Perf "Specimen" ..		..	*Set of 15*	£225	

1946 (14 Oct). *Victory. As Nos.* 110/11 *of Antigua.*

110	1d. carmine ..	..	..	.. 20	10
111	3½d. blue ..	..	..	.. 20	10
110/11 Perf "Specimen"			*Set of 2* 48·00		

1948 (1 Dec). *Royal Silver Wedding. As Nos.* 112/13 *of
Antigua.*

112	1d. scarlet ..	..	.. 15	10
113	10s. red-brown ..	..	.. 8·00	21·00

(New Currency. 100 cents = 1 B.W.I., later East Caribbean dollar)

1949 (10 Oct). *75th Anniv of Universal Postal Union. As Nos.*
114/17 *of Antigua.*

114	5 c. blue	..	..	.. 15	15
115	6 c. brown	..	..	.. 1·00	2·00
116	12 c. purple	..	..	.. 45	1·00
117	24 c. olive	..	..	.. 30	30
114/17	..	..	..	*Set of 4* 1·75	3·00

1951 (16 Feb). *Inauguration of B.W.I. University College. As Nos.*
118/19 *of Antigua.*

118	3 c. yellow-green and reddish violet..	..	50	45
119	12 c. deep green and carmine ..	..	75	30

22 King George VI

23 Drying Cocoa

(Photo Harrison (½ c.). Recess B.W. (others))

1951 (1 July). *T* **22** *and designs as T* **23**. *Wmk Mult Script CA.
Chalk-surfaced paper* (½ c.). *P* 15×14 (½ c.), 13½×13 ($2.40),
13×13½ (*others*).

120	½ c. chocolate	..	..	.. 10	15
121	1 c. black and vermilion ..	..	.. 10	30
	b. "A" of "CA" missing from wmk		..	£500	
	c. "JA" for "CA" in wmk		..	£500	
122	2 c. red-brown and deep green	..	.. 10	20
	a. "C" of "CA" missing from wmk		..	†	—
	b. "A" of "CA" missing from wmk		..	£600	
123	3 c. green and reddish violet	..	.. 15	70
	a. "C" of "CA" missing from wmk		..	£600	
	c. "JA" for "CA" in wmk		..	£500	
124	4 c. brown-orange and sepia	..	.. 30	80
	a. "C" of "CA" missing from wmk		..	£600	
	b. "A" of "CA" missing from wmk		..	£600	
125	5 c. black and carmine	..	.. 85	30
	a. "C" of "CA" missing from wmk		..	£800	
	b. "A" of "CA" missing from wmk		..	£800	
126	6 c. olive and chestnut	..	.. 90	30
	a. "C" of "CA" missing from wmk		..	£1000	
127	8 c. blue-green and blue ..	..	.. 60	60
	b. "A" of "CA" missing from wmk		..		
128	12 c. black and bright green	..	.. 45	1·25
	a. "C" of "CA" missing from wmk		..	£1200	
129	14 c. blue and violet	..	.. 95	1·25
	a. "C" of "CA" missing from wmk		..	£1200	
	b. "A" of "CA" missing from wmk		..	†	
	c. "JA" for "CA" in wmk		..		
130	24 c. reddish violet and rose-carmine	..	75	30
	a. "C" of "CA" missing from wmk		..	£1200	
131	48 c. bright green and red-orange	..	3·00	6·50
	a. "C" of "CA" missing from wmk		..	£1200	
	b. "A" of "CA" missing from wmk		..	£1200	
	c. "JA" for "CA" in wmk		..		
132	60 c. carmine and black ..	..	.. 3·00	5·00
	c. "JA" for "CA" in wmk		..	£800	
133	$1.20, emerald and black	..	.. 4·00	6·00
	a. "C" of "CA" missing from wmk		..	£1400	
	b. "A" of "CA" missing from wmk		..	£1400	
134	$2.40, orange and black	..	.. 23·00	29·00
120/34	..	..	..	*Set of 15* 30·00	45·00

Designs: *Horiz*—2 c., 60 c. Making Carib baskets; 3 c., 48 c. Lime plantation; 4 c. Picking oranges; 5 c. Bananas; 6 c. Botanical Gardens; 8 c. Drying vanilla beans; 12 c., $1.20, Fresh Water Lake; 14 c. Layou River; 24 c. Boiling Lake. *Vert*—$2.40, Picking oranges.

Examples of Nos. 121b, 122b, 124b, 125b, 126b, 129b, 131b and 133b show traces of the *left leg* of the "A", *as seen from the back of the stamp*.

Nos. 121c, 123c, 129c and 131c may represent an attempt to repair the missing "C" variety.

NEW
CONSTITUTION
1951
(34)

1951 (15 Oct). *New Constitution. Nos.* 123, 125, 127 *and* 129 *optd with* T **34** *by B.W.*

135	3 c. emerald and reddish violet	..	..	15	70
136	5 c. black and carmine	..	..	15	70
	a. "JA" for "CA" in wmk	..	..	£700	
137	8 c. blue-green and blue (R.)	..	..	15	15
	a. "JA" for "CA" in wmk	..	..		
138	14 c. blue and violet (R.)	..	..	15	20
	b. "A" of "CA" missing from wmk	..	£900	
135/8	.. ..	*Set of* 4	55	1·60

Falkland Islands

12 pence (d) = 1 shilling; 20 shillings = 1 pound

CROWN COLONY

1937 (12 May). *Coronation. As Nos. 95/7 of Antigua.*
P 11×11½.

143	½d. green			30	10
144	1d. carmine			40	45
145	2½d. blue ..			80	80
143/5			*Set of* 3	1·40	1·25
143/5 Perf "Specimen"			*Set of* 3	£160	

27 Whales' Jaw Bones

(Des G. Roberts (Nos. 146, 148/9, 158 and 160/3), K. Lellman (No. 159). Recess B.W.)

1938 (3 Jan)–**50.** *Horiz designs as T* **27.** *Wmk Mult Script CA.*
P 12.

146	½d. black and green (*shades*)			30	75
147	1d. black and carmine			27·00	80
	a. Black and scarlet..			3·75	85
148	1d. black and violet (14.7.41)			2·50	1·75
	a. Black and purple-violet (1.43)			7·00	1·75
149	2d. black and deep violet			1·00	50
150	2d. black and carmine-red (14.7.41)..			75	2·25
	a. Black and red (1.43)			2·75	1·00
151	2½d. black and bright blue			1·25	30
152	2½d. black and blue (15.6.49) ..			6·50	7·00
153	3d. black and blue (14.7.41)..			6·50	2·50
	a. Black and deep blue (1.43)			9·00	2·50
154	4d. black and purple ..			2·75	50
155	6d. black and brown ..			3·25	1·50
156	6d. black (15.6.49)			5·00	3·75
157	9d. black and grey-blue			13·00	90
158	1s. pale blue ..			65·00	18·00
	a. Deep blue (1941) ..			16·00	2·50
159	1s. 3d. black and carmine-red (11.12.46)			2·50	1·40
160	2s. slate ..			55·00	10·00
161	5s. bright blue and pale brown			£110	60·00
	b. Indigo and yellow-brown (1942)			£600	£100
	c. Blue and buff-brown (9.2.50)			£140	£170
162	10s. black and orange			55·00	27·00
163	£1 black and violet ..			£110	48·00
146/63			*Set of* 18	£350	£140
146/63 (*ex* 152, 156) Perf "Specimen"		*Set of* 16	£950	

Designs:—Nos. 147 and 150, Black-necked Swan; Nos. 148/9, Battle Memorial; Nos. 151 and 153, Flock of sheep; Nos. 152 and 154, Magellan Goose; Nos. 155/6, *Discovery II* (polar supply vessel); No. 157, *William Scoresby* (research ship); No. 158, Mount Sugar Top; No. 159; Turkey Vultures; No 160 Gentoo Penguins; No. 161, Southern Sealion; No. 162, Deception Island; No. 163, Arms of Falkland Islands.

1946 (7 Oct). *Victory. As Nos. 110/11 of Antigua.*

164	1d. dull violet			30	15
165	3d. blue ..			45	15
164/5 Perf "Specimen"		*Set of* 2	£140	

1948 (1 Nov). *Royal Silver Wedding. As Nos. 112/13 of Antigua.*

166	2½d. ultramarine			2·00	85
167	£1 mauve ..			90·00	55·00

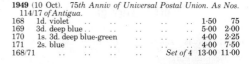

1949 (10 Oct). *75th Anniv of Universal Postal Union. As Nos. 114/17 of Antigua.*

168	1d. violet	..	..	..	..	1·50	75
169	3d. deep blue ..		..	..	..	5·00	2·00
170	1s. 3d. deep blue-green		..	..	4·00	2·25
171	2s. blue	..	..	..		4·00	7·50
168/71		..	..		*Set of* 4	13·00	11·00

39 Sheep   **43** Arms of the Colony

(Des from sketches by V. Spencer. Recess Waterlow)

1952 (2 Jan). *T* **39, 43** *and similar designs. Wmk Mult Script CA. P* 13×13½ (*vert*) *or* 13½×13 (*horiz*).

172	½d. green	..	..	70	70
173	1d. scarlet	..	..	1·50	40
174	2d. violet	..	..	3·50	2·50
175	2½d. black and light ultramarine	..	95	50
176	3d. deep ultramarine	..	..	1·00	1·00
177	4d. reddish purple	..	..	7·50	1·50
178	6d. bistre-brown	..	..	12·00	1·00
179	9d. orange-yellow	..	..	9·00	2·00
180	1s. black	..	..	22·00	80
181	1s. 3d. orange	..	..	13·00	5·00
182	2s. 6d. olive-green	..	..	16·00	10·00
183	5s. purple	..	..	10·00	7·00
184	10s. grey	..	..	23·00	15·00
185	£1 black	..	..	25·00	17·00
172/185			*Set of* 14	£130	55·00

Designs: *Horiz*—1d. *Fitzroy* (supply ship); 2d. Magellan Goose; 2½d. Map of Falkland Islands; 4d. Auster Autocrat aircraft; 6d. *John Biscoe I* (research ship); 9d. View of the Two Sisters; 1s. 3d. Kelp goose and gander; 10s. Southern Sealion and South American Fur Seal; £1 Hulk of *Great Britain*. *Vert*—1s. Gentoo Penguins; 2s. 6d. Sheep-shearing; 5s. Battle Memorial.

FALKLAND ISLANDS DEPENDENCIES

A. GRAHAM LAND

For use at Port Lockroy (established 16 February 1944) and Hope Bay (established 12 February 1945) bases.
Falkland Islands definitive stamps with face values of 1s. 3d. and above were valid for use from Graham Land in conjunction with Nos. A1/8 and subsequently Nos. G1/16.

Stamps of FALKLAND ISLANDS *cancelled at Port Lockroy or Hope Bay with Graham Land circular datestamps between* 16 February 1944 *and* 31 January 1954.

1938–50. *King George VI (Nos. 159/63).*

Z1	1s. 3d. black and carmine-red	..		..	75·00
Z2	2s. 6d. slate	..		..	30·00
Z3	5s. indigo and yellow-brown	..		..	£130
Z4	10s. black and orange	..		..	40·00
Z5	£1 black and violet	..		..	60·00

1952. *King George VI* (*Nos.* 181/5)
Z 6	1s. 3d. orange	..	..	..	..	..	
Z 7	2s. 6d. olive-green	..	..	..	..	
Z 8	5s. purple	..	..	..	..	..	
Z 9	10s. grey	..	..	..	..	..	
Z10	£1 black..	..	..	..	..	..	

GRAHAM LAND

DEPENDENCY OF

(A 1)

1944 (12 Feb)–**45**. *Falkland Islands Nos.* 146, 148, 150, 153/5, 157 *and* 158*a optd with Type* A 1, *in red, by B.W.*
A1	½d. black and green	..	..	30	1·75
	a. *Blue-black and green*	..	..	£600	£375
A2	1d. black and violet	..	..	30	1·00
A3	2d. black and carmine-red	..	..	40	1·00
A4	3d. black and blue	..	..	30	1·00
A5	4d. black and purple	..	..	3·00	1·75
A6	6d. black and brown	..	..	14·00	2·25
	a. *Blue-black and brown* (24.9.45)		..	20·00	
A7	9d. black and grey-blue	..	..	1·00	1·25
A8	1s. deep blue	..	..	1·00	1·25
A1/8		..	*Set of* 8	18·00	10·00
A1/8 Perf "Specimen"	..	..	*Set of* 8	£325	

B. SOUTH GEORGIA

Stamps of FALKLAND ISLANDS *cancelled at Grytviken with South Georgia circular datestamps.*

1937. *Coronation* (*Nos.* 143/5).
Z70	½d. green	..	..	..	..	2·00
Z71	1d. carmine	..	..	..	..	2·00
Z72	2½d. blue ..	..	..	..	..	2·00

1938–50. *King George VI* (*Nos.* 146/63).
Z73	½d. black and green	..	..	..	3·00
Z74	1d. black and carmine	..	..	..	5·00
	a. *Black and scarlet*	..	..	..	2·00
Z75	1d. black and violet	..	..	..	4·50
Z76	2d. black and deep violet	..	..	..	6·00
Z77	2d. black and carmine-red	..	..	..	7·00
Z78	2½d. black and bright blue (No. 151)	..	..	2·00
Z79	3d. black and blue	..	..	..	6·00
Z80	4d. black and purple	..	..	..	6·00
Z81	6d. black and brown	..	..	..	8·00
Z82	9d. black and grey-blue	..	..	..	10·00
Z83	1s. pale blue	..	..	..	30·00
	a. *Deep blue*	..	..	..	30·00
Z84	1s. 3d. black and carmine-red	..	..	30·00
Z85	2s. 6d. slate	..	..	..	20·00
Z86	5s. bright blue and pale brown ..	..	..	£100
	a. *Indigo and yellow-brown*	..	..	£130
	b. *Blue and buff-brown*	..	..	£200
Z87	10s. black and orange	..	..	..	40·00
Z88	£1 black and violet	..	..	..	60·00

Falkland Islands definitive stamps with values of 1s. 3d. and above continued to be valid from South Georgia after the introduction of Nos. B1/8 and subsequently Nos. G1/16.

1952. *King George VI* (*Nos.* 181/5).
Z89	1s. 3d. orange	..	..	..	..	25·00
Z90	2s. 6d. olive-green	..	..	..	..	
Z91	5s. purple	..	..	..	..	
Z92	10s. grey	..	..	..	..	
Z93	£1 black..	..	..	..	..	

1944 (24 Feb)–**45**. *Falkland Islands Nos.* 146, 148, 150, 153/5, 157 *and* 158*a optd* "SOUTH GEORGIA/DEPENDENCY OF", *in red, as Type* A 1 *of Graham Land.*
B1	½d. black and green	..	..	30	1·75
	a. *Wmk sideways*	..	..	£2750	
B2	1d. black and violet	..	..	30	1·00
B3	2d. black and carmine-red	..	..	40	1·00
B4	3d. black and blue	..	..	30	1·00
B5	4d. black and purple	..	..	3·00	1·75
B6	6d. black and brown	..	..	14·00	2·25
	a. *Blue-black and brown* (24.9.45)		..	20·00	

B7	9d. black and grey-blue	..	..	1·00	1·25
B8	1s. deep blue	..	..	1·00	1·25
B1/8		..	*Set of* 8	18·00	10·00
B1/8 Perf "Specimen"	..	*Set of* 8	£325	

For later issues, see after No. G44.

C. SOUTH ORKNEYS

Used from the *Fitzroy* in February 1944 and at Laurie Island (established January 1946).

Falkland Islands definitive stamps with face values of 1s. 3d. and above were valid for use from the South Orkneys in conjunction with Nos. C1/8 and subsequently Nos. G1/16.

Stamps of FALKLAND ISLANDS *cancelled on the* Fitzroy, *at Laurie Island or at Signy Island with South Orkneys circular datestamps between* 21 *February* 1944 *and* 31 *January* 1954.

1938–50. *King George VI* (*Nos.* 160/3).
Z95	2s. 6d. slate	..	..	..	30·00
Z96	5s. indigo and yellow-brown	..	..	£130
Z97	10s. black and orange	..	..	40·00
Z98	£1 black and violet	..	..	60·00

1952. *King George VI* (*Nos.* 181/5).
Z 99	1s. 3d. orange	..	..	..	
Z100	2s. 6d. olive-green	..	..	..	
Z101	5s. purple	..	..	..	
Z102	10s. grey	..	..	..	
Z103	£1 black	..	..	..	

1944 (21 Feb)–**45**. *Falkland Islands Nos.* 146, 148, 150, 153/5, 157 *and* 158*a optd* "SOUTH ORKNEYS/DEPENDENCY OF", *in red as Type* A 1 *of Graham Land.*
C1	½d. black and green	..	..	30	1·75
C2	1d. black and violet	..	..	30	1·00
	w. *Wmk inverted*	..	..	£3750	
C3	2d. black and carmine-red	..	..	40	1·00
C4	3d. black and blue	..	..	30	1·00
C5	4d. black and purple	..	..	3·00	1·75
C6	6d. black and brown	..	..	14·00	2·25
	a. *Blue-black and brown* (24.9.45)		..	20·00	
C7	9d. black and grey-blue	..	..	1·00	1·25
C8	1s. deep blue	..	..	1·00	1·25
C1/8		..	*Set of* 8	18·00	10·00
C1/8 Perf "Specimen"	..	*Set of* 8	£325	

D. SOUTH SHETLANDS

Stamps of FALKLAND ISLANDS *cancelled at Port Foster or Admiralty Bay with South Shetlands circular datestamps between* 5 *February* 1944 *and* 31 *January* 1954

1938–50. *King George VI* (*Nos.* 160/3).
Z159	2s. 6d. slate	..	..	..	30·00
Z160	5s. indigo and yellow-brown	..	..	£130
Z161	10s. black and orange	..	..	40·00
Z162	£1 black and violet	..	..	60·00

1952. *King George VI* (*Nos.* 181/5).
Z163	1s. 3d. orange	..	..	..	
Z164	2s. 6d. olive-green	..	..	..	
Z165	5s. purple	..	..	..	
Z166	10s. grey	..	..	..	
Z167	£1 black	..	..	..	

1944 (5 Feb)–**45**. *Falkland Islands Nos.* 146, 148, 150, 153/5, 157 *and* 158*a optd* "SOUTH SHETLANDS/DEPENDENCY OF", *in red, as Type* A 1 *of Graham Land.*
D1	½d. black and green	..	..	30	1·75
D2	1d. black and violet	..	..	30	1·00
D3	2d. black and carmine-red	..	..	40	1·00
D4	3d. black and blue ..	..	..	30	1·00
D5	4d. black and purple	..	..	3·00	1·75
D6	6d. black and brown	..	..	14·00	2·25
	a. *Blue-black and brown* (24.9.45)		..	20·00	

)7	9d. black and grey-blue	..	..	..	1·00	1·25
)8	1s. deep blue	..	..	..	1·00	1·25
)1/8	..	..	..	*Set of* 8	18·00	10·00
)1/8 Perf "Specimen"		..	..	*Set of* 8	£325	

E. FALKLAND ISLANDS DEPENDENCIES

G 1

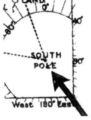

Extra island (Plate 1 R. 3/9)　　"SOUTH POKE" flaw (Plate 2 R. 6/8)

Missing "I" in "S. Shetland Is." (Plate 1 R. 1/2)

Nos. G1/8

NEW INFORMATION

The editor is always interested to correspond with people who have new information that will improve or correct the Catalogue.

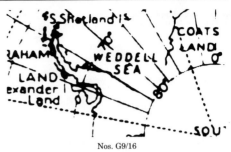

Nos. G9/16

On Nos. G9 to G16 the map is redrawn; the "o⁰" meridian does not pass through the "S" of "COATS", the "n" of "Alexander" is not joined to the "L" of "Land" below, and the loops of letters "s" and "t" are generally more open.

(Map litho, frame recess D.L.R.)

1946 (12 July*)–**49**. *Wmk Mult Script CA* (*sideways*). P 12.

(a) Map thick and coarse

G 1	G 1	½d. black and green		..	1·00	2·25
		a. Extra island	..		65·00	
		b. Missing "I"	..		65·00	
		c. "SOUTH POKE"			65·00	
G 2		1d. black and violet		..	1·25	1·75
		a. Extra island	..		65·00	
		b. Missing "I"	..		65·00	
G 3		2d. black and carmine		..	1·25	2·50
		a. Extra island	..		70·00	
		b. Missing "I"	..		70·00	
G 4		3d. black and blue		..	1·25	4·00
		a. Extra island	..		80·00	
		b. Missing "I"	..		80·00	
G 5		4d. black and claret		..	2·25	4·75
		c. "SOUTH POKE"			95·00	
G 6		6d. black and orange		..	3·25	4·75
		a. Extra island	..		£110	
		b. Missing "I"	..		£110	
		c. "SOUTH POKE"			£110	
		d. *Black and ochre*		..	48·00	90·00
		da. Extra island	..		£275	
		db. Missing "I"			£275	
		dc. "SOUTH POKE"			£275	
G 7		9d. black and brown		..	2·00	3·75
		c. "SOUTH POKE"			95·00	
G 8		1s. black and purple		..	2·00	4·25
		c. "SOUTH POKE"			95·00	
G1/8		..	..	*Set of* 8	13·00	25·00
G1/8 Perf "Specimen"		..	..	*Set of* 8	£450	

(b) Map thin and clear (16.2.48)

G 9	G 1	½d. black and green		..	2·25	11·00
		a. Recess frame printed double, one albino and inverted		..	£900	
G10		1d. black and violet		..	1·50	14·00
G11		2d. black and carmine		..	3·75	19·00
G11*a*		2½d. black and deep blue (6.3.49)		..	7·50	7·00
G12		3d. black and blue	..		2·75	4·50
G13		4d. black and claret		..	16·00	20·00
G14		6d. black and orange		..	23·00	11·00
G15		9d. black and brown		..	23·00	10·00
G16		1s. black and purple		..	23·00	10·00
G9/16		..	..	*Set of* 9	90·00	95·00

*This is the date of issue for South Georgia. Nos. G1/8 were released in London on 11 February.

In Nos. G1/8 a variety with a gap in the 80th parallel occurs six times in each sheet of all values in positions R. 1/4, 1/9, 3/4, 3/9, 5/4 and 5/9 (*Price for set of* 8 £40 *mint, in pairs with normal*).

A constant variety, dot on "T" of "SOUTH", occurs on R. 5/2, 5/4, 5/6, 5/8 and 5/10 of all values of the "thin map" set with the exception of the 2½d.

1946 (4 Oct*). *Victory. As Nos.* 110/11 *of Antigua.*

G17	1d. deep violet	..	..	..	50	15
G18	3d. blue	..	..	..	75	15
G17/18 Perf "Specimen"	..	..	*Set of* 2	£120		

*This is the date of issue for South Georgia. The stamps were placed on sale from the South Orkneys on 17 January 1947, from the South Shetlands on 30 January 1947 and from Graham Land on 10 February 1947.

1948 (6 Dec). *Royal Silver Wedding. As Nos.* 112/13 *of Antigua, but* 1s. *in recess.*

G19	2½d. ultramarine	..	..	..	..	1·50	1·00
G20	1s. violet-blue	..	..	..	..	2·25	1·75

1949 (10 Oct). *75th Anniv of U.P.U. As Nos.* 114/17 *of Antigua.*

G21	1d. violet	..	..	..	..	1·50	1·50
G22	2d. carmine-red	..	..	..	..	5·00	2·50
G23	3d. deep blue..	..	..	..	..	4·00	1·25
G24	6d. red-orange	..	..	..	..	7·00	3·00
G21/4		..	..	..	..	*Set of* 4 16·00	7·50

Fiji

12 pence (d) = 1 shilling; 20 shillings = 1 pound

CROWN COLONY

1937 (12 May). *Coronation. As Nos. 95/7 of Antigua.*
P 11×11½.
246	1d. purple	..	..	..	..	60	45
247	2d. grey-black		..	..	..	60	1·25
248	3d. Prussian blue			..	..	60	1·25
246/8 ..				*Set of 3*	1·60	2·75
246/8 Perf "Specimen"				*Set of 3*	55·00	

28 Native sailing Canoe

29 Native Village

30 Camakua (canoe)

31 Map of Fiji Islands

Two Dies of Type **30**:

Die I — Empty Canoe Die II — Native in Canoe

Two Dies of Type **31**:

Die I — Without "180°" Die II — With "180°"

Extra palm frond (R. 5/8)

Extra line (R. 2/1)

Spur on arms medallion (Pl 2 R. 4/2) (ptg of 26 Nov 1945)

(Des V. E. Ousey (½d., 1s., 2s. 6d.), Miss C. D. Lovejoy (1d., 1½d., 5d.), Miss I. Stinson (3d., 5s.) and A. V. Guy (Nos. 253/4), 2½d., 6d., 2s.). Recess De La Rue (½d., 1½d., 2d., (Nos. 253/5a), 2½d., 6d., 8d., 1s. 5d., 1s. 6d.), Waterlow (others))

1938 (5 Apr)**–1955.** *T* **28/31** *and similar designs. Wmk Mult Script CA. Various perfs.*

249	28	½d. green (*p* 13½) ..	..	.. 20	75
		a. Perf 14 (5.41) ..	..	.. 20·00	3·50
		b. Perf 12 (8.48) ..	..	.. 80	3·00
		ba. Extra palm frond	..	38·00	
250	29	1d. brown and blue (*p* 12½)	..	40	20
251	30	1½d. carmine (Die I) (*p* 13½)	..	15·00	35
252		1½d. carmine (Die II) (*p* 13½) (1.10.40)	1·40	3·00
		a. Deep carmine (10.42)	..	4·00	1·25
		b. Perf 14 (6.42) ..	..	18·00	19·00
		c. Perf 12 (21.7.49)	..	90	1·25
253	31	2d. brown and green (Die I) (*p* 13½)	38·00	40
		a. Extra line	..	£275	42·00
254		2d. brown & green (Die II) (*p* 13½)		
		(1.10.40)	..	16·00	16·00
255	–	2d. grn & magenta (*p* 13½) (19.5.42)	40	60
		a. Perf 12 (27.5.46)	..	55	70
256	31	2½d. brown & grn (Die II) (*p* 14) (6.1.42)	60	1·00
		a. Perf 13½ (1.44) ..	..	70	80
		b. Perf 12 (19.1.48)	..	90	50
257	–	3d. blue (*p* 12½) ..	..	1·00	30
		a. Spur on arms medallion	..	£150	
258	–	5d. blue and scarlet (*p* 12½)	..	42·00	10·00
259	–	5d. yell-green & scar (*p* 12½) (1.10.40)	20	30
260	31	6d. black (Die I) (*p* 13×12) ..	60·00	12·00
261		6d. black (Die II) (*p* 13½) (1.10.40)	3·00	2·25
		a. Violet-black (1.44)	..	25·00	28·00
		b. Perf 12. *Black* (5.6.47) ..	1·50	1·50
261c	–	8d. carmine (*p* 14) (15.11.48)	..	1·00	1·75
		d. Perf 13 (7.6.50) ..	..	70	2·75
262	–	1s. black and yellow (*p* 12½)	..	75	70
263	–	1s. 5d. black & carm (*p* 14) (13.6.40)	20	1·00
263a	–	1s. 6d. ultramarine (*p* 14) (1.8.50) ..	3·50	2·75
		b. Perf 13 (16.2.55) ..	..	1·25	15·00
264	–	2s. violet and orange (*p* 12½)	..	2·50	40
265	–	2s. 6d. green and brown (*p* 12½)	..	2·50	1·50

266	–	5s. green and purple (p 12½)			2·50	1·75
266a	–	10s. orange & emer (p 12½) (13.3.50)		35·00	40·00
266b	–	£1 ultram & carm (p 12½) (13.3.50)		48·00	50·00
249/66b				Set of 22	£250	£120

249/66 excl 261c and 263a Perf
"Specimen" .. .. .. *Set of 18* £450

Designs: *Horiz (as T 30)*—2d. (Nos. 255/a) Government Offices.
(As T **29**)—3d. Canoe and arms of Fiji; 8d., 1s. 5d., 1s. 6d. Arms of
Fiji; 2s. Suva Harbour; 2s. 6d. River scene; 5s. Chief's hut. *Vert (as
T **29**)—5d. Sugar cane; 1s. Spearing fish by torchlight; 10s. Paw-
paw Tree; £1 Police bugler.

2½d.

(42)

1941 (10 Feb). *No. 254 surch with T **42** by Govt Printer, Suva.*
267 **31** 2½d. on 2d. brown and green 65 20

1946 (17 Aug). *Victory. As Nos. 110/11 of Antigua.*
268	2½d. green				10	75
	a. Printed double, one albino			£275	
269	3d. blue				10	10
268/9 Perf "Specimen"			Set of 2	60·00	

1948 (17 Dec). *Royal Silver Wedding. As Nos. 112/13 of
Antigua.*
| 270 | 2½d. green | | | | 40 | 1·00 |
| 271 | 5s. violet-blue | | | | 14·00 | 7·00 |

1949 (10 Oct). *75th Anniv of U.P.U. As Nos. 114/17 of Antigua.*
272	2d. bright reddish purple			30	30
273	3d. deep blue				2·25	2·25
274	8d. carmine-red				45	1·25
275	1s. 6d. blue				45	1·00
272/5				Set of 4	3·00	4·25

43 Children Bathing

44 Rugby Football

(Recess B.W.)

1951 (17 Sept). *Health Stamps. Wmk Mult Script CA. P 13½.*
| 276 | **43** | 1d. + 1d. brown | | | | 10 | 60 |
| 277 | **44** | 2d. + 1d. green | | | | 30 | 60 |

STAMP BOOKLETS

1939 (10 Mar)–**40.** *Black on green covers. No advertising
pages. Stapled.*
SB3 3s. booklet containing eight ½d. and eight 1d.
   (Nos. 249/50) in blocks of 8 and twelve 2d. (No.
   253) in blocks of 6 .. .. .. £700
   a. Including four advertising pages (black on buff
   cover) (1940) .. .. ..
SB4 5s. 9d. booklet containing ten ½d. and ten 1d.
   (Nos. 249/50) in blocks of 10 and twenty-seven
   2d. (No. 253) in blocks of 9 .. .. £2000
   a. Including four advertising pages (black on pink
   cover) (1940) .. .. ..
Nos. SB3/4 were produced locally and Nos. SB3a/4a by De La
Rue.

POSTAGE DUE STAMPS

D 4

(Typo Waterlow)

1940 (3 July). *Wmk Mult Script CA. P 12½.*
D11	D 4	1d. emerald-green				7·00	60·00
D12		2d. emerald-green				9·00	60·00
D13		3d. emerald-green				12·00	65·00
D14		4d. emerald-green				15·00	70·00
D15		5d. emerald-green				16·00	70·00
D16		6d. emerald-green				18·00	75·00
D17		1s. carmine-lake				22·00	£100
D18		1s. 6d. carmine-lake				23·00	£150
D11/18					Set of 8	£110	£600
D11/18 Perf "Specimen"				Set of 8	£180	

All values are known with forged postmarks, including one of
Levuka dated "8 APR 41" and others of Suva dated "12 AUG
42", "14 AU 42" or "20 MR 45".
The use of postage due stamps was discontinued on 30 April
1946.

Gambia

12 pence (d) = 1 shilling; 20 shillings = 1 pound

CROWN COLONY

1937 (12 May). *Coronation. As Nos. 95/7 of Antigua.*
P 11×11½
147	1d. yellow-brown	..	..	..	30	15
148	1½d. carmine ..	..	..	..	30	30
149	3d. blue	..	..	..	55	45
147/9 ..	..	..		Set of 3	1·00	80
147/9 Perf "Specimen"	..	..	Set of 3	60·00	

11 Elephant (from Colony Badge)

(Recess B.W.)

1938 (1 Apr)–**46.** *Wmk Mult Script CA. P 12.*
150	**11**	½d. black and emerald-green			15	60
151		1d. purple and brown		..	20	50
152		1½d. brown-lake and bright carmine	..	£150	12·00	
		a. Brown-lake and scarlet ..			2·50	2·25
		b. Brown-lake and vermilion		..	30	2·00
152c		1½d. blue and black (2.1.45) ..		..	30	1·25
153		2d. blue and black	..	..	2·75	3·00
153a		2d. lake and scarlet (1.10.43)		..	60	2·25

154	**11**	3d. light blue and grey-blue		..	30	10
154a		5d. sage-green & purple-brn (13.3.41)			45	45
155		6d. olive-green and claret	..	..	1·50	35
156		1s. slate-blue and violet	..	..	2·00	10
156a		1s. 3d. chocolate & lt blue (28.11.46)			2·75	2·50
157		2s. carmine and blue		..	4·50	3·25
158		2s. 6d. sepia and dull green ..		..	12·00	2·00
159		4s. vermilion and purple		..	21·00	2·50
160		5s. blue and vermilion		..	21·00	4·00
161		10s. orange and black		..	21·00	7·00
150/61		..	..	..	Set of 16	80·00 28·00
150/61 Perf "Specimen"	..	..	Set of 16	£250		

1946 (6 Aug). *Victory. As Nos. 110/11 of Antigua.*
162	1½d. black	..	..	..	10	10
163	3d. blue	..	..	..	10	10
162/3 Perf "Specimen"	..	..	Set of 2	55·00		

1948 (24 Dec). *Royal Silver Wedding. As Nos. 112/13 of Antigua.*
164	1½d. black	..	..	..	..	25	10
165	£1 mauve	..	..	..	..	12·00 14·00

1949 (10 Oct). *75th Anniv of Universal Postal Union. As Nos. 114/17 of Antigua.*
166	1½d. blue-black	..	..	..	40	40
167	3d. deep blue	..	..	..	1·50	80
168	6d. magenta ..	..	..	..	60	40
169	1s. violet	..	..	..	60	30
166/9 ..	..	..	..	Set of 4	2·75	1·75

Gibraltar

12 pence (d) = 1 shilling; 20 shillings = 1 pound

CROWN COLONY

1937 (12 May). *Coronation. As Nos. 95/7 of Antigua.*
P 11×11½.

118	½d. green ..	..	..	..	25	15
119	2d. grey-black	..	..	..	80	2·25
120	3d. blue ..	..	..	..	2·00	2·25
118/20	..	..	..	*Set of* 3	2·75	4·00
118/20 Perf "Specimen"	..	..	*Set of* 3	75·00	

14 King George VI   **15** Rock of Gibraltar

16 The Rock (North Side)

Broken second "R" in "GIBRALTAR"
(Frame Pl.2 R.9/4)

(Des Captain H. St. C. Garrood. Recess D.L.R.)

1938 (25 Feb)–**51**. *Designs as T* **14/16**. *Wmk Mult Script CA.*
121	½d. deep green (*p* 13½×14)	..	..	10	40
122	1d. yellow-brown (*p* 14)	..	..	24·00	2·25
	a. Perf 13½	..	..	..	26·00	2·25
	ab. Perf 13½. Wmk sideways (1940)	..	6·50	7·00
	b. Perf 13. Wmk sideways. *Red-brown*		
	(1942)	..	..	..	50	55
	c. Perf 13. Wmk sideways. *Deep brown*		
	(1944)	..	..	..	30	3·50
	d. Perf 13. *Red-brown* (1949) ..	..	1·50	1·50
123	1½d. carmine (*p* 14)	..	..	35·00	75
	a. Perf 13½	..	..	..	£250	35·00
123*b*	1½d. slate-violet (*p* 13) (1.1.43) ..	30	1·25
124	2d. grey (*p* 14) ..	..	..	26·00	40
	a. Perf 13½	..	..	..	55	35
	ab. Perf 13½. Wmk sideways (1939)	..	£600	42·00
	b. Perf 13. Wmk sideways (1943)	..	30	1·25
	ba. "A" of "CA" missing from wmk	..	£1200	
124*c*	2d. carm (*p* 13) (*wmk sideways*) (15.7.44)	40	60
125	3d. light blue (*p* 13½) ..	..	16·00	1·00
	a. Perf 14	..	..	..	£130	5·00
	b. Perf 13 (1942)	..	..	30	30
	ba. Greenish blue (2.51)	..	..	3·50	2·50
125*c*	5d. red-orange (*p* 13) (1.10.47) ..	..	70	1·25

126	6d. carm & grey-violet (*p* 13½) (16.3.38)	48·00	3·00
	a. Perf 14	..	..	..	£120	1·25
	b. Perf 13 (1942)	..	..	2·25	1·75
	c. Perf 13. *Scarlet and grey-violet* (1945)	4·25	3·50
127	1s. black and green (*p* 14) (16.3.38)	..	38·00	23·00
	a. Perf 13½	..	..	..	60·00	7·00
	b. Perf 13 (1942)	..	..	3·00	4·00
	ba. Broken "R" ..	..	..	£150	
128	2s. black and brown (*p* 14) (16.3.38)	..	65·00	25·00
	a. Perf 13½	..	..	..	£120	32·00
	b. Perf 13 (1942)	..	..	4·00	6·50
	ba. Broken "R" ..	..	..	£170	
129	5s. black and carmine (*p* 14) (16.3.38)	95·00	£150
	a. Perf 13½	..	..	..	38·00	17·00
	b. Perf 13 (1944)	..	..	12·00	17·00
	ba. Broken "R" ..	..	..	£225	
130	10s. black and blue (*p* 14) (16.3.38)	..	65·00	£120
	a. Perf 13 (1943)	..	..	35·00	25·00
	ab. Broken "R" ..	..	..	£325	
131	£1 orange (*p* 13½×14) (16.3.38)	..	38·00	45·00
121/31	..	..	..	*Set of* 14	£120	85·00
121/31 Perf "Specimen"	..	..	*Set of* 14	£500	

Designs:—½d., £1, Type **14**. *Horiz as T* **15/16**—1d., 1½d. (*both*)
Type **15**; 2d. (*both*), Type **16**; 3d., 5d. Europa Point; 6d. Moorish
Castle; 1s. Southport Gate; 2s. Eliott Memorial; 5s. Government
House; 10s. Catalan Bay.
The ½d., 1d. and both colours of the 2d. exist in coils constructed
from normal sheets. These were originally joined vertically, but
because of technical problems, the 1d. and 2d. grey were
subsequently issued in horizontal coils. The 2d. carmine only exists
in the horizontal version.

1946 (12 Oct). *Victory. As Nos. 110/11 of Antigua.*
132	½d. green	..	..	..	10	15
133	3d. ultramarine	..	..	..	30	40
132/3 Perf "Specimen"	..	..	*Set of* 2	60·00	

1948 (1 Dec). *Royal Silver Wedding. As Nos. 112/13 of Antigua.*
134	½d. green	..	..	..	..	70	1·00
135	£1 brown-orange	..	..	..	50·00	65·00

1949 (10 Oct). *75th Anniv of Universal Postal Union. As Nos. 114/17 of Antigua.*
136	2d. carmine	..	..	..	1·00	1·25
137	3d. deep blue ..	..	..	..	2·50	1·25
138	6d. purple	..	..	..	2·00	1·25
139	1s. blue-green	..	..	..	1·60	2·75
136/9	..	..	..	*Set of* 4	6·50	6·00

NEW
CONSTITUTION
1950
(23)

1950 (1 Aug). *Inauguration of Legislative Council. Nos.* 124*c*, 125*b*, 126*b and* 127*b optd as T* **23**.
140	**16**	2d. carmine	..	..	..	30	1·00
141	—	3d. light blue	..	..	..	55	1·00
142	—	6d. carmine and grey-violet	..	..	65	1·60
		a. Opt double	..	..	..	£650	£750
143	—	1s. black and green (R.)	..	..	65	1·60
		a. Broken "R" ..	..	..	50·00	
140/3		..	..	..	*Set of* 4	1·90	4·75

On stamps from the lower part of the sheet of No. 142a the two
impressions are almost coincident.

Gilbert and Ellice Islands

12 pence (d) = 1 shilling; 20 shillings = 1 pound

CROWN COLONY

1937 (12 May). *Coronation. As Nos. 95/7 of Antigua, but ptd by D.L.R. P 14.*

40	1d. violet	..	..	..	..	35	65
41	1½d. scarlet			..	..	35	65
42	3d. bright blue	..	..	..	..	40	70
40/2	..	..	..		*Set of 3*	1·00	1·75
40/2 Perf "Specimen"		..		*Set of 3*	65·00	

6 Great Frigate Bird   **7** Pandanus Pine

8 Canoe crossing Reef

(Recess B.W. (½d., 2d., 2s. 6d.), Waterlow (1d., 5d., 6d., 2s., 5s.), D.L.R. (1½d., 2½d., 3d., 1s.))

1939 (14 Jan)–**55.** *T* 6/8 *and similar horiz designs. Wmk Mult Script CA (sideways on ½d., 2d. and 2s. 6d.). P* 11½×11 *(½d., 2d., 2s. 6d.),* 12½ *(1d., 5d., 6d., 2s., 5s.) or* 13½ *(1½d., 2½d., 1s.).*

43	½d. indigo and deep bluish green	..	30	85
	a. "A" of "CA" missing from wmk	∴		
44	1d. emerald and plum	..	30	1·50
45	1½d. brownish black and bright carmine	..	30	90
46	2d. red-brown and grey-black	..	60	1·00
47	2½d. brownish black and deep olive	..	40	70
	a. *Brownish black & olive-green* (12.5.43)	3·00	3·25
48	3d. brownish black and ultramarine	..	45	1·00
	a. *Perf 12. Black and bright blue* (24.8.55)	50	2·25
49	5d. deep ultramarine and sepia	..	4·25	1·25
	a. *Ultramarine and sepia* (12.5.43)	4·75	5·00
	b. *Ultramarine & blackish brn* (20.10.44)	4·25	4·25
50	6d. olive-green and deep violet	..	40	50
51	1s. brownish black and turquoise-green	..	8·50	2·00
	a. *Brownish black & turquoise-bl* (12.5.43)	4·50	2·25
	ab. *Perf 12* (8.5.51)	..	..	3·75	13·00
52	2s. deep ultramarine and orange-red	..	16·00	12·00

53	2s. 6d. deep blue and emerald	..	..	17·00	14·00
54	5s. deep rose-red and royal blue	..	..	18·00	16·00
43/54	..	..	..	*Set of 12*	55·00	42·00
43/54 Perf "Specimen"	..	..	*Set of 12*	£250	

Designs: *As T* **6**—2d. Canoe and boat-house; 2s. 6d. Gilbert Islands canoe. *As T* **7**—5d. Ellice Islands canoe; 6d. Coconut palms; 2s. H.M.C.S. *Nimanoa*; 5s. Coat of arms. *As T* **8**—2½d. Native house; 3d. Seascape; 1s. Cantilever jetty, Ocean Island.

1946 (16 Dec). *Victory. As Nos. 110/11 of Antigua.*

55	1d. purple	..	..	..	..	15	40
56	3d. blue	..	..	..	..	15	40
55/6 Perf "Specimen"	..	..	*Set of 2*	55·00	

1949 (29 Aug). *Royal Silver Wedding. As Nos. 112/13 of Antigua.*

57	1d. violet	..	..	..	..	40	50
58	£1 scarlet	..	..	..	..	15·00	18·00

1949 (10 Oct). *75th Anniv of U.P.U. As Nos. 114/17 of Antigua.*

59	1d. purple	..	..	..	..	55	90
60	2d. grey-black	..	..	..	..	2·25	2·25
61	3d. deep blue	..	..	..	..	1·00	2·00
62	1s. blue	..	..	..	..	1·25	2·00
59/62	..	..	..	..	*Set of 4*	4·50	6·50

POSTAGE DUE STAMPS

D 1

(Typo B.W.)

1940 (Aug). *Wmk Mult Script CA. P 12.*

D1	D 1	1d. emerald-green	..	..	8·50	22·00
D2		2d. scarlet	..	..	9·50	22·00
D3		3d. brown	..	..	14·00	23·00
D4		4d. blue	..	..	16·00	29·00
D5		5d. grey-green	..	..	21·00	29·00
D6		6d. purple	..	..	21·00	29·00
D7		1s. violet	..	..	23·00	40·00
D8		1s. 6d. turquoise-green	..		45·00	85·00
D1/8	..	..	..	*Set of 8*	£140	£250
D1/8 Perf "Specimen"	..	..	*Set of 8*	£160	

Examples of all values are known showing a forged Post Office Ocean Island postmark dated "16 DE 46".

Gold Coast

12 pence (d) = 1 shilling; 20 shillings = 1 pound

CROWN COLONY

1937 (12 May). *Coronation. As Nos. 95/7 of Antigua.*
P 11×11½.

117	1d. buff	..	..	..	..	..	1·00	1·50
118	2d. slate	..	..	..	..	..	1·10	3·00
119	3d. blue	..	..	..	..	..	1·25	1·25
117/19	..	..	..	..	*Set of* 3	3·00	5·25
117/19 Perf "Specimen"		..	..	*Set of* 3	50·00	

14

15 King George VI and
Christiansborg Castle, Accra

(Recess B.W.)

1938 (1 Apr)–**44**. *Wmk Mult Script CA. P* 11½×12 (1s. 3d.,
10s.) *or* 12 (*others*).

120	**14**	½d. green	..	..	..	2·00	1·25
		a. Perf 12×11½ (1940)		..	..	40	50
121		1d. red-brown	..	..	..	2·00	30
		a. Perf 12×11½ (1939)		..	..	40	10
122		1½d. scarlet	..	..	..	2·00	1·25
		a. Perf 12×11½ (1940)		..	..	40	50
123		2d. slate	..	..	..	2·00	80
		a. Perf 12×11½ (1940)		..	..	40	10
124		3d. blue	..	..	..	2·00	60
		a. Perf 12×11½ (1940)		..	..	40	35
125		4d. magenta	..	..	..	2·75	2·50
		a. Perf 12×11½ (1942)		..	..	70	1·25
126		6d. purple	..	..	..	2·75	45
		a. Perf 12×11½ (1939)		..	..	70	20
127		9d. orange	..	..	..	2·75	1·25
		a. Perf 12×11½ (1944)		..	..	90	55
128	**15**	1s. black and olive-green	..	..	5·00	2·00
		a. Perf 11½×12 (1940)		..	1·00	50
129		1s. 3d. brown & turquoise-bl (12.4.41)		2·00	40
130		2s. blue and violet	..	..	16·00	9·00
		a. Perf 11½×12 (1940)		..	4·50	9·00
131		5s. olive-green & carmine	..	..	27·00	12·00
		a. Perf 11½×12 (1940)		..	9·00	12·00
132		10s. black and violet (7.40)	..	..	7·00	17·00
120/32	..	..	..	*Set of* 13	25·00	38·00
120/32 Perf "Specimen"	..	..	*Set of* 13	£170	

All values except 1s. 3d. and 10s. exist in two perforations: (*a*)
Line-perforated 12, from early printings; (*b*) Comb-perforated
12×11.8 (vertical design) or 11.8×12 (horiz design) from later
printings. The 1s. 3d. and 10s. only exist comb-perforated
11.8×12.
The ½d. and 1d. values exist in coils constructed from normal
sheets.

1946 (14 Oct). *Victory. As Nos.* 110/11 *of Antigua. P* 13½×14.

133	2d. slate-violet	..	..	..	..	12·00	2·25
	a. Perf 13½	..	..	..	..	10	10
134	4d. claret	..	..	..	..	1·50	2·75
	a. Perf 13½	..	..	..	..	1·00	2·75
133/4 Perf "Specimen"	..	..	*Set of* 2	50·00	

16 Northern Territories
Mounted Constabulary

17 Christiansborg Castle

(Des B. A. Johnston (1½d.), M. Ziorkley and B. A. Abban (2d.), P.C
draughtsman (2½d.), C. Gomez (1s.), M. Ziorkley (10s.); other
from photographs. Recess B.W.)

1948 (1 July). *T* **16/17** *and similar designs. Wmk Mult Script CA.
P* 12 × 11½ (*vert*) *or* 11½ × 12 (*horiz*).

135	½d. emerald-green	..	..	..	..	20	3
136	1d. blue	..	..	..	..	15	1
137	1½d. scarlet	..	..	..	..	1·25	7
138	2d. purple-brown	..	..	..	55	1
139	2½d. yellow-brown and scarlet	..	..	2·00	2·7
140	3d. light blue	..	..	..	..	4·00	4
141	4d. magenta	..	..	..	..	3·50	1·2
142	6d. black and orange	..	..	..	30	3
143	1s. black and vermilion	..	..	60	3
144	2s. sage-green and magenta	..	..	3·00	2·0
145	5s. purple and black	..	..	..	20·00	4·5
146	10s. black and sage-green	..	..	8·00	4·5
135/46	..	..	..	*Set of* 12	40·00	15·0
135/46 Perf "Specimen"	..	*Set of* 12	£225	

Designs: *Horiz*—1½d. Emblem of Joint Provincial Counci
2½d. Map showing position of Gold Coast; 3d. Nsuta mangane
mine; 4d. Lake Bosumtwi; 1s. Breaking cocoa pods; 2s. Go
Coast Regt Trooping the Colour; 5s. Surfboats. *Vert*—2
Talking drums; 6d. Cocoa farmer; 10s. Forest.
Nos. 135/6 exist in coils constructed from normal sheets.

1948 (20 Dec). *Royal Silver Wedding. As Nos.* 112/13 *o
Antigua.*

147	1½d. scarlet	..	..	..	..	30	3
148	10s. grey-olive	..	..	..	..	13·00	3·0

1949 (10 Oct). *75th Anniv of U.P.U. As Nos.* 114/17 *of Antigu*

149	2d. red-brown	..	..	..	..	30	3
150	2½d. orange	..	..	..	..	2·00	2·0
151	3d. deep blue	..	..	..	..	50	5
152	1s. blue-green	..	..	..	..	50	5
149/52	..	..	..	..	*Set of* 4	3·00	3·2

POSTAGE DUE STAMPS

D 1

3ᵈ

Normal

3ᵈ

Lower serif
at left of
"3" missing
(R. 9/1)

1/-

Row 4
(No. D8)

1/-

Row 5
(No. D8c)

The degree of inclination of the stroke on the 1s. value varies
for each vertical row of the sheet: Rows 1, 2 and 6 104°, Row 3
108°, Row 4 107° and Row 5 (No. D8c) 100°.

1951–52. *Chalk-surfaced paper. Wmk Mult Script CA. P* 14.

D5	D 1	2d. black (13.12.51)	..	..	3·00	18·00
		a. Error. Crown missing, W 9*a*		..	£550	
		b. Error. St. Edward's Crown, W 9*b*			£300	
		c. Large "d" (R. 9/6, 10/6)	..		18·00	
D6		3d. black (13.12.51)	..	..	1·50	16·00
		a. Error. Crown missing, W 9*a*		..	£550	
		b. Error. St. Edward's Crown, W 9*b*			£300	
		c. Missing serif	..		22·00	
D7		6d. black (1.10.52)	..	..	1·75	8·00
		a. Error. Crown missing, W 9*a*		..	£700	
		b. Error. St. Edward's Crown, W 9*b*			£500	
D8		1s. black (1.10.52)	..	..	1·75	60·00
		b. Error. St. Edward's Crown, W 9*b*			£650	
		c. Upright stroke	..		12·00	
D5/8		..	..	*Set of* 4	7·25	90·00

For illustration of No. D5c see above Nos. D4/6 of
Bechuanaland Protectorate.

Grenada

1937. 12 pence (d) = 1 shilling; 20 shillings = 1 pound
1949. 100 cents = 1 West Indian dollar

CROWN COLONY

1937 (12 May). *Coronation. As Nos. 95/7 of Antigua.*
P 11x11½.

149	1d. violet	..	..	..	..	40	20
150	1½d. carmine ..	..	..	..	..	40	20
151	2½d. blue	..	..	..	..	80	30
149/51	..	..	..	..	*Set of 3*	1·40	65
149/51 Perf "Specimen"	..	..		*Set of 3*	50·00	

35 King George VI

(Photo Harrison)

1937 (12 July)–50. *Wmk Mult Script CA. Chalk-surfaced paper. P* 15×14.

152	**35**	¼d. brown	..	..	..	1·40	10
	a. Ordinary paper (11.42)	..	..	30	60		
	b. Ordinary paper. *Chocolate* (1.45)		20	60			
	c. Chalk-surfaced paper. *Chocolate* (8.50)	..	..	50	3·00		

The ordinary paper is thick, smooth and opaque.

36 Grand Anse Beach    **40** Badge of the Colony

Colon flaw
(R. 5/8. Corrected on
ptg of Nov 1950)

(Recess D.L.R. (10s.), Waterlow (others))

1938 (16 Mar)–50. *As T* **31/4** (*but portrait of King George VI as in T* **36**) *and T* **40**. *Wmk Mult Script CA* (*sideways on T* 32). *P* 12½ *or* 12 × 13 (10s.).

153	**36**	½d. yellow-green..	..	..	..	4·50	1·00
	a. Perf 12½ × 13½ (1938)	..	..	6·00	80		
	b. Perf 12½. *Blue-green*	..	..	60	1·25		
	ba. Perf 12½ × 13½. *Blue-green*	..	6·00	5·00			
154	**32**	1d. black and sepia	..	..	1·00	20	
	a. Perf 13½ × 12½ (1938)	..	..	50	50		

155	**33**	1½d. black and scarlet	..	..	..	50	70
	a. Perf 12½ × 13½ (1938)	..	..	2·25	30		
156	**32**	2d. black and orange	..	..	30	50	
	a. Perf 13½ × 12½ (1938)	..	..	2·50	70		
157	**34**	2½d. bright blue	..	..	..	30	30
	a. Perf 12½ × 13½ (?March 1950)	.. £4250	£225				
158	**32**	3d. black and olive-green	..	..	9·50	1·40	
	a. Perf 13½ × 12½ (16.3.38)	..	6·00	80			
	ab. Perf 13½ × 12½. *Black and brown-olive* (1942)	..	..	30	80		
	b. Perf 12½. *Black and brown-olive* (16.8.50)	..	..	30	1·60		
	ba. Colon flaw	..	..	..	.. 50·00		
159		6d. black and purple	..	..	1·25	40	
	a. Perf 13½ × 12½ (1942)	..	..	2·25	50		
160		1s. black and brown	..	..	2·25	30	
	a. Perf 13½ × 12½ (1941)	..	..	3·50	1·25		
161		2s. black and ultramarine	..	..	16·00	1·50	
	a. Perf 13½ × 12½ (1941)	..	..	20·00	1·50		
162		5s. black and violet	..	..	3·50	1·50	
	a. Perf 13½ × 12½ (1947)	..	..	2·75	5·50		
163	**40**	10s. steel blue and carmine (*narrow*) (*p* 12 × 13)	..	..	55·00	9·00	
	a. Perf 14. *Steel blue and bright carmine* (*narrow*)	..	..	£180	45·00		
	b. Perf 14. *Slate-blue and bright carmine* (*narrow*) (1943)	..	£190	£110			
	c. Perf 12. *Slate-blue and bright carmine* (*narrow*) (1943)	..	£450	£800			
	d. Perf 14. *Slate-blue and carmine-lake* (*wide*) (1944)..	..	90·00	8·00			
	e. Perf 14. *Blue-black and carmine* (*narrow*) (1943)	..	..	27·00	8·50		
	f. Perf 14. *Blue-black and bright carmine* (*wide*) (1947)	..	25·00	25·00			
152/63e	..	..	..	*Set of 12*	45·00	13·00	
152/63 Perf "Specimen"	..	..	*Set of 12*	£225			

In the earlier printings of the 10s. the paper was dampened before printing and the subsequent shrinkage produced narrow frames 23½ to 23¾ mm wide. Later printings were made on dry paper producing wide frames 24¼ mm wide.

No. 163a is one of the earlier printings line perf 13.8×14.1. Later printings of the 10s. are line perf 14.1.

Nos. 163b/c show a blurred centre caused by the use of a worn plate.

Nos. 163a and 163b may be found with gum more or less yellow due to local climatic conditions.

Examples of No. 163c are known showing forged St. George's postmarks dated "21 AU 42", "21 AU 43" or "2 OC 43".

1946 (25 Sept). *Victory. As Nos. 110/11 of Antigua.*

164	1½d. carmine ..	..	..	..	..	10	10
165	3½d. blue	..	..	..	..	10	20
164/5 Perf "Specimen"	..		*Set of 2*	50·00		

1948 (27 Oct). *Royal Silver Wedding. As Nos.* 112/13 *of Antigua.*

166	1½d. scarlet	..	..	..	..	15	10
167	10s. slate-green	..	..	..	8·00	16·00	

(New Currency. 100 cents = 1 West Indian, later Eastern Caribbean, dollar)

1949 (10 Oct). *75th Anniv of Universal Postal Union. As Nos.* 114/17 *of Antigua.*

168	5 c. ultramarine	..	..	..	..	20	10
169	6 c. olive	..	..	..	..	90	1·25
170	12 c. magenta ..	..	..	..	..	35	30
171	24 c. red-brown	..	..	..	..	35	30
168/71	..	..	..	..	*Set of 4*	1·60	1·60

41 King
George VI

42 Badge of the
Colony

43 Badge of the
Colony

(Recess B.W. (T **41**), D.L.R. (others))

1951 (8 Jan). *Wmk Mult Script CA. P* 11½ (*T* **41**), 11½ × 12½
(*T* **42**), *and* 11½ × 13 (*T* **43**).

172	**41**	½ c. black and red-brown	..	..	15	1·00
173		1 c. black and emerald-green	..	..	15	25
174		2 c. black and brown	..	..	15	30
175		3 c. black and rose-carmine	..	..	15	10
176		4 c. black and orange	..	..	35	40
177		5 c. black and violet	..	..	20	10
178		6 c. black and olive	..	..	30	60
179		7 c. black and light blue	..	..	1·75	10
180		12 c. black and purple	..	..	2·25	30
181	**42**	25 c. black and sepia	..	..	2·25	50
182		50 c. black and blue	..	..	6·50	40
183		$1.50, black and yellow-orange	..		7·50	6·50
184	**43**	$2.50, slate-blue and carmine	..		5·50	5·50
172/184		.. ..	*Set of* 13	24·00	14·00

1951 (16 Feb). *Inauguration of B.W.I. University College. As Nos.*
118/19 *of Antigua.*

185	3 c. black and carmine	..	..	45	20
186	6 c. black and olive	..	..	45	20

NEW CONSTITUTION

1951

(44)

1951 (21 Sept). *New Constitution. Nos.* 175/7 *and* 180 *optd*
with T **44** *by B.W.*

187	**41**	3 c. black and rose-carmine	..	..	10	10
188		4 c. black and orange	..	..	10	10
189		5 c. black and violet (R.)	..	..	10	10
190		12 c. black and purple	..	..	10	15
187/90		.. ..	*Set of* 4	30	40

POSTAGE DUE STAMPS

D 1

1952 (1 Mar). *As Type* D **1**, *but inscr* "POSTAGE DUE". *Value in*
cents. Chalk-surfaced paper. Wmk Mult Script CA. P 14.

D15	2 c. black	..	..	30	5·50
	a. Error. Crown missing. W **9**a	..	..	90·00	
	b. Error. St. Edward Crown. W **9**b	..		45·00	
D16	4 c. black	..	..	30	11·00
	a. Error. Crown missing. W **9**a	..	..	90·00	
	b. Error. St. Edward Crown. W **9**b	..		45·00	
D17	6 c. black	..	..	45	11·00
	a. Error. Crown missing. W **9**a	..		130	
	b. Error. St. Edward Crown. W **9**b	..		85·00	
D18	8 c. black	..	..	75	11·00
	a. Error. Crown missing. W **9**a	..		£225	
	b. Error. St. Edward Crown. W **9**b	..		£140	
D15/18	.. ..	*Set of* 4	1·60	35·00

Hong Kong

100 cents = 1 Hong Kong dollar

CROWN COLONY

1937 (12 May). *Coronation. As Nos. 95/7 of Antigua.*
P 11×11½.

137	4 c. green		4·50	2·50
138	15 c. carmine		10·00	3·25
139	25 c. blue		13·00	2·50
137/9		*Set of* 3	25·00	7·50
137/9	Perf "Specimen"	*Set of* 3	£180	

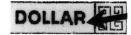

29 King George VI   Short right leg to "R" (Right pane R. 7/3, left pane R. 3/1)

1938–52. *Wmk Mult Script CA. Chalk-surfaced paper* (80 c.,
$1 (No. 155), $2 (No. 157), $5 (No. 159), $10 (No. 161)). *P* 14.

140	29	1 c. brown (24.5.38)	1·75	80
		a. Pale brown (4.2.52)	2·00	4·75
141		2 c. grey (5.4.38)	2·00	30
		a. Perf 14½×14 (28.9.45)	1·75	4·50
142		4 c. orange (5.4.38)	3·25	1·25
		a. Perf 14½×14 (28.9.45)	4·50	3·25
143		5 c. green (24.5.38)	1·25	20
		a. Perf 14½×14 (28.9.45)	2·50	5·00
144		8 c. red-brown (1.11.41)	1·75	2·25
		a. Imperf (pair)	£23000	
145		10 c. bright violet (13.4.38)	50·00	75
		a. Perf 14½×14. *Dull violet* (28.9.45)	8·50	20
		b. Dull reddish violet (9.4.46)	6·00	70
		c. Reddish lilac (9.4.47)	15·00	20
146		15 c. scarlet (13.4.38)	1·75	30
147		20 c. black (1.2.46)	1·25	30
148		20 c. scarlet-vermilion (1.4.48)	7·00	40
		a. Rose-red (25.4.51)	15·00	5·50
149		25 c. bright blue (5.4.38)	26·00	80
150		25 c. pale yellow-olive (9.4.46)	4·75	1·25
151		30 c. yellow-olive (13.4.48)	£150	1·40
		a. Perf 14½×14. *Yellowish olive* (28.9.45)	22·00	8·00
152		30 c. blue (9.4.46)	7·00	20
153		50 c. reddish purple (13.4.38)	45·00	70
		a. Perf 14½×14. *Deep magenta* (28.9.45)	29·00	1·10
		ab. Printed both sides, inverted on reverse	£7500	
		b. Chalk-surfaced paper. *Brt purple* (9.4.47)	9·00	20
154		80 c. carmine (2.2.48)	5·00	95
155		$1 dull lilac and blue (*chalk-surfaced paper*) (27.4.38)	8·00	2·50
		a. Short right leg to "R"	£110	
		b. Ordinary paper. *Pale reddish lilac and blue* (28.9.45)	11·00	6·50
156		$1 red-orange and green (9.4.46)	17·00	30
		a. Short right leg to "R"	£160	
		b. Chalk-surfaced paper (21.6.48)	45·00	3·50
		ba. Short right leg to "R"	£275	
		c. Chalk-surfaced paper. *Yellow-orange and green* (6.11.52)	70·00	15·00
157		$2 red-orange and green (24.5.38)	70·00	14·00
158		$2 reddish violet and scarlet (9.4.46)	26·00	2·00
		a. Chalk-surfaced paper (9.4.47)	32·00	95
159		$5 dull lilac and scarlet (2.6.38)	55·00	48·00
160		$5 green and violet (9.4.46)	80·00	5·00
		a. Yellowish green and violet (9.4.46)	£150	16·00
		ab. Chalk-surfaced paper (9.4.47)	95·00	2·75
161	29	$10 green and violet (2.6.38)	£400	85·00
162		$10 bright lilac and blue (9.4.46)	£140	23·00
		a. Chalk-surfaced paper. *Reddish violet and blue* (9.4.47)	£180	18·00
140/62		*Set of* 23	£750	£150
140/62	Perf "Specimen"	*Set of* 23	£2000	

Following bomb damage to the De La Rue works on the night of 29 December 1940 various emergency arrangements were made to complete current requisitions for Hong Kong stamps:

Nos. 141a, 143a, 145a, 151a and 153a (all printings perforated 14½×14 except the 4 c.) were printed and perforated by Bradbury, Wilkinson & Co. Ltd. using De La Rue plates. These stamps are on rough-surfaced paper.

Nos. 142a and 144 were printed by Harrison & Sons in sheets of 120 (12×10) instead of the normal 120 two panes (6×10).

Printings of the $1 and $2 values were made by Williams, Lea & Co. using De La Rue plates.

With the exception of the 8 c. it is believed that none of these printings were issued in Hong Kong before its occupation by the Japanese on 25 December 1941, although examples could be obtained in London from late 1941. The issue dates quoted are those on which the stamps were eventually released in Hong Kong following liberation in 1945.

Nos. 160/*a* were separate printings released in Hong Kong on the same day.

No. 144a. One imperforate sheet was found and most of the stamps were sold singly to the public at a branch P.O. and used for postage.

30 Street Scene   31 *Empress of Japan* (liner) and Junk

(Des W. E. Jones. Recess B.W.)

1941 (26 Feb). *Centenary of British Occupation. T* **30**/1 *and similar designs. Wmk Mult Script CA* (*sideways on horiz designs*). *P* 13½ × 13 (2 c. *and* 25 c.) *or* 13 × 13½ (*others*).

163	2 c. orange and chocolate		4·50	1·75
164	4 c. bright purple and carmine		4·50	1·75
165	5 c. black and green		2·50	50
166	15 c. black and scarlet		5·50	1·00
167	25 c. chocolate and blue		12·00	3·50
168	$1 blue and orange		45·00	7·00
163/168		*Set of* 6	65·00	14·00
163/8	Perf "Specimen"	*Set of* 6	£325	

Designs: *Horiz*—5 c. The University; 15 c. The Harbour; $1 Falcon (clipper) and Short S.23 Empire "C" Class flying boat. *Vert*—25 c. The Hong Kong Bank.

Hong Kong was under Japanese occupation from 25 December 1941 until 30 August 1945. The Japanese post offices in the colony were closed from 31 August and mail was carried free, marked with cachets reading "HONG KONG/1945/ POSTAGE PAID". Military administration lasted until 1 May 1946. Hong Kong stamps were re-introduced on 28 September 1945.

36 King George VI and Phoenix

Extra stroke (R. 1/2)

(Des W. E. Jones. Recess D.L.R.)

)46 (29 Aug). *Victory. Wmk Mult Script CA. P* 13.

59	**36**	30 c. blue and red (*shades*)			2·00	1·25
		a. Extra stroke			45·00	
70		$1 brown and red			3·50	75
		a. Extra stroke			80·00	
59/70		Perf "Specimen"		*Set of* 2	£160	

Spur on "N" of "KONG" (R. 2/9)

948 (22 Dec). *Royal Silver Wedding. As Nos.* 112/13 *of Antigua.*

71	10 c. violet				2·75	80
	a. Spur on "N"				55·00	
72	$10 carmine				£250	75·00

949 (10 Oct). *75th Anniv of Universal Postal Union. As Nos.* 114/17 *of Antigua.*

73	10 c. violet				3·75	50
74	20 c. carmine-red				15·00	3·00
75	30 c. deep blue				12·00	1·75
76	80 c. bright reddish purple			35·00	9·50
73/6				*Set of* 4	60·00	13·00

POSTAGE DUE STAMPS

D 1 Post-office Scales

(Typo D.L.R.)

938 (Feb)–**63**. *Wmk Mult Script CA* (*sideways*). *Ordinary paper. P* 14.

)6	D 1	2 c. grey			13·00	9·00
		a. Chalk-surfaced paper (21.3.56)		1·10	10·00
) 7		4 c. orange			17·00	6·50
		a. Chalk-surfaced paper. *Orange-yellow* (23.5.61)		2·50	9·50

D 8	D 1	6 c. scarlet				9·50	5·50
D 9		8 c. chestnut (26.2.46)				5·50	32·00
D10		10 c. violet				30·00	45
		a. Chalk-surfaced paper (17.9.63)		16·00	8·50
D11		20 c. black (26.2.46)				11·00	3·00
D12		50 c. blue (7.47)				40·00	15·00
D6a/12					*Set of* 7	75·00	65·00
D6/12		Perf "Specimen"			*Set of* 7	£300	

POSTAL FISCAL STAMPS

F 8

1938 (11 Jan). *Wmk Mult Script CA. P* 14.

| F12 | F 8 | 5 c. green | | | | 50·00 | 9·50 |

No. F12 was authorised for postal use between 11 and 20 January 1938 due to a shortage of the 5 c., No. 121.

Forged cancellations are known on this stamp inscribed "VICTORIA 9.AM 11 JA 38 HONG KONG" without side bars between the rings.

JAPANESE OCCUPATION OF HONG KONG

Hong Kong surrendered to the Japanese on 25 December 1941. The postal service was not resumed until 22 January 1942 when the G.P.O. and Kowloon Central Office re-opened.

Japanese postmarks used in Hong Kong can be identified by the unique combination of horizontal lines in the central circle and three stars in the lower segment of the outer circle. Dates shown on such postmarks are in the sequence Year/Month/Day with the first shown as a Japanese regnal year number so that Showa 17 = 1942 and so on.

Initially six current Japanese definitives, 1, 2, 3, 4, 10 and 30 s. (Nos. 297, 315/17, 322 and 327). were on sale, but the range gradually expanded to cover all values between ½ s. and 10 y. with Nos. 313/14, 318, 325, 328/31, 391, 395/6, 398/9 and 405 of Japan also available from Hong Kong post offices during the occupation. Philatelic covers exist showing other Japanese stamps, but these were not available from the local post offices. Supply of these Japanese stamps was often interrupted and, during the period between 28 July 1942 and 21 April 1943, circular "Postage Paid" handstamps were sometimes used. A substantial increase in postage rates on 16 April 1945 led to the issue of the local surcharges, Nos. J1/3.

(1)   (2)

1945 (16 Apr). *Stamps of Japan surch with T* 1 (*No.* J1) *or as T* 2.

J1	1.50 yen on 1 s. brown			26·00	21·00
J2	3 yen on 2 s. scarlet			12·00	18·00
J3	5 yen on 5 s. claret			£850	£130

Designs (18½ × 22 *mm*):—1 s. Girl Worker; 2 s. Gen. Nogi; 5 s. Admiral Togo.

No. J3 has four characters of value similarly arranged but differing from T 2.

India

12 pies = 1 anna; 16 annas = 1 rupee

91 King George VI   **92** Dak Runner

93 King George VI

1937 (23 Aug)–**40.** *Typo.* W **69**. *P* 13½×14 *or* 14×13½ (*T* **93**)

247	**91**	3 p. slate (15.12.37)	..	50	10
248		½ a. red-brown (15.12.37)	..	1·75	10
249		9 p. green	..	5·00	20
250		1 a. carmine	..	70	10
		a. *Tête-bêche* (vert pair) (1940)	..	1·40	1·75
		w. Wmk inverted (from booklets)	..	70	70
251	**92**	2 a. vermilion (15.12.37)	..	3·25	30
252	–	2 a. 6 p. bright violet (15.12.37)	..	75	20
253	–	3 a. yellow-green (15.12.37)	..	4·75	30
254	–	3 a. 6 p. bright blue (15.12.37)	..	3·25	50
255	–	4 a. brown (15.12.37)	..	13·00	20
256	–	6 a. turquoise-green (15.12.37)	..	14·00	80
257	–	8 a. slate-violet (15.12.37)	..	7·50	50
258	–	12 a. lake (15.12.37)	..	18·00	1·10
259	**93**	1 r. grey and red-brown (15.12.37)	..	1·00	15
260		2 r. purple and brown (15.12.37)	..	3·75	30
		w. Wmk inverted	..	20·00	
261		5 r. green and blue (15.12.37)	..	17·00	50
		w. Wmk inverted	..	35·00	
262		10 r. purple and claret (15.12.37)	..	15·00	70
263		15 r. brown and green (15.12.37)	..	70·00	60·00
		w. Wmk inverted	..	80·00	65·00
264		25 r. slate-violet and purple (15.12.37)	..	95·00	17·00
247/64		.. .. .. *Set of* 18	£250	75·00

Designs: *Horiz as T* **92**—2 a. 6 p. Dak bullock cart; 3 a. Dak tonga; 3 a. 6 p. Dak camel; 4 a. Mail train; 6 a. *Strathnaver* (liner); 8 a. Mail lorry; 12 a. Armstrong Whitworth A.W.27 Ensign I mail plane (small head).

No. 250a comes from surplus booklet sheets issued as normal stock following the rise in postal rates.

100a King George VI   **101**   King George VI   **102**

103 Armstrong Whitworth
A.W.27 Ensign I Mail Plane
(large head)

(T **100a/102** des T. I. Archer. Typo)

1940–43. W **69**. *P* 13½×14.

265	**100a**	3 p. slate	..	..	30	10
266		½ a. purple (1.10.42)	..	..	60	10
		w. Wmk inverted	..			
267		9 p. green	..	..	60	10
268		1 a. carmine (1.4.43)	..	..	60	10
269	**101**	1 a. 3 p. yellow-brown	..	..	90	10
		aw. Wmk inverted	..			
269b		1½ a. dull violet (9.42)	..	..	75	10
270		2 a. vermilion	..	..	1·50	10
271		3 a. bright violet (1942)	..	..	2·50	10
		w. Wmk inverted	..	..	—	10·00
272		3½ a. bright blue	..	..	70	10
273	**102**	4 a. brown	..	..	45	10
274		6 a. turquoise-green	..	..	3·50	10
275		8 a. slate-violet	..	..	1·50	30
276		12 a. lake	..	..	3·00	50
277	**103**	14 a. purple (15.10.40)	..	..	18·00	1·25
265/77		.. .. .. *Set of* 14	32·00	2·25

The 1½ a. and 3 a. were at first printed by lithography and were of finer execution and without Jubilee lines in the sheet margins.

= =

3 PIES

105 "Victory" and King   **(106)**
George VI

1946 (2 Jan). *Victory. Litho.* W **69**. *P* 13.

278	**105**	9 p. yellow-green (8.2.46)	..		30	40
279		1½ a. dull violet	..	..	30	30
280		3½ a. bright blue	..	..	75	60
281		12 a. claret (8.2.46)	..	..	1·50	65
278/81		.. .. .. *Set of* 4	2·50	1·75

1946 (8 Aug). *Surch with T* **106.**

282	**101**	3 p. on 1 a. 3 p. yellow-brown..	..	10	10

DOMINION

301 Asokan Capital   **302** Indian National Flag
(Inscr reads
"Long Live India")

303 Douglas DC-4

(Des T. I. Archer. Litho)

947 (21 Nov–15 Dec). *Independence. W* **69**. *P* 14 × 13½ (1½ *a*.)
or 13½ × 14 (*others*).
01	**301**	1½ a. grey-green (15 Dec)	..	15	10
02	**302**	3½ a. orange-red, blue and green		30	1·10
		w. Wmk inverted ..	..	5·50	5·50
03	**303**	12 a. ultramarine (15 Dec)	..	1·50	2·00
01/3		..	*Set of* 3	1·75	2·75

304 Lockheed Constellation

(Des T. I. Archer. Litho)

948 (29 May). *Air. Inauguration of India-U.K. Air Service. W* **69**.
P 13½ × 14.
304	**304**	12 a. black and ultramarine	..	1·00	2·00

305 Mahatma Gandhi 306

(Photo Courvoisier)

1948 (15 Aug). *First Anniv of Independence. P* 11½.
305	**305**	1½ a. brown	..	..	..	1·75	30
306		3½ a. violet	..	..	..	4·25	1·50
307		12 a. grey-green		..	..	6·00	60
308	**306**	10 r. purple-brown and lake	..		55·00	40·00
305/8	..	..	..	..	*Set of* 4	60·00	40·00

307 Ajanta   308 Konarak Horse   309 Trimurti
Panel

310 Bodhisattva   311 Nataraja   312 Sanchi Stupa,
East Gate

313 Bodh Gaya   314 Bhuvanesvara   315 Gol Gumbad,
Temple   Bijapur

316 Kandarya Mahadeva   317 Golden Temple,
Temple   Amritsar

318 Victory Tower,   319 Red Fort, Delhi
Chittorgarh

320 Taj Mahal, Agra   321 Qutb Minar,
Delhi

322 Satrunjaya Temple, Palitana

(Des T. I. Archer and I. M. Das. Typo (low values), litho (rupee
values))

1949 (15 Aug). *W* **69** (*sideways* * *on* 6 *p*., 1 *r*. *and* 10 *r*.). *P* 14
(3 *p*. *to* 2 *a*.), 13½ (3 *a*. *to* 12 *a*.), 14×13½ (1 *r*. *and* 10 *r*.),
13½×14 (2 *r*. *and* 5 *r*.), 13 (15 *r*.).
309	**307**	3 p. slate-violet	..	..	15	10
		w. Wmk inverted ..				
310	**308**	6 p. purple-brown	..	..	25	10
		w. Wmk star pointing right	..	3·25	90
311	**309**	9 p. yellow-green	..	..	40	10
312	**310**	1 a. turquoise	..	..	60	10
313	**311**	2 a. carmine	..	..	80	10
		w. Wmk inverted ..	..	..	9·00	90

314	312	3 a. brown-orange	..	..	1·50	10
315	313	3½ a. bright blue	..	..	1·50	2·75
316	314	4 a. lake	..	..	4·00	20
		w. Wmk inverted	..		13·00	1·00
317	315	6 a. violet	..	..	1·50	10
		w. Wmk inverted	..		3·00	45
318	316	8 a. turquoise-green	..		1·50	10
		w. Wmk inverted	..			
319	317	12 a. dull blue	..	..	1·50	20
		w. Wmk inverted	..		5·00	80
320	318	1 r. dull violet and green	..		9·00	10
		w. Wmk star pointing left		20·00	80
321	319	2 r. claret and violet	..		10·00	20
		w. Wmk inverted	..		24·00	1·00
322	320	5 r. blue-green and red-brown		28·00	90
		w. Wmk inverted	..		50·00	1·75
323	321	10 r. purple-brown and deep blue		45·00	5·00
		a. *Purple-brown and blue*		90·00	3·75
		aw. Wmk star pointing left			
324	322	15 r. brown and claret	..		14·00	17·00
309/24	..	..	..	*Set of* 16	£110	22·00

*The normal sideways watermark has the star pointing to the
left on the 6 p. value and to the right on the 1 r. and 10 r. (323*a*)
when seen from the back of the stamp.
For T 310 with statue reversed see No. 333.

323 Globe and Asokan Capital

1949 (10 Oct). *75th Anniv of U.P.U. Litho.* W **69**. *P* 13.

325	323	9 p. green	..	..	1·00	2·00
326		2 a. rose	..	..	1·00	2·00
327		3½ a. bright blue	..	..	1·75	2·25
328		12 a. brown-purple	..	..	3·00	2·50
325/8	..	..	..	*Set of* 4	6·00	8·00

REPUBLIC

REPUBLIC OF INDIA

INAUGURATION JAN 26.1950

324 Rejoicing Crowds	**328** As T **310**, but statue reversed

(Des D. J. Keymer & Co. Litho)

1950 (26 Jan). *Inauguration of Republic.* T **324** *and similar
designs.* W **69** (*sideways on* 3½ a.). *P* 13.

329		2 a. scarlet	..	..	1·00	40
		w. Wmk inverted	..	..	12·00	1·75
330		3½ a. ultramarine	..	..	1·50	2·75
331		4 a. violet	..	..	1·50	65
332		12 a. maroon	..	..	3·25	2·25
		w. Wmk inverted	..	..	14·00	4·50
329/32	..	..	..	*Set of* 4	6·50	5·50

Designs: *Vert*—3½ a. Quill, ink-well and verse. *Horiz*—4 a. Ear
of corn and plough; 12 a. Spinning-wheel and cloth.

1950 (15 July)–**51**. *Typo.* W **69**. *P* 14 (1 a.), 13½ (*others*).

333	328	1 a. turquoise	..	..	2·50	10
		aw. Wmk inverted	..	..		
333*b*	313	2½ a. lake (30.4.51)	..		2·50	2·50
333*c*	314	4 a. bright blue (30.4.51)	..		6·00	10
333/*c*	..	..	..	*Set of* 3	10·00	2·50

329 Stegodon ganesa	**330** Torch

1951 (13 Jan). *Centenary of Geological Survey of India. Litho*
W **69**. *P* 13.

334	329	2 a. black and claret	..	..	2·00	5

1951 (4 Mar). *First Asian Games, New Delhi. Litho.* W **69** (*sideways*). *P* 14.

335	330	2 a. reddish purple and brown-orange	..	1·00	3
336		12 a. chocolate and light blue	..	..	4·00	9

STAMP BOOKLETS

1937. *Black on red cover. Stamps with wmk upright or
inverted. Stitched.*

SB22   1 *r.* booklet containing sixteen 1 a. (No. 250) in
blocks of 4 .. .. £200

OFFICIAL STAMPS

SERVICE	**SERVICE**
(O **17**)(13½ mm)	(O **18**) (19½ mm)

1937–39. *Stamps of King George VI optd as Types* O **17** *or* O **18**
(*rupee values*).

O135	91	½ a. red-brown (1938)	..	..	16·00	20
O136		9 p. green (1937)	..	..	17·00	30
O137		1 a. carmine (1937)	..	..	3·00	10
O138	93	1 r. grey and red-brown (5.38)	..	50	50
O139		2 r. purple and brown (5.38)	..	1·50	2·50
		w. Wmk inverted	..	..	—	21·00
O140		5 r. green and blue (10.38)	..	2·50	5·50
O141		10 r. purple and claret (1939)	..	14·00	4·75
O135/41	..	..	..	*Set of* 7	48·00	12·50

SERVICE	**INDIA POSTAGE**
(O **19**)	O **20**

1939 (May). *Stamp of King George V, surch with Type* O **19**.

O142	82	1 a. on 1¼ a. mauve	..	..	11·00	20

(Des T. I. Archer)

1939 (1 June)–**42**. *Typo.* W **69**. *P* 14.

O143	O 20	3 p. slate	..	..	40	10
O144		½ a. red-brown	..	..	4·00	10
O144*a*		½ a. purple (1942)	..		30	10
O145		9 p. green	..	..	30	10
O146		1 a. carmine	..	..	30	10
O146*a*		1 a. 3 p. yellow-brown (1941)	..	3·00	70
O146*b*		1½ a. dull violet (1942)	..	65	10
		aw. Wmk inverted	..			
O147		2 a. vermilion	..	..	60	10
O148		2½ a. bright violet	..	..	60	50
O149		4 a. brown	..	..	60	10
O150		8 a. slate-violet	..	..	90	30
O143/50	..	..	..	*Set of* 11	10·50	1·60

1948 (15 Aug). *First Anniv of Independence. Nos. 305/8 optd as Type* O **17**.

)150a	**305**	1½ a. brown	..	..	.. 42·00 30·00
)150b		3½ a. violet	..	..	.. £750 £450
)150c		12 a. grey-green		..	£2000 £1600
)150d	**306**	10 r. purple-brown and lake		.. £11000

Nos. O150a/d were only issued to the Governor-General's Secretariat.

O **21**   Asokan Capital   O **22**

(Des T. I. Archer)

1950 (2 Jan)–**51.** *Typo* (O **21**) *or litho* (O **22**). W **69**. *P* 14.

O151	O **21**	3 p. slate-violet (1.7.50)	..		10	10
O152		6 p. purple-brown (1.7.50)		..	10	10
O153		9 p. green (1.7.50)			30	10
O154		1 a. turquoise (1.7.50)		..	70	10
O155		2 a. carmine (1.7.50)		..	1·00	10
		w. Wmk inverted		..		
O156		3 a. red-orange (1.7.50)	..	..	3·00	1·75
O157		4 a. lake (1.7.50)	..	..	5·00	20
O158		4 a. ultramarine (1.10.51)		..	50	10
O159		6 a. bright violet (1.7.50)	..		3·00	40
O160		8 a. red-brown (1.7.50)		..	1·50	10
		w. Wmk inverted			8·00	
O161	O **22**	1 r. violet	..	..	2·75	10
		w. Wmk inverted		..		
O162		2 r. rose-carmine	..		1·00	70
O163		5 r. bluish green	..		2·00	1·75
O164		10 r. reddish brown		..	3·00 16·00
O151/64	..	..	..	..	*Set of* 14 21·00 19·00

INDIAN NATIONAL ARMY

The following are stated to have been used in the Japanese occupied areas of India during the drive on Imphal. Issued by the Indian National Army.

Genuine examples are inscribed "PROVISIONAL GOVERNMENT OF FREE INDIA". Forgeries also exist inscribed "PROVISIONAL GOVT. OF FREE INDIA".

Typo in Rangoon. No gum. Perf 11½ or imperf. 1 p. violet, 1 p. maroon, 1 a. green   *Price from* £50 *each unused*

JAPANESE OCCUPATION OF THE ANDAMAN AND NICOBAR ISLANDS

The Andaman Islands in the Bay of Bengal were occupied on the 23 March 1942 and the Nicobar Islands in July 1942. Civil administration was resumed in October 1945.

The following Indian stamps were surcharged with large figures preceded by a decimal point:—

Postage stamps—.3 on ½ a. (No. 248), .5 on 1 a. (No. 250), .10 on 2 a. (No. 236b), .30 on 6 a. (No. 274).

Official stamps—.10 on 1 a. 3 p. (No. O146a), .20 on 3 p. (No. O143), .20 in red on 3 p. (No. O143).

Prices from £400 *each unused*

INDIAN CONVENTION STATES

The following issues resulted from a series of postal conventions agreed between the Imperial Government and the state administrations of Patiala (1 October 1884), Gwalior, Jind and Nabha (1 July 1885), and Chamba and Faridkot (1 January 1887).

Under the terms of these conventions the British Indian Post Office supplied overprinted British India issues to the state administrations which, in turn, had to conform to a number of conditions covering the issue of stamps, rates of postage and the exchange of mail.

Such overprinted issues were valid for postage within the state of issue, to other "Convention States" and to destinations in British India.

Stamps of Chamba, Gwalior, Jind, Nabha and Patiala ceased to be valid for postage on 1 January 1951, when they were replaced by those of the Republic of India, valid from 1 April 1950.

RULERS OF INDIAN CONVENTION AND FEUDATORY STATES. Details of the rulers of the various states during the period when stamps were issued are now provided in a somewhat simplified form which omits reference to minor titles. Dates quoted are of the various reigns, extended to 1971 when the titles of the surviving rulers of the former princely states were abolished by the Indian Government.

During the absorption of the Convention and Feudatory States there was often an interim period during which the administration was handed over. In some instances it is only possible to quote the end of this interim period as the point of transfer.

Stamps of India overprinted

CHAMBA

Raja Lakshman Singh, 1935–1971

CHAMBA STATE   **CHAMBA STATE**
(3)   (4)

CHAMBA STATE   CHAMBA   **CHAMBA**
(5)   (6)   (7)

1938. *King George VI. Nos.* 247/64 *optd with T* **3** (3 *p. to* 1 *a.*), *T* **5** (2 *a. to* 12 *a.*) *or T* **4** (*rupee values*).

82	**91**	3 p. slate	..		..	..	3·50	8·00
83		½ a. red-brown	..			..	90	4·50
84		9 p. green	..	..	..	..	4·50	21·00
85		1 a. carmine	..			..	90	1·40
86	**92**	2 a. vermilion	..		..	..	3·00	7·00
87	–	2 a. 6 p. bright violet		..		..	3·50	15·00
88	–	3 a. yellow-green		..		..	4·50	16·00
89	–	3 a. 6 p. bright blue			..	..	4·50	18·00
90	–	4 a. brown	..		..	..	14·00	12·00
91	–	6 a. turquoise-green		..		..	13·00	38·00
92	–	8 a. slate-violet ..			..	..	14·00	32·00
93	–	12 a. lake	..	..		..	9·00	38·00
94	**93**	1 r. grey and red-brown			..	..	29·00	45·00
95		2 r. purple and brown		..		..	42·00	£190
96		5 r. green and blue			..	..	70·00	£300
97		10 r. purple and claret		..		..	£120	£450
98		15 r. brown and green		..		..	£200	£650
99		25 r. slate-violet and purple			..	..	£225	£700
82/99		..	..	..	..	*Set of* 18	£650 £2250

1942–47. *Optd with T* **6** (*to* 12 *a*), "CHAMBA" *only, as in T* **5** (14 *a.*) *or T* **7** (*rupee values*). (*a*) *Stamps of* 1937. W **69** (*inverted on* 15 *r.*).

100	**91**	½ a. red-brown	..	..		..	25·00 16·00
101		1 a. carmine	..	..		..	28·00 17·00
102	**93**	1 r. grey and red-brown		..		..	21·00 45·00
103		2 r. purple and brown		..		..	28·00 £170
104		5 r. green and blue		..		..	60·00 £180
105		10 r. purple and claret		..		..	85·00 £350
106		15 r. brown and green		..		..	£180 £550
107		25 r. slate-violet and purple		..		..	£200 £550
100/107		..	..	..	..	*Set of* 8	£550 £1700

(b) *Stamps of* 1940–43

108	100a	3 p. slate	..	..	..	60	3·50
109		½ a. purple (1943)	..	..	..	70	2·50
110		9 p. green	..	..	..	80	9·00
111		1 a. carmine (1943)	..	..	..	90	2·25
112	101	1½ a. dull violet (1943)	..	..	..	90	6·00
113		2 a. vermilion (1943)	..	..	..	2·50	6·50
114		3 a. bright violet	..	..	..	7·50	18·00
115		3½ a. bright blue	..	..	..	4·00	24·00
116	102	4 a. brown	..	..	..	5·50	7·50
117		6 a. turquoise-green	..	..	..	15·00	35·00
118		8 a. slate-violet	..	..	..	14·00	40·00
119		12 a. lake	..	..	..	27·00	50·00
120	103	14 a. purple (1947)	..	..	..	7·00	3·00
108/120			..	..	Set of 13	75·00	£190

The 3 a. exists printed by lithography or typography.

OFFICIAL STAMPS

CHAMBA STATE SERVICE (O 2)

CHAMBA STATE SERVICE
(O 3)

1938—40. *King George VI. Optd with Type* O **2** *or* O **3** (*rupee values*).

O66	91	9 p. green	..	..	..	8·00	35·00
O67		1 a. carmine	..	..	..	6·50	1·50
O68	93	1 r. grey and red-brown (1940?)	..	£500	£750
O69		2 r. purple and brown (1939)	..	50·00	£250
O70		5 r. green and blue (1939)	..	80·00	£325
O71		10 r. purple and claret (1939)	..	£120	£550
O66/71			..	..	Set of 6	£700	£1700

CHAMBA SERVICE
(O 4)

1940–43. (a) *Official stamps optd with T* **6**.

O72	O 20	3 p. slate	..	..	..	60	60
O73		½ a. red-brown	..	..	..	12·00	1·40
O74		½ a. purple (1943)	..	..	..	60	1·60
O75		9 p. green	..	..	..	3·50	5·50
		w. Wmk inverted	..	..	..	12·00	9·00
O76		1 a. carmine (1941)	..	..	60	1·25
O77		1 a. 3 p. yellow-brown (1941)	..	40·00	14·00
O78		1½ a. dull violet (1943)	..	..	3·75	4·75
O79		2 a. vermilion	..	..	..	3·50	4·00
O80		2½ a. bright violet (1941)	..	..	1·75	16·00
O81		4 a. brown	..	..	..	3·50	7·00
O82		8 a. slate-violet	..	..	..	10·00	40·00
		w. Wmk inverted	..	..	..	9·50	40·00

(b) *Postage stamps optd with Type* O **4**.

O83	93	1 r. grey and red-brown (1942)	..	32·00	£140
O84		2 r. purple and brown (1942)	..	50·00	£200
O85		5 r. green and blue (1942)	..	80·00	£300
O86		10 r. purple and claret (1942)	..	£120	£500
O72/86		..	..	..	Set of 15	£325	£1100

Chamba became part of Himachal Pradesh on 15 April 1948.

GWALIOR

Maharaja George Jivaji Rao Sindhia, 1925–1961

GWALIOR गवालियर (4)

GWALIOR
गवालियर (5)

1938–48. *King George VI. Nos.* 247/50, 253, 255/6, *and* 259/64 *optd with T* **4** *or* **5** (*rupee values*).

105	91	3 p. slate	..	..	..	4·00	10
106		½ a. red-brown	..	..	..	4·00	10
107		9 p. green (1939)	..	..	..	32·00	2·75
108		1 a. carmine	..	..	..	4·00	15
109	–	3 a. yellow-green (1939)	..	..	10·00	2·75
110	–	4 a. brown	..	..	..	38·00	1·75

111	–	6 a. turquoise-green (1939)	..	..	2·50	6·00
112	93	1 r. grey and red-brown (1942)	..	6·00	1·50
113		2 r. purple and brown (1948)	..	28·00	7·00
114		5 r. green and blue (1948)	..	38·00	32·00
115		10 r. purple and claret (1948)	..	38·00	40·00
116		15 r. brown and green (1948)	..	£120	£160
117		25 r. slate-violet and purple (1948)	..	£110	£120
105/117		..	..	..	Set of 13	£400	£325

1942–5. *King George VI. Optd with T* **4**.

118	100a	3 p. slate	..	..	..	45	10
		w. Wmk inverted	..	..	—	13·00
119		½ a. purple (1943)	..	..	45	10
120		9 p. green	..	..	..	45	10
121		1 a. carmine (1943)	..	..	40	10
		a. Opt double	..	..	..	—	£120
122	101	1½ a. dull violet	..	..	3·50	20
123		2 a. vermilion	..	..	..	55	20
124		3 a. bright violet	..	..	6·50	30
		a. Opt double	..	..	..	—	£120
125	102	4 a. brown	..	..	..	1·25	20
126		6 a. turquoise-green (1945)	..	20·00	18·00
127		8 a. slate-violet (1944)	..	2·75	2·75
128		12 a. lake (1943)	..	..	4·50	16·00
118/28			..	..	Set of 11	35·00	32·00

The 1½ a. and 3 a. exist printed by lithography or typography.

GWALIOR
गवालियर (6)

1949 (Apr). *King George VI. Optd with T* **6** *at the Alizah Printing Press, Gwalior.*

129	100a	3 p. slate	..	..	..	60	50
130		½ a. purple	..	..	..	60	50
131		1 a. carmine	..	..	..	75	60
132	101	2 a. vermilion	..	..	..	15·00	1·75
133		3 a. bright violet	..	..	..	38·00	21·00
134	102	4 a. brown	..	..	..	2·75	2·75
135		6 a. turquoise-green	..	..	35·00	45·00
136		8 a. slate-violet	..	..	80·00	45·00
137		12 a. lake	..	..	..	£300	£130
129/137			..	..	Set of 9	£425	£225

OFFICIAL STAMPS

गवालियर

गवालियर

सरविस (O 1)

सरविस (O 2)

1938. *King George VI. Optd as Type* O **1** (13 *mm*).

O78	91	½ a. red-brown	..	..	..	6·50	3
O79		1 a. carmine	..	..	..	1·10	2

गवालियर (O 3)

1A —— **1**A (O 4)

1940–42. *Official stamps optd with Type* O **3**.

O80	O 20	3 p. slate	..	..	..	50	10
O81		½ a. red-brown	..	..	..	3·00	25
O82		½ a. purple (1942)	..	..	50	10
O83		9 p. green (1942)	..	..	70	50
O84		1 a. carmine	..	..	..	2·25	10
O85		1 a. 3 p. yellow-brown (1942)	..	30·00	1·60
		w. Wmk inverted	..	..	—	12·00
O86		1½ a. dull violet (1942)	..	1·00	30
O87		2 a. vermilion	..	..	..	1·00	30
O88		4 a. brown (1942)	..	..	1·25	1·60
O89		8 a. slate-violet (1942)	..	2·50	6·00
O80/9			..	..	Set of 10	38·00	9·75

1941. *Stamp of 1932 (King George V) optd with Type* O **1** *and surch with Type* O **4**.

O90	**82**	1 a. on 1 a. 3 p. mauve	..	..	18·00	2·75
		w. Wmk inverted	..	..	21·00	4·75

1942–47. *King George VI. Optd with Type* O **2**.

O91	**93**	1 r. grey and red-brown	..	..	8·00	13·00
O92		2 r. purple and brown	..	..	21·00	70·00
O93		5 r. green and blue (1943)	..		38·00	£375
O94		10 r. purple and claret (1947)	..		£110	£750
O91/4 ..		..	..	*Set of 4*	£160	£1100

Gwalior became part of Madhya Bharat by 1 July 1948.

JIND

Raja (Maharaja from 1911) Ranbir Singh, 1887–1959

JIND STATE	**JIND STATE**
(5)	(6)

1937–38. *King George VI. Nos. 247/64 optd with T* **5** *or T* **6** *(rupee values)*.

109	**91**	3 p. slate	..	..	6·00	1·50
110		½ a. red-brown	..	..	60	2·50
111		9 p. green (1937)	..	..	60	2·25
112		1 a. carmine (1937)	..	..	60	45
113	**92**	2 a. vermilion ..	..	..	1·50	11·00
114	—	2 a. 6 p. bright violet	..	..	1·00	12·00
115	—	3 a. yellow-green	..	..	5·00	11·00
116	—	3 a. 6 p. bright blue	..	..	2·00	12·00
117	—	4 a. brown	..	..	6·00	12·00
118	—	6 a. turquoise-green	..	..	3·50	15·00
119	—	8 a. slate-violet	..	..	2·50	15·00
120	—	12 a. lake	..	..	1·75	17·00
121	**93**	1 r. grey and red-brown	..	..	15·00	28·00
122		2 r. purple and brown	..	..	17·00	80·00
123		5 r. green and blue	..	..	30·00	60·00
124		10 r. purple and claret	..	..	55·00	60·00
125		15 r. brown and green	..	..	£150	£600
126		25 r. slate-violet and purple	..	..	£325	£600
109/26		..	..	*Set of 18*	£550	£1400

JIND
(7)

1941–43. *King George VI. Optd with T* **7**. (*a*) *Stamps of 1937. W* **69** *(inverted on 15 r.)*.

127	**91**	3 p. slate	..	..	10·00	14·00
128		½ a. red-brown..	..	..	1·00	50
129		9 p. green	..	..	9·00	11·00
130		1 a. carmine	..	..	1·00	3·25
131	**93**	1 r. grey and red-brown	..	..	8·00	20·00
132		2 r. purple and brown..	..	..	16·00	26·00
133		5 r. green and blue	..	..	38·00	70·00
134		10 r. purple and claret ..	..	..	55·00	70·00
135		15 r. brown and green ..	..	..	£120	£130
136		25 r. slate-violet and purple	..	..	£100	£325
127/136		..	..	*Set of 10*	£325	£550

(*b*) *Stamps of 1940–43*

137	**100a**	3 p. slate (1942)	..	..	50	60
138		½ a. purple (1943)	..	..	50	85
139		9 p. green (1942)	..	..	60	2·25
140		1 a. carmine (1942)	..	..	65	85
141	**101**	1 a. 3 p. yellow-brown	..	..	1·00	2·75
142		1½ a. dull violet (1942) ..	..	..	5·00	3·50
143		2 a. vermilion ..	..	..	1·75	2·50
144		3 a. bright violet (1942)	..	..	12·00	2·75
145		3½ a. bright blue	..	..	6·00	6·00
146	**102**	4 a. brown	..	..	3·50	2·75
147		6 a. turquoise-green	..	..	3·75	9·50
148		8 a. slate-violet	..	..	2·50	9·00
149		12 a. lake	..	..	11·00	9·00
137/149		..	..	*Set of 13*	42·00	48·00

The 1½ a. and 3 a. exist printed by lithography or typography.

JIND STATE SERVICE	**JIND STATE SERVICE**	JIND SERVICE
(O 17)	(O 18)	(O 19)

1937–40. *King George VI. Optd with Types* O **17** *or* O **18** (*rupee values*).

O66	**91**	½ a. red-brown (1938)	..	..	48·00	30
O67		9 p. green	..	..	85	7·50
O68		1 a. carmine	..	..	55	30
O69	**93**	1 r. grey and red-brown (1940)..	..	26·00	42·00
O70		2 r. purple and brown (1940)	..	45·00	£180
O71		5 r. green and blue (1940)	..	85·00	£325
O72		10 r. purple and claret (1940)	..	£180	£750
O66/72		..	*Set of 7*	£350	£1200

1939–43. (*a*) *Official stamps optd with T* **7**.

O73	O **20**	3 p. slate	..	..	50	70
O74		½ a. red-brown	..	..	1·50	50
O75		½ a. purple (1943)	..	..	60	30
O76		9 p. green	..	..	1·50	7·50
O77		1 a. carmine	..	..	1·60	15
O78		1½ a. dull violet (1942)	..	..	6·00	1·00
O79		2 a. vermilion	..	..	3·00	30
		w. Wmk inverted	..	..	—	2·50
O80		2½ a. bright violet	..	..	2·00	6·00
O81		4 a. brown	..	..	3·75	1·40
O82		8 a. slate-violet	..	..	3·50	3·00

(*b*) *Postage stamps optd with Type* O **19**

O83	**93**	1 r. grey and red-brown (1942)..	..	18·00	42·00
O84		2 r. purple and brown (1942)	..	42·00	£120
O85		5 r. green and blue (1942)	..	90·00	£300
O86		10 r. purple and claret (1942)	..	£160	£375
O73/86		..	*Set of 14*	£300	£750

Jind was absorbed into the Patiala and East Punjab States Union by 20 August 1948.

NABHA

Maharaja Partab Singh, 1928–1971

NABHA STATE	**NABHA STATE**
(3)	(4)

NABHA STATE	**NABHA**
(5)	(6)

1938. *King George VI. Nos. 247/64 optd as T* **3** (*3 p. to 1 a.*), *T* **5** (*2 a. to 12 a.*) *or T* **4** (*rupee values*). *W* **69** (*inverted on 15 r.*).

77	**91**	3 p. slate	..	..	5·50	30
78		½ a. red-brown	..	..	3·25	60
79		9 p. green	..	..	17·00	3·25
80		1 a. carmine	..	..	1·50	35
81	**92**	2 a. vermilion ..	..	..	1·00	4·25
82	—	2 a. 6 p. bright violet	..	..	1·00	7·00
83	—	3 a. yellow-green	..	..	1·10	3·75
84	—	3 a. 6 p. bright blue	..	..	1·10	14·00
85	—	4 a. brown	..	..	5·00	5·00
86	—	6 a. turquoise-green	..	..	2·50	14·00
87	—	8 a. slate-violet	..	..	1·90	14·00
88	—	12 a. lake	..	..	2·25	15·00
89	**93**	1 r. grey and red-brown	..	..	10·00	21·00
90		2 r. purple and brown	..	..	19·00	75·00
91		5 r. green and blue	..	..	45·00	£150
92		10 r. purple and claret ..	..	..	70·00	£300
93		15 r. brown and green ..	..	..	£180	£550
94		25 r. slate-violet and purple	..	..	£180	£550
		w. Wmk inverted	..	..	£300	£650
77/94		..	..	*Set of 18*	£500	£1500

1941–45. *King George VI. Optd with T* **6**. (*a*) *Stamps of 1937.*

95	**91**	3 p. slate (1942)..	.. .. ..	28·00	2·75
96		½ a. red-brown (1942)	.. ..	65·00	3·75
97		9 p. green (1942)	.. ..	10·00	10·00
98		1 a. carmine (1942)	.. ..	10·00	2·25
95/8	..	.. .. ..	*Set of* 4	£100	17·00

(*b*) *Stamps of 1940-43*

105	**100***a*	3 p. slate (1942)	.. ..	80	55
106		½ a. purple (1943)	.. ..	4·00	65
107		9 p. green (1942)	.. ..	3·25	60
108		1 a. carmine (1945)	.. ..	80	2·25
109	**101**	1 a. 3 p. yellow-brown	.. ..	80	1·75
110		1½ a. dull violet (1942) ..	.. ..	1·00	1·10
111		2 a. vermilion (1943) ..	.. ..	80	3·00
112		3 a. bright violet (1943)	.. ..	2·50	2·75
113		3½ a. bright blue (1944)	.. ..	10·00	38·00
114	**102**	4 a. brown	.. ..	1·60	75
115		6 a. turquoise-green (1943)	.. ..	8·00	38·00
116		8 a. slate-violet (1943)	.. ..	6·00	26·00
117		12 a. lake (1943)	.. ..	4·50	38·00
105/117	..	.. ..	*Set of* 13	40·00	£140

The 1½ a. exists printed by lithography or typography.

OFFICIAL STAMPS

NABHA STATE SERVICE	**NABHA SERVICE**
(O 10)	(O 11)

1938. *King George VI. Optd as Type* O **10.**

O53	**91**	9 p. green	.. ..	1·75	2·50
O54		1 a. carmine	.. ..	9·00	55

1940–43. (*a*) *Official stamps optd with T* **6.**

O55	**O 20**	3 p. slate (1942)	.. ..	60	70
O56		½ a. red-brown (1942)	.. ..	70	30
O57		½ a. purple (1943) ..	.. ..	2·75	50
O58		9 p. green	.. ..	1·25	20
O59		1 a. carmine (1942)	.. ..	50	20
O61		1½ a. dull violet (1942)	.. ..	60	40
O62		2 a. vermilion (1942)	.. ..	1·40	75
		w. Wmk inverted	.. ..	2·50	1·25
O64		4 a. brown (1942) ..	.. ..	3·50	2·00
O65		8 a. slate-violet (1942)	.. ..	5·50	13·00

(*b*) *Postage stamps optd with Type* O **11.**

O66	**93**	1 r. grey and red-brown (1942)	..	8·50	28·00
O67		2 r. purple and brown (1942)	..	24·00	£150
O68		5 r. green and blue (1942)	..	£200	£475
O55/68	..	.. ..	*Set of* 12	£225	£600

Nabha was absorbed into the Patiala and East Punjab States Union by 20 August 1948.

PATIALA

Maharaja Bhupindra Singh, 1900–1938

PATIALA STATE	**PATIALA STATE**
(4)	(5)

PATIALA STATE	**PATIALA**	**PATIALA**
(6)	(7)	(8)

1937–8. *King George VI. Nos. 247/64 optd with T* **4** (3 *p. to* 1 *a.*), *T* **5** (2 *a. to* 12 *a.*), *or T* **5** (*rupee values*).

80	**91**	3 p. slate	.. ..	26·00	30
81		½ a. red-brown ..	.. ..	7·00	20
82		9 p. green (1937)	.. ..	2·50	60
83		1 a. carmine (1937)	.. ..	1·60	20
84	**92**	2 a. vermilion	.. ..	1·50	5·50
85	–	2 a. 6 p. bright violet ..	.. ..	3·00	12·00
86	–	3 a. yellow-green	.. ..	2·25	5·00

87	–	3 a. 6 p. bright blue	.. ..	3·25	16·0•
88	–	4 a. brown	.. ..	17·00	9·5•
89	–	6 a. turquoise-green	.. ..	18·00	32·0•
90	–	8 a. slate-violet ..	.. ..	18·00	24·0•
91	–	12 a. lake ..	.. ..	19·00	38·0•
92	**93**	1 r. grey and red-brown	..	19·00	35·0•
93		2 r. purple and brown	..	27·00	75·0•
94		5 r. green and blue	..	38·00	£16•
95		10 r. purple and claret	..	55·00	£25•
96		15 r. brown and green	..	£100	£40•
97		25 r. slate-violet and purple	..	£130	£47•
80/97	..	.. ..	*Set of* 18	£425	£140•

Maharaja Yadavindra Singh, 1938–1971

1941–6. *King George VI. Optd with T* **7** *or* **8** (*rupee value*).

(*a*) *Stamps of 1937*

98	**91**	3 p. slate	.. ..	8·50	7•
99		½ a. red-brown	.. ..	6·50	4•
100		9 p. green	.. ..	£140	2·7•
		w. Wmk inverted	.. ..		
101		1 a. carmine	.. ..	19·00	7•
102	**93**	1 r. grey and red-brown (1946)	..	9·00	60·0•
98/102	..	.. ..	*Set of* 5	£160	60·0•

(*b*) *Stamps of 1940–43*

103	**100***a*	3 p. slate (1942)	.. ..	1·75	1•
104		½ a. purple (1943)	.. ..	1·90	1•
		a. Pair, one without opt	..	£4250	
105		9 p. green (1942)	.. ..	1·00	1•
		a. Vert pair, one without opt	..	£2750	
106		1 a. carmine (1944)	.. ..	80	1•
107	**101**	1 a. 3 p. yellow-brown	.. ..	1·60	1·9•
108		1½ a. violet (1942)	.. ..	7·50	1·7•
109		2 a. vermilion (1944)	.. ..	6·50	2•
110		3 a. bright violet (1944)	.. ..	4·50	1·0•
111		3½ a. bright blue (1944)	.. ..	15·00	22·0•
112	**102**	4 a. brown (1944)	.. ..	5·00	1·5•
113		6 a. turquoise-green (1944)	.. ..	2·50	15·0•
114		8 a. slate-violet (1944)	.. ..	3·00	8·0•
115		12 a. lake (1945)	.. ..	10·00	48·0•
103/15	..	.. ..	*Set of* 13	55·00	90·0•

The 1½ a. exists printed by lithography or typography.

OFFICIAL STAMPS

PATIALA STATE SERVICE	**PATIALA STATE SERVICE**
(O 5)	(O 6)

1937–39. *King George VI. Optd with Types* O **5** *or* O **6** (*rupee values*).

O63	**91**	½ a. red-brown (1938)	.. ..	75	20•
O64		9 p. green (1938)	.. ..	13·00	55·00•
O65		1 a. carmine	.. ..	75	20•
O66	**93**	1 r. grey and red-brown (1939)..	..	1·00	4·00•
O67		2 r. purple and brown (1939)	..	6·00	5·00•
O68		5 r. green and blue (1939)	..	15·00	50·00•
O63/8	..	.. .. ..	*Set of* 6	32·00	£100•

1ᴬ——1ᴬ	**1ᴬ SERVICE 1ᴬ**	**PATIALA SERVICE**
(O 7)	(O 8)	(O 9)

1939–40. *Stamp of 1932* (*King George V*).

(*a*) *Optd with Types* O **5** *and* O **7**

O69	**82**	1 a. on 1 a. 3 p. mauve	..	7·00	1·60
		w. Wmk inverted	..	7·00	2·25

(*b*) *Optd with T* **4** *and* O **8**

O70	**82**	1 a. on 1 a. 3 p. mauve (1940)	..	5·00	1·75
		w. Wmk inverted	..	5·50	2·25

"SERVICE" measures 9¼ mm on No. O69 but only 8¾ mm on O70.

1939–44. *(a) Official stamps optd with T* **7.**

)71	O **20**	3 p. slate (1940)	..	..	45	10
)72		½ a. red-brown		..	3·50	10
)73		½ a. purple (1942)	..	..	45	10
)74		9 p. green	..	..	45	20
		w. Wmk inverted		..		
)75		1 a. carmine		..	1·25	10
)76		1 a. 3 p. yellow-brown (1941)		..	85	25
)77		1½ a. dull violet (1944)		..	3·50	50
)78		2 a. vermilion (1940)		..	5·00	15
		w. Wmk inverted		..		
)79		2½ a. bright violet (1940)		..	1·25	65
)80		4 a. brown (1943)	..	..	85	1·25
)81		8 a. slate-violet (1944)		..	1·75	4·00

(b) Postage stamps optd with Type O **9.**

)82	**93**	1 r. grey and red-brown (1943)	..	6·00	7·00
)83		2 r. purple and brown (1944)	..	15·00	45·00
)84		5 r. green and blue (1944)	..	22·00	65·00
)71/84	..	..	..	*Set of* 14	55·00	£110

Patiala became part of the Patiala and East Punjab States Union by 20 August 1948.

INDIAN FEUDATORY STATES

These stamps were only valid for use within their respective tates, *unless otherwise indicated.*

Postage stamps of the Indian States, current at that date, were eplaced by those of the Republic of India on 1 April 1950.

Unless otherwise stated, all became obsolete on 1 May 1950 (with he exception of the "Anchal" stamps of Travancore-Cochin, which emained current until 1 July 1951 or Sept 1951 for the Official ssues).

BARWANI

Rana Devi Singh, 1930–1971

1    2    3

4   Rana Devi Singh   5

932 (Oct)–**47.** *Medium to thick wove paper.*

A. *Close setting* (2½–4½ *mm*). P 11, 12 *or compound* (1932–41)

·2A	**4**	¼ a. slate	..	..	1·40	15·00
·3A		½ a. blue-green	..		1·90	15·00
·4A		1 a. brown	..	..	1·90	14·00
		a. Imperf between (horiz pair)	..	£1300		
·5A		2 a. purple (*shades*)	..	..	3·25	24·00
·6A		4 a. olive-green	..	..	6·00	27·00
·2A/6A	..	..	..	*Set of* 5	13·00	85·00

B. *Wide setting* (6–7 *mm*). P 11 (1945–47)

·2B	**4**	¼ a. slate	..	..	3·75	20·00
·3B		½ a. blue-green	..		3·25	15·00
·4B		1 a. brown	..	..	8·50	15·00
		b. Chocolate. Perf 8½ (1947)	..	12·50	35·00	
·5aB		2 a. rose-carmine	..	..	£170	£350
·6B		4 a. olive-green	..	..	20·00	32·00

The measurements given in the heading indicate the vertical pacing between impressions. There are eight settings of this nteresting issue: four "Close" where the overall stamp size limensions from centre to centre of perfs vary in width from 1½ to 23 mm and in height from 25 to 27½ mm; three "Wide", vidth 23–23½ mm and height 29–30 mm and one "Medium" 26½×31 mm) (No. 34B*b* only).

1933–47. P 11.

A. *Close setting* (3–4½ *mm*). *Thick, cream-surfaced wove paper* 1933 *and* 1941 (*No.* 38A*a*)

37A	**1**	¼ a. black	..	..	3·00	42·00
38A		½ a. blue-green	..	..	10·00	23·00
		a. Yellowish green (1941)	..	7·50	20·00	
39A	**2**	1 a. brown (*shades*)	..	..	15·00	21·00
42A	**3**	4 a. sage-green	..	..	25·00	60·00

B. *Wide setting* (7–10 *mm*). *Medium to thick wove paper* (1939–47)

37B	**1**	¼ a. black (1945)	..	..	2·75	24·00
38aB		½ a. yellowish green (1945)	..	4·25	26·00	
39B	**2**	1 a. brown (*shades*)	..	..	11·00	20·00
		a. Perf 8½ (5 mm) (1947)	..	11·00	32·00	
40B		2 a. bright purple	..	..	70·00	£170
41B		2 a. rose-carmine (1945)	..	..	22·00	85·00
42B	**3**	4 a. sage-green (1941)	..	..	24·00	45·00
		a. Pale sage-green (1939)	..	10·00	32·00	

There were two "Close" settings (over-all stamp size 25×29 mm) and five "Wide" settings with all sizes 26½–31½ × 31–36½ mm. There was also one "Medium" setting (26½×31 mm) but this was confined to the 1 a. perf 8½, No. 39a.

1938. P 11.

43	**5**	1 a. brown	..	..	26·00	50·00

Stamps printed in red with designs similar to Types **3** and **5** were intended for fiscal use.

STAMP BOOKLETS

Nos. 1/17, 18d/da and 20/5 are believed to have been issued in sewn or stapled booklets, usually containing thirty-two examples of one value in blocks of 8. All these early booklets had plain covers, often in shades of brown. Few complete booklets have survived from this period.

Nos. 32/47, produced by the *Times of India* Press in a series of nine printings between 1932 and 1947, were only issued in booklet form. Booklets from the 1932, 1933, 1937 and 1939 printings had plain card or paper covers in various colours, usually containing eight blocks of 4, except for the 1933 printing, which contained twenty blocks of 4. Booklets from the 1945 printing had plain white tissue covers from the same stock as the interleaving. All these booklets were stapled at left.

The following booklets, from a printing in 1941 and a series of three printings in 1947, had printed covers, produced by a handstamp in the case of Nos. SB14/15.

1941. *Buff, green* (*No.* SB3) *or blue* (*No.* SB7) *card covers inscribed* "BARWANI STATE POSTAGE STAMPS", *booklet value in brackets and number and value of stamps thus* "(Rs 4) 32 2 Annas". *Panes of 4 with margin at left only. Stapled.*

(a) Booklets 59×55 *mm*

SB1	8 a. booklet containing thirty-two ¼ a. (No. 32A)	£250
SB2	1 r. booklet containing thirty-two ½ a. (No. 33A)	£425
SB3	2 r. booklet containing thirty-two 1 a. (No. 34A)	£475
SB4	4 r. booklet containing thirty-two 2 a. (No. 35A)	£275
SB5	8 r. booklet containing thirty-two 4 a. (No. 36A)	£400

(b) Booklets 63×60 *mm* (*No.* SB6) *or* 73×72 *mm* (*No.* SB7)

SB6	1 r. booklet containing thirty-two ½ a. (No. 38A*a*)	£550
SB7	8 r. booklet containing thirty-two 4 a. (No. 42B)	£800

1947. *Grey tissue covers inscribed* "32 STAMPS VALUE...." *Panes of 4 with margins at left. Stapled at left.*

(a) Booklets 70×95 *mm*

SB 8	1 r. booklet containing thirty-two ½ a. (No. 33B)	£500
SB 9	2 r. booklet containing thirty-two 1 a. (No. 34B)	£750
SB10	8 r. booklet containing thirty-two 4 a. (No. 36B)	£850

(b) Booklets 76×95 *mm*

SB11	8 a. booklet containing thirty-two ¼ a. (No. 37B)	£650
SB12	4 r. booklet containing thirty-two 2 a. (No. 41B)	£700
SB13	8 r. booklet containing thirty-two 4 a. (No. 42B*a*)	£400

1947. *Buff paper covers with violet handstamp inscribed* "32 STAMPS VALUE Rs 2/-". *Panes of 4 with margins all round, Sewn with twine at left.*

SB14	2 r. booklets (71×69 *mm*) containing thirty-two 1 a. (No. 34B*b*)	£450
SB15	2 r. booklet (71×73 *mm*) containing thirty-two 1 a. (No. 39B*a*)	£375

1947. *Grey tissue covers inscribed* "32 STAMPS VALUE As 8".
Panes of 4 with margins all round. Stapled at left.

SB16	8 a. booklet (70×75 *mm*) containing thirty-two ¹/₄ a. (No. 32B)	£150
SB17	8 a. booklet (85×75 *mm*) containing thirty-two ¹/₄ a. (No. 37B)	£170

Barwani became part of Madhya Bharat by 1 July 1948

BHOPAL

**Nawab Mohammad Hamidullah. Khan
17 May 1926 to transfer of administration to India, 1 June 1949**

OFFICIAL STAMPS

PRINTERS. From No. O333 all issues were printed by the Bhopal Govt Ptg Wks in typography.

O 8

O 9   O 10 The Moti Mahal

1936 (July)–**38.** *Optd* "SERVICE". *P* 12.

O333	O 9	¹/₄ a. orange (Br.)	90	20
		a. Imperf between (vert pair)	£120	
		ab. Imperf between (horiz pair)	†	£190
		b. Opt inverted	£225	£170
		c. Black opt	7·00	75
		ca. Opt inverted	†	£225
		cb. Opt double	†	£200
O334		¹/₄ a. yellow (Br.) (1938)	2·00	60
O335		1 a. scarlet..	1·25	10
		a. Imperf between (horiz pair)	90·00	85·00
		b. Imperf between (vert pair)	†	£160
		c. Imperf between (block of four)	£225	£225
		d. Imperf vert (horiz pair)	†	95·00

1936–49. *As Type* O 10 (*various palaces*). *P* 12.

(a) Optd "SERVICE" (13¹/₂ *mm*)

O336	¹/₂ a. purple-brown and yellow-green	70	55
	a. Imperf between (vert pair)	†	£130
	ab. Imperf between (horiz pair)	†	£130
	b. Opt double	£190	£130
	c. Frame double..	95·00	15·00
	d. Purple-brown and green (1938)	70	30

(b) Optd "SERVICE" (11 *mm*)

O337	2 a. brown and blue (1937)	1·40	30
	a. Imperf between (vert pair)	†	£190
	ab. Imperf between (horiz pair)	†	£140
	b. Opt inverted	£200	£200
	c. Pair, one without opt	£375	
	d. As c. but opt inverted	£550	
O338	2 a. green and violet (1938)	6·50	25
	a. Imperf between (vert pair)	†	£140
	b. Imperf between (vert strip of 3)	95·00	£100
	c. Frame double	†	£150
	d. Centre double	†	£150

O339	4 a. blue and brown (1937)	2·75	5C
	a. Imperf between (horiz pair)	†	£37£
	b. Opt omitted	†	£19C
	c. Opt double	†	£12C
	d. Centre double	†	£20C
	e. *Blue and reddish brown* (1938)	2·75	5£
	ea. Frame double	†	£15C
O340	8 a. bright purple and blue (1938)	3·75	7£
	a. Imperf between (vert pair)	†	£22£
	b. Opt omitted	†	£10C
	c. Opt double	†	£12C
	d. Imperf vert (horiz pair) and opt omitted	†	£18C
	e. Imperf (pair) and opt omitted	†	£18C
O341	1 r. blue and reddish purple (Br.) (1938)	12·00	5·0C
	a. Imperf horiz (vert pair)	†	£80C
	b. Opt in black (1942)	13·00	4·0C
	ba. Light blue and bright purple	32·00	27·0C
	bb. Laid paper	£425	£45C
O336/41		Set of 6	24·00	5·5C

(c) Optd "SERVICE" (11¹/₂ *mm*) *with serifs*

O342	1 r. dull blue and bright purple (Blk.) (1949)	40·00	65·0C
	a. "SREVICE" for "SERVICE" (R. 6/6)	£130	£17C
	b. "SERVICE" omitted	£550	

(d) Optd "SERVICE" (13¹/₂ *mm*) *with serifs*

O343	8 a. bright purple and blue (1949)	60·00	85·0
	a. "SERAICE" for "SERVICE" (R. 6/5)	£250	£35
	b. Fig "1" for "I" in "SERVICE" (R. 7/1)	£250	£35

The ¹/₂ a. is inscr "BHOPAL GOVT" below the arms, other value have "BHOPAL STATE".
Designs:—(37¹/₂ × 22¹/₂ *mm*) 2 a. The Moti Masjid; 4 a. Ta Mahal and Be-Nazir Palaces. (39 × 24 *mm*)—8 a. Ahmadaba Palace. (45¹/₂ × 27¹/₂ *mm*)—1 r. Rait Ghat.

O 11 Tiger   O 13 The Moti Mahal

1940. *As Type* O 11 (*animals*). *P* 12.

O344	¹/₄ a. bright blue	2·75	8
O345	1 a. bright purple (Spotted Deer)..	15·00	1·0

1941. *As Type* O 8 *but coloured centre inscr* "SERVICE"; *bottom frame inscr* "BHOPAL STATE POSTAGE". *P* 12.

O346	1 a. 3 p. emerald-green	80	8C
	a. Imperf between (pair)..	£325	£32£

1944–47. *As Type* O 13 (*various palaces*). *P* 12.

O347	¹/₂ a. green	85	5C
	a. Imperf (pair)	†	65·0C
	b. Imperf between (vert pair)	†	£12£
	c. Doubly printed	†	£10C
O348	2 a. violet	6·00	2·5C
	a. Imperf (pair)	†	65·0C
	c. Bright purple (1945)	1·75	2·2£
	d. Mauve (1947)	11·00	12·0C
	e. Error. Chocolate (imperf)	£120	£12C
O349	4 a. chocolate	3·75	1·1C
	a. Imperf (pair)	†	80·0C
	b. Imperf vert (horiz pair)	†	£15C
	c. Doubly printed	†	£12C
O347/9		Set of 3	5·75	3·5C

Design inscr "BHOPAL STATE":—2 a. The Moti Masjid; 4 a. Be-Nazir Palaces.

 — — ✳ ✳

O 14 Arms of Bhopal   (O 15)   (O 16)

2 As.   2 As.

944–49. *P* 12.

)350	O **14**	3 p. bright blue	..	65	30
		a. Imperf between (vert pair)	..	80·00	85·00
		b. Imperf between (horiz pair)	..	†	£150
		c. Stamp doubly printed	..	42·00	
)351		9 p. chestnut (*shades*) (1945)	..	7·00	2·00
		a. Imperf (pair) ..		†	£130
		b. *Orange-brown*	..	2·00	2·50
)352		1 a. purple (1945)	..	3·75	90
		a. Imperf horiz (vert pair)		†	£225
		b. *Violet* (1946) ..		6·50	1·90
)353		1½ a. claret (1945)	..	1·25	50
		a. Imperf between (horiz pair)	..	†	£200
		b. Imperf between (vert pair)	..		
)354		3 a. yellow	..	7·50	8·00
		a. Imperf (pair) ..		†	£130
		b. Imperf horiz (vert pair)	..	†	£170
		c. Imperf vert (horiz pair)			
		d. *Orange-brown* (1949)	..	70·00	65·00
)355		6 a. carmine (1945)	..	11·00	30·00
		a. Imperf (pair) ..		†	£140
		b. Imperf horiz (vert pair)	..	†	£170
		c. Imperf vert (horiz pair)	..	†	£170
)350/5		.. .. ..	*Set of* 6	23·00	38·00

949 (July). *Surch with Type* O **15.** *P* 12.

)356	O **14**	2 a. on 1½ a. claret ..	..	2·25	5·00
		a. Stop omitted	..	12·00	20·00
		b. Imperf (pair)	..	£150	£170
		ba. Stop omitted (pair)	..	£425	£450
		c. "2" omitted (in pair with normal)	£500	

The "stop omitted" variety occurs on positions 60 and 69 in the
sheet of 81.

949. *Surch with Type* O **16.** *Imperf.*

)357	O **14**	2 a. on 1½ a. claret	..	£550	£550
		a. Perf 12	..	£550	£550

Three different types of "2" occur in the setting of Type O **16.**

BIJAWAR

Maharaja Sarwant Singh, 1899–1941

1

2

(Typo Lakshmi Art Ptg Works, Bombay)

)35 (1 July)**–36.** (*a*) *P* 11.

1		3 p. brown	..	4·25	3·00
		a. Imperf (pair) ..	..	6·50	
		b. Imperf between (vert pair)	..	85·00	
		c. Imperf horiz (vert pair)	..	50·00	
		6 p. carmine	..	4·00	3·00
		a. Imperf (pair) ..	..	85·00	
		b. Imperf between (vert pair)	..	80·00	
		c. Imperf between (horiz pair)	..	85·00	£120
		d. Imperf horiz (vert pair)	..	85·00	
		9 p. violet..	..	4·50	3·50
		a. Imperf (pair) ..	..	£140	
		b. Imperf between (vert pair)	..	85·00	
		c. Imperf between (horiz pair)	..	80·00	
		d. Imperf horiz (vert pair)	..	80·00	
		1 a. blue ..	..	5·00	4·00
		a. Imperf (pair) ..	..	85·00	
		b. Imperf between (vert pair)	..	85·00	
		c. Imperf between (horiz pair)	..	£120	
		d. Imperf horiz (vert pair)	..	85·00	
		e. Imperf vert (horiz strip of 3)	..	£140	
		2 a. deep green	..	5·50	4·75
		a. Imperf (pair) ..	..	£100	
		b. Imperf horiz (vert pair)	..	11·00	
		c. Imperf between (vert pair)	..	35·00	
		d. Imperf between (horiz pair)	..	50·00	80·00
)5		.. .. ..	*Set of* 5	21·00	16·00

(*b*) *Roul* 7 (1936)

6	1	3 p. brown	..	2·75	2·75
		a. Printed on gummed side	..	£400	
7		6 p. carmine	..	4·25	15·00
8		9 p. violet	..	5·50	75·00
9		1 a. blue ..	..	7·00	80·00
10		2 a. deep green ..	..	7·50	85·00
6/10	..		*Set of* 5	24·00	£225

1937 (May). *Typo. P* 9.

11	**2**	4 a. orange ..	..	8·00	60·00
		a. Imperf between (vert pair)	..	£140	
		b. Imperf (pair) ..	..	£200	
12		6 a. lemon ..	..	8·50	60·00
		a. Imperf between (vert pair)	..	£140	
		b. Imperf (pair) ..	..	£200	
13		8 a. emerald-green..	..	9·00	75·00
		a. Imperf (pair) ..	..	£225	
14		12 a. greenish blue ..	..	9·00	75·00
		a. Imperf (pair) ..	..	£250	
15		1 r. bright violet	..	29·00	£110
		a. "1 Rs" for "1 R" (R. 1/2)	..	48·00	£300
		b. Imperf (pair)	..	£300	
		ba. "1 Rs" for "1 R" (R. 1/2)	..	£850	
11/15	..	.. .. ..	*Set of* 5	55·00	£350

The stamps of Bijawar were withdrawn in 1941.

BUNDI

Maharao Raja Ishwari Singh, 1927–1945

20

1941–44. *Typo. P* 11.

79	**20**	3 p. bright blue ..	..	..	1·25	3·00
80		6 p. deep blue	..	..	3·00	4·50
81		1 a. orange-red	..	..	3·25	5·50
82		2 a. chestnut	..	..	4·50	12·00
		a. *Deep brown* (*no gum*) (1944)	..	13·00	15·00
83		4 a. bright green	..	..	9·00	35·00
84		8 a. dull green	..	..	11·00	£120
85		1 r. deep blue	..	..	30·00	£180
79/85		.. ..	*Set of* 7	55·00	£325

The first printing only of Nos. 79/85 is usual with gum; all further
printings, including No. 82*a*, are without gum.

Maharao Raja Bahadur Singh, 1945–1971

21 Maharao Raja
Bahadur Singh

22 Bundi

(Typo *Times of India* Press, Bombay)

1947. *P* 11.

86	**21**	¼ a. blue-green ..	..	..	1·25	24·00
87		½ a. violet	..	..	1·25	24·00
88		1 a. yellow-green	..	..	1·25	24·00
89	—	2 a. vermilion ..	..	..	1·25	45·00
90	—	4 a. orange	..	..	1·25	65·00
91	**22**	8 a. ultramarine	..	..	2·00	
92		1 r. chocolate	..	..	13·00	
86/92		.. ..	*Set of* 7	19·00	

On the 2 and 4 a. the Maharao is in Indian dress.

OFFICIAL STAMPS

1941. *Nos. 79 to 85 optd* "SERVICE".

O53	20	3 p. bright blue (R.)	..	..	4·00	8·50
O54		6 p. deep blue (R.)	..	..	11·00	8·50
O55		1 a. orange-red ..	..	..	10·00	7·50
O56		2 a. brown	..	..	8·00	8·50
O57		4 a. bright green	..	..	26·00	70·00
O58		8 a. dull green ..	..	..	£100	£325
O59		1 r. deep blue (R.)	..	..	£130	£350
O53/9..		..	..	*Set of* 7	£250	£700

Two different types of "R" occur in the "SERVICE" overprint. On five positions in the sheet of 12 the "R" shows a larger loop and a pointed diagonal leg.

Bundi became part of the Rajasthan Union by 15 April 1948.

CHARKHARI

Maharaja Arimardan Singh, 1920–1942

6 (Left-hand sword over right)

$\frac{1}{2}$ **As.**

(8)

(Typo State Ptg Press, Charkhari)

1930–45. *Wove paper. No gum. Imperf.*

31	6	1 p. deep blue	..	..	35	12·00
		a. Vert pair, top ptd inverted on back, bottom normal upright	..	..	13·00	
		b. Tête-bêche (vert pair)	..	..	£190	
		c. Perf 11×imperf (horiz pair) (1939)	..	35·00	35·00	
		d. Bluish slate	..	..	21·00	
		e. Laid paper (1944)	..	..	—	£300
32		1 p. dull *to* light green (*pelure*) (1943)	..	42·00	£150	
33		1 p. violet (1943)	..	..	14·00	£110
		a. Tête-bêche (vert pair)	..	..	50·00	
34		¹/₂ a. deep olive	..	..	85	12·00
35		¹/₂ a. red-brown (1940)	..	..	3·75	22·00
		a. Tête-bêche (vert pair)	..	..	£350	
36		¹/₂ a. black (*pelure*) (1943)	..	..	48·00	£130
37		¹/₂ a. red (*shades*) (1943)	..	..	17·00	£350
		a. Tête-bêche (vert pair)	..	..	35·00	
		b. Laid paper (1944)	..	..	—	£275
38		¹/₂ a. grey-brown ..	..	..	60·00	75·00
39		1 a. green	..	..	60	12·00
		a. *Emerald* (1938)	..	..	27·00	45·00
40		1 a. chocolate (1940)	..	..	6·00	22·00
		a. Tête-bêche (vert pair)	..	..	75·00	
		b. *Lake-brown*	..	..	—	40·00
41		1 a. red (1940)	..	..	80·00	55·00
		a. *Carmine*	..	..	—	55·00
		b. Laid paper (1944)	..	..	—	£300
42		2 a. light blue	..	..	1·25	16·00
		a. Tête-bêche (vert pair)	..	..	9·50	
43		2 a. greenish grey (1941?)	..	..	38·00	50·00
		a. Tête-bêche (vert pair)	..	..	70·00	
		b. Laid paper (1944)	..	..	—	£325
		c. *Greyish green*	..	..	60·00	£110
43d		2 a. yellow-green (1945)	..	..	—	£450
44		4 a. carmine	..	..	3·50	18·00
		a. Tête-bêche (vert pair)	..	..	14·00	

There are two different versions of No. 37a, one with the stamps tête-bêche base to base and the other showing them top to top.

1939 (Dec)–40. *Nos. 21/2 surch as T* 8.

54	2	¹/₂ a. on 8 a. brown-red (1940)	..	..	26·00	£120
		a. No space between "¹/₂" and "As"	..	32·00	£120	
		b. Surch inverted	..	..	£250	
		c. "1" of "¹/₂" inverted ..	..	..	£225	
55		1 a. on 1 r. chestnut (1940)	..	..	75·00	£300
		a. Surch inverted	..	..	£275	
56		"1 ANNA" on 1 r. chestnut	..	..	£500	£550

Maharaja Jaiendra Singh, 1942–1971

Charkhari became part of Vindhya Pradesh by 1 May 1948

COCHIN

Maharaja Rama Varma III, 1932–1941

8a

18 Maharaja Rama Varma III

(Recess Perkins, Bacon & Co)

1933–38. *T* 18 (*but frame and inscription of* 1 *a. as T* 9). W 8*a*. P 13 × 13½.

54	18	2 p. brown (1936)	..	..	60	20
55		4 p. green	..	..	60	10
56		6 p. red-brown..	..	..	70	10
57	—	1 a. brown-orange	..	..	70	10
58	18	1 a. 8 p. carmine	..	..	3·00	4·00
59		2 a. grey (1938)	..	..	4·25	55
60		2¼ a. yellow-green	..	..	1·50	10
61		3 a. vermilion (1938) ..	..	4·00	1·25	
62		3 a. 4 p. violet ..	..	..	1·50	1·40
63		6 a. 8 p. sepia ..	..	..	1·75	9·00
64		10 a. blue	..	..	3·00	10·00
54/64 ..		..	..	*Set of* 11	19·00	24·00

For stamps in this design, but lithographed, see Nos. 67/71.

"DOUBLE PRINTS". The errors previously listed under this description are now identified as blanket offsets, a type of variety outside the scope of this catalogue. Examples occur on issues from 1938 onwards.

SPACING OF OVERPRINTS AND SURCHARGES. The typeset overprints and surcharges issued from 1939 onwards show considerable differences in spacing. Except for specialists, however these differences have little significance as they occur within the same settings and do not represent separate printings.

(Litho The Associated Printers, Madras)

1938. W 8*a*. P 11.

67	18	2 p. brown	..	..	1·00	35
		aw. Wmk inverted	..	..		
		b. Perf 13×13½	..	..	5·50	60
68		4 p. green	..	..	85	15
		aw. Wmk inverted	..	..		
		b. Perf 13×13½	..	..	8·00	13·00
69		6 p. red-brown ..	..	..	2·25	10
		aw. Wmk inverted	..	..		
		b. Perf 13×13½	..	..	†	£250
70		1 a. brown-orange	..	..	65·00	75·00
		aw. Wmk inverted	..	..		
		b. Perf 13×13½	..	..	75·00	80·00
71		2¼ a. sage-green	..	..	6·00	15
		a. Perf 13×13½	..	..	12·00	4·00
67/71				*Set of* 5	65·00	75·00

Most examples of Nos. 70/b were used fiscally. Collectors are warned against examples which have been cleaned and regummed or provided with forged postmarks.

STANLEY GIBBONS STAMP COLLECTING SERIES

Introductory booklets on *How to Start, How to Identify Stamps* and *Collecting by Theme.* A series of well illustrated guides at a low price.
Write for details.

ANCHAL
(19)

ANCHAL
(19a)

THREE PIES
(20)

SURCHARGED

ANCHAL

27 (*The actual measurement of this wmk is* 6¼ × 3⅝ *in.*)

**ONE ANNA
THREE PIES**
(21)

NINE PIES
(22)

ANCHAL

ANCHAL

NINE PIES
(23)

**SURCHARGED
NINE PIES**
(24)

(Litho The Associated Printers, Madras)

1943. *Frame of* 1 *a. inscr* "ANCHAL & REVENUE".
P 13×13½. (a) *W* 8a.

85	**26**	2 p. grey-brown	..	..	1·00	1·75
		a. Perf 11	..	..	†	£1700
85b		4 p. green	..	..	£475	£225
85c		1 a. brown-orange	..	..	80·00	90·00
85/c		..	..	Set of 3	£500	£275

(b) *W* 27

86	**26**	2 p. grey-brown	..	..	25·00	1·75
		a. Perf 11	..	..	†	£2000
87		4 p. green	..	..	7·00	16·00
		a. Perf 11	..	..	3·00	3·25
88		6 p. red-brown	..	..	1·25	10
		a. Perf 11	..	..	8·00	1·40
89		9 p. ultramarine (*p* 11)	..	..	25·00	1·00
		a. Imperf between (horiz pair)	..	£1400		
90		1 a. brown-orange	..	..	£200	£150
		a. Perf 11	..	..	21·00	40·00
91		2¼ a. yellow-green	..	..	20·00	1·75
		a. Perf 11	..	..	25·00	7·50

Part of W 27 appears on many stamps in each sheet, while
others are entirely without wmk.

Although inscribed "ANCHAL (= Postage) & REVENUE"
most examples of Nos. 85c and 90/a were used fiscally. Collectors
are warned against examples which have been cleaned and
regummed or provided with forged postmarks.

1939 (Jan). *Nos. 57 and 70 optd with T* 19/a.

72	**18**	1 a. brown-orange (*recess*) (T **19**)	..	1·90	55
73		1 a. brown-orange (*litho*) (T **19**)	..	£250	65
		aw. Wmk inverted	..	..	†
		b. Perf 13×13½	..	..	—	£275
74		1 a. brown-orange (*litho*) (T **19a**)	..	75	1·60
		a. Perf 13×13½	..	..	10·00	50

In 1939 it was decided that there would be separate 1 a.
stamps for revenue and postal purposes. The "ANCHAL"
overprints were applied to stamps intended for postal purposes.

1942–44. *T* 18 *variously optd or surch.*

I. *Recess-printed stamp. No.* 58

75	3 p. on 1 a. 8 p. carmine (T **20**)	..	£160	75·00
76	3 p. on 1 a. 8 p. carmine (T **21**)	..	2·50	6·50
77	6 p. on 1 a. 8 p. carmine (T **20**)	..	3·00	17·00
78	1 a. 3 p. on 1 a. 8 p. carmine (T **21**)	..	1·00	30

II. *Lithographed stamps. Nos.* 68, 70 *and* 70b

79	3 p. on 4 p. (T **21**)	..	5·50	3·50
	a. Perf 13×13½	..	13·00	3·50
80	6 p. on 1 a. (T **22**)	..	£250	£170
	a. "SIX PIES" double	..	†	£700
81	6 p. on 1 a. (T **23**)	..	£225	£150
	a. Perf 13×13½	..	90·00	48·00
82	9 p. on 1 a. (T **22**)	..	95·00	£100
83	9 p. on 1 a. (T **23**) (*p* 13×13½)	..	£180	30·00
84	9 p. on 1 a. (T **24**) (*p* 13×13½)	..	14·00	4·50

Maharaja Kerala Varma II, 1941–1943

26 Maharaja Kerala Varma II

Maharaja Ravi Varma 1943-1946

1943. *T* 26 *variously optd or surch. P* 13×13½. (a) *W* 8a

92	3 p. on 4 p. (T **21**) ..	..	50·00	16·00
92a	9 p. on 1 a. (T **23**)	..	4·75	1·75
92b	9 p. on 1 a. (T **24**)	..	3·75	2·00
92c	1 a. 3 p. on 1 a. (T **21**)	..	—	£2750

(b) *W* 27

93	2 p. on 6 p. (T **20**)	..	75	2·50
	a. Perf 11	..	85	2·50
94	3 p. on 4 p. (T **20**) (*p* 11)	..	2·50	10
95	3 p. on 4 p. (T **21**)	..	3·25	10
96	3 p. on 6 p. (T **20**)	..	85	20
	a. Perf 11	..	85	50
97	4 p. on 6 p. (T **20**)	..	3·00	8·50

No. 92c is believed to be an error; a sheet of No. 85b having
been included in a stock of No. O52 intended to become No. O66.

PRICES OF SETS

Set prices are given for many issues, generally
those containing three stamps or more. Definitive
sets include one of each value or major colour
change, but do not cover different perforations,
die types or minor shades. Where a choice is
possible the set prices are based on the cheapest
versions of the stamps included in the listings.

28 Maharaja Ravi Varma 29

I　　　　II

(Litho The Associated Printers, Madras)

1944–48. *W* 27. *No gum.* (*a*) *Type* I. *P* 11.
98　28　9 p. ultramarine (1944) .. 　　.. 　10·00　1·75

(*b*) *Type* II. *P* 13
98*a*　28　9 p. ultramarine (1946) .. 　　.. 　6·00　12·00
　　　ab. Perf 13 × 13½ 　　　.. 　.. 　30·00　2·50
99　　　1 a. 3 p. magenta (1948) 　　.. 　5·00　7·50
　　　a. Perf 13 × 13½ 　　　.. 　.. 　£160　35·00
100　　1 a. 9 p. ultramarine (*shades*) (1948) 　.. 　8·00　11·00
98*a*/100　　.. 　　.. 　　.. 　*Set of* 3　17·00　19·00
Nos. 98*a*/100 are line-perforated, Nos. 98ab and 99a comb-perforated.

Maharaja Kerala Varma III, 1946–48
(Litho The Associated Printers, Madras)

1946–48. *Frame of* 1 *a. inscr* "ANCHAL & REVENUE". *W* 27.
No gum (*except for stamps perf* 11). *P* 13.
101　29　2 p. chocolate .. 　　.. 　.. 　1·50　10
　　　a. Imperf horiz (vert pair) 　.. 　£1300　£1300
　　　c. Perf 11 　　.. 　　.. 　.. 　8·00　60
　　　d. Perf 11×13 　　.. 　　.. 　£375　£140
102　　3 p. carmine 　.. 　　.. 　.. 　50　10
103　　4 p. grey-green 　　.. 　　.. 　£1600　80·00
104　　6 p. red-brown (1947) 　.. 　.. 　20·00　3·00
　　　a. Perf 11 　　.. 　　.. 　.. 　£150　3·00
105　　9 p. ultramarine 　.. 　　.. 　50　10
　　　a. Imperf between (horiz pair) 　.. 　†£1400
106　　1 a. orange (1948) 　　.. 　.. 　6·50　25·00
　　　a. Perf 11 　　.. 　　.. 　.. 　£500
107　　2 a. black 　　.. 　　.. 　.. 　80·00　7·00
　　　a. Perf 11 　　.. 　　.. 　.. 　£110　5·50
108　　3 a. vermilion .. 　　.. 　.. 　50·00　50
101/8　　.. 　　.. 　　.. 　*Set of* 8　£1600　£100
Although inscribed "ANCHAL (=Postage) & REVENUE" most examples of No. 106 were used fiscally.
The 1 a. 3 p. magenta, 1 a. 9 p. ultramarine and 2¼ a. yellow-green in Type **29** subsequently appeared surcharged or overprinted for official use. Examples of the 1 a. 3 p. magenta exist without overprint, but may have not been issued in this state (*Price* £275 *unused*).

Tail to turban flaw (R. 1/7)

(Litho The Associated Printers, Madras)

1948–50. *W* 27 (*upright or inverted*). *P* 11.
109　30　2 p. grey-brown 　　.. 　.. 　1·50　15
　　　a. Imperf vert (horiz pair) 　.. 　†£1300
110　　3 p. carmine 　.. 　　.. 　75　15
　　　a. Imperf between (vert pair) 　.. 　†£1300
111　　4 p. green 　　.. 　　.. 　10·00　1·50
　　　a. Imperf vert (horiz pair) 　.. 　£275　£325
112　　6 p. chestnut 　.. 　　.. 　12·00　20
　　　a. Imperf vert (horiz pair) 　.. 　£800
113　　9 p. ultramarine 　.. 　　.. 　40·00　15
114　　2 a. black 　.. 　　.. 　40·00　40
115　　3 a. orange-red 　.. 　　.. 　50·00　50
　　　a. Imperf vert (horiz pair) 　.. 　£1600
116　　3 a. 4 p. violet (1950) .. 　　.. 　90·00　£350
　　　a. Tail to turban flaw 　　.. 　£250
109/16　　.. 　　.. 　　.. 　*Set of* 8　£180　£350

Maharaja Rama Varma IV, 1948–1964

31 Chinese Nets　　　32 Dutch Palace

(Litho The Associated Printers, Madras)

1949. *W* 27. *P* 11.
117　31　2 a. black 　　.. 　　.. 　3·25　5·00
　　　a. Imperf vert (horiz pair) .. 　.. 　£425
118　32　2¼ a. green 　.. 　　.. 　2·50　4·50
　　　a. Imperf vert (horiz pair) .. 　.. 　£425

30 Maharaja Kerala Varma III

SIX PIES

ആറു പൈ

(33)

ഐെപ Normal

ഐെപ Error

Due to similarities between two Malayalam characters some values of the 1948 provisional issue exist with an error in the second word of the Malayalam surcharge. On Nos. 119, 122 and 0103 this occurs twice in the setting of 48. No. 125 shows four examples and No. O104b one. Most instances are as illustrated above, but in two instances on the setting for No. 125 the error occurs on the second character.

1949. *Surch as T 33.* (i) *On 1944–48 issue. P 13.*

119	28	6 p. on 1 a. 3 p. magenta	..	..	3·00	3·25
		a. Incorrect character ..		..	24·00	24·00
120		1 a. on 1 a. 9 p. ultramarine (R.)		..	80	90

(ii) *On 1946–48 issue*

121	29	3 p. on 9 p. ultramarine..		..	8·00	16·00
122		6 p. on 1 a. 3 p. magenta		..	10·00	11·00
		a. Surch double	..	..	†	£400
		b. Incorrect character ..		..	70·00	70·00
123		1 a. on 1 a. 9 p. ultramarine (R.)		..	3·00	1·50
		a. Surch in black	..		†	£2000
		b. Black surch with smaller native characters 7½ mm instead of 10 mm long ..	..	..	†	£2750

(iii) *On 1948–50 issue*

124	30	3 p. on 9 p. ultramarine		..	1·75	1·75
		a. Larger native characters 20 mm instead of 16½ mm long ..		..	2·25	50
		ab. Imperf between (vert pair)		..	†	£1200
		b. Surch double	..			£400
		c. Surch both sides ..		..		£325
125		3 p. on 9 p. ultramarine (R.) ..		..	3·00	2·25
		a. Incorrect character		..	17·00	14·00
126		6 p. on 9 p. ultramarine (R.)		..	75	40
119/26		..	..	*Set of 8*	27·00	32·00

The 9 p. ultramarine (T 29) with 6 p. surcharge (T 33) in red was prepared for use but not issued (*Price £250 unused*)

1949. *Surch as T 20. W 27. P 13.*

27	29	6 p. on 1 a. orange	..	..	55·00	£120
28		9 p. on 1 a. orange	..	..	70·00	£120

OFFICIAL STAMPS

ON ON

C G Cʻ G

S S

(O 5 Straight back to "C̈") (O 6 Circular "O"; "N" without serifs)

1933–38. *Recess-printed stamps of 1933–38 optd.*

(a) *With Type O 5*

O34	18	4 p. green	..	..	2·00	10
O35		6 p. red-brown (1934) ..		..	2·25	10
O36		1 a. brown-orange	..	..	9·50	10
O37		1 a. 8 p. carmine	..	..	1·50	20
O38		2 a. grey	..	..	9·50	10
O39		2¼ a. yellow-green	..	..	4·00	10
O40		3 a. vermilion ..		..	35·00	10
O41		3 a. 4 p. violet ..		..	1·50	15
O42		6 a. 8 p. sepia ..		..	1·50	20
O43		10 a. blue	..	..	1·50	50
O34/43		..	..	*Set of 10*	60·00	1·50

(b) *With Type O 6* (*typo*)

O44	18	1 a. brown-orange (1937) ..		..	35·00	45
O45		2 a. grey-black (1938)	..	..	21·00	1·10
O46		3 a. vermilion (1938)	..	..	10·00	1·10
O44/6..		..	..	*Set of 3*	60·00	2·25

ON ON

C G C G

S S

(O 7 Curved back to "c") (O 8)

ON ON ON

C G C G C G

S S S

(O 9 Circular "O"; N with serifs) (O 10 Oval "O") (O 11)

1938–44. *Lithographed stamps of 1938. W 8a, optd.*

(a) *With Type O 7 or O 8* (1 a.) *P 11*

O47	18	4 p. green	..	..	22·00	1·60
		a. Inverted "S"	..	..	26·00	1·60
		b. Perf 13×13½	..	..	19·00	1·75
O48		6 p. red-brown	..	..	20·00	40
		a. Inverted "S"	..	..	23·00	50
O49		1 a. brown-orange	..	..	£250	2·50
O50		2 a. grey-black	..	..	16·00	70
		a. Inverted "S"	..	..	17·00	70

(b) *With Type O 9* (*litho*) *or O 10* (6 p.)

O51	18	6 p. red-brown (p 13×13½)		..	8·00	2·25
O52		1 a. brown-orange	..	..	1·00	10
O53		3 a. vermilion	..	..	2·75	70

(c) *With Type O 11*

O53a	18	6 p. red-brown	..	..	£750	£325

The inverted "S" varieties, Nos. O47a, O48a and O50a, occur 21 times in the setting of 48.

1942–43. *Unissued stamps optd with Type O 10. Litho. W 27. P 11.*

O54	18	4 p. green	..	..	60·00	13·00
		a. Perf 13×13½ ..		..	1·75	60
O55		6 p. red-brown	..	..	90·00	11·00
		a. Perf 13×13½ ..		..	18·00	90
		ab. Optd both sides	..	..	†	£100
O56		1 a. brown-orange	..	..	16·00	5·00
		a. Perf 13×13½ ..		..	1·40	3·75
		ab. Optd both sides	..	..	1·40	3·75
O56b		2 a. grey-black (1943)	..	..	48·00	65
		ba. Opt omitted	..	..	†	£1200
O56c		2¼ a. sage-green (1943)	..	..	£900	4·25
O56d		3 a. vermilion (1943)	..	..	12·00	3·75

1943. *Official stamps variously surch with T 20 or 21.*

(i) *On 1½ a. purple, of 1919–33*

O57	10	9 p. on 1½ a. (T 20)	..	..	£400	20·00

(ii) *On recess-printed 1 a. 8 p. carmine of 1933–44* (*Type O 5 opt*)

O58		3 p. on 1 a. 8 p. (T 21)..		..	4·50	75
O59		9 p. on 1 a. 8 p. (T 20)..		..	£100	26·00
O60		1 a. 9 p. on 1 a. 8 p. (T 20)	..	..	1·75	1·60
O61		1 a. 9 p. on 1 a. 8 p. (T 21)	..	..	80	30

(iii) *On lithographed stamps of 1938–44. P 11. (a) W 8a*

O62	18	3 p. on 4 p. (Types O 7 and 20) (p 13×13½)		..	19·00	5·00
		a. Surch double	..	..	£300	£150
O63		3 p. on 4 p. (Types O 7 and 21) (p 13×13½)		..	85·00	45·00
O64		3 p. on 1 a. (Types O 9 and 20)	..	..	1·75	2·25
O65		9 p. on 1 a. (Types O 9 and 20)	..	..	£180	45·00
O66		1 a. 3 p. on 1 a. (Types O 9 and 21)	..	..	£250	90·00

(*b*) *W* **27**

O67 **18** 3 p. on 4 p. (Types O **10** and **20**) (*p* 13×13½) .. .. .. 75·00 45·00
O67*a* 3 p. on 4 p. (Types O **10** and **21**) (*p* 13×13½) £450
O67*b* 3 p. on 1 a. (Types O **10** and **20**) .. £110 60·00
ba. Perf 13×13½ .. .. .. 85·00 60·00

1944. *Optd with Type* O **10**. *W* **27**. *P* 13×13½.

O68 **26** 4 p. green .. .. 18·00 2·75
a. Perf 11 .. .. £110 4·50
b. Perf 13 .. .. £250 65·00
O69 6 p. red-brown .. .. .. 1·10 10
a. Opt double .. .. .. — 55·00
b. Perf 11 .. .. 70 10
ba. Opt double .. .. .. — 55·00
c. Perf 13 .. .. 7·00 2·00
O70 1 a. brown-orange .. .. .. £1600 45·00
O71 2 a. black .. .. 3·25 45
O72 2¼ a. yellow-green .. .. .. 2·00 45
a. Optd both sides .. .. .. † £110
O73 3 a. vermilion .. .. .. 5·50 45
a. Perf 11 .. .. 4·50 40

Stamps perforated 13 × 13½ are from a comb machine; those perforated 13 from a line perforator.

1944. *Optd with Type* O **10** *and variously surch as Types* **20** *and* **21**. *W* **27**.

O74 **26** 3 p. on 4 p. (T **20**) .. .. .. 1·75 10
a. Perf 11 .. .. 5·50 45
ab. Optd Type O **10** on both sides .. † £120
O75 3 p. on 4 p. (T **21**) .. .. .. 3·75 30
a. Perf 11 .. .. £375 £160
O76 3 p. on 1 a. (T **20**) .. .. .. 14·00 3·00
O77 9 p. on 6 p. (T **20**) .. .. .. 6·00 1·50
a. Stamp printed both sides .. ..
O78 9 p. on 6 p. (T **21**) .. .. .. 3·00 25
O79 1 a. 3 p. on 1 a. (T **20**) .. .. 5·00 90
O80 1 a. 3 p. on 1 a. (T **21**) .. .. 3·00 10
O74/80 .. .. *Set of* 7 32·00 5·50

1946–47. *Stamps of* 1944–48 (*Head Type II*) *optd with Type* O **10**. *P* 13.

O81 **28** 9 p. ultramarine .. .. .. 2·25 10
a. Stamp printed both sides .. .. † £350
b. Perf 13×13½ .. .. .. 3·25 10
O82 1 a. 3 p. magenta (1947) .. .. 1·25 20
a. Opt double .. .. .. 19·00 12·00
b. Optd on both sides .. ..
ba. Optd both sides, opt double and inverted on reverse .. .. 48·00
O83 1 a. 9 p. ultramarine (1947) 40 70
a. Opt double .. .. ..
O81/3 .. .. *Set of* 3 3·50 90

1948. *Stamps of* 1946–48 *and unissued values optd with Type* O **2**. *P* 13.

O84 **29** 3 p. carmine 50 10
a. Stamp printed both sides .. † —
O85 4 p. grey-green .. .. 23·00 4·50
O86 6 p. red-brown .. .. 4·50 60
O87 9 p. ultramarine 75 10
O88 1 a. 3 p. magenta .. .. .. 2·00 40
O89 1 a. 9 p. ultramarine .. .. .. 1·75 40
O90 2 a. black .. .. 13·00 2·50
O91 2¼ a. yellow-green .. .. .. 16·00 2·50
O84/91 .. .. *Set of* 8 55·00 10·00

1949. *Stamps of* 1948–50 *and unissued values optd with Type* O **7**.

O92 **30** 3 p. carmine 75 15
a. "C" for "G" in opt .. .. 8·50 3·00
O93 4 p. green 85 25
a. Imperf between (horiz or vert pair) † £1100
b. Optd on reverse .. .. .. 65·00 65·00
c. "C" for "G" in opt .. .. 11·00 4·25
O94 6 p. chestnut .. .. 2·25 10
a. Imperf between (vert pair) .. † £1200
b. "C" for "G" in opt .. .. 17·00 2·75
O95 9 p. ultramarine .. .. .. 2·00 10
a. "C" for "G" in opt .. .. 14·00 3·75
O96 2 a. black 85 15
a. "C" for "G" in opt .. .. 13·00 4·25
O97 2¼ a. yellow-green .. .. .. 2·25 4·25
a. "C" for "G" in opt .. .. 21·00 32·00
O98 **30** 3 a. orange-red .. .. .. 1·10 45
a. "C" for "G" in opt .. .. 16·00 8·00
O99 3 a. 4 p. violet .. .. .. 27·00 25·00
a. "C" for "G" in opt £250 £250
b. Tail to turban flaw £190
O92/9 .. .. *Set of* 8 32·00 27·00

The "C" for "G" variety occurs on R. 1/4. Nos. O92/9, O103/4 and O104b also exist with a flat back to "G" which occurs twice in each sheet on R. 1/5 and R. 2/8.

No. O93 exists with watermark sideways, but can usually only be identified when in multiples.

1949. *Official stamps surch as T* **33**. (i) *On* 1944 *issue*.

O100 **28** 1 a. on 1 a. 9 p. ultramarine (R.) .. 60 40

(ii) *On* 1948 *issue*

O101 **29** 1 a. on 1 a. 9 p. ultramarine (R.) .. 16·00 12·00

(iii) *On* 1949 *issue*

O103 **30** 6 p. on 3 p. carmine 45 50
a. Imperf between (vert pair) .. † £800
b. Surch double .. .. .. † £275
c. "C" for "G" in opt .. .. 8·00 8·50
d. Incorrect character .. .. 8·00 8·50
O104 9 p. on 4 p. green (18 *mm long*) .. 55 1·50
a. Imperf between (horiz pair) .. £650 £750
b. Larger native characters, 22 mm long 90 70
ba. Ditto. Imperf between (horiz pair) £650 £650
bb. Incorrect character .. .. 15·00 12·00
c. "C" for "G" in opt .. .. 12·00 17·00
ca. Ditto. Larger native characters, 22 mm long .. .. 15·00 12·00
O100/4 .. .. *Set of* 4 16·00 12·00

No. O104 exists with watermark sideways, but can usually only be identified when in multiples.

1949. *No.* 124*a, but with lines of surch* 17½ *mm apart, optd* "SERVICE".

O105 **30** 3 p. on 9 p. ultramarine 60 55
a. Imperf between (horiz pair) .. † £1100

From 1 July 1949 Cochin formed part of the new state of Travancore-Cochin. Existing stocks of Cochin issues continued to be used in conjunction with stamps of Travancore surcharged in Indian currency.

DUNGARPUR

Maharawal Lakshman Singh, 1918–1971

1 State Arms

(Litho Shri Lakshman Bijaya Printing Press, Dungarpur)

1933–47. *P* 11.

1 **1** ¼ a. bistre-yellow .. .. — £120
2 ¼ a. rose (1935) .. .. — £350
3 ¼ a. red-brown (1937) .. .. .. — £225
4 1 a. pale turquoise-blue .. .. .. — £100
5 1 a. rose (1938) .. .. — £1100
6 1 a. 3 p. deep reddish violet (1935) .. — £160
7 2 a. deep dull green (1947) .. .. — £190
8 4 a. rose-red (1934) .. .. .. — £375

Nos. 2 and 5 are known in a *se-tenant* strip of 3, the centre stamp being the 1 a. value.

NEW INFORMATION

The editor is always interested to correspond with people who have new information that will improve or correct the Catalogue.

2   3   4

Maharawal Lakshman Singh

Three dies of ½ a. (*shown actual size*):

Die I. Size 21×25½ mm. Large portrait (head 5 mm and turban 7½ mm wide), correctly aligned (sheets of 12 and left-hand stamps in subsequent blocks of four *se-tenant* horizontally with Die II)

Die II. Size 20×24½ mm. Large portrait (head 4¾ mm and turban 7 mm wide), but with less detail at foot and with distinct tilt to left (right-hand stamps in sheets of four horizontally *se-tenant* with Die I)

Die III. Size 21×25½ mm. Small portrait (head 4½ mm and turban 6½ mm wide) (sheets of 4)

(Typo L.V. Indap & Co, Bombay)

1939–46. *T* 2 *(various frames) and* 3/4. *Various perfs.*
9	2	¼ a. orange (*p* 12, 11, 10½ *or* 10)	£375	50·00
10		½ a. verm (Die I) (*p* 12, 11 *or* 10½) (1940)	£170	38·00
		a. Die II (*p* 10½) (1944)	£170	48·00
		ab. Horiz pair. Die I and Die II	£375	£120
		b. Die III (*p* 10) (1945)	£225	38·00
		c. Imperf between (vert pair)	† £1700	
11		1 a. deep blue (*p* 12, 11, 10½ *or* 10)	£160	29·00
12	3	1 a. 3 p. brt mauve (*p* 10½ *or* 10) (1944)	£425	£150
13	4	1½ a. deep violet (*p* 10) (1946)	£450	£150

14	2	2 a. brt green (*p* 12, *pin* perf 11½) (1943)	£500	£275
15		4 a. brown (*p* 12, 10½ *or* 10) (1940)	£425	£120

Stamps perforated 12, 11 and 10½ were printed in sheets of 12 (4×3) which were imperforate along the top, bottom and, sometimes, at right so that examples exist with one or two adjacent sides imperforate. Stamps perforated 10 were printed in sheets of 4 either imperforate at top, bottom and right-hand side or fully perforated.

Dungarpur became part of Rajasthan by 15 April 1948.

HYDERABAD

Nawab Mir Osman Ali Khan Asaf Jah VII, 1911–1967

12 Symbols   13 The Char Minar

14 Bidar College

(Plates by De La Rue. Recess Stamps Office, Hyderabad)

1931 (12 Nov)–**47**. *T* 12 *to* 14 *(and similar types).* W 7. *Wove paper.*
P 13½.
41	12	4 p. black				30	10
		a. Laid paper (1947)				2·50	4·75
		b. Imperf (pair)				48·00	75·00
42		8 p. green				35	10
		a. Imperf between (vert pair)				—	£550
		b. Imperf (pair)				60·00	90·00
		c. Laid paper (1947)				3·00	4·25
43	13	1 a. brown (*shades*)				35	10
		a. Imperf between (horiz pair)				—	£550
44	—	2 a. violet (*shades*)				2·00	10
		a. Imperf (pair)				£130	£180
45	—	4 a. ultramarine				1·25	30
		a. Imperf (pair)				£140	£225
46	—	8 a. orange				4·00	2·50
		a. *Yellow-orange* (1944)				65·00	30·00
47	14	12 a. scarlet				4·00	8·50
48	—	1 r. yellow				4·00	3·00
41/8					*Set of* 8	14·50	13·00

Designs (*as T* 14): *Horiz*—2 a. High Court of Justice; 4 a. Osman Sagar Reservoir. *Vert*—8 a. Entrance to Ajanta Caves; 1 r. Victory Tower, Daulatabad.

Nos. 41a and 42c have a large sheet watermark "THE NIZAM's GOVERNMENT HYDERABAD DECCAN" and arms within a circle, but this does not appear on all stamps.

15 Unani General Hospital   16 Family Reunion

(Litho Indian Security Printing Press, Nasik)

1937 (13 Feb). *Various horiz designs as T* 15, *inscr* "H.E.H. THE NIZAM'S SILVER JUBILEE". *P* 14.

49	4 p. slate and violet				40	80
50	8 p. slate and brown				70	85
51	1 a. slate and orange-yellow				70	60
52	2 a. slate and green				90	3·00
49/52				*Set of* 4	2·50	4·75

Designs:—8 p. Osmania General Hospital; 1 a. Osmania University; 2 a. Osmania Jubilee Hall.

(Des T. I. Archer. Typo)

1945 (6 Dec). *Victory. W* 7 (*very faint*). *Wove paper. P* 13½.

53	16	1 a. blue			10	10
		a. Imperf between (vert pair)			£500	
		b. Laid paper			65	65

No. 53b shows the sheet watermark described beneath Nos. 41/8.

17 Town Hall   **18** Power House, Hyderabad

(Des. T. I. Archer. Litho Government Press)

1947 (17 Feb). *Reformed Legislature. P* 13½.

54	17	1 a. black			70	1·00
		a. Imperf between (pair)			—	£700

(Des Γ. I. Archer. Typo)

1947–49. *As T* 18 (*inscr* "H. E. H. THE NIZAM'S GOVT. POSTAGE"). *W* 7. *P* 13½.

55	1 a. 4 p. green			75	1·50
56	3 a. greenish blue			85	2·25
	a. *Bluish green*			1·50	2·50
57	6 a. sepia			3·00	10·00
	a. *Red-brown* (1949)			18·00	25·00
	ab. Imperf (pair)			£110	
55/7			*Set of* 3	4·25	12·50

Designs:—3 a. Kaktyai Arch, Warangal Fort; 6 a. Golkunda Fort.

1947. *As 1915 issue but colour changed. P* 13½.

58	8	½ a. claret		1·25	50
		a. Imperf between (horizontal pair)		—	£275
		b. Imperf between (vert pair)		—	£425

An Independence commemorative set of four, 4 p., 8 p., 1 a. and 2 a., was prepared in 1948, but not issued.

1948. *As T* 12 ("POSTAGE" *at foot*). *Recess. W* 7. *P* 13½.

59	6 p. claret			6·00	5·00

Following intervention by the forces of the Dominion of India during September 1948 the Hyderabad postal system was taken over by the Dominion authorities, operating as an agency of the India Post Office.

1949. *T* 12 ("POSTAGE" *at top*). *Litho. W* 7. *P* 13½.

60	12	2 p. bistre-brown			1·00	1·75
		a. Imperf between (horizontal pair)		†	£650
		b. Imperf (pair)			£325	£475

No. 60 was produced from a transfer taken from a plate of the 4 p., No. 41, with each impression amended individually.

OFFICIAL STAMPS

سرکاری

(O 2)

1934–44. *Nos.* 41/8 *optd with Type* O 2.

O46	4 p. black			1·00	10
	a. Imperf (pair)			60·00	
	b. Imperf between (vert pair)			£500	£500
	c. Imperf between (horiz pair)			—	£500
O47	8 p. green			40	10
	a. Opt inverted			†	£150
	b. Imperf between (horiz pair)			—	£500
	c. Opt double			†	£120
	d. Imperf (pair)			£120	£150
O48	1 a. brown			60	10
	a. Imperf between (vert pair)		£400	£400
	b. Imperf between (horiz pair)		—	£400
	c. Imperf (pair)			£140	£180
	d. Opt double			—	£160
O49	2 a. violet			4·00	10
	a. Imperf between (horiz pair)		†	£900
O50	4 a. ultramarine			1·75	20
	a. Opt double			†	£375
	b. Imperf between (vert pair)		†	£950
O51	8 a. orange (1935)			8·00	50
	a. *Yellow-orange* (1944)			—	38·00
O52	12 a. scarlet (1935)			5·50	1·25
O53	1 r. yellow (1935)			13·00	2·00
O46/53			*Set of* 8	30·00	3·75

1947. *No.* 58 *optd with Type* O 2.

O54	8 ½ a. claret			9·00	5·50

1949. *No.* 60 *optd with Type* O 2.

O55	12	2 p. bistre-brown		7·00	6·00

1950. *No.* 59 *optd with Type* O 2.

O56	6 p. claret			8·50	17·00

IDAR

Maharaja Himmat Singh, 1931–1960

1 Maharaja Himmat Singh **2**

(Typo M. N. Kothari & Sons, Bombay)

1932 (1 Oct)–**43.** *P* 11. (*a*) *White panels.*

1	1	½ a. light green		—	25·00
		a. *Pale yellow-green* (*thick paper*) (1939)	13·00	18·00
		b. *Emerald* (1941)		12·00	18·00
		ba. Imperf between (pair)		£950	
		c. *Yellow-green* (1943)		10·00	16·00
		ca. Imperf between (horiz pair)		£900	

(*b*) *Coloured panels*

2	1	½ a. pale yellow-green (*thick paper*) (1939)	22·00	22·00
		a. *Emerald* (1941)		17·00	19·00
		b. *Yellow-green* (1943)		9·50	18·00

In No. 2 the whole design is composed of half-tone dots. In No. 1 the dots are confined to the oval portrait.

(Typo P. G. Mehta & Co, Hitmatnagar)

1944 (21 Oct). *P* 12.

3	2	½ a. blue-green		2·00	50
		a. Imperf between (vert pair)		£250	
		b. *Yellow-green*		2·00	50·00
		ba. Imperf between (vert pair)		12·00	
4		1 a. violet		2·25	45·00
		a. Imperf (pair)		£200	
		b. Imperf vert (horiz pair)		£225	

5	2	2 a. blue	2·50	75·00
		a. Imperf between (vert pair) ..	75·00	
		b. Imperf between (horiz pair) ..	£190	
6		4 a. vermilion	2·75	80·00
		a. Doubly printed	£550	
3/6		.. .. *Set of* 4	8·50	£225

Nos. 1 to 6 are from booklet panes of 4 stamps, producing single stamps with one or two adjacent sides imperf.
The 4 a. violet is believed to be a colour trial.

POSTAL FISCAL STAMPS

F 1

1940 (?)–45. *Typo. P* 11 (*No.* F1) *or* 12 *on two or three sides.*

F1	–	1 a. violet	65·00	£100
F2	F 1	1 a. violet (1943)	—	£100
F3		1¼ a. on 1 a. violet	95·00	£200
F4		1¼ a. yellow-green (1945) ..	13·00	
		a. Imperf between (vert pair) ..	30·00	
		b. *Blue-green* (1945) ..	48·00	95·00

No. F1 shows the portrait as Type **1**. Used prices are. for examples with postal cancellations. No. F3 shows a handstamped surcharge in Gujerati.

Idar became part of Bombay Province on 10 June 1948.

INDORE

Maharaja Yeshwant Rao Holkar II, 1926–1961

7 Maharaja Yeshwant
Rao Holkar II

(Recess Perkins, Bacon & Co)

1927–37. *P* 13 *to* 14.

16	7	¼ a. orange (*a*) (*d*) (*e*)	30	10
17		½ a. claret (*a*) (*d*) (*e*)	40	10
18		1 a. green (*a*) (*d*) (*e*)	90	10
19		1¼ a. green (*c*) (*d*) (1933) ..	1·50	25
20		2 a. sepia (*a*)	3·75	1·00
21		2 a. bluish green (*d*) (1936) ..	10·00	70
		a. Imperf (pair)	25·00	£110
22		3 a. deep violet (*a*)	1·50	9·00
23		3 a. Prussian blue (*d*) (1935?) ..	15·00	
		a. Imperf (pair)	30·00	£275
24		3½ a. violet (*d*) (1934)	4·75	9·50
		a. Imperf (pair)	50·00	£275
25		4 a. ultramarine (*a*)	3·25	3·25
26		4 a. yellow-brown (*d*) (1937) ..	22·00	1·50
		a. Imperf (pair)	30·00	£190
27		8 a. slate-grey (*a*)	5·50	4·50
28		8 a. red-orange (*d*) (1937) ..	16·00	19·00
29		12 a. carmine (*d*) (1934)	5·00	10·00
30	–	1 r. black and light blue (*b*) ..	8·00	14·00
31	–	2 r. black and carmine (*b*) ..	35·00	35·00
32	–	5 r. black & brown-orange (*b*) ..	55·00	60·00

Nos. 30/32 are as Type **7**, but larger, size 23 × 28 mm.
Five different perforating heads were used for this issue: (*a*) comb 13·6; (*b*) comb 13·9; (*c*) line 13·2; (*d*) line 13·8; (*e*) line 14·2. Values on which each perforation occur are indicated above.

Nos. 21a, 23a, 24a and 26a were specifically ordered by the state government in 1933 and are known used for postage *circa* 1938–42. A plate proof of the 1 r. in green and carmine is also known postally used (*Price of pair* £32 *unused,* £300 *used*).
Nos. 16/19 and 28/32 also exist as imperforate plate proofs, but these were never sent to India.

(8)    9

1940 (1 Aug).   *Surch in words as T* **8** *by* Times of India *Press, Bombay.*

33	7	¼ a. on 5 r. black and brown-orange (*b*)	7·50	85
		a. Surch double (Blk. + G.)	†	£400
34		½ a. on 2 r. black and carmine (*b*) ..	11·00	1·75
35		1 a. on 1¼ a. green (*c*) (*d*) (*e*) ..	11·00	40
		b. Surch inverted (*d*)	90·00	
		c. Surch double (*c*)	£325	
33/5		.. .. *Set of* 3	27·00	2·75

(Typo *"Times of India"* Press, Bombay)

1941–46. *P* 11.

36	9	¼ a. red-orange	2·00	10
37		½ a. claret	1·60	10
38		1 a. green	8·00	10
39		1¼ a. yellow-green	14·00	45
		a. Imperf (pair)	£190	
40		2 a. turquoise-blue	11·00	1·00
41		4 a. yellow-brown (1946) ..	12·00	9·50

Larger size (23 × 28 *mm*)

42		2 r. black and carmine (1943) ..	9·00	£100
43		5 r. black and yellow-orange (1943) ..	9·00	£140
36/43	..	.. .. .. *Set of* 8	60·00	£225

JAIPUR

Maharaja Sawai Man Singh II, 1922–1970

7 Maharaja Sawai
Man Singh II

10 Maharaja Sawai
Man Singh II

(Des T. I. Archer. Litho Indian Security Printing Press, Nasik)

1932–46. *P* 14. (*a*) *Inscr* "POSTAGE & REVENUE".

52	10	1 a. black and blue	50	55
53		2 a. black and buff	1·75	1·10
54		4 a. black and grey-green	3·25	5·50
55		8 a. black and chocolate.. ..	4·50	8·50
56		1 r. black and yellow-bistre ..	16·00	70·00
57		2 r. black and yellow-green ..	70·00	£275
52/7		.. .. *Set of* 6	85·00	£325

(*b*) *Inscr* "POSTAGE"

58	7	¼ a. black and brown-lake	30	15
59		¾ a. black and brown-red (1943?) ..	4·50	2·75
60		1 a. black and blue (1943?) ..	5·50	2·00
61		2 a. black and buff (1943?) ..	5·50	2·75
62		2½ a. black and carmine	2·25	1·50
63		3 a. black and green	1·40	40

64	7	4 a. black and grey-green (1943?)	..	17·00	80·00
65		6 a. black and deep blue	..	2·25	18·00
		a. Black and pale blue (1946)..		6·50	45·00
66		8 a. black and chocolate (1946)..	..	14·00	75·00
67		1 r. black and yellow-bistre (1946)	..	20·00	£100
58/67	..	.. ..	*Set of* 10	65·00	£250

One Rupee

(11)

1936. *Nos. 57 and 51 surch with* T **11.**

68	10	1 r. on 2 r. black and yellow-green (R.)		6·00	65·00
69	–	1 r. on 5 r. black and purple	.. ..	6·00	50·00

पाव आना

(12)   13 Maharaja and Amber Palace

1938 (Dec). *No.* 41 *surch* "QUARTER ANNA" *in Devanagari,* T **12.**

70	7	¼ a. on ½ a. black and violet (R.)	..	9·00	12·00

(Recess D.L.R.)

1947 (Dec)–48. *Silver Jubilee of Maharaja's Accession to Throne. Various designs as* T **13.** P 13½ × 14.

71		¼ a. red-brown and green (5.48)	.. ..	70	2·75
72		½ a. green and violet ..	..	20	2·50
73		¾ a. black and lake (5.48)	..	70	3·25
74		1 a. red-brown and ultramarine	..	40	2·50
75		2 a. violet and scarlet..	.. ..	40	4·25
76		3 a. green and black (5.48)	.. ..	90	3·75
77		4 a. ultramarine and brown	..	50	2·50
78		8 a. vermilion and brown	..	60	3·50
79		1 r. purple and green (5.48) ..	..	1·40	19·00
71/9		.. ..	*Set of* 9	5·25	38·00

Designs:—¼ a. Palace Gate; ¾ a. Map of Jaipur; 1 a. Observatory; 2 a. Wind Palace; 3 a. Coat of Arms; 4 a. Amber Fort Gate; 8 a. Chariot of the Sun; 1 r. Maharaja's portrait between State flags.

3 PIES

(14)

1947 (Dec). *No.* 41 *surch with* T **14.**

80	7	3 p. on ½ a. black and violet (R.)	..	14·00	22·00
		a. "PIE" for "PIES" ..	..	42·00	75·00
		b. Bars at left vertical..	..	55·00	85·00
		c. Surch inverted ..	..	35·00	32·00
		d. Surch inverted and "PIE" for "PIES"		£150	£140
		e. Surch double, one inverted..	..	48·00	45·00
		f. As variety e, but inverted surch showing "PIE" for "PIES" ..		£300	£275

There were three settings of Type **14**, each applied to quarter sheets of 30 (6×5). No. 80a occurs in two of these settings on R.5/5 and one of these settings also shows No. 80b on R.6/1.

OFFICIAL STAMPS

SERVICE   **SERVICE**

(O 2)   (O 3)

1932–7. *Nos.* 52/6 *optd at Nasik with Type* O **3,** *in red.*

O18	10	1 a. black and blue	.. ..	1·50	10
O19		2 a. black and buff	..	2·00	10
O20		4 a. black and grey-green (1937)		£225	5·50
O21		8 a. black and chocolate..	..	5·50	1·10
O22		1 r. black and yellow-bistre	..	14·00	15·00
O18/22		.. ..	*Set of* 5	£225	19·00

1936–46. *Stamps of* 1932–46, *inscr* "POSTAGE".

(a) *Optd at Nasik with Type* O **3,** *in red*

O23	7	¼ a. black and brown-lake (1936)	..	40	10
O24		¾ a. black and brown-red (1944)	..	1·50	40
O25		1 a. black and blue (1941?)	..	7·50	30
O26		2 a. black and buff (date?)	..	6·50	1·75
O27		2½ a. black and carmine (1946)	..	9·00	70·00
O28		4 a. black and grey-green (1942)	..	5·00	3·25
O29		8 a. black and chocolate (1943)	..	5·00	4·50
O30		1 r. black and yellow-bistre (date?)	..	£100	
O23/9		.. ..	*Set of* 7	32·00	75·00

(b) *Optd locally as Type* O **2** (16 *mm long), in black*

O31	7	¼ a. black and red-brown (1936)	..	65·00	55·00

9 PIES

(O 5)

1947. *No.* O25 *surch with Type* O **5,** *in red.*

O32	7	9 p. on 1 a. black and blue	.. ..	2·50	2·50

1947 (Dec). *No.* O13 *surch as* T **14,** *but* "3 PIES" *placed higher.*

O33	7	3 p. on ½ a. black and violet (R.)	..	4·00	10·00
		a. Surch double, one inverted..	..	35·00	35·00
		ab. "PIE" for "PIES" in inverted surcharge	.. ..	£190	£200
		c. Surch inverted	.. ..	—	£1100

1949. *No.* O13 *surch* "THREE-QUARTER ANNA" *in Devanagari, as* T **12,** *but with two bars on each side.*

O34	7	¾ a. on ½ a. black and violet (R.)	..	13·00	13·00
		a. Surch double	.. ..	—	£1100

There are three different types of surcharge in the setting of 30, which vary in one or other of the Devanagari characters.

Jaipur became part of Rajasthan by 7 April 1949.

JASDAN

Darbar Ala Khachar, 1919–1971

1 Sun

(Typo L. V. Indap & Co, Bombay)

1942 (15 Mar)–47. *Stamps from booklet panes. Various perfs.*

1		1 a. deep myrtle-green (*p* 10½×*imperf*)		£650	£425
2		1 a. light green (*p* 12×*imperf*)	..	£375	£425
3		1 a. light green (*p* 10½×*imperf*) (1943)	..	£100	£130

4		1 a. pale yellow-green (p 8½×$imperf$)			12·00	95·00
5		1 a. dull yellow-green (p 10) (1946)			17·00	£110
6		1 a. bluish green (p 9) (1947)			13·00	95·00

Nos. 1/4 were issued in panes of four with the stamps imperforate on one or two sides; Nos. 5/6 were in panes of eight perforated all round.

A 1 a. rose with the arms of Jasdan in the centre is a fiscal stamp.

Jasdan was merged with the United State of Kathiawar (later Saurashtra) by 15 April 1948.

KISHANGARH

Maharaja Sumar Singh, 1939–1971

16 Maharaja Yagyanarayan Singh 17

1943–47. *Thick, soft, unsurfaced paper. Poor impression. Typo. Pin-perf.*

81	16	¼ a. pale dull blue (1945)			3·75	8·50
		a. Imperf (pair)			32·00	
82		¼ a. greenish blue (1947)			1·60	7·00
		a. Imperf (pair)			28·00	
83		½ a. deep green (1944)			90	2·00
		a. Imperf (pair)			25·00	25·00
		b. Imperf between (vert or horiz pair)			42·00	
84		½ a. yellow-green (1946)			4·75	7·00
		a. Imperf (pair)			28·00	28·00
		b. Imperf between (vert or horiz pair)			42·00	
85	17	1 a. carmine-red (1944)			6·50	2·75
		a. Double print			£300	
		b. Imperf (pair)			28·00	28·00
		c. Imperf between (vert or horiz pair)			42·00	
		d. *Red-orange* (1947)			60·00	24·00
		da. Imperf (pair)			95·00	75·00
86		2 a. bright magenta			7·50	13·00
		a. Imperf (pair)			55·00	60·00
87		2 a. maroon (1947)			65·00	16·00
		a. Imperf (pair)			42·00	42·00
		b. Imperf between (vert or horiz pair)			75·00	
88	16	4 a. brown (1944)			22·00	16·00
		a. Imperf (pair)				
89		8 a. violet (1945)			45·00	£110
90		1 r. green (1945)			50·00	£120
		a. Imperf (pair)			£170	£250
90b		2 r. yellow (date?)			£375	
		ba. Imperf (pair)				
91		5 r. claret (1945)			£425	£450
		a. Imperf (pair)			£275	

MORVI

Maharaja Lakhdirji, 1922–1948

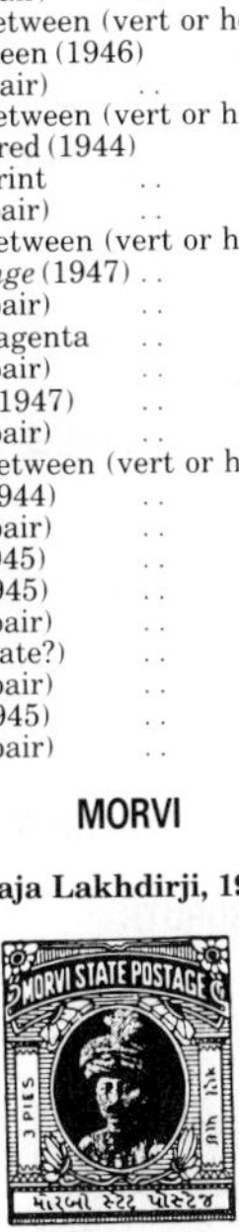

3

1935–48. *Typo. Morvi Press ptg. Rough perf 11.*

16	3	3 p. scarlet (shades)			70	2·50
		a. Imperf between (horiz pair)			£1300	
17		6 p. grey-green			75	2·00
		a. *Emerald-green*			5·50	23·00
18		1 a. brown			12·00	14·00
		a. *Pale yellow-brown*			16·00	25·00
		b. *Chocolate*			22·00	30·00
19		2 a. dull violet (to deep)			2·50	15·00
16/19				Set of 4	14·00	30·00

Nos. 17a, 18a and 18b were issued between 1944 and 1948.

Maharaja Mahendra Singh, 1948–1957

Morvi was merged with the United State of Kathiawar (later Saurashtra) by 15 April 1948.

ORCHHA

Maharaja Vir Singh II, 1930–1956

5 Maharaja Vir Singh II 6

(Litho Indian Security Printing Press, Nasik)

1939–42? P 13½ × 14 (T 5) *or* 14 × 13½ (T 6).

31	5	¼ a. chocolate				2·50	48·00
32		½ a. yellow-green				2·75	40·00
33		¾ a. bright blue				2·75	65·00
34		1 a. scarlet				2·75	13·00
35		1¼ a. blue				2·75	65·00
36		1½ a. mauve				3·00	80·00
37		2 a. vermilion				2·75	48·00
38		2½ a. turquoise-green				2·75	£140
39		3 a. slate-violet				4·00	75·00
40		4 a. slate				5·00	21·00
41		8 a. magenta				8·50	£140
42	6	1 r. grey-green				15·00	
43		2 r. bright violet				32·00	£375
44		5 r. yellow-orange				90·00	
45		10 r. turquoise-green (1942)				£350	
46		15 r. slate-lilac (date ?)				£7500	
47		25 r. claret (date ?)				£5500	

Orchha became part of Vindhya Pradesh by 1 May 1948.

RAJASTHAN

Rajasthan was formed in 1948–49 from a number of States in Rajputana; these included Bundi, Jaipur and Kishangarh, whose posts continued to function more or less separately until ordered by the Indian Government to close on 1 April 1950.

BUNDI

(1)

1949. *Nos. 86/92 of Bundi. (a) Handstamped with T 1.*

A. *In black.* B. *In violet.* C. *In blue*

						A	B	C
1		¼ a. blue-green				4·75	4·50	24·00
		a. Pair, one without opt				£170	†	†
2		½ a. violet				3·50	3·00	27·00
		a. Pair, one without opt				†	£180	†
3		1 a. yellow-green				4·50	9·50	28·00
		a. Pair, one without opt				†	£180	†
4		2 a. vermilion				8·00	20·00	—
5		4 a. orange				29·00	23·00	70·00
6		8 a. ultramarine				4·00	6·00	45·00
7		1 r. chocolate				£160	60·00	

The above prices are for unused, used stamps being worth about six times the unused prices. Most of these handstamps are known, sideways, inverted or double.

(b) Machine-printed as T 1 in black

8	¼ a. blue-green	..	..	..
9	½ a. violet ..			
10	1 a. yellow-green	..	..	
11	2 a. vermilion	..	..	4·00 55·00
	a. Opt inverted	..	..	£250
12	4 a. orange ..			2·00 55·00
	a. Opt double	..	..	£225
13	8 a. ultramarine	..	..	25·00
	a. Opt inverted	..		£450
	b. Opt double	..	..	£375
14	1 r. chocolate	..	..	7·50

JAIPUR

राजस्थान

RAJASTHAN
(2)

1950 (26 Jan). *T 7 of Jaipur optd with T 2.*

15	¼ a. black and brown-lake (No. 58) (B.)	..	3·75 13·00
16	½ a. black and violet (No. 41) (R.)	..	3·25 14·00
17	¾ a. black and brown-red (No. 59) (Blue-blk.)	6·00 16·00
	a. Opt in pale blue	..	14·00 32·00
18	1 a. black and blue (No. 60) (R.)	..	4·00 29·00
19	2 a. black and buff (No. 61) (R.)	..	6·50 38·00
20	2½ a. black and carmine (No. 62) (B.)	..	7·00 18·00
21	3 a. black and green (No. 63) (R.)	..	7·50 42·00
22	4 a. black and grey-green (No. 64) (R.)	..	7·50 48·00
23	6 a. black and pale blue (No. 65a) (R.)	..	8·50 75·00
24	8 a. black and chocolate (No. 66) (R.)	..	12·00 95·00
25	1 r. black and yellow-bistre (No. 67) (R.)	..	13·00 £140
15/25 ..	.. .. .. *Set of* 11	70·00 £475

KISHANGARH

1948–49. *Various stamps of Kishangarh handstamped with T 1 in red.*

(a) On stamps of 1899–1901

26	¼ a. rose-pink (No. 5a) (B.)	..	£150
26a	¼ a. rose-pink (No. 22a)	..	..	— £140
27	½ a. deep blue (No. 26)	..	..	£250
29	1 a. brown-lilac (No. 29)	..	..	14·00 38·00
	b. Imperf (pair)	..	..	40·00 80·00
	c. Violet handstamp	..	..	— £225
	d. Black handstamp	..	..	— £275
30	4 a. chocolate (No. 31)	..	55·00 75·00
	a. Violet handstamp	..	..	— £325
31	1 r. dull green (No. 32)	..	£170 £180
31a	2 r. brown-red (No. 34)	..	..	£200
32	5 r. mauve (No. 35)	..	..	£190 £190

(b) On stamps of 1904–10

33	13	½ a. chestnut	..	..	— 95·00
33a		1 a. blue ..	..	..	— £130
34		4 a. brown	..	..	13·00
		a. Blue handstamp	..	£160
35	12a	8 a. grey ..	..	75·00 £120
36	13	8 a. violet	..	11·00
37		1 r. green	..	11·00
38		2 r. olive-yellow..	..	18·00
39		5 r. purple-brown	..	23·00
		a. Blue handstamp	..	£275

(c) On stamps of 1912–16

40	14	½ a. green (No. 64)	..	— £120
41		1 a. red	..	..	— £120
42		2 a. deep violet (No. 51)	..	£250
43		2 a. purple (No. 66)	..	2·50 5·50
44		4 a. bright blue	..	— £325
45		8 a. brown	..	..	5·00
		a. Pair, one without handstamp	..	£250
46		1 r. mauve	..	..	10·00
47		2 r. deep green	..	..	10·00
48		5 r. brown	..	..	£225

(d) On stamps of 1928–36

49	16	½ a. yellow-green	..	90·00
49a		2 a. magenta ..	..	..	— £225
50		4 a. chestnut ..	..	£140
51		8 a. violet	..	..	6·00 50·00
		a. Pair, one without handstamp	..	£225
52		1 r. light green	..	20·00
53		2 r. lemon-yellow	..	14·00
54		5 r. claret	..	..	15·00

(e) On stamps of 1943–47

55	16	¼ a. pale dull blue	..	65·00 65·00
56		¼ a. greenish blue	..	38·00 38·00
		a. Imperf (pair)	..	£150
57		½ a. deep green ..	..	25·00 27·00
		a. Violet handstamp ..	..	— £140
57b		½ a. yellow-green	..	35·00 38·00
		ba. Imperf (pair)	..	£150
		bb. Blue handstamp	..	— £140
58	17	1 a. carmine-red ..	..	38·00 38·00
		a. Violet handstamp ..	..	— £150
58b		1 a. orange-red (*imperf*)..	..	95·00
		ba. Blue handstamp	..	£100
59		2 a. bright magenta	..	£110 £110
60		2 a. maroon (*imperf*)	..	£120
61	16	4 a. brown	..	..	2·00 6·00
62		8 a. violet	..	..	15·00 45·00
63		1 r. green	..	..	6·00
64		2 r. yellow	..	..	90·00
65		5 r. claret	..	..	50·00

A 1 a. value in deep violet-blue was issued for revenue purposes, but is known postally used (*Price* £60 *used*).

SHAHPURA

POSTAL FISCAL

Rajadhiraj Umaid Singh, 1932–1947

Rajadhiraj Sudarshan Deo, 1947–1971

F 1

1932–47. *Typo. P 11, 11½ or 12.*

F1	F 1	1 a. red (*shades*)	..	50·00 £130
		a. Pin-perf 7 (1947)	..	

Nos. F1/a were used for both fiscal and postal purposes. Manuscript cancellations must be assumed to be fiscal, unless on cover showing other evidence of postal use. The design was first issued for fiscal purposes in 1898.

Shahpura became part of Rajasthan by 15 April 1948.

SORUTH

JUNAGADH

Nawab Mahabat Khan III, 1911–1959

17 Nawab
Mahabat Khan III

1935. *As T* 17, *but inscr* "POSTAGE AND REVENUE". *P* 14.
57 **17** 1 a. black and carmine   ..   ..   ..   4·50   90

OFFICIAL STAMPS

SARKARI

(O 1)

1938. *No.* 57 *optd with Type* O 1, *in vermilion.*
O13   **17**   1 a. black and carmine ..   ..   ..   12·00   1·90
      a. Brown-red opt   ..   ..   9·50   1·40
The state was occupied by Indian troops on 9 November 1947 following the flight of the Nawab to Pakistan.

UNITED STATE OF SAURASHTRA

The administration of Junagadh state was assumed by the Government of India on 7 November 1947. An Executive Council took office on 1 June 1948.
   Under the new Constitution of India the United State of Saurashtra was formed on 15 February 1948, comprising 221 former states and estates of Kathiawar, including Jasdan, Morvi, Nawanagar and Wadhwan, but excluding Junagadh. A referendum was held by the Executive Council of Junagadh which then joined the United State on 20 January 1949. It is believed that the following issues were only used in Junagadh. The following issues were surcharged at the Junagadh State Press.

POSTAGE & REVENUE

ONE ANNA

(19)

Postage & Revenue

ONE ANNA

(20)

1949. *Stamps of* 1929 *surch.* (a) *With T* 19 *in red.*
58   **16**   1 a. on ¹⁄₂ a. black and deep blue (6.49)   9·00   4·50
      a. Surch double   ..   ..   † £425
      b. "AFNA" for "ANNA" and inverted
        "N" in "REVENUE" £1600
      c. Larger first "A" in "ANNA" (R. 2/5)   80·00 60·00

           (b) *With T* 20 *in green*
59   **18**   1 a. on 2 a. grey and dull yellow (2.49) ..   9·50 20·00
      a. "evenue" omittted   ..   — £425
A number of other varieties occur on No. 58, including: small "V" in "REVENUE" (R. 2/3); small "N" in "REVENUE" (R. 2/4, 3/4); small "E" in "POSTAGE" (R. 3/2); thick "A" in "POSTAGE" (R. 4/4); inverted "N" in "REVENUE" and small second "A" in "ANNA" (R. 4/5); small "O" in "ONE" (R. 5/1); small "V" and "U" in "REVENUE" (R. 6/3); small "N" in "ONE" (R. 7/2).
   In No. 59 no stop after "ANNA" is known on R. 1/4, 4/2, 7/4 and 8/3 and small "N" in "ONE" on R. 2/4.

21

(Typo Waterlow)

1949 (Sept). *Court Fee stamps of Bhavnagar state optd* "SAURASHTRA" *and further optd* "U.S.S. REVENUE & POSTAGE" *as in T* 21, *in black. P* 11.
60 **21** 1 a. purple   ..   ..   ..   8·00   8·50
      a. "POSTAGE" omitted (R. 1/2)   .. £250 £180
      b. Opt double £250 £300
   The Count Fee stamps were in sheets of 80 (8×10) and were overprinted in a setting of 40 applied twice to each sheet.
   Minor varieties include small "S" in "POSTAGE" (R. 2/1 of the setting); small "N" in "REVENUE" (R. 2/7); small "U" in "REVENUE" (R. 3/2); small "V" in "REVENUE" (R. 3/8, 5/5); and small "O" in "POSTAGE" (R. 4/7).
   Various missing stop varieties also occur.

POSTAGE & REVENUE
ONE ANNA
(22)

1950 (2 Mar). *Stamp of* 1929 *surch with T* 22.
61 **15** 1 a. on 3 p. black and blackish green   ..   48·00 50·00
      a. "P" of "POSTAGE" omitted (R. 8/1)   £550 £550
      b. "O" of "ONE" omitted (R. 6/1)   .. £700
Other minor varieties include small second "A" in "ANNA" (R. 1/2); small "S" in "POSTAGE" with small "V" in "REVENUE" (R. 3/4, 6/1) and small "V" in "REVENUE" (R. 2/3, 3/1).

OFFICIAL STAMPS

1948 (July–Dec). *Nos.* O4/O7 *surch* "ONE ANNA" (2¹⁄₄ *mm high*) *by Junagadh State Press.*
O14 **18** 1 a. on 2 a. grey & dull yellow (B.)   .. £5000 20·00
O15 **15** 1 a. on 3 a. black and carmine (Aug)   .. £1700 45·00
      a. Surch double   ..   ..   † £1600
O16 **16** 1 a. on 4 a. black and purple (Dec)   .. £275 40·00
      a. "ANNE" for "ANNA" (R. 5/4)   .. £2000 £350
      b. "ANNN" for "ANNA" (R. 7/5)   .. £2000 £350
O17 **18** 1 a. on 8 a. black & yellow-green (Dec)   £250 30·00
      a. "ANNE" for "ANNA" (R. 5/4)   .. £2000 £275
      b. "ANNN" for "ANNA" (R. 7/5)   .. £2000 £275
Numerous minor varieties of fount occur in this surcharge.

1948 (Nov). *Handstamped* "ONE ANNA" (4 *mm high*).
O18 **17** 1 a. on 1 r. (No. O8)   ..   .. £950 29·00
O19   1 a. on 1 r. (No. O12a) ..   ..   .. £350 32·00
      a. Optd on No. O12   ..   ..   — 50·00
A used copy of No. O12a is known surcharged in black as on Nos. O14/17. This may have come from a proof sheet.

1949 (Jan). *Postage stamps optd with Type* O 3, *in red.*
O20 **15** 3 p. black and blackish green   ..   .. £225 10·00
O21 **16** ¹⁄₂ a. black and deep blue   ..   .. £500 10·00
O22 **18** 1 a. on 2 a. grey and dull yellow (No. 59)   60·00 18·00
Various wrong fount letters occur in the above surcharges.

MANUSCRIPT OVERPRINTS. Nos. 49, 50, 57, 58, 59 and 60 are known with manuscript overprints reading "Service" (or "SARKARI" (in English or Gujerati script), usually in red. Such provisionals were used at Gadhada and Una between June and December 1949 (*Price from* £85 *each, used on piece*).

   The United State of Saurashtra postal service was incorporated into that of India on 30 March 1950.

MINIMUM PRICE

The minimum price quote is 10p which represents a handling charge rather than a basis for valuing common stamps. For further notes about prices see introductory pages.

TRAVANCORE

Maharaja Bala Rama Varma XI, 1924–1971

16 Maharaja Bala Rama
Varma XI and Subramania
Shrine

(Plates by Indian Security Printing Press, Nasik. Typo Stamp
Manufactory, Trivandrum)

1937 (29 Mar). *Temple Entry Proclamation. T* **16** *and similar
horiz designs. Wmk* C. *P* 12.

60	6 ca. carmine			60	70
	a. Imperf between (horiz strip of 3)			£400	
	b. Perf 12½			1·10	1·50
	c. Compound perf			25·00	25·00
61	12 ca. bright blue			1·40	20
	a. Perf 12½			2·00	60
	ab. Imperf between (vert pair)			£375	
	b. Compound perf			40·00	
62	1½ ch. yellow-green			1·00	70
	a. Imperf between (vert pair)			£300	
	b. Perf 12½			21·00	5·00
	c. Compound perf				
63	3 ch. violet			2·75	1·40
	a. Perf 12½			3·50	1·90
60/3			*Set of* 4	5·25	2·75

Designs:—Maharaja's portrait and temples—12 ca. Sri Padmanabha; 1½ ch. Mahadeva; 3 ch. Kanyakumari.

COMPOUND PERFS. This term covers stamps perf compound of
12½ and 11, 12 and 11 or 12 and 12½, and where two or more
combinations exist the prices are for the commonest. Such
compounds can occur on values which do not exist perf 12 all round.

17 Lake Ashtamudi

18 Maharaja Bala
Rama Varma XI

(Des Nilakantha Pellai. Plates by Indian Security Printing
Press, Nasik. Typo Stamp Manufactory, Trivandrum)

1939 (9 Nov). *Maharaja's 27th Birthday. T* **17/18** *and similar
designs. Wmk* C. *P* 12½.

64	1 ch. yellow-green			3·25	10
	a. Imperf between (horiz pair)			20·00	
	b. Perf 11			7·00	10
	ba. Imperf between (vert pair)			30·00	35·00
	bb. Imperf between (vert strip of 3)			20·00	32·00
	c. Perf 12			14·00	75
	ca. Imperf between (horiz pair)			20·00	
	cb. Imperf between (vert pair)			30·00	
	d. Compound perf			17·00	1·90
	da. Imperf between (vert pair)			85·00	
65	1½ ch. scarlet			1·60	1·90
	a. Doubly printed			£190	
	b. Imperf between (horiz pair)			25·00	
	c. Imperf between (vert pair)			20·00	
	d. Perf 11			3·00	17·00
	da. Imperf horiz (vert pair)			8·00	
	e. Perf 12			23·00	3·00
	f. Perf 13½			13·00	48·00
	g. Compound perf			32·00	4·25
	h. Imperf (pair)			30·00	

66	2 ch. orange			3·75	75
	a. Perf 11			12·00	35
	b. Perf 12			70·00	3·75
	c. Compound perf			70·00	4·50
67	3 ch. brown			4·75	10
	a. Doubly printed			—	£100
	b. Imperf between (horiz pair)			32·00	45·00
	c. Perf 11			15·00	30
	ca. Doubly printed			40·00	48·00
	d. Perf 12			29·00	2·25
	da. Imperf between (vert pair)			£100	£100
	e. Compound perf			22·00	1·00
68	4 ch. red			3·75	40
	a. Perf 11			24·00	50
	b. Perf 12			22·00	4·75
	c. Compound perf			£110	90·00
69	7 ch. pale blue			6·50	12·00
	a. Perf 11			55·00	22·00
	ab. Blue			55·00	20·00
	b. Compound perf			70·00	25·00
70	14 ch. turquoise-green			6·00	38·00
	a. Perf 11			7·50	65·00
64/70			*Set of* 7	27·00	48·00

Designs: *Vert as T* **18**—1½ ch., 3 ch. Portraits of Maharaja in
different frames. *Horiz as T* **17**—4 ch. Sri Padmanabha Shrine;
7 ch. Cape Comorin; 14 ch. Pachipari Reservoir.

19 Maharaja and Aruvikara Falls

2 CASH
(20)

(Des Nilakantha Pellai. Plates by Indian Security Printing Press,
Nasik. Typo Stamp Manufactory, Trivandrum)

1941 (20 Oct). *Maharaja's 29th Birthday. T* **19** *and similar horiz
design. Wmk* C. *P* 12½.

71	6 ca. blackish violet			4·50	10
	a. Perf 11			4·50	10
	ab. Imperf between (vert pair)			20·00	
	ac. Imperf horiz (vert pair)			32·00	45·00
	b. Perf 12			16·00	1·00
	ba. Imperf between (horiz pair)			24·00	
	bb. Imperf between (vert pair)			32·00	
	bc. Imperf between (vert strip of 3)			21·00	
	c. Compound perf			4·75	80
72	¾ ch. brown			4·75	15
	a. Perf 11			6·50	15
	ab. Imperf between (horiz pair)			£100	
	ac. Imperf between (vert pair)			26·00	35·00
	ad. Imperf between (vert strip of 3)			23·00	
	ae. Block of four imperf between (horiz and vert)			£140	
	b. Perf 12			38·00	6·50
	c. Compound perf			9·00	1·10

Design:—¾ ch. Maharaja and Marthanda Varma Bridge,
Alwaye.

1943 (17 Sept). *Nos.* 65, 71 (*colour changed*) *and* 72 *surch as T* **20**.
P 12½.

73	2 ca. on 1½ ch. scarlet			1·10	45
	a. Imperf between (vert pair)			32·00	
	b. "2" omitted			£180	£180
	c. "CA" omitted			£275	
	d. "ASH" omitted			£275	
	e. Perf 11			30	20
	ea. "CA" omitted			£275	
	f. Compound perf			55	85
	fa. Imperf between (vert pair)			95·00	
	fb. "2" omitted			£190	
74	4 ca. on ¾ ch. brown			2·75	1·00
	a. Perf 11			3·00	20
	b. Perf 12			—	90·00
	c. Compound perf			3·75	1·00
75	8 ca. on 6 ca. scarlet			3·50	10
	a. Perf 11			2·25	10
	ab. Imperf between (horiz pair)			30·00	
	b. Perf 12			—	65·00
	c. Compound perf			10·00	5·00
73/5			*Set of* 3	4·75	45

SPECIAL

21 Maharaja Bala   **(22)**
Rama Varma XI

(Des Nilakantha Pellai. Plates by Indian Security Printing Press,
Nasik. Typo Stamp Manufactory, Trivandrum)

1946 (24 Oct).   *Maharaja's 34th Birthday. Wmk C. P 12½.*

76	21	8 ca. carmine	..	..	20·00	2·75
		a. Perf 11	..	..	65	85
		b. Perf 12	..	..	28·00	2·50
		ba. Imperf between (horiz pair)	..	30·00	42·00
		bb. Imperf between (horiz strip of 3)	45·00	
		c. Compound perf .	..	..		

1946. *No. O103 revalidated for ordinary postage with opt T 22, in
orange. P 12½.*

77	19	6 ca. blackish violet	..	..	6·00	2·25
		a. Perf 11	..	..	28·00	5·00
		b. Compound perf	..	..	6·00	5·00

OFFICIAL STAMPS

SERVICE	SERVICE	**SERVICE**
		8 CASH
(O 10)	(O 11)	(O 12)
13 mm ("R"	13½ mm	
with curved	("R" with	
tail)	straight tail)	

1939–41. *Nos. 35 and 40 with type-set opt, Type O 10. P 12½.*

O85	1	6 ca. brown-red (1941) ..	..	..	70	20
		a. Perf 11	..	..	1·25	75
		b. Perf 12	..	..	70	30
		c. Compound perf	..	..	70	1·10
O86	5	¾ ch. reddish violet	..	..	90·00	48·00
		a. Perf 12	..	..	21·00	1·25
		b. Compound perf	..	..	85·00	48·00

1939 (9 Nov).   *Maharaja's 27th Birthday. Nos. 64/70 with type-set
opt, Type O 10. P 12½.*

O87		1 ch. yellow-green ..	..	..	3·75	25
O88		1½ ch. scarlet	..	..	3·75	75
		a. "SESVICE"	..	..	80·00	26·00
		b. Perf 12	..	..	30·00	5·50
		ba. "SESVICE"	..	..	—	95·00
		bb. Imperf between (horiz pair) ..	†	£130
		c. Compound perf	..	..	9·00	1·75
O89		2 ch. orange	..	..	3·75	4·25
		a. "SESVICE"	..	..	95·00	£110
		b. Compound perf	..	..	70·00	70·00
O90		3 ch. brown ..	..	..	3·00	20
		a. "SESVICE"	..	..	60·00	21·00
		b. Perf 12	..	..	16·00	45
		ba. "SESVICE"	..	..	£150	42·00
		c. Compound perf	..	..	7·00	2·75
O91		4 ch. red	..	..	7·50	3·00
O92		7 ch. pale blue	..	..	8·50	1·90
O93		14 ch. turquoise-green	..	..	11·00	3·00
O87/93		..	..	..	Set of 7	38·00	12·00

1940 (?)–**45.** *Nos. 40a and 42b optd with Type O 11 from
stereos. P 12½.*

O94	5	¾ ch. reddish violet	..	..	10·00	20
		a. Imperf between (horiz pair)	..	£100	
		b. Perf 11	..	..	50·00	1·10
		c. Perf 12	..	..	15·00	20
		d. Compound perf ..	..	..	42·00	75
O95	1	1½ ch. rose (1945)	..	..	13·00	8·00
		a. Perf 12	..	..	4·50	1·00
		b. Compound perf	..	..	18·00	12·00

1942 (?).   *Nos. 64/70 optd with Type O 11 from stereos. P 12½.*

O 96		1 ch. yellow-green	..	..	75	10
		a. Imperf between (vert pair)	..	42·00	45·00
		b. Opt inverted	..	..	†	38·00
		c. Opt double	..	..	21·00	
		d. Perf 11	..	..	60	10
		da. Imperf between (vert pair)	..	27·00	
		db. Opt double	..	..	85·00	85·00
		e. Perf 12	..	..	2·75	50
		ea. Imperf between (vert pair)	..	80·00	80·00
		eb. Stamp doubly printed	..	£110	
		ec. Opt inverted	..	..	†	85·00
		ed. Opt double	..	..	23·00	
		f. Compound perf	..	..	5·50	1·00
		fa. Imperf between (vert pair)	..	†	£110
O 97		1½ ch. scarlet	..	..	2·75	10
		a. Imperf between (horiz pair)	..	50·00	
		b. Perf 11	..	..	1·10	15
		ba. Imperf between (vert pair)	..	85·00	85·00
		bb. Imperf between (vert strip of 3)	65·00	
		bc. Imperf between (horiz pair)	..	†	90·00
		c. Perf 12	..	..	4·25	50
		ca. Imperf between (vert strip of 3)	£110	
		d. Compound perf	..	..	2·00	30
		e. Imperf (pair)	..	..	26·00	
O 98		2 ch. orange	..	..	1·00	30
		a. Perf 11	..	..	6·50	1·00
		ab. Imperf between (vert pair)	..		
		b. Perf 12	..	..	70·00	70·00
		ba. Imperf between (vert pair)	..	£275	£275
		c. Compound perf	..	..	70·00	70·00
O 99		3 ch. brown	..	..	60	10
		a. Imperf between (vert pair)	..		
		b. Perf 11	..	..	1·75	10
		c. Perf 12	..	..	4·00	1·40
		ca. Imperf between (vert pair)	..	£200	£200
		d. Compound perf	..	..	14·00	75
O100		4 ch. red	..	..	1·75	65
		a. Perf 11	..	..	2·75	45
		b. Perf 12	..	..	13·00	3·50
		c. Compound perf	..	..	55·00	20·00
O101		7 ch. pale blue ..	..	..	5·50	35
		a. Perf 11	..	..	4·50	3·50
		b. Perf 12	..	..	17·00	6·50
		c. Compound perf	..	..	14·00	4·50
		d. Blue (p 11)	..	..	8·50	4·00
		da. Perf 12	..	..	6·50	4·00
		db. Compound perf	..	..	21·00	14·00
O102		14 ch. turquoise-green	..	..	9·50	70
		a. Perf 11	..	..	9·50	1·50
		b. Perf 12	..	..	7·50	2·40
		c. Compound perf	..	..	48·00	6·00
O96/102		..	..	..	Set of 7	15·00	1·90

1942. *Maharaja's 29th Birthday. Nos 71/2 optd with Type O 11.
P 12½.*

O103		6 ca. blackish violet	..	..	40	40
		a. Perf 11	..	..	70	80
		b. Perf 12	..	..	48·00	4·50
		c. Compound perf	..	..	1·50	1·00
O104		¾ ch. brown	..	..	3·00	10
		a. Imperf between (vert pair) ..	†	£250
		b. Perf 11	..	..	5·50	10
		c. Perf 12	..	..	48·00	1·75
		d. Compound perf	..	..	6·50	85

1943. *Surch with Type O 12. P 12½.*

O105	19	8 ca. on 6 ca. scarlet	..	..	1·75	20
		a. Perf 11	..	..	1·25	10
		ab. Surch inverted	..	..	†	£700
		b. Compound perf	..	..	5·50	1·25

1945. *Nos. 73/4 optd with Type O 11. P 12½.*

O106		2 ca. on 1½ ch. scarlet	..	..	50	50
		a. Perf 11	..	..	45	15
		ab. Pair, one without surch	..	£225	
		b. Compound perf	..	..	70	1·00
		ba. "2" omitted ..	..	..	£200	£200
		c. Perf 12	..		
O107		4 ca. on ¾ ch. brown	..	..	2·25	30
		a. Perf 11	..	..	1·25	20
		b. Compound perf	..	..	1·40	1·00

1947. *Maharaja's 34th Birthday. Optd with Type* O 11. *P* 11.

O108	21	8 ca. carmine	..	..	..	1·75	70
		a. Imperf between (horiz pair)		..	35·00	
		ab. Imperf between (vert pair)	..	†	£120	
		b. Opt double..	..	..	†	£170	
		c. Perf 12½ ..	..	..	3·50	1·10
		ca. Stamp doubly printed	..	..	30·00	
		d. Perf 12	..	..	3·50	1·40
		da. Stamp doubly printed	..	..	38·00	

From 1 July 1949 Travancore formed part of the new State of Travancore-Cochin and stamps of Travancore surcharged in Indian currency were used.

TRAVANCORE-COCHIN

On 1 July 1949 the United State of Travancore and Cochin was formed ("U.S.T.C.") and the name was changed to State of Travancore-Cochin ("T.C.") by the new constitution of India on 26 January 1950.

NO WATERMARK VARIETIES. These were formerly listed but we have now decided to omit them as they do not occur in full sheets. They are best collected in pairs, with and without watermarks.

COMPOUND PERFS. The notes above Type **17** of Travancore also apply here.

VALIDITY OF STAMPS. From 6 June 1950 the stamps of Travancore-Cochin were valid on mail from both Indian and state post offices to destinations in India and abroad.

ONE ANNA
ഒരണ
(1)

2 p. on 6 ca.

രണ്ട രപ്പെസ	രണ്ട രപ്പെസ
Normal	1st character of 2nd group as 1st character of 1st group (Rt pane R.14/2)

1949 (1 July). *Stamps of Travancore surch in* "PIES" *or* "ANNAS" *as T* 1. *P* 12½.

1	19	2 p. on 6 ca. blackish violet (R.) ..		..	2·00	90
		a. Surch inverted		..	32·00	
		b. Character error	..	..	£100	70·00
		c. "O" inverted ..	..	..	25·00	13·00
		d. Perf 11	..	..	1·25	20
		da. Imperf between (vert pair)	..	£110	£110
		db. Pair, one without surch	..	..	85·00	
		dc. Character error	..	..	95·00	70·00
		dd. "O" inverted ..	..	..	26·00	13·00
		e. Perf 12	..	..	40	20
		ea. Imperf between (horiz pair)	..	48·00	
		eb. Imperf between (vert pair)	..	5·00	13·00
		ec. Surch inverted	..	..	75·00	
		ed. Character error	..	..	£100	70·00
		ee. Imperf between (vert strip of 3)	..	32·00	
		ef. Block of four imperf between (horiz and vert)	..	..	45·00	
		eg. "O" inverted ..	..	..	26·00	13·00
		f. Perf 14	..	..	†	£400
		g. Imperf (pair)	..	..	8·50	
		h. Compound perf	..	..	—	30·00
2	21	4 p. on 8 ca. carmine	..	..	1·10	30
		a. Surch inverted	..	..	38·00	
		b. "S" inverted ..	..	..	75·00	38·00
		c. Perf 11	..	..	1·60	30
		ca. Imperf between (vert pair)	..	£120	£120
		cb. Surch inverted	..	..	75·00	
		cc. Pair, one without surch	..	..	90·00	
		cd. "FOUP" for "FOUR"	..	..	£120	85·00

(2)	ce. "S" inverted ..	..	..	..	75·00	38·00
	d. Perf 12	..	..	..	45	30
	da. Imperf between (vert pair)	..	17·00	
	db. Pair, one without surch	..	85·00	
	dc. "FOUP" for "FOUR"	..	..	£100	80·00
	dd. "S" inverted ..	..	..	80·00	45·00
	de. Surch inverted	..	..	95·00	
	e. Imperf (pair) ..	..	..	70·00	
	f. Compound perf	..	..	—	30·00
	g. Perf 13½	..	..	..	†	£425
3 17	½ a. on 1 ch. yellow-green	..	..	2·50	30
	a. "NANA" for "ANNA" (Lt pane R.3/3)	£120	85·00
	b. Inverted "H" in "HALF"		—	75·00
	c. Imperf between (vert pair)	..	†	£100
	d. Perf 11	..	..	..	1·75	20
	da. Imperf between (vert pair)	..	26·00	
	db. Surch inverted	..	..	†	£140
	dc. "NANA" for "ANNA" (Lt pane R.3/3)	£140	90·00
	dd. Inverted "H" in "HALF"	..	—	80·00
	e. Perf 12	..	..	..	65	40
	ea. Imperf between (horiz pair) ..	38·00	42·00
	eb. Imperf between (vert pair)	..	4·50	11·00
	ec. Surch inverted	..	..	5·00	
	ed. "NANA" for "ANNA" (Lt pane R.3/3)	£160	£100
	ee. Block of four imperf between (horiz and vert) ..	..	..	42·00	
	f. Perf 14	..	..	..	†	£375
	g. Imperf (pair) ..	..	..	8·50	18·00
	h. Compound perf	..	..	—	28·00
4 18	1 a. on 2 ch. orange	..	..	2·75	30
	a. Perf 11	..	..	..	55	20
	ab. Surch double	..	..	50·00	
	b. Perf 12	..	..	..	2·75	50
	ba. Imperf between (horiz pair) ..	6·00	
	bb. Imperf between (vert pair)	..	4·25	11·00
	bc. Block of four imperf between (horiz and vert)	..	..	..	42·00	
	c. Perf 13½	..	..	..	£140	2·00
	d. Imperf (pair)	..	..	8·50	
	e. Compound perf	..	..	32·00	22·00
5 —	2 a. on 4 ch. red (68)	..	..	2·25	60
	a. Surch inverted	..	..	†	£200
	b. "O" inverted ..	..	..	30·00	16·00
	c. Perf 11	..	..	..	2·25	60
	ca. "O" inverted ..	..	..	—	18·00
	d. Perf 12	..	..	..	1·75	60
	da. "O" inverted ..	..	..	35·00	18·00
	e. Compound perf	..	..	35·00	26·00
6 18	3 a. on 7 ch. pale blue (69)	..	..	8·50	3·75
	a. Perf 11	..	..	..	4·50	2·00
	ab. *Blue* ..	..	..	..	48·00	4·50
	ac. "3" omitted ..	..	..	†	£400
	b. Perf 12	..	..	..	8·00	2·75
	c. Compound perf	..	..	—	48·00
	ca. *Blue* ..	..	..	..	—	65·00
7 —	6 a. on 14 ch. turquoise-green (70)	..	11·00	18·00
	a. Accent omitted from native surch (Rt pane R.13/4) ..	..	£180	£190
	b. Perf 11	..	..	..	9·00	16·00
	ba. Accent omitted from native surch (Rt pane R.13/4) ..	..	£180	£190
	c. Perf 12	..	..	..	11·00	17·00
	ca. Accent omitted from native surch (Rt pane R. 13/4) ..	..	£190	£200
	d. Compound perf	..	..	25·00	27·00
	da. Accent omitted from native surch (Rt pane R.13/4) ..	..	£275	
	e. Imperf (pair) ..	..	..	
1/7	..	..	..	*Set of* 7	15·50	17·50

There are two settings of the ½ a. surcharge. In one the first native character is under the second downstroke of the "H" and in the other it's under the first downstroke of the "A" of "HALF". They occur on stamps perf 12½, 11 and 12 equally commonly and also on the Official stamps.

U. S. T. C.	**T.–C.**		**SIX PIES**
(2)	(3)		(4)

1949. *No. 106 of Cochin optd with T* 2.

8	29	1 a. orange	..	..	..	4·50	50·00
		a. No stop after "S" (R. 1/6)	..	..	70·00	
		b. Raised stop after "T" (R. 4/1) ..	..	70·00	

1950 (1 Apr).   *No. 106 of Cochin optd with T* 3.

9	29	1 a. orange	..	..	5·50	48·00
		a. No stop after "T"	..	..	50·00	
		b. Opt inverted	..	..	£190	
		ba. No stop after "T"	..	..	£1500	

The no stop variety occurs on No. 5 in the sheet and again on No. 8 in conjunction with a short hyphen.

1950 (1 Apr).   *No. 9 surch as T* 4.

10	29	6 p. on 1 a. orange	..	..	2·75	35·00
		a. No stop after "T" (R. 1/5)	..	..	17·00	
		b. Error. Surch on No. 8	..	..	25·00	
		ba. No stop after "S"	..	..	£200	
		bb. Raised stop after "T"	..	..	£200	
11		9 p. on 1 a. orange	..	..	2·00	30·00
		a. No stop after "T" (R. 1/5)	..	..	17·00	
		b. Error. Surch on No. 8	..	..	£160	
		ba. No stop after "S"	..	..	£600	
		bb. Raised stop after "T"	..	..	£600	

5 Conch or Chank Shell   **6** Palm Trees

(Litho Indian Security Printing Press, Nasik)

1950 (24 Oct).   *W* 69 *of India. P* 14.

12	5	2 p. rose-carmine	..	..	1·50	1·40
13	6	4 p. ultramarine	..	..	2·25	11·00

The ordinary issues of Travancore-Cochin became obsolete on 1 July 1951.

OFFICIAL STAMPS

VALIDITY. Travancore-Cochin official stamps were valid for use throughout India from 30 September 1950.

SERVICE   SERVICE
(O 1)   (O 2)

1949 (1 July)–51.   *Stamps of Travancore surch with value as T* 1 *and optd* "SERVICE". *No gum. P* 12½. (*a*) *With Type* O 1.

(i) *Wmk* C *of Travancore*

O 1	19	2 p. on 6 ca. blackish violet (R.)	..		1·00	20
		a. Imperf between (vert pair)	..		£120	£120
		b. Character error (Rt pane R. 14/2)	32·00	24·00		
		c. "O" inverted	..		21·00	10·00
		d. Pair, one without surch	..		£110	
		e. Perf 11	..		70	20
		ea. Imperf between (vert pair)	..		£120	£120
		eb. Character error (Rt pane R. 14/2)	42·00	32·00		
		ec. "O" inverted	..		21·00	12·00
		f. Perf 12	..		35	20
		fa. Imperf between (horiz pair)	..		7·50	17·00
		fb. Imperf between (vert pair)	..		6·00	
		fc. Character error (Rt pane R.14/2)	35·00	28·00		
		fd. "O" inverted	..		21·00	
		fe. Block of four imperf between (horiz and vert)	..		25·00	
		g. Imperf (pair)	..		8·50	18·00
		ga. Character error (Rt pane R. 14/2)	..		£170	

O 2	21	4 p. on 8 ca. carmine	..	..	2·00	55
		a. "FOUB" for "FOUR" (Lt pane R. 2/3)	..	..	£150	95·00
		b. Perf 11	..	..	1·90	30
		ba. "FOUB" for "FOUR" (Lt pane R. 2/3)	..	..	80·00	32·00
		c. Perf 12	..	..	1·90	55
		ca. "FOUB" for "FOUR" (Lt pane R. 2/3)	..	..	90·00	50·00
		d. Compound perf	..	..	17·00	17·00
O 3	17	½ a. on 1 ch. yellow-green	..	..	50	25
		a. Pair, one without surch	..	..	70·00	
		b. Surch inverted	..	..	24·00	
		c. "NANA" for "ANNA" (Lt pane R. 3/3)	..	..	£170	60·00
		d. Perf 11	..	..	1·00	25
		da. Pair, one without surch	..	..	£100	
		db. Surch inverted	..	..	55·00	
		dc. "NANA" for "ANNA" (Lt pane R. 3/3)	..	..	£160	70·00
		e. Perf 12	..	..	8·00	2·00
		ea. "NANA" for "ANNA" (Lt pane R. 3/3)	..	..	£300	£140
		eb. Pair, one without surch	..	..	90·00	
		ec. Surch inverted on back only	..	..	£180	
		f. Compound perf	..	..	—	21·00
O 4	18	1 a. on 2 ch. orange	..	..	16·00	5·00
		a. Surch inverted	..	..	85·00	
		b. Pair, one without surch	..	..	£475	
		c. Perf 11	..	..	14·00	7·50
O 5	—	2 a. on 4 ch. red (68)	..	..	1·00	60
		b. Perf 11	..	..	4·00	60
		ba. Surch inverted	..	..	£500	
		bb. "O" inverted	..	..	—	32·00
		c. Perf 12	..	..	4·75	3·75
		ca. "O" inverted	..	..	—	55·00
		cb. Pair, one without surch	..	..	£190	
		d. Compound perf	..	..	—	27·00
O 6	—	3 a. on 7 ch. pale blue (69)	..	..	4·00	1·40
		a. Imperf between (vert pair)	..	..	17·00	
		b. Blue	..	..	30·00	5·50
		c. Perf 11	..	..	2·40	90
		ca. Blue	..	..	30·00	5·50
		d. Perf 12	..	..	2·50	3·50
		da. Imperf between (horiz pair)	..	..	15·00	
		db. Imperf between (vert pair)	..	..	8·00	
		dc. Block of four imperf between (horiz and vert)	..	..	35·00	
		dd. Blue	..	..	30·00	5·00
		e. Imperf (pair)	..	..	11·00	
O 7	—	6 a. on 14 ch. turquoise-green (70)	..	..	11·00	6·00
		a. Imperf between (vert pair)	..	..	27·00	
		b. Perf 11	..	..	9·50	5·00
		c. Perf 12	..	..	40·00	6·00
		ca. Imperf between (horiz pair)	..	..	24·00	
		cb. Imperf between (vert pair)	..	..	29·00	
		cc. Block of four imperf between (horiz and vert)	..	..	55·00	
		d. Imperf (pair)	..	..	14·00	
O1/7		..	..	*Set of* 7	27·00	11·00

(ii) *W* 27 *of Cochin*

O 8	19	2 p. on 6 ca. blackish violet (R.)	..	..	30	1·10
		a. Type O 1 double	..	..	18·00	
		b. Perf 11	..	..	75	1·25
		c. Perf 12	..	..	45	1·10
O 9	—	2 a. on 4 ch. red (68)	..	..	1·25	85
		a. Perf 11	..	..	60	65
		ab. Imperf between (vert pair)	..	..	£190	£190
		b. Compound perf	..	..	—	30·00

(*b*) *With Type* O 2

(i) *Wmk* C *of Travancore*

O10	21	4 p. on 8 ca. carmine	..	..	30	20
		a. "FOUR" for "FOUR" (Lt pane R.2/3)	95·00	38·00		
		b. 2nd "E" of "SERVICE" in wrong fount	..	..	—	48·00
		c. "S" in "PIES" inverted	..	..	—	50·00
		d. Imperf between (vert pair)	..	..	†	£100
		e. Perf 11	..	..	30	20
		ea. Imperf between (horiz pair)	..	..	4·50	
		eb. Imperf between (vert pair)	..	..	27·00	
		ec. "FOUB" for "FOUR" (Lt pane R.2/3)	90·00	32·00		
		ed. 2nd "E" of "SERVICE" in wrong fount	..	..	£100	50·00
		ee. "S" in "PIES" inverted	..	..	—	55·00

(O10)	ef.	Block of four imperf between (horiz and vert)	32·00	
	f.	Perf 12	30	20
	fa.	Imperf between (horiz pair) ..	4·00	
	fb.	Imperf between (vert pair) ..	2·00	
	fc.	Block of four imperf between (horiz and vert)	12·00	21·00
	fd.	"FOUB" for "FOUR" (Lt pane R.2/3)	£110	40·00
	ff.	2nd "E" of "SERVICE" in wrong fount	95·00	48·00
	fg.	"FOUK" for "FOUR"	†	£375
	g.	Perf 13½	3·25	1·25
	h.	Compound perf	8·00	8·00
	i.	Imperf (pair)	6·00	
	ia.	2nd "E" of "SERVICE" in wrong fount	£130	

O11 **17**	½ a.	on 1 ch. yellow-green	50	20
	a.	"AANA" for "ANNA" (Rt pane R.13/1)	£140	60·00
	b.	Perf 11	30	20
	ba.	Imperf between (horiz pair) ..	55·00	55·00
	bb.	Imperf between (vert pair) ..	8·00	
	bc.	Block of four imperf between (horiz and vert)	48·00	
	bd.	"AANA" for "ANNA" (Rt pane R.13/1)	75·00	40·00
	c.	Perf 12	60	15
	ca.	Imperf between (horiz pair) ..	3·50	
	cb.	Imperf between (vert pair) ..	3·50	8·50
	cc.	"AANA" for "ANNA" (Rt pane R.13/1)	90·00	55·00
	cd.	Block of four imperf between (horiz and vert)	23·00	
	d.	Compound perf	20·00	15·00
	da.	"AANA" for "ANNA" (Rt pane R.13/1)	—	£160
	e.	Imperf (pair)	6·00	15·00

O12 **18**	1 a.	on 2 ch. orange	40	30
	a.	Imperf between (vert pair) ..	†	£110
	ab.	Imperf between (horiz pair) ..	†	£110
	b.	Perf 11	2·25	50
	ba.	Imperf between (horiz pair) ..	6·00	15·00
	bb.	Imperf between (vert pair) ..	70·00	70·00
	c.	Perf 12	40	20
	ca.	Imperf between (horiz pair) ..	6·00	
	cb.	Imperf between (vert pair) ..	3·50	9·00
	cc.	Block of four imperf between (horiz and vert)	20·00	
	d.	Compound perf	24·00	16·00
	e.	Imperf (pair)	14·00	

O13 —	2 a.	on 4 ch. red (68)	2·50	80
	a.	"O" inverted (Lt pane R. 14/3)	60·00	35·00
	b.	Perf 11	1·50	1·10
	ba.	"O" inverted (Lt pane R. 14/3)	50·00	35·00

(O13)	c.	Perf 12	7·50	1·10
	ca.	Imperf between (vert pair) ..	£120	£130
	cb.	"O" inverted (Lt pane R. 14/3) ..	95·00	35·00
	d.	Compound perf	23·00	13·00
O14 —	3 a.	on 7 ch. pale blue (69)	5·50	1·10
	a.	"S" inverted in "SERVICE" (Lt pane R.6/3)	75·00	32·00
	b.	First "E" inverted (Lt pane R.7/4)	£170	£130
	c.	"C" inverted (Lt pane R.4/1 and 5/1)	90·00	75·00
	d.	Second "E" inverted (Lt pane R.3/2)	£160	£120
	e.	Perf 11	1·50	1·10
	ea.	"S" inverted in "SERVICE" (Lt pane R.6/3)	50·00	32·00
	f.	Perf 12	3·75	1·60
	fa.	"S" inverted in "SERVICE" (Lt pane R.6/3)	£130	80·00
	g.	Compound perf	—	40·00
O15 —	6 a.	on 14 ch. turquoise-green (70) ..	1·50	3·25
	a.	Accent omitted from native surch	16·00	13·00
	b.	"S" inverted in "SERVICE" (Lt pane R.6/3)	70·00	42·00
	c.	Perf 11	11·00	3·25
	ca.	Accent omitted from native surch	60·00	22·00
	cb.	"S" inverted in "SERVICE" (Lt pane R.6/3)	£130	50·00
	d.	Perf 12	42·00	4·50
	da.	Accent omitted from native surch	£130	30·00
	db.	"S" inverted in "SERVICE" (Lt pane R.6/3)	£275	65·00
	e.	Compound perf	70·00	70·00
O10/15		.. .. *Set of* 6	5·00	5·00

(ii) W 27 of *Cochin*

O16 **17**	½ a.	on 1 ch. yellow-green	1·25	65
	a.	Perf 11	40	35
	b.	Perf 12	17·00	8·50
	c.	Compound perf	11·00	3·00
O17 **18**	1 a.	on 2 ch. orange	65	65
	a.	Perf 11	50	40
	b.	Perf 12	11·00	4·00
	c.	Perf 13½	2·00	1·00
	d.	Compound perf	5·00	3·00

Nos. O2, O10, O12 and O17 have the value at top in English and at bottom in native characters with "SERVICE" in between. All others have "SERVICE" below the surcharge.

Type O **2** was overprinted at one operation with the surcharges.

Nos. O10b, O10ed, O10ff and O10ia, show the second "E" of "SERVICE" with serifs matching those on the surcharge.

The "accent omitted" varieties on No. O15 occur on Left pane R. 5/1, 11/4 and Right pane R. 1/4, 12/4, 14/1 and 13/4.

The Official stamps became obsolete in September 1951.

Ireland

12 pence (d) = 1 shilling; 20 shillings = 1 pound

IRISH FREE STATE

6 "Sword of Light"

7 Map of Ireland

8 Arms of Ireland

9 Celtic Cross

10

18 St. Patrick

19 Ireland and New Constitution

1937 (8 Sept). *W* **10**. *P* 14×15.

102	18	2s. 6d. emerald-green ..	..	..	£140	65·00
		w. Wmk inverted	..	..	£600	£225
103		5s. maroon ..	..	..	£180	£110
		w. Wmk inverted	..	..	£500	£225
104		10s. deep blue ..	..	..	£140	50·00
		w. Wmk inverted				
102/4		.. .. ..	..	*Set of 3*	£425	£200

See also Nos. 123/5.

EIRE
29 December 1937—17 April 1949

1937 (29 Dec). *Constitution Day*. *W* **10**. *P* 15×14.

105	19	2d. claret	..	..	1·00	20
		w. Wmk inverted	..	..	—	£180
106		3d. blue ..	..	..	4·00	3·75

For similar stamps see Nos. 176/7.

20 Father Mathew

(Des S. Keating. Typo)

1938 (1 July). *Centenary of Temperance Crusade*. *W* **10**.
P 15×14.

107	20	2d. agate	..	..	..	1·50	30
		w. Wmk inverted	..	..	..		
108		3d. blue	..	..	..	8·50	6·00

21 George Washington, American
Eagle and Irish Harp

22

(Des G. Atkinson. Typo)

1939 (1 Mar). *150th Anniv of U.S. Constitution and Installation
of First U.S. President*. *W* **10**. *P* 15 × 14.

109	21	2d. scarlet	..	..	..	1·75	65
110		3d. blue ..	..	..	..	3·25	4·25

SIZE OF WATERMARK. T **22** can be found in various sizes from
about 8 to 10 mm high. This is due to the use of two different dandy
rolls supplied by different firms and to the effects of paper
shrinkage and other factors such as pressure and machine speed.

White line above left
value tablet joining
horizontal line to
ornament (R. 3/7)

1940–68. *Typo*. *W* **22**. *P* 15×14 *or* 14×15 (2s. 6d. *to* 10s.).

111	6	½d. bright green (24.11.40) ..	..	2·00	40
		w. Wmk inverted ..	..	50·00	6·50
112	7	1d. carmine (26.10.40) ..	..	30	10
		aw. Wmk inverted ..	..	1·75	30
		b. From coils. Perf 14×imperf (9.40)	60·00	65·00
		c. From coils. Perf 15×imperf		
		(20.3.46) ..	..	35·00	15·00
		cw. Wmk inverted ..	..	35·00	15·00
		d. Booklet pane. Three stamps plus		
		three printed labels	..	£1500	
		dw. Wmk inverted ..			
113		1½d. claret (1.40)	..	..	14·00	30
		w. Wmk inverted ..	..	32·00	7·50
114		2d. grey-green (1.40)	..	..	30	10
		w. Wmk inverted ..	..	2·25	75
115	8	2½d. red-brown (3.41)	..	..	9·00	15
		w. Wmk inverted ..	..	20·00	4·00
116	9	3d. blue (12.40)	..	..	60	10
		w. Wmk inverted ..	..	3·50	50
117	8	4d. slate-blue (12.40)	..	..	55	10
		w. Wmk inverted ..	..	14·00	2·75
118	6	5d. deep violet (7.40)	..	..	65	10
		w. Wmk inverted ..	..	26·00	1·50

119	6	6d. claret (3.42)	..	..	2·25	50
		aw. Wmk inverted	..	..	18·00	3·00
		b. Chalk-surfaced paper (1967)	..	1·25	20
		bw. Wmk inverted	..	..	13·00	2·50
119c		8d. scarlet (12.9.49)	..	..	80	80
		cw. Wmk inverted	..	..	32·00	10·00
120	8	9d. deep violet (7.40)	..	..	1·50	80
		w. Wmk inverted	..	..	9·50	2·00
121	9	10d. brown (7.40)	..	..	60	80
		aw. Wmk inverted	..	..	10·00	3·50
121b		11d. rose (12.9.49)	..	..	1·50	2·25
122	6	1s. light blue (6.40)	..	..	70·00	17·00
		w. Wmk inverted	..	..	£600	£150
123	18	2s. 6d. emerald-green (10.2.43)	..	40·00	1·25
		aw. Wmk inverted	..	..	85·00	20·00
		b. Chalk-surfaced paper (1968?)	..	1·50	2·25
124		5s. maroon (15.12.42)	..	..	40·00	3·00
		a. Line flaw	..	..		
		bw. Wmk inverted	..	..	£160	32·00
		c. Chalk-surfaced paper (1968?)	..	13·00	4·00
		ca. *Purple*	..	..	6·00	7·50
		cb. Line flaw	..	..	95·00	
		cw. Wmk inverted	..	..	35·00	9·00
125		10s. deep blue (7.45)	..	..	60·00	6·00
		aw. Wmk inverted	..	..	£180	70·00
		b. Chalk-surfaced paper (1968)	..	19·00	12·00
		ba. *Blue*	..	..	7·00	16·00
		bw. Wmk inverted	..	..	£130	60·00
111/25		..	..	*Set of* 17	£100	30·00

There is a wide range of shades and also variation in paper used in this issue.

1941
1 ȚCUIṁne
ΔISéIRȚE
1916

(**23** *Trans* "In memory of the rising of 1916") **24** Volunteer and G.P.O., Dublin

1941 (12 Apr). *25th Anniv of Easter Rising* (1916). *Provisional issue. T* **7** *and* **9** (2d. in new colour), optd with T **23**.
126	7	2d. orange (G.)	..	..	1·00	50
127	9	3d. blue (V.)	..	..	24·00	9·50

(Des V. Brown. Typo)

1941 (27 Oct). *25th Anniv of Easter Rising* (1916). *Definitive issue.*
W **22**. P 15 × 14.
128	24	2½d. blue-black	..	..	70	60

25 Dr. Douglas Hyde   **26** Sir William Rowan Hamilton   **27** Bro. Michael O'Clery

(Des S. O'Sullivan. Typo)

1943 (31 July). *50th Anniv of Founding of Gaelic League.* W **22**.
P 15 × 14.
129	25	½d. green	..	..	40	30
130		2½d. claret	..	..	1·25	10

(Des S. O'Sullivan from a bust by Hogan. Typo)

1943 (13 Nov). *Centenary of Announcement of Discovery of Quaternions.* W **22**. P 15 × 14.
131	26	½d. green	..	..	40	40
		w. Wmk inverted	..	..		
132		2½d. brown	..	..	1·75	10

(Des R. J. King. Typo)

1944 (30 June). *Tercentenary of Death of Michael O'Clery.* (*Commemorating the "Annals of the Four Masters"*). W **22** (*sideways**). P 14×15.
133	27	½d. emerald-green	..	..	10	10
		w. Wmk facing right	..		55	20
134		1s. red-brown	..	..	70	10
		w. Wmk facing right	..	..	2·25	50

*The normal sideways watermark shows the top of the e facing left, *as seen from the back of the stamp.*
Although issued as commemoratives these two stamps were kept in use as part of the current issue, replacing Nos. 111 and 122.

28 Edmund Ignatius Rice   **29** "Youth Sowing Seeds of Freedom"

(Des S. O'Sullivan. Typo)

1944 (29 Aug). *Death Centenary of Edmund Rice (founder of Irish Christian Brothers).* W **22**. P 15 × 14.
135	28	2½d. slate	..	..	60	45
		w. Wmk inverted	..	..		

(Des R. J. King. Typo)

1945 (15 Sept). *Centenary of Death of Thomas Davis (founder of Young Ireland Movement).* W **22**. P 15 × 14.
136	29	2½d. blue	..	..	1·00	25
		w. Wmk inverted	..	..	—	£130
137		6d. claret	..	..	6·00	3·75

30 "Country and Homestead"

(Des R. J. King. Typo)

1946 (16 Sept). *Birth Centenaries of Davitt and Parnell (land reformers).* W **22**. P 15 × 14.
138	30	2½d. scarlet	..	..	1·50	20
139		3d. blue	..	..	2·75	3·50

31 Angel Victor over Rock of Cashel

(Des R. J. King. Recess Waterlow (1d. to 1s. 3d. until 1961), D.L.R. (8d., 1s. 3d. from 1961 and 1s. 3d.))

1948 (7 Apr)–**65**. *Air. T* **31** *and similar horiz designs.* W **22**. P 15 (1s. 5d.) or 15 × 14 (*others*).
140	31	1d. chocolate (4.4.49)	..	..	1·50	3·50
141	–	3d. blue (4.4.49)	..	..	3·00	2·25
142	–	6d. magenta	..	..	80	1·50
		aw. Wmk inverted	..	..		
142b	–	8d. lake-brown (13.12.54)	..	6·00	7·00
143	–	1s. green (4.4.49)	..	..	80	1·50
143a	31	1s. 3d. red-orange (13.12.54)	..	7·00	1·50
		aw. Wmk inverted	..	..	£550	£250
143b		1s. 5d. deep ultramarine (1.4.65)	..	2·75	1·00
140/3b				*Set of* 7	20·00	16·00

Designs:—3d., 8d. Lough Derg; 6d. Croagh Patrick; 1s. Glendalough.

35 Theobald Wolfe Tone

(Des K. Uhlemann. Typo)

1948 (19 Nov). *150th Anniv of Insurrection.* W **22**. P 15×14.
144 **35** 2½d. reddish purple .. .. .. 1·00 10
145   3d. violet .. .. 3·25 3·25

REPUBLIC OF IRELAND
18 April 1949

36 Leinster House and Arms   37 J. C. Mangan
    of Provinces

(Des Muriel Brandt. Typo)

1949 (21 Nov). *International Recognition of Republic.* W **22**.
P 15 × 14.
146 **36** 2½d. reddish brown .. .. .. 1·50 10
147   3d. bright blue .. .. 5·50 4·25

(Des R. J. King. Typo)

1949 (5 Dec). *Death Centenary of James Clarence Mangan (poet).*
W **22**. P 15 × 14.
148 **37** 1d. green .. .. 1·50 20
     w. Wmk inverted .. .. ..

38 Statue of
St. Peter, Rome

(Recess Waterlow & Sons)

1950 (11 Sept). *Holy Year.* W **22**. P 12½.
149 **38** 2½d. violet .. .. 1·00 40
150   3d. blue .. .. 8·00 8·50
151   9d. brown .. .. 8·00 10·00
149/51 .. .. *Set of* 3 15·00 17·00

MINIMUM PRICE

The minimum price quote is 10p which represents
a handling charge rather than a basis for valuing
common stamps. For further notes about prices
see introductory pages.

STAMP BOOKLETS

B 2 Harp and "EIRE"

1940. *Black on red cover as Type* B **2**.
SB2   2s. booklet containing six ½d., six 2d. (Nos. 71,
     74), each in block of 6, and nine 1d. (No. 72) in
     block of 6 and pane of 3 stamps and 3 labels
     (No. 112d or 112dw) £6500
   Edition No.:—22—40

1940. *Black on red cover as Type* B **2**.
SB3   2s. booklet containing six ½d., six 2d. (Nos. 111,
     114), each in block of 6, and nine 1d. (No. 112)
     in block of 6 and pane of 3 stamps and 3 labels
     (No. 112d or 112dw) £6500
   Edition No.:—23—40

1941–44. *Black on red cover as Type* B **2**.
SB4   2s. booklet containing twelve ½d., six 1d. and six
     2d. (Nos. 111/12, 114) in blocks of 6 .. .. £750
   Edition Nos.:—24—41, 25—42, 26—44

B 3

1945. *Black on red cover as Type* B **3**.
SB5   2s. booklet containing twelve ½d., six 1d. and six
     2d. (Nos. 111/12, 114) in blocks of 6 .. .. £650
   Edition No.:—27—45

1946. *Black on buff cover as Type* B **2**.
SB6   2s. booklet containing twelve ½d., six 1d. and six
     2d. (Nos. 111/12, 114) in blocks of 6 .. .. £475
   Edition No.:—28—46

1946–47. *Black on buff cover as Type* B **2**.
SB7   2s. booklet containing twelve ½d., six 1d. and six
     2d. (Nos. 133, 112, 114) in blocks of 6 .. *From* £225
   Edition Nos.:—29—46, 30—47

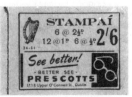

B 4 Harp only

1948–50. *Black on red cover as Type* B 4.
SB8   2s. 6d. booklet containing six ¹/₂d., twelve 1d. and
    six 2¹/₂d. (Nos. 133, 112, 115) in blocks of 6 .. £130
    Edition Nos.:—31–48, 32–49, 33–50

1951–53. *Black on buff cover as Type* B 4.
SB9   2s. 6d. booklet containing six ¹/₂d., twelve 1d. and
    six 2¹/₂d. (Nos. 133, 112, 115) in blocks of 6 .. 50·00
    Edition Nos.:—34–51, 35–52, 36–53

POSTAGE DUE STAMPS

D 1

1940–70. W 22. P 14×15.

D 5	D 1	¹/₂d. emerald-green (1942)	..	..	35·00	22·00
		w. Wmk inverted ..	..		£250	£130
D 6		1d. carmine (1941) ..	..	..	1·50	70
		w. Wmk inverted ..	..		55·00	6·50
D 7		1¹/₂d. vermilion (1953) ..		..	1·75	6·50
		w. Wmk inverted ..	..		15·00	21·00
D 8		2d. deep green (1940) ..		..	2·75	70
		w. Wmk inverted ..	..		20·00	6·50
D 9		3d. blue (10.11.52) ..	..	..	2·25	2·75
		w. Wmk inverted ..	..		6·00	5·00
D10		5d. blue-violet (3.3.43)	..	..	4·50	3·00
		w. Wmk inverted ..	..		6·50	7·00
D11		6d. plum (21.3.60) ..	..	..	3·00	2·00
		a. Wmk sideways (1968)	..		80	95
D12		8d. orange (30.10.62)	..	..	8·50	8·00
		w. Wmk inverted ..	..		17·00	18·00
D13		10d. bright purple (27.1.65) ..		..	8·50	7·50
D14		1s. apple-green (10.2.69)	..	..	6·00	9·00
		a. Wmk sideways (1970)	..		70·00	8·50
D5/14	..	..	..	.. *Set of* 10	65·00	55·00

Jamaica

12 pence (d) = 1 shilling; 20 shillings = 1 pound

CROWN COLONY

47 King George VI and
Queen Elizabeth

(Des and recess D.L.R.)

1937 (12 May). *Coronation. Wmk Mult Script CA.* P 14.

118	**47**	1d. scarlet		30	15
119		1½d. grey-black		50	30
120		2½d. bright blue		85	70
118/20			*Set of* 3	1·50	1·00
118/20 Perf "Specimen"			*Set of* 3	55·00	

48 King
George VI

49 Coco Palms at
Don Christopher's
Cove

50 Bananas

51 Citrus Grove

52 Kingston Harbour

53 Sugar Industry

54 Bamboo Walk

55 King George VI

56 Tobacco Growing and
Cigar Making

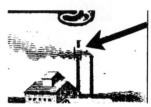

Repaired chimney (Centre plate 1 R. 11/1)

(Recess D.L.R. (T **48**, 5s. and 10s.), Waterlow (others))

1938 (10 Oct)–**52.** *T* **48/56** *and similar designs with inset portrait of King George VI, as in T* **49***. Wmk Mult Script CA.* P 13½×14 (½d., 1d., 1½d.), 14 (5s., 10s.) *or* 12½ (*others*).

121	**48**	½d. blue-green (10.10.38)	1·50	10
		a. Wmk sideways	† £3500	
121b		½d. orange (25.10.51)	30	30
122		1d. scarlet	80	10
122a		1d. blue-green (25.10.51)	50	10
123		1½d. brown	80	10
124	**49**	2d. grey and green (10.12.38)	60	60
		a. Perf 13×13½ (1939)	2·00	40
		ab. "C" of "CA" missing from wmk	£750	
		b. Perf 12½×13 (1951)	75	10
125	–	2½d. greenish blue & ultram (10.12.38)	3·00	1·50
126	**50**	3d. ultramarine and green (10.12.38)	70	1·25
		a. "A" of "CA" missing from wmk	£750	
126b		3d. greenish blue and ultram (15.8.49)	1·25	1·25
126c		3d. green and scarlet (1.7.52)	1·50	30
127	**51**	4d. brown and green (10.12.38)	40	10
128		6d. grey and purple (10.12.38)	3·25	30
		a. Perf 13½×13 (10.10.50)	1·75	10
129	**52**	9d. lake (10.12.38)	40	50
		a. "A" of "CA" missing from wmk		
130	**53**	1s. green and purple-brown (10.12.38)	6·00	20
		a. Repaired chimney	£475	£100
131	**54**	2s. blue and chocolate (10.12.38)	20·00	90
132	–	5s. slate-blue & yellow-orge (10.12.38)	14·00	3·75
		a. Perf 14, line (1941)	£2750	£190
		b. Perf 13 (24.10.49)	6·50	3·00
		ba. *Blue and orange* (10.10.50)	6·50	3·00
133	**55**	10s. myrtle-green (10.12.38)	11·00	7·50
		aa. Perf 13 (10.10.50)	9·00	5·00
133a	**56**	£1 chocolate and violet (15.8.49)	27·00	26·00
121/33a		*Set of* 18	70·00	35·00
121/33 Perf "Specimen"		*Set of* 13	£200	

Designs: *Vert*—2½d. Wag Water River, St. Andrew; 5s. Jamaican scenery. *Horiz*—6d. Priestman's River, Portland.

No. 130a occurred in conjunction with Frame plate 2 on printings between 1943 and 1951.

No. 132a shows the emergency use of a line perforation machine, giving an irregular gauge of 14–14.15, after the De La Rue works were damaged in December 1940. The normal comb measures 13.8×13.7.

Nos. 121 and 122 exist in coils constructed from normal sheets.

SELF-GOVERNMENT

57 Courthouse, Falmouth

58 King Charles II and King George VI

59 Institute of Jamaica

(Recess Waterlow)

1945 (20 Aug)–**46**. *New Constitution. T* 57/9 *and similar designs. Wmk Mult Script CA. P* 12½.

134	**57**	1½d. sepia	..	..	20	30
		a. Perf 12½×13 (1946)	..	..	3·00	50
135	**58**	2d. green	..	..	6·50	90
		a. Perf 12½×13 (1945)	..	..	30	50
136	**59**	3d. ultramarine	..	..	20	50
		a. Perf 13 (1946)	..	..	1·25	2·50
137	–	4½d. slate	..	..	30	30
		a. Perf 13 (1946)	..	..	1·50	2·00
138	–	2s. red-brown	..	..	30	50
139	–	5s. indigo	..	..	1·00	1·00
140	**59**	10s. green	..	..	85	2·25
134/40				Set of 7	2·75	4·75
134/40 Perf "Specimen"		..		Set of 7	£140	

Designs: *Vert* (as *T* 57)—2s. "Labour and Learning". *Horiz* (as *T* 59)—4½d. House of Assembly; 5s. Scroll, flag and King George VI.

60 Houses of Parliament, London

(Des and recess D.L.R.)

1946 (14 Oct). *Victory. Wmk Mult Script CA. P* 13½×14.

141	**60**	1½d. purple-brown	..	..	2·50	10
		a. Perf 13½	..	..	30	65
142		3d. blue	..	..	2·50	2·25
		a. Perf 13½	..	..	30	4·25
141/2 Perf "Specimen"		..		Set of 2	50·00	

61
King George VI and Queen Elizabeth
62

(Des and photo Waterlow (T **61**). Design recess, name typo B.W. (T **62**))

1948 (1 Dec). *Royal Silver Wedding. Wmk Mult Script CA.*

143	**61**	1½d. red-brown (*p* 14×15)	..	..	30	10
144	**62**	£1 scarlet (*p* 11½×11)	..	..	24·00	45·00

63 Hermes, Globe and Forms of Transport

64 Hemispheres, Vickers Viking Airplane and Steamer

65 Hermes and Globe

66 U.P.U. Monument

(Recess Waterlow (T **63**, **66**). Design recess, name typo B.W. (T **64**/5))

1949 (10 Oct). *75th Anniv of Universal Postal Union. Wmk Mult Script CA.*

145	**63**	1½d. red-brown (*p* 13½–14)	..	..	30	15
146	**64**	2d. deep blue-green (*p* 11×11½)	..	1·00	1·75
147	**65**	3d. deep blue (*p* 11×11½)	..	..	55	1·25
148	**66**	6d. purple (*p* 13½–14)	..	..	65	2·50
145/8		..	..	..	Set of 4	2·25	5·00

67 Arms of University

68 Princess Alice

(Recess Waterlow)

1951 (16 Feb). *Inauguration of B.W.I. University College. Wmk Mult Script CA. P* 14×14½.

149	**67**	2d. black and red-brown	..	..	30	30
150	**68**	6d. grey-black and purple	..	..	35	30

69 Scout Badge and Map of Caribbean

70 Scout Badge and Map of Jamaica

(Litho B.W.)

1952 (5 Mar). *First Caribbean Scout Jamboree. Wmk Mult Script CA. P 13½×13 (2d.) or 13×13½ (6d.).*
151	**69**	2d. blue, apple-green and black	..	15	10
152	**70**	6d. yellow-green, carmine-red and black		15	50

STAMP BOOKLETS

1938–40. *Black on green cover inscr "JAMAICA POSTAGE STAMPS" in one line. Inland Postage Rates on interleaf. Stapled.*
SB9 2s. booklet containing twelve ½d. and eighteen 1d. (Nos. 121/2), each in blocks of 6 (inland letter rate 1d. per oz) £350
    a. Inland letter rate 1½d. for first 2 oz (1940) ..

1942–47. *Black on blue cover inscr "JAMAICA POSTAGE STAMPS" in three lines. Inland Postage Rates on inside front cover. Stapled.*
SB10 2s. booklet containing twelve ½d. and eighteen 1d. (Nos. 121/2), each in blocks of 6 (Inland letter rate 1½d. for first 2 oz) £225
    a. Black on yellow cover (1947) £130

1946. *New Constitution. Black on blue cover. Stapled.*
SB12 2s. booklet containing sixteen 1½d. (No. 134a) in blocks of 4 .. .. £225

1952. *Black on yellow cover. Stapled.*
SB13 2s. booklet containing twelve ½d and eighteen 1d. (Nos. 121b, 122a), each in blocks of 6 .. 42·00

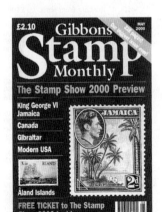

Kenya, Uganda and Tanganyika

100 cents = 1 East Africa shilling

COMBINED POSTAL ADMINISTRATION

1937 (12 May). *Coronation. As Nos.* 118/20 *of Jamaica.*

128	5 c. green	..	..	..	20	10
129	20 c. orange	..	..	..	40	30
130	30 c. bright blue	..	..	..	60	1·25
128/30		..	..	*Set of* 3	1·10	1·50
128/30 Perf "Specimen"		..	..	*Set of* 3	65·00	

14a South African
Crowned Cranes

15b Lion

15 Dhow on Lake Victoria

15a Kilimanjaro

Damaged left-hand
value tablet (Frame
Pl 2–2, with Centre
Pl 4B only, R. 9/6)

Retouched value
tablet (Frame Pl
2–2, with Centre Pls
4B, 5, 6 or 7, R. 9/6)

Break in bird's breast
(Frame Pl 2–2, with
Centre Pls 4A or 4B,
R. 2/5)

Damage on mountain
(Pl 7B R. 6/7. August 1948
ptg. Retouched in June
1949 for 10 c. and 1 s.)

Mountain retouch (Pl 7B,
R. 5/10 and 6/7. Ptgs from
June 1949 onwards)

With dot

Dot removed

In the 50 c. printing of 14 June 1950, using Frame-plate 3, the dot was removed by retouching on all but five stamps (R. 5/2, 6/1, 7/2, 7/4, and 9/1). In addition, other stamps show traces of the dot where the retouching was not completely effective.

PERFORATIONS. In this issue, to aid identification, the perforations are indicated to the nearest quarter.

(£1 typo, others recess D.L.R.)

1938 (11 Apr)–**54.** *T* 14a/15b *and similar designs showing portrait of King George VI. Wmk Mult Script CA. Chalk-surfaced paper* (£1).

131	14a	1 c. black & red-brown (p 13¼) (2.5.38)		1·75	85
		a. Perf 13¼×13¾. *Black & choc-*			
		brown (1942) ..	..	30	40
		ab. "A" of "CA" missing from wmk ..	..	£1000	
		ac. Damaged value tablet ..	..	85·00	
		ad. Retouched value tablet ..	..	45·00	65·00
		ae. Break in bird's breast ..	..	75·00	
		af. Black & dp chocolate-brn (10.6.46)	2·25	1·75	
		ag. Ditto. Retouched tablet ..	..	50·00	70·00
		ah. Black and red-brown (26.9.51)	..	2·50	1·75
132	15	5 c. black and green (p 13×11¾)		2·75	50
133		5 c. reddish brown & orge (p 13×11¾)			
		(1.6.49) ..	..	40	30
		a. Perf 13×12½ (14.6.50) ..		1·60	3·00
134	–	10 c. red-brn & orge (p 13×11¾) (2.5.38)	1·75	10	
		aw. Wmk inverted ..	..		
		b. Perf 14 (22.4.41) ..	..	£110	6·50
135	–	10 c. black & green (p 13×11¾) (1.6.49)	30	85	
		a. Mountain retouch ..	..	70·00	50·00
		b. Perf 13×12½ (14.6.50) ..	..	1·25	10
136	–	10 c. brown & grey (p 13×12½) (1.4.52)	75	55	
137	15a	15 c. black and rose-red (p 13¼) (2.5.38)	12·00	55	
		a. Perf 13¾×13¼ (2.43) ..	..	3·75	3·75
		ab. "A" of "CA" missing from wmk ..			
138		15 c. black & grn (p 13¾×13¼) (1.4.52)	1·60	3·00	
139	14a	20 c. black and orange (p 13¼) (2.5.38)	35·00	30	
		a. Perf 14 (19.5.41) ..	..	55·00	1·75
		b. Perf 13¼×13¾ (25.2.42) ..	..	6·00	10
		ba. Deep black and deep orange (8.51)	11·00	1·25	
		bw. Wmk inverted ..	..		†
140	15	25 c. blk & car-red (p 13×12½) (1.4.52)	1·25	2·25	
141	–	30 c. black & dull vio-bl (p 13¼) (2.5.38)	50·00	60	
		a. Perf 14 (3.7.41) ..	..	£140	11·00
		b. Perf 13¼×13¾ (10.5.42) ..		2·75	10
142	–	30 c. dull purple & brown (p 13¼×13¾)			
		(1.4.52) ..	..	1·50	40
143	14a	40 c. black & blue (p 13¼×13¾) (1.4.52)	1·75	3·00	

144	15	50 c. purple & blk (II) (*p* 13×11³/₄) (2.5.38)	13·00	1·00
		a. Rope not joined to sail (I) (R. 2/5)	£225	£225
		b. *Dull claret and black* (29.7.47) ..	28·00	4·50
		c. *Brown-purple and black* (4.48) ..	26·00	4·50
		d. *Reddish purple and black* (28.4.49)	20·00	2·50
		e. Ditto. Perf 13×12¹/₂ (10.49) ..	7·00	55
		ea. Dot removed (14.6.50)	12·00	55
		eb. Ditto. In pair with normal ..	£275	£100
		ew. Wmk inverted	† £2250	
145	–	1 s. black & yellowish brn (*p* 13×11³/₄)		
		(2.5.38)	12·00	30
		a. *Black and brown* (9.42)	9·50	30
		ab. Damage on mountain	£250	
		ac. Mountain retouch	£800	£160
		aw. Wmk inverted	† £1900	
		b. Perf 13×12¹/₂ (10.49)	10·00	60
		ba. *Deep black and brown* (clearer		
		impression) (14.6.50)	13·00	1·50
146	15a	2 s. lake-brn & brn-pur (*p* 13¹/₄) (2.5.38)	£110	2·00
		a. Perf 14 (1941)	70·00	11·00
		b. Perf 13³/₄×13¹/₄ (24.2.44) ..	15·00	30
147	–	3 s. dull ultramarine & blk (*p* 13×11³/₄)		
		(2.5.38)	35·00	3·50
		a. *Deep violet-blue and black* (29.4.47)	45·00	7·50
		ab. Damage on mountain	£1200	
		ac. Perf 13×12¹/₂ (14.6.50)	23·00	2·00
148	–	5 s. black and carmine (*p* 13¹/₄) (2.5.38)	£130	14·00
		a. Perf 14 (1941)	28·00	2·00
		b. Perf 13¹/₄×13³/₄ (24.2.44) ..	23·00	1·00
149	14a	10 s. purple and blue (*p* 13¹/₄) (2.5.38)	£120	21·00
		a. Perf 14. *Reddish purple & bl* (1941)	30·00	17·00
		b. Perf 13¹/₄×13³/₄ (24.2.44) ..	30·00	3·00
150	15b	£1 black and red (*p* 11³/₄×13) (12.10.38)	£300	£120
		a. Perf 14 (1941)	17·00	15·00
		ab. Ordinary paper (24.2.44)	17·00	16·00
		b. Perf 12¹/₂ (21.1.54)	10·00	29·00
131/50ab (*cheapest*) .. .. Set of 20			£120	30·00
131/50 Perf "Specimen" .. Set of 13			£450	

Designs: *Vert* (*as T* 14a)—30 c., 5 s. Nile Railway Bridge,
Ripon Falls. *Horiz* (*as T* 15)—10 c., 1 s., 3 s. Lake Naivasha.
The first printing of the 50 c. utilised the King George V
centre plate on which each impression had been individually
corrected to show the rope joined to sail. R. 2/5 was missed,
however, and this continued to show Type I until replaced by a
further printing from a new plate in September 1938.
Stamps perf 14, together with Nos. 131a, 137a, 139b, 141b,
146b, 148b and 149b, are the result of air raid damage to the De
La Rue works which destroyed the normal perforators. Dates
quoted for these stamps represent earliest known postmarks.

1941 (1 July)–**42.** *Pictorial Stamps of South Africa variously
surch as T* **16** *by Government Printer, Pretoria. Inscr alternately
in English and Afrikaans.*

			Un.	Used	Used
			pair	pair	single
151	5 c. on 1d. grey & carmine (No. 56)	60	1·75	15
152	10 c. on 3d. ultramarine (No. 59) ..	1·00	5·00	30
153	20 c. on 6d. green & verm (No. 61a)	1·00	2·25	20
154	70 c. on 1s. brown and chalky blue			
	(No. 62) (20.4.42)	9·50	4·50	40
	a. Crescent moon flaw	60·00		
151/4	.. .. .. *Set of 4*	11·00	12·00	95
151/4 Handstamped "Specimen"	*Set of 4*	£190		

1946 (11 Nov). *Victory. As Nos. 141/2 of Jamaica.*

				Unused	Used
155	20 c. red-orange	.. .. ..		30	10
156	30 c. blue	.. .. ..		30	50
155/6 Perf "Specimen"	.. ..	*Set of 2*	55·00		

Examples of Nos. 155/6 were prereleased at Lindi on 15
October 1946.

1948 (1 Dec). *Royal Silver Wedding. As Nos. 143/4 of Jamaica.*

157	20 c. orange	15	10
158	£1 scarlet	35·00	50·00

1949 (10 Oct). *75th Anniv of Universal Postal Union. As Nos.
145/8 of Jamaica.*

159	20 c. red-orange	.. .. ..	20	10
160	30 c. deep blue ..	.. .. ..	1·50	1·25
161	50 c. grey	.. .. ..	75	20
162	1 s. red-brown	.. .. ..	75	40
159/62	.. .. ..	*Set of 4*	2·75	1·75

(Recess D.L.R.)

1952 (1 Feb). *Visit of Princess Elizabeth and Duke of Edinburgh. Nos.* 135b *and* 145b *additionally inscr* "ROYAL VISIT
1952". *Wmk Mult Script CA. P* 13×12¹/₂.

163	10 c. black and green	.. ..	10	1·50
164	1 s. black and brown	.. ..	20	1·75

STAMP BOOKLETS

1938. *Black on pink cover. Stapled.*

SB3   3 s. 40, booklet containing twelve 15 c. and eight
20 c. (Nos. 137, 139), each in blocks of 4   .. £190

1950–52. *Blue on yellow cover. Stapled.*

SB4   1 s. booklet containing four 5 c. and eight 10 c.
(Nos. 133a, 135b), each in blocks of 4   .. £120
a. Stitched   .. .. 50·00
ab. Contents as No. SB4a, but 10 c. changed to No.
136 (1952)   .. .. 35·00

POSTAGE DUE STAMPS

D 2

(Typo D.L.R.)

1935 (1 May)–**60.** *Wmk Mult Script CA. P* 14.

D 7	D 2	5 c. violet	.. .. ..	2·75	1·75
D 8		10 c. scarlet	.. .. ..	30	50
D 9		20 c. green	.. .. ..	40	50
D10		30 c. brown	.. .. ..	80	50
		a. *Bistre-brown* (19.7.60)	.. ..	3·00	7·00
D11		40 c. ultramarine	.. ..	1·50	3·00
D12		1 s. grey ..	.. ..	19·00	19·00
D7/12 ..	..	..	*Set of 6*	22·00	23·00
D7/12 Perf "Specimen"	..	*Set of 6*	£110	

10ᶜ
KENYA
TANGANYIKA
UGANDA

(16)

A screw head in the
surcharging forme appears
as a crescent moon (R. 20/4)

Kuwait

16 annas = 1 rupee

INDIAN POSTAL ADMINISTRATION

1939. *Nos. 248, 250/1, 253, 255/63 of India (King George VI) optd with T 3 or 4 (rupee values).*

36	½ a. red-brown	..	..	..	7·00	1·75
38	1 a. carmine	..	..	..	7·00	1·50
39	2 a. vermilion	..	..	..	7·00	2·50
41	3 a. yellow-green	..	..	..	7·00	2·00
43	4 a. brown	..	..	..	35·00	14·00
44	6 a. turquoise-green	..	..	..	25·00	7·50
45	8 a. slate-violet	..	..	..	28·00	32·00
46	12 a. lake	..	..	..	20·00	48·00
47	1 r. grey and red-brown	..	..	6·50	2·75
	a. Extended "T"	..	..	..	£300	
	b. Opt triple, one inverted	..	..		
48	2 r. purple and brown	..	..	3·75	13·00
	a. Extended "T"	..	..	..	£275	
49	5 r. green and blue	..	..	12·00	18·00
	a. Extended "T"	..	..	..	£425	
50	10 r. purple and claret	..	..	60·00	75·00
	a. Opt double	..	..	..	£325	
	b. Extended "T"	..	..	..	£600	
51	15 r. brown and green	..	..	£130	£190
	a. Extended "T"	..	..	..	£850	
	w. Wmk inverted	..	..	85·00	£150
36/51w	..	..	..	*Set of 13*	£275	£325

On later printings the extended "T" variety was corrected in two stages.

Examples of most values are known showing a forged Kuwait postmark dated "17 NOV 39".

> Following the rebellion in Iraq control of the Kuwait postal service was assumed by the Indian authorities on 2 June 1941.
> Unoverprinted stamps of INDIA were used in Kuwait between 1941 and 1945.

1945. *Nos. 265/8 and 269a of India (King George VI, on white background) optd with T 3.*

52	3 p. slate	..	..	..	1·25	2·50
53	½ a. purple	..	..	..	1·25	2·50
54	9 p. green	..	..	..	2·75	7·50
55	1 a. carmine	..	..	..	1·50	2·00
56	1½ a. dull violet	..	..	..	3·25	7·50
57	2 a. vermilion	..	..	..	3·50	2·75
58	3 a. bright violet	..	..	..	3·75	3·50
59	3½ a. bright blue	..	..	..	4·00	7·50
60	4 a. brown	..	..	..	3·50	2·50
60a	6 a. turquoise-green	..	..	..	14·00	8·50
61	8 a. slate-violet	..	..	..	7·00	3·75
62	12 a. lake	..	..	..	7·50	3·25
63	14 a. purple	..	..	..	14·00	16·00
52/63	..	..	..	*Set of 13*	60·00	60·00

Following a short period of Pakistani control, from August 1947 the Kuwait postal service passed to British administration on 1 April 1948.

BRITISH POSTAL ADMINISTRATION

KUWAIT

(5)

KUWAIT

1 ANNA

(5)

KUWAIT

5 RUPEES

(6)

NOTE. From 1948 onwards, for stamps with similar surcharges but without name of country, see British Postal Agencies in Eastern Arabia.

1948 (1 Apr)–49. *Nos. 470, 475, 476a/7, 478a and 485/90 of Great Britain (King George VI), surch as T 5 or 6 (rupee values).*

64	½ a. on ½d. pale green	..	..	1·25	1·25
65	1 a. on 1d. pale scarlet	..	..	1·25	1·25
66	1½ a. on 1½d. pale red-brown	..	..	1·75	75
67	2 a. on 2d. pale orange	..	..	1·25	90
68	2½ a. on 2½d. light ultramarine	..	..	1·75	1·00
69	3 a. on 3d. pale violet	..	..	1·25	30
	a. Pair, one surch albino	..	..		
70	6 a. on 6d. purple	..	..	1·25	60
71	1 r. on 1s. bistre-brown	..	..	3·00	1·00
72	2 r. on 2s. 6d. yellow-green	..	..	3·50	4·50
73	5 r. on 5s. red	..	..	5·50	4·50
73a	10 r. on 10s. ultramarine (4.7.49)	..	..	38·00	6·00
64/73a	..	..	..	*Set of 11*	55·00	20·00

KUWAIT 2½ ANNAS

(7)

KUWAIT 15 RUPEES ═

(8)

1948 (1 May). *Royal Silver Wedding. Nos. 493/4 of Great Britain surch with T 7 or 8.*

74	2½ a. on 2½d. ultramarine	..	..	1·50	60
75	15 r. on £1 blue	..	..	30·00	30·00
	a. Short bars (R. 3/4)	..	..	£130	

No. 75a has the bars cancelling the original face value 3 mm long instead of the 3½ mm of the normal surcharge.

1948 (29 July). *Olympic Games. Nos. 495/8 of Great Britain surch as T 7, but in one line (6 a.) or two lines (others).*

76	2½ a. on 2½d. ultramarine	..	..	1·00	1·50
77	3 a. on 3d. violet	..	..	1·00	1·50
78	6 a. on 6d. bright purple	..	..	1·25	1·50
79	1 r. on 1s. brown	..	..	1·25	1·50
76/9	..	..	..	*Set of 4*	4·00	5·50

1949 (10 Oct). *75th Anniv of U.P.U. Nos. 499/502 of Great Britain surch "KUWAIT" and new values.*

80	2½ a. on 2½d. ultramarine	..	..	90	1·75
81	3 a. on 3d. violet	..	..	1·25	2·25
82	6 a. on 6d. bright purple	..	..	1·25	2·25
83	1 r. on 1s. brown	..	..	1·25	1·25
80/3	..	..	..	*Set of 4*	4·25	6·75

═ KUWAIT   **═ KUWAIT**

═ 2 RUPEES
Type I

(8a)

═ 2 RUPEES
Type II

KUWAIT

Type I

1O RUPEES ═══

KUWAIT

Type II

1O RUPEES ═══

(8b)

2 r. Type I   Type-set surcharge. "2" level with "RUPEES". Surcharge sharp.
Type II.   Plate-printed surcharge. "2" raised. Surcharge worn.
10 r. Type I.   Type-set surcharge. "1" and "O" spaced. Surcharge sharp and clean.
Type II.   Plate-printed surcharge. "1" and "O" closer together. Surcharge appears heavy and worn, see especially "A", "R" and "P".

═══ **KUWAIT**   ═══ **KUWAIT**
Extra bar in centre   Extra bar at top
(R. 7/2)   (R. 2/2)

1950 (2 Oct)–54.   *Nos. 503/11 of Great Britain (King George VI)
surch as T 5 or 8a/b (rupee values).*

84	½ a. on ½d. pale orange (3.5.51) ..	.. 1·75	1·50
85	1 a. on 1d. light ultramarine (3.5.51)	.. 1·75	1·10
86	1½ a. on 1½d. pale green (3.5.51) ..	.. 1·75	2·25
87	2 a. on 2d. pale red-brown (3.5.51)	.. 1·75	85
88	2½ a. on 2½d. pale scarlet (3.5.51)	.. 1·75	2·25
89	4 a. on 4d. light ultramarine ..	.. 1·50	90
90	2 r. on 2s. 6d. yellow-green (I) (3.5.51)	.. 15·00	4·50
	a. Extra bar in centre	.. £400	£350
	b. Type II surch (1954)	.. £180	50·00
91	5 r. on 5s. red (3.5.51)	.. 21·00	5·00
	a. Extra bar at top	.. £275	£225
92	10 r. on 10s. ultramarine (I) (3.5.51)	.. 29·00	6·50
	a. Type II surch (1952)	.. £225	50·00
84/92	.. ..	*Set of* 9 65·00	22·00

No. 92a is known with surch spaced 10 mm apart instead of 9 mm.

Leeward Islands

1937. 12 pence (d) = 1 shilling; 20 shillings = 1 pound
1951. 100 cents = 1 West Indian dollar

FEDERAL COLONY

1937 (12 May). *Coronation. As Nos. 118/20 of Jamaica.*

92	1d. scarlet	..	..	..	30	15
93	1½d. buff	..	..	..	40	35
94	2½d. bright blue	..	..		40	45
92/4	..	..	..	Set of 3	1·00	85
92/4 Perf "Specimen"		..	..	Set of 3	60·00	

14

15

(Die A)

(Die B)

In Die B the figure "1" has a broader top and more projecting serif.

"ISLANDS" flaw (R. 1/2 of right pane) (Pl. 2 ptgs from November 1942 until corrected in July 1949)

Broken second "E" in "LEEWARD" (R. 4/1 of right pane) (Pl. 3 ptgs from August 1942 until corrected in June 1949)

"D I" shaved at foot (1d. R. 7/3 of left pane from all ptgs between Sept 1947 and July 1949. 1s. R. 9/6 of right pane from all ptgs between 1932 and 1938)

NEW INFORMATION

The editor is always interested to correspond with people who have new information that will improve or correct the Catalogue.

Broken top right scroll (R. 5/11) (1942 ptg of 10s. only. Corrected on £1 value from same period)

Broken lower right scroll (R. 5/12. 1942 ptgs only)

Missing pearl (R. 5/1. 1944 ptgs only)

Gash in chin (R. 2/5. 1942 ptgs only)

1938 (25 Nov)–51. *T* **14** *(and similar type, but shaded value tablet, ½d., 1d., 2½d., 6d.) and* **15** *(10s., £1). Chalk-surfaced paper (3d. to £1). P* 14.

(a) Wmk Mult Script CA

95	½d. brown	..	..	..	30	1·25
	a. Chalk-surfaced paper. *Dp brn* (13.6.49)				10	1·25
96	½d. emerald	..	..	..	60	60
	a. "ISLANDS" flaw	..	..	48·00		
97	½d. slate-grey (*chalk-surfaced paper*) (1.7.49)		..	..	30	1·25
98	1d. scarlet (Die A)	..	..	9·00	1·75
99	1d. scarlet (*shades*) (Die B) (1940)	..	1·75	1·50
	a. "D I" flaw (9.47)	..	..	£150	
	b. *Carmine* (9.42)	..	..	1·00	4·25
	c. *Red* (13.9.48) ..	..	..	5·50	3·00
	ca. "D I" flaw	..	..	£150	
100	1d. blue-green (*chalk-surfaced paper*) (1.7.49)		..	..	55	15
	a. "D I" flaw	..	..	£140	
101	1½d. chestnut	..	..	..	90	50
102	1½d. yellow-orange and black (*chalk-surfaced paper*) (1.7.49)		..	..	60	30
103	2d. olive-grey	..	..	..	2·50	1·00
	a. *Slate-grey* (11.42)	..	..	5·50	2·75
104	2d. scarlet (*chalk-surfaced paper*) (1.7.49)		..	1·40	90
	a. *Vermilion* (24.10.51) ..	..	..	15·00	9·00

105	2½d. bright blue	..	..	8·50	2·25
	a. *Light bright blue* (11.42)	..	..	60	1·25
106	2½d. black and purple (*chalk-surfaced*				
	paper) (1.7.49)	..	..	55	15
107	3d. orange	..	..	35·00	2·75
	a. Ordinary paper. *Pale orange* (11.42)		40	85
108	3d. bright blue (1.7.49)	..	..	65	15
109	6d. deep dull purple and bright purple		20·00	4·75
	a. Ordinary paper (8.42)	..	..	4·50	2·25
	ab. Broken "E"	..	..	£200	
	b. *Purple and deep magenta* (29.9.47)	..	£200	2·75
	ba. Broken "E"	..	..	£200	
110	1s. black/*emerald*	..	..	16·00	2·00
	a. "D I" flaw	..	..	£325	
	b. Ordinary paper (3.42)	..	..	4·25	90
	ba. *Grey and black/emerald* (8.42)	..	23·00	4·00
	bb. *Black and grey/emerald* (11.42)	..	£130	11·00
111	2s. reddish purple and blue/*blue*	..	20·00	2·25
	a. Ordinary paper (3.42)	..	..	10·00	1·50
	ab. *Deep purple and blue/blue* (29.9.47)		10·00	2·25
112	5s. green and red/*yellow* ..	..	48·00	15·00
	a. Ordinary paper (12.43)	..	..	32·00	14·00
	ab. Broken "E" (R. 3/4 of left pane)	..	£500	
	b. *Bright green and red/yellow* (24.10.51)	55·00	50·00
113	10s. bluish green and deep red/*green*	..	£190	£120
	a. Ordinary paper. *Pale green and dull*			
	red/green (26.6.44*)	..	..	£425	£250
	ad. Broken top right scroll	..	..	£3000	
	ae. Broken lower right scroll	..	£3000	£3000
	af. Gash in chin ..	..	..	£2750	
	b. Ordinary paper. *Green and red/green*			
	(22.2.45*)	..	..	£150	65·00
	c. Ordinary paper. *Deep green and deep*			
	vermilion/green (17.7.48*)	..	..	£120	70·00
	ca. Missing pearl	..	..	£1200	
	(b) Wmk Mult Crown CA				
114	£1 brown-purple and black/*red* ..	..	£300	£225
	a. *Purple and black/carmine* (21.9.42*)	85·00	45·00
	ae. Broken lower right scroll	..	£1100	£550
	af. Broken top right scroll	..	£1100	£550
	b. *Brown-purple & black/salmon* (5.2.45*)	35·00	24·00
	ba. Missing pearl	..	..	£950	£650
	c. Perf 13. *Violet & black/scarlet* (4.1.52*)	32·00	38·00
	ca. Wmk sideways	..	..	£3000	
	cw. Wmk inverted	..	..	£2250	
	95/114*b*	..	..	*Set of* 19	£190	£100
	95/114 Perf "Specimen" ..	..	*Set of* 13	£500

*Dates quoted for Nos. 113a/14c are earliest known postmark dates. Nos. 113a and 114a were despatched to the Leeward Islands in March 1942, Nos. 113b and 114b in December 1943, No. 113c in June 1944 and No. 114c on 13 December 1951.

Nos. 96, 98/9 and 99b exist in coils constructed from normal sheets.

Printings of the 10s. in March 1942 (No. 113a) and of the £1 in February and October 1942 (No. 114a) were made by Williams Lea & Co. Ltd. following bomb damage to the De La Rue works in 1940.

1946 (1 Nov). *Victory. As Nos. 141/2 of Jamaica.*

115	1½d. brown	..	..	..	15	30
116	3d. red-orange	..	..	..	15	30
115/16 Perf "Specimen"	..	..	*Set of* 2	55·00	

1949 (2 Jan). *Royal Silver Wedding. As Nos. 143/4 of Jamaica.*

117	2½d. ultramarine	..	..	..	10	10
118	5s. green	..	..	..	3·75	2·75

1949 (10 Oct). *75th Anniv of Universal Postal Union. As Nos. 145/8 of Jamaica.*

119	2½d. blue-black	..	..	..	15	80
120	3d. deep blue	..	..	..	1·25	80
121	6d. magenta..	..	..	..	30	80
122	1s. blue-green	..	..	..	30	80
119/22	..	..	..	*Set of* 4	1·75	2·75

(New Currency. 100 cents = 1 B.W.I. dollar)

1951 (16 Feb). *Inauguration of B.W.I. University College. As Nos. 149/50 of Jamaica.*

123	3 c. orange and black..	..	..	..	30	60
124	12 c. rose-carmine and reddish violet..	..	60	60

Malaya

100 cents = 1 Malayan dollar

STRAITS SETTLEMENTS

CROWN COLONY

1937 (12 May). *Coronation. As Nos. 118/20 of Jamaica.*

275	4 c. orange				30	10
276	8 c. grey-black				70	10
277	12 c. bright blue				1·25	60
275/7				*Set of 3*	2·00	65
275/7 Perf "Specimen"			*Set of 3*	70·00	

58

1937–41. *Chalk-surfaced paper. Wmk Mult Script CA. P 14 or 15×14 (15 c.). (a) Die I (printed at two operations).*

278	58	1 c. black (1.1.38)			4·00	10
279		2 c. green (6.12.37)			18·00	10
280		4 c. orange (1.1.38)			13·00	20
281		5 c. brown (19.11.37)			20·00	30
282		6 c. scarlet (10.1.38)			10·00	50
283		8 c. grey (26.1.38)			40·00	10
284		10 c. dull purple (8.11.37)			7·50	10
285		12 c. ultramarine (10.1.38)			8·00	30
286		25 c. dull purple and scarlet (11.12.37)		42·00	1·10
287		30 c. dull purple and orange (1.12.37)		30·00	2·00
288		40 c. scarlet and dull purple (20.12.37)		10·00	2·25
289		50 c. black/*emerald* (26.1.38)		10·00	10
290		$1 black and red/*blue* (26.1.38)		15·00	20
291		$2 green and scarlet (26.1.38)		30·00	4·00
292		$5 green and red/*emerald* (26.1.38)		25·00	3·25

(b) Die II (printed at one operation)

293	58	2 c. green (28.12.38)			50·00	40
294		2 c. orange (6.10.41)			2·00	9·00
295		3 c. green (*ordinary paper*) (5.9.41)		3·25	4·00
296		4 c. orange (29.10.38)			70·00	10
297		5 c. brown (18.2.39)			28·00	10
298		15 c. ultram (*ordinary paper*) (6.10.41)	5·00	10·00
278/98				*Set of 18*	£275	32·00
278/92, 294/5, 298 Perf "Specimen"		*Set of 18*	£375	

Die I. Lines of background outside central oval touch the oval and the foliage of the palm tree is usually joined to the oval frame. The downward-pointing palm frond, opposite the King's eye, has two points.

Die II. Lines of background are separated from the oval by a white line and the foliage of the palm trees does not touch the outer frame. The palm frond has only one point.

Nos. 295 and 298 were printed by Harrison and Sons following bomb damage to the De La Rue works on 29 December 1940.

The 6 c. grey, 8 c. scarlet and $5 purple and orange were only issued with the BMA overprint, but the 8 c. without overprint is known although in this state it was never issued (*Price* £14).

STAMP BOOKLETS

1938. *Black on buff (No. SB11) or black on green (No. SB12) covers. Stapled.*

SB11 $1 booklet containing twenty 5 c. (No. 281) in
     blocks of 10 .. .. £1200
SB12 $1.30, booklet containing 5 c. and 8 c. (Nos. 281,
     283) in blocks of 10 and pane of airmail labels £1500

MALAYAN POSTAL UNION

The Malayan Postal Union was organised in 1934 and, initially, covered the Straits Settlements and the Federated Malay States. Stamps of the Straits Settlements together with issues for the individual States continued to be used, but Malayan Postal Union postage due stamps were introduced in 1936.

Following the end of the Second World War the use of these postage dues spread throughout Malaya and to Singapore.

POSTAGE DUE STAMPS

10

cents

D 1   (D 2)

(Typo Waterlow until 1961, then D.L.R.)

1936 (June)**–38.** *Wmk Mult Script CA. P 15 × 14.*

D1	D 1	1 c. slate-purple (4.38)			4·00	70
D2		4 c. green (9.36)..			13·00	1·00
D3		8 c. scarlet			6·50	3·50
D4		10 c. yellow-orange			9·00	30
D5		12 c. pale ultramarine (9.36)		10·00	14·00
D6		50 c. black (1.38)..			28·00	6·00
D1/6				*Set of 6*	60·00	23·00
D1/6 Perf "Specimen"		*Set of 6*	£140	

For use in Negri Sembilan, Pahang, Perak, Selangor and Straits Settlements including Singapore.

1945–49. *New values and colours. Wmk Mult Script CA. P 15 × 14.*

D 7	D 1	1 c. purple			2·75	1·75
D 8		3 c. green			6·00	6·00
D 9		5 c. scarlet			6·00	8·50
D10		8 c. yell-orange (1949) (Perf S. £75)	16·00	16·00
D11		9 c. yellow-orange			50·00	48·00
D12		15 c. pale ultramarine			£140	35·00
D13		20 c. blue (1948) (Perf S. £75)		8·00	5·00
D7/13 ..				*Set of 7*	£200	£110

1951 (8 Aug)**–63.** *Wmk Mult Script CA. P 14.*

D14	D 1	1 c. violet (21.8.52)			40	1·40
D15		2 c. deep slate-blue (16.11.53)		90	2·25
		a. Perf 12½ (15.11.60)			40	11·00
		ab. Chalk-surfaced paper (10.7.62)	35	6·50
		ac. Ditto. Imperf between (vert pair)		
D16		3 c. deep green (21.8.52)		24·00	12·00
D17		4 c. sepia (16.11.53)			45	4·50
		a. Perf 12½ (15.11.60)			60	16·00
		ab. Chalk-surfaced paper. *Bistrebrown* (10.7.62)		70	13·00
D18		5 c. vermilion			48·00	12·00
D19		8 c. yellow-orange			2·00	4·25
D20		12 c. bright purple (1.2.54)		1·00	5·50
		a. Perf 12½. Chalk-surfaced paper (10.7.62) ..		1·50	22·00
D21		20 c. blue			4·00	6·50
		a. Perf 12½. *Deep blue* (10.12.57)	6·50	26·00
		ab. Chalk-surfaced paper (15.10.63)	3·00	32·00
D14/21				*Set of 8*	70·00	42·00

Nos. D7 to D21b were for use in the Federation and Singapore, and from 1963 throughout Malaysia.

MALAYA (BRITISH MILITARY ADMINISTRATION)

For use throughout all Malay States and in Singapore. From 1948 this general issue was gradually replaced by individual issues for each state. The last usage was in Kelantan where B M A overprints were not withdrawn until 10 July 1951.

B M A
MALAYA

(1)

1945 (19 Oct)–48. *T 58 of Straits Settlements from Die I (double-plate printing) or Die II (single-plate printing) optd with T 1. Wmk Mult Script CA. Chalk-surfaced paper. P 14 or 15×14 (No. 11).*

1	1 c. black (I) (R.)		2·50	40
	a. Ordinary paper		10	30
2	2 c. orange (II) (8.7.47)		4·00	60
	a. Ordinary paper (19.10.45)		20	10
	w. Wmk inverted		†£1300	
3	2 c. orange (I) (*ordinary paper*) (9.46)		16·00	3·25
4	3 c. yellow-green (II) (*ordinary paper*)		30	50
	a. *Blue-green* (27.1.47)		3·50	3·00
	b. Chalk-surfaced paper. *Blue-grn* (8.7.47)		9·00	60
5	5 c. brown (I) (11.45)		70	90
6	6 c. grey (II) (22.3.48)		10·00	2·25
	a. Ordinary paper (19.10.45)		30	20
7	8 c. scarlet (II) (*ordinary paper*)		30	10
8	10 c. purple (I) (12.45)		3·25	60
	a. Ordinary paper (19.10.45)		40	10
	b. *Slate-purple* (12.45)		2·50	30
	c. *Magenta* (22.3.48)		5·50	70
9	10 c. purple (II) (28.7.48)		18·00	2·25
10	12 c. bright ultramarine (I) (11.45)		1·75	4·50
11	15 c. brt ultram (II) (*ordinary paper*) (11.45)		2·25	7·50
12	15 c. bright ultramarine (II) (R.) (22.3.48)		22·00	90
	a. Ordinary paper (12.45)		75	20
	b. *Blue* (27.11.47)		45·00	85
	ba. Ordinary paper (8.7.47)		90·00	13·00
13	25 c. dull purple and scarlet (I) (22.3.48)		8·50	1·25
	a. Ordinary paper (12.45)		1·40	30
	ab. Opt double		£4250	
14	50 c. black/*emerald* (R.) (12.45)		18·00	1·50
	a. Ordinary paper		60	10
15	$1 black and red (I) (*ordinary paper*) (12.45)		2·00	10
16	$2 green & scar (I) (*ordinary paper*) (12.45)		2·75	75
17	$5 green and red/*emerald* (I) (11.45)		85·00	80·00
18	$5 pur & orge (I) (*ordinary paper*) (12.45)		3·75	3·00
1/18		*Set of 15*	90·00	80·00
1/11, 13/16, 18 Perf "Specimen"		*Set of 14*	£400	

The 8 c. grey with "BMA" opt was prepared but not officially issued (*Price £275 unused*).

Nos. 3 and 9 do not exist without the overprint.

Initial printings on ordinary paper were produced by Harrison and Sons in 1941 following bomb damage to the De La Rue works on 29 December 1940.

No. 8 with reddish purple medallion and dull purple frame is from a 1947 printing with the head in fugitive ink which discolours with moisture.

Postal forgeries of the 50 c. value exist made by dyeing examples of the 1 c. and then altering the face value to 50 c.

In 1946 8 c. and 15 c. stamps in the Crown Colony Victory design were prepared for the Malayan Union, but not issued. Examples of the 8 c. carmine from this issue exist from unofficial leakages (*Price £275 unused*).

MALAYAN STATES

JOHORE

33   34   35 Sultan Sir Ibrahim

1922–40. *Wmk Mult Script CA. Chalk-surfaced paper. P 14.*

103	33	1 c. dull purple and black	30	20
104		2 c. purple and sepia (1924)	85	3·00
105		2 c. green (1928)	40	40
106		3 c. green (1925)	1·50	4·00
107		3 c. purple and sepia (1928)	1·10	1·50
108		4 c. purple and carmine (1924)	2·50	20
109		5 c. dull purple and sage-green	30	30
		w. Wmk inverted		
110		6 c. dull purple and claret	40	45
111	34	10 c. dull purple and blue	16·00	28·00
112		10 c. dull purple and yellow	30	25
113	33	12 c. dull purple and blue	1·00	1·25
114		12 c. ultramarine (1940)	35·00	4·00
115	34	21 c. dull purple and orange (1928)	2·00	3·00
116		25 c. dull purple and myrtle	2·25	1·00
117	35	30 c. dull purple and orange (1936)	5·00	4·00
118		40 c. dull purple and brown (1936)	5·00	4·50
119	34	50 c. dull purple and red	3·00	1·60
120	33	$1 green and mauve	3·00	85
121	35	$2 green and carmine (1923)	5·50	3·50
122		$3 green and blue (1925)	45·00	75·00
123		$4 green and brown (1926)	75·00	£150
		w. Wmk inverted		
124		$5 green and orange	50·00	50·00
125	34	$10 green and black (1924)	£160	£250
126		$50 green and ultram (Optd S. £150)	£600	
127		$100 green and scarlet (Optd S. £250)	£1400	
128	35	$500 blue and red (1926) (Optd S. £750)	£16000	
103/25			*Set of 23*	£375	£500
103/25 Optd/Perf "Specimen"			*Set of 23*	£500	

38   Sultan Sir Ibrahim   39

(Recess D.L.R.)

1940 (Feb). *Wmk Mult Script CA. P 13½.*

130	38	8 c. black and pale blue	14·00	30
130 Perf "Specimen"			42·00	

1948 (1 Dec). *Royal Silver Wedding. As Nos. 143/4 of Jamaica.*

131		10 c. violet	20	30
132		$5 green	24·00	35·00

1949 (2 May)–**55.** *Wmk Mult Script CA. Chalk-surfaced paper. P 17½ × 18.*

133	39	1 c. black	10	10
134		2 c. orange	10	10
		a. *Orange-yellow* (22.1.52)	10	60
135		3 c. green	35	60
		a. *Yellow-green* (22.1.52)	8·00	2·25
136		4 c. brown	10	10
136a		5 c. bright purple (1.9.52)	30	30
137		6 c. grey	20	10
		a. *Pale grey* (22.1.52)	30	30
		ac. Error. St. Edward's Crown W 9b	£1000	
138		8 c. scarlet	2·50	90
138a		8 c. green (1.9.52)	3·00	1·50
139		10 c. magenta	40	10
		aa. Imperf (pair)	£1500	
139a		12 c. scarlet (1.9.52)	2·25	3·00
140		15 c. ultramarine	2·00	10
141		20 c. black and green	45	1·00
141a		20 c. bright blue (1.9.52)	80	10
142		25 c. purple and orange	60	10
142a	39	30 c. scarlet and purple (5.9.55)	1·75	2·25
142b		35 c. scarlet and purple (1.9.52)	3·25	1·00
143		40 c. red and purple	3·50	7·50
144		50 c. black and blue	1·00	10
145		$1 blue and purple	3·50	1·50
146		$2 green and scarlet	14·00	3·50
147		$5 green and brown	40·00	9·00
133/47			*Set of 21*	70·00	27·00

1949 (10 Oct).   *75th Anniv of U.P.U. As Nos. 145/8 of Jamaica.*
148	10 c. purple	..	..	30	15
149	15 c. deep blue	..	..	1·25	1·00
150	25 c. orange	..	..	65	2·25
151	50 c. blue-black	..	..	1·25	2·25
148/51	..	..	Set of 4	3·00	5·00

POSTAGE DUE STAMPS

D 1

(Typo Waterlow)

1938 (1 Jan).   *Wmk Mult Script CA. P 12½.*
D1	D 1	1 c. carmine	..	12·00	35·00
D2		4 c. green	..	40·00	40·00
D3		8 c. orange	..	48·00	£140
D4		10 c. brown	..	48·00	48·00
D5		12 c. purple	..	55·00	£110
D1/5	..	..	Set of 5	£180	£325
D1/5 Perf "Specimen"	..	Set of 5	£130	

KEDAH

1 Sheaf of Rice   2 Malay ploughing

1922–40.   *New colours, etc. Wmk Mult Script CA (sideways* on 12, 35 c.). P 14.*
52	1	1 c. black (ii) (Type I)	..	50	10
53		3 c. green (ii) (1924)	..	1·75	90
54		4 c. violet (ii) (1926)	..	90	10
55		5 c. yellow (ii)	..	1·50	10
	w.	Wmk inverted	..	65·00	
	x.	Wmk reversed	..	†	£130
	y.	Wmk inverted and reversed	..	†	£130
56		6 c. carmine (ii) (1926)	..	70	65
	a.	Carmine-red (1940)	..	14·00	48·00
57		8 c. grey-black (ii) (10.36)	..	9·50	10
58	2	12 c. black and indigo (II) (1926)	..	2·25	4·00
59		35 c. purple (II) (1926)	..	5·00	25·00
52/9	..		Set of 8	20·00	27·00
52/9 Optd/Perf "Specimen"		Set of 8	£190	

*The normal sideways watermark shows Crown to left of CA, as seen from the back of the stamp.

With the exception of the 6 c. and 8 c. the printing plates for the Type **1** values listed above were, as for the previous issue, produced by electrotyping with the face values added to the plates by pantograph. The plates for the 6 c. and 8 c. values were constructed by the more modern method of using a transfer die to enter each impression.

Printings after November 1933 were normally produced by the "dry" method as described beneath Nos. 26/40. There were late "wet" printings of the 1 c. (No. 68a) and 2 c. (No. 27) in August 1936. The 3 c. only exists from a "wet" printing, the 6 c. (No. 56a) and 8 c. from dry printings and the remainder from either method.

Stamps as Type **1** can be found perforated either comb or line. The 3 c. and 6 c. (No. 56) come comb only, the 6 c. (No. 56a) and 8 c. line only and the 1, 4 and 5 c. either way.

For the 1 c. Type II see No. 68a.

6 Sultan Abdul Hamid Halimshah

(Recess Waterlow)

1937 (30 June).   *Wmk Mult Script CA. P 12½.*
60	6	10 c. ultramarine and sepia	..	4·00	80
61		12 c. black and violet	..	27·00	12·00
62		25 c. ultramarine and purple	..	7·50	4·50
63		30 c. green and scarlet	..	8·00	10·00
64		40 c. black and purple	..	4·00	16·00
65		50 c. brown and blue	..	6·00	4·50
66		$1 black and green	..	4·00	10·00
67		$2 green and brown	..	£120	90·00
68		$5 black and scarlet	..	32·00	£140
60/8	..	..	Set of 9	£190	£250
60/8 Perf "Specimen"	..	Set of 9	£200	

I   II   I   II

1938 (May)–**40.**   *As Nos. 52 and 27, but face values redrawn as Types II.*
68a	1	1 c. black	..	80·00	3·00
69		2 c. bright green (1940) ..	..	£160	6·00

1 c. Type II. Figures "1" have square-cut corners instead of rounded, and larger top serif. Larger "C". Line perf. Produced from a new electrotyped Plate 2 with different engraved face values. Printings exist from either the "wet" or "dry" methods.

2 c. Type II. Figures "2" have circular instead of oval drops and the letters "c" are thin and tall instead of thick and rounded. Produced from a new plate, made from a transfer die, and printed by the "dry" method.

1948 (1 Dec).   *Royal Silver Wedding. As Nos. 143/4 of Jamaica.*
70	10 c. violet	..	..	20	20
71	$5 carmine	..	..	25·00	32·00

1949 (10 Oct).   *75th Anniv of U.P.U. As Nos. 145/8 of Jamaica.*
72	10 c. purple	..	..	25	20
73	15 c. deep blue ..	..	..	1·50	1·25
74	25 c. orange	..	..	65	2·25
75	50 c. blue-black	..	..	1·00	2·25
72/5	..	..	Set of 4	3·00	4·50

7 Sheaf of Rice   8 Sultan Badlishah

1950 (1 June)–**55.**   *Wmk Mult Script CA. Chalk-surfaced paper. P 17½ × 18.*
76	7	1 c. black	..	..	30	30
77		2 c. orange	..	..	30	15
78		3 c. green	..	..	1·40	1·00
79		4 c. brown	..	..	60	10
79a		5 c. bright purple (1.9.52)	..	60	1·25
		ab. Bright mauve (24.9.53)	..	60	60

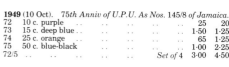

80	7	6 c. grey					50	15
81		8 c. scarlet					1·25	2·25
81a		8 c. green (1.9.52)					75	1·75
		ab. Deep green (24.9.53)					8·00	8·50
82		10 c. magenta					50	10
82a		12 c. scarlet (1.9.52)					85	2·50
83		15 c. ultramarine					80	35
84		20 c. black and green					85	2·50
84a		20 c. bright blue (1.9.52)					85	10
85	8	25 c. purple and orange					90	30
85a		30 c. scarlet and purple (5.9.55)					1·25	1·25
85b		35 c. scarlet and purple (1.9.52)					85	1·50
86		40 c. red and purple					2·25	6·00
87		50 c. black and blue					1·75	20
88		$1 blue and purple					2·75	2·50
89		$2 green and scarlet					20·00	22·00
90		$5 green and brown					42·00	32·00
76/90						Set of 21	70·00	65·00

KELANTAN

4 Sultan Ismail

(Recess B.W.)

1937 (July)**–40.** *Wmk Mult Script CA. P* 12.

40	4	1 c. grey-olive and yellow				30	55
41		2 c. green				2·50	10
42		4 c. scarlet				4·75	70
43		5 c. red-brown				4·75	10
44		6 c. lake (10.37)				11·00	5·50
45		8 c. grey-olive				4·75	10
46		10 c. purple (10.37)				22·00	2·75
47		12 c. blue				3·25	4·00
48		25 c. vermilion and violet				4·75	3·50
49		30 c. violet and scarlet (10.37)				40·00	16·00
50		40 c. orange and blue-green				8·00	23·00
51		50 c. grey-olive and orange (10.37)				55·00	4·75
52		$1 violet and blue-green (10.37)				48·00	12·00
53		$2 red-brown and scarlet (3.40)				£180	£180
54		$5 vermilion and lake (3.40)				£325	£450
40/54					Set of 15	£650	£650
40/54 Perf "Specimen"					Set of 15	£400	

For above issue surcharged see issues under "Japanese Occupation".

1948 (1 Dec). *Royal Silver Wedding. As Nos. 143/4 of Jamaica.*

55	10 c. violet					60	1·75
56	$5 carmine					24·00	48·00

1949 (10 Oct). *75th Anniv of U.P.U. As Nos. 145/8 of Jamaica.*

57	10 c. purple				25	30
58	15 c. deep blue				1·50	90
59	25 c. orange				60	2·25
60	50 c. blue-black				1·00	2·25
57/60				Set of 4	3·00	5·00

5 Sultan Ibrahim

Normal   No. 62a
Tiny stop (R. 1/2)

1951 (11 July)**–55.** *Chalk-surfaced paper. Wmk Mult Script CA. P* 17½ × 18.

61	5	1 c. black					30	30
62		2 c. orange					80	35
		a. Tiny stop					22·00	
		b. Orange-yellow (11.5.55)					2·25	30
63		3 c. green					3·50	1·25
64		4 c. brown					40	15
65		5 c. bright purple (1.9.52)					45	50
		a. Bright mauve (9.12.53)					1·75	50
66		6 c. grey					40	20
67		8 c. scarlet					1·75	3·25
68		8 c. green (1.9.52)					75	1·75
69		10 c. magenta					40	10
70		12 c. scarlet (1.9.52)					75	2·25
71		15 c. ultramarine					3·25	60
72		20 c. black and green					45	5·50
73		20 c. bright blue (1.9.52)					80	25
74		25 c. purple and orange					1·00	85
75		30 c. scarlet and purple (5.9.55)					1·25	1·75
76		35 c. scarlet and purple (1.9.52)					90	1·50
77		40 c. red and purple					5·50	12·00
78		50 c. black and blue					2·00	40
79		$1 blue and purple					7·00	4·25
80		$2 green and scarlet					23·00	20·00
81		$5 green and brown					48·00	40·00
		a. Green and sepia (8.12.53)					75·00	80·00
61/81						Set of 21	90·00	80·00

MALACCA

1948 (1 Dec). *Royal Silver Wedding. As Nos. 143/4 of Jamaica.*

1	10 c. violet					30	70
2	$5 brown					26·00	35·00

1949 (1 Mar)**–52.** *As T 58 of Straits Settlements, but inscr* "MALACCA" *at foot. Wmk Mult Script CA. Chalk-surfaced paper. P* 17½ × 18.

3	1 c. black					30	70
4	2 c. orange					70	45
5	3 c. green					30	1·75
6	4 c. brown					20	10
6a	5 c. bright purple (1.9.52)					45	1·50
7	6 c. grey					60	85
8	8 c. scarlet					30	5·50
8a	8 c. green (1.9.52)					85	4·50
9	10 c. purple					20	10
9a	12 c. scarlet (1.9.52)					95	4·25
10	15 c. ultramarine					70	60
11	20 c. black and green					30	6·00
11a	20 c. bright blue (1.9.52)					1·75	2·50
12	25 c. purple and orange					30	70
12a	35 c. scarlet and purple (1.9.52)					1·00	3·00
13	40 c. red and purple					1·25	11·00
14	50 c. black and blue					75	1·25
15	$1 blue and purple					7·00	19·00
16	$2 green and scarlet					20·00	21·00
17	$5 green and brown					42·00	35·00
3/17					Set of 20	70·00	£110

1949 (10 Oct). *75th Anniv of U.P.U. As Nos. 145/8 of Jamaica.*

18	10 c. purple					20	45
19	15 c. deep blue					1·40	1·75
20	25 c. orange					45	3·75
21	50 c. blue-black					1·00	4·00
18/21					Set of 4	2·75	9·00

NEGRI SEMBILAN

6   Arms of Negri Sembilan   **7**

1935 (2 Dec)–**41.** *Wmk Mult Script CA. Ordinary paper (6 c. grey, 15 c.) or chalk-surfaced paper (others). P 14.*

21	**6**	1 c. black (1.1.36)	..	85	20
22		2 c. green (1.1.36)	..	85	20
23		2 c. orange (11.12.41)	..	3·75	60·00
24		3 c. green (21.8.41)	..	6·50	8·00
		a. Ordinary paper	..	17·00	8·00
25		4 c. orange	..	70	10
26		5 c. brown (5.12.35)	..	1·50	10
27		6 c. scarlet (1.1.37)	..	9·50	2·50
		a. Stop omitted at right (R. 10/4)	..	£275	85·00
28		6 c. grey (18.12.41)	..	4·25	70·00
		a. Stop omitted at right (R. 10/4)	..	£120	£425
29		8 c. grey ..	..	2·00	10
30		10 c. dull purple (1.1.36) ..	..	70	10
31		12 c. bright ultramarine (1.1.36) ..	..	1·40	10
32		15 c. ultramarine (1.10.41)	..	9·00	48·00
33		25 c. dull purple and scarlet (1.4.36)	..	90	70
34		30 c. dull purple and orange (1.1.36)	..	3·50	2·00
35		40 c. scarlet and dull purple	..	85	2·00
36		50 c. black/*emerald* (1.2.36)	..	3·75	2·25
37		$1 black and red/*blue* (1.4.36)	..	2·25	3·25
38		$2 green and scarlet (16.5.36) ..	..	26·00	16·00
39		$5 green and red/*emerald* (16.5.36)	..	15·00	48·00
21/39			*Set of* 19	80·00	£225
21/39 Perf "Specimen"		..	*Set of* 19	£250	

The stamps issued in 1941 were printed by Harrison and Sons following bomb damage to the De La Rue works on 29 December 1940.

An 8 c. scarlet was issued but only with opt during Japanese Occupation of Malaya. Unoverprinted specimens result from leakages.

During shortages in 1941 stamps of STRAITS SETTLE-MENTS (2 c.), SELANGOR (2 c., 8 c.), PERAK (2 c., 25 c., 50 c.) and PAHANG (8 c.) were issued in Negri Sembilan.

1948 (1 Dec). *Royal Silver Wedding. As Nos. 143/4 of Jamaica.*

40	10 c. violet	..	..	15	50
41	$5 green	..	..	18·00	28·00

1949 (1 Apr)–**55.** *Chalk-surfaced paper. Wmk Mult Script CA. P* 17½ × 18.

42	**7**	1 c. black ..	..	10	10
43		2 c. orange	..	10	10
44		3 c. green	..	10	30
45		4 c. brown	..	10	10
46		5 c. bright purple (1.9.52)	..	30	50
		a. Bright mauve (25.8.53)	..	30	45
47		6 c. grey	..	30	10
		a. Pale grey (25.8.53)	..	3·25	30
48		8 c. scarlet	..	30	75
49		8 c. green (1.9.52)	..	1·50	1·60
50		10 c. purple	..	20	10
51		12 c. scarlet (1.9.52)	..	1·50	2·50
52		15 c. ultramarine ..	..	2·25	10
53		20 c. black and green	..	30	75
54		20 c. bright blue (1.9.52)	..	80	10
55		25 c. purple and orange	..	30	10
56		30 c. scarlet and purple (5.9.55)	..	1·25	2·50
57		35 c. scarlet and purple (1.9.52)	..	70	1·00
58		40 c. red and purple	..	80	4·75
59		50 c. black and blue	..	80	10
60		$1 blue and purple	..	3·00	2·00
61		$2 green and scarlet	..	12·00	15·00
62		$5 green and brown	..	50·00	38·00
42/62			*Set of* 21	65·00	60·00

1949 (10 Oct). *75th Anniv of U.P.U. As Nos. 145/8 of Jamaica.*

63	10 c. purple ..	..	..	20	10
64	15 c. deep blue	..	..	1·10	2·00
65	25 c. orange ..	..	..	50	2·00
66	50 c. blue-black	..	..	1·00	2·50
63/6	..	..	*Set of* 4	2·50	6·00

STAMP BOOKLETS

1935. *Stapled.*

SB1 $1 booklet containing twenty 5 c. (No. 26) in blocks of 10

SB2 $1.30, booklet containing 5 c. and 8 c. (Nos. 26, 29), each in block of 10

PAHANG

15 Sultan Sir Abu   **16** Sultan Sir Abu
        Bakar   Bakar

1935 (2 Dec)–**41.** *Chalk-surfaced paper. Wmk Mult Script CA. P* 14.

29	**15**	1 c. black (1.1.36)	..	15	40
30		2 c. green (1.1.36)	..	60	10
31		3 c. green (21.8.41)	..	12·00	13·00
		a. Ordinary paper	..	24·00	4·25
32		4 c. orange	..	30	50
33		5 c. brown (5.12.35)	..	60	10
34		6 c. scarlet (1.1.37)	..	8·50	2·25
35		8 c. grey	..	60	10
36		8 c. scarlet (11.12.41)	..	1·00	42·00
37		10 c. dull purple (1.1.36) ..	..	30	10
38		12 c. bright ultramarine (1.1.36)	..	1·00	1·75
39		15 c. ultram (*ordinary paper*) (1.10.41)	..	7·00	48·00
40		25 c. dull purple and scarlet (1.4.36)	..	80	1·75
41		30 c. dull purple and orange (1.1.36)	..	80	1·10
42		40 c. scarlet and dull purple	..	75	2·50
43		50 c. black/*emerald* (1.2.36)	..	2·75	1·75
44		$1 black and red/*blue* (1.4.36) ..	..	2·00	7·50
45		$2 green and scarlet (16.5.36) ..	..	18·00	26·00
46		$5 green and red/*emerald* (16.5.36)	..	7·00	50·00
29/46			*Set of* 18	55·00	£170
29/46 Perf "Specimen"		..	*Set of* 18	£225	

The stamps issued during 1941 were printed by Harrison and Sons following bomb damage to the De La Rue works on 29 December 1940.

A 2 c. orange and a 6 c. grey were prepared but not officially issued. (*Price mint £4 each*).

During shortages in 1941 stamps of STRAITS SETTLE-MENTS (2 c.), SELANGOR (2 c., 8 c.) and PERAK (2 c.) were issued in Pahang.

1948 (1 Dec). *Royal Silver Wedding. As Nos. 143/4 of Jamaica.*

47	10 c. violet	..	..	15	60
48	$5 green	..	..	22·00	40·00

1949 (10 Oct). *75th Anniv of U.P.U. As Nos. 145/8 of Jamaica.*

49	10 c. purple	..	..	30	20
50	15 c. deep blue ..	..	..	90	70
51	25 c. orange	..	..	35	1·10
52	50 c. blue-black	..	..	70	2·00
49/52 ..	..	..	*Set of* 4	2·00	3·50

1950 (1 June)–**56**. *Wmk Mult Script CA. Chalk-surfaced paper. P* 17½×18.

53 **16**	1 c. black	..	..	..	10	10
54	2 c. orange	..	..	..	10	10
55	3 c. green	..	..	..	30	60
56	4 c. brown	..	..	..	50	10
	a. *Chocolate* (24.3.54)	..	..	4·50	1·75
57	5 c. bright purple (1.9.52)	..	..	25	70
	a. *Bright mauve* (10.9.53)	..	25	15
58	6 c. grey	..	..	..	15	20
59	8 c. scarlet	..	..	..	20	1·25
60	8 c. green (1.9.52)	..	..	85	75
61	10 c. magenta	..	..	..	15	10
62	12 c. scarlet (1.9.52)	..	..	85	1·25
63	15 c. ultramarine	..	..	50	10
64	20 c. black and green	..	..	25	2·75
65	20 c. bright blue (1.9.52)	..	..	75	10
	a. *Ultramarine* (8.3.56)	..	4·25	2·75
66	25 c. purple and orange	..	..	30	10
67	30 c. scarlet and brown-purple (5.9.55)	1·25	35
	a. *Scarlet and purple* (8.3.56)	..	10·00	3·25
68	35 c. scarlet and purple (1.9.52)	..	60	25
69	40 c. red and purple	..	..	1·00	7·50
70	50 c. black and blue	..	..	1·00	10
71	$1 blue and purple	..	..	2·50	2·50
72	$2 green and scarlet	..	..	13·00	20·00
73	$5 green and brown	..	..	55·00	50·00
	a. *Green and sepia* (24.3.54)	..	85·00	85·00
53/73	..	..	..	*Set of* 21	70·00	75·00

STAMP BOOKLETS

1935. *Stapled.*

SB1	$1 booklet containing twenty 5 c. (No. 33) in blocks of 10	..
SB2	$1.30, booklet containing 5 c. and 8 c. (Nos. 33, 35) each in block of 10	..

PENANG

1948 (1 Dec). *Royal Silver Wedding. As Nos.* 143/4 *of Jamaica.*

1	10 c. violet	..	..	..	30	20
2	$5 brown	..	..	..	30·00	28·00

1949 (21 Feb)–**52**. *As T* **58** *of Straits Settlements, but inscr* "PENANG" *at foot. Wmk Mult Script CA. Chalk-surfaced paper. P* 17½ × 18.

3	1 c. black	..	..	..	10	10
4	2 c. orange	..	..	..	55	10
5	3 c. green	..	..	..	20	30
6	4 c. brown	..	..	..	20	10
7	5 c. bright purple (1.9.52)	..	..	60	1·75
8	6 c. grey	..	..	..	20	20
9	8 c. scarlet	..	..	..	40	2·75
10	8 c. green (1.9.52)	..	..	80	1·00
11	10 c. purple	..	..	..	15	10
12	12 c. scarlet (1.9.52)	..	..	80	3·50
13	15 c. ultramarine	..	..	20	30
14	20 c. black and green	..	..	20	1·00
15	20 c. bright blue (1.9.52)	..	..	55	50
16	25 c. purple and orange	..	..	1·00	10
17	35 c. scarlet and purple (1.9.52)	..	60	80
18	40 c. red and purple	..	..	85	8·00
19	50 c. black and blue	..	..	1·25	15
20	$1 blue and purple	..	..	13·00	1·75
21	$2 green and scarlet..	..	..	16·00	1·75
22	$5 green and brown..	..	..	48·00	2·50
3/22	..	..	*Set of* 20	75·00	23·00

1949 (10 Oct). *75th Anniv of U.P.U. As Nos.* 145/8 *of Jamaica.*

23	10 c. purple	..	..	..	20	10
24	15 c. deep blue..	..	..	1·50	1·75
25	25 c. orange	..	..	..	45	2·00
26	50 c. blue-black	..	..	1·50	2·75
23/6	..	..	..	*Set of* 4	3·25	6·00

PERAK

50   Sultan Iskandar   **51**

1935 (2 Dec)–**37**. *Chalk-surfaced paper. Wmk Mult Script CA. P* 14.

88 **50**	1 c. black (1.1.36)..	..	..	..	30	10
89	2 c. green (1.1.36)..	..	..	30	10
90	4 c. orange	..	..	..	30	10
91	5 c. brown (5.12.35)	..	..	30	10
92	6 c. scarlet (1.1.37)	..	..	10·00	3·50
93	8 c. grey	..	..	..	50	10
94	10 c. dull purple (1.1.36)	..	..	30	15
95	12 c. bright ultramarine (1.1.36)	..	70	90
96	25 c. dull purple and scarlet (1.4.36)	1·00	85
97	30 c. dull purple and orange (1.1.36)	..	1·25	1·50
98	40 c. scarlet and dull purple	..	3·00	4·25
99	50 c. black/*emerald* (1.2.36)	..	3·75	1·00
100	$1 black and red/*blue* (1.4.36)	..	2·50	1·00
101	$2 green and scarlet (16.5.36)	..	15·00	8·50
102	$5 green and red/*emerald* (16.5.36)	..	65·00	28·00
88/102			*Set of* 15	90·00	45·00
88/102 Perf "Specimen"	..	..	*Set of* 15	£170

No. 91 exists in coils constructed from normal sheets in 1936.

1938 (2 May)–**41**. *Wmk Mult Script CA. Chalk-surfaced paper. P* 14.

103 **51**	1 c. black (4.39)	..	..	6·00	10
104	2 c. green (13.1.39)	..	..	2·75	10
105	2 c. orange (30.10.41)	..	..	2·25	6·00
	a. *Ordinary paper*	..	..	2·50	16·00
106	3 c. green (21.8.41)	..	..	1·75	4·25
107	4 c. orange (5.39)	..	..	30·00	10
108	5 c. brown (1.2.39)	..	..	4·75	10
109	6 c. scarlet (12.39)	..	..	27·00	10
110	8 c. grey (1.12.38)	..	..	22·00	10
111	8 c. scarlet (18.12.41)	..	..	1·00	60·00
112	10 c. dull purple (17.10.38)	..	22·00	10
113	12 c. bright ultramarine (17.10.38)	..	20·00	2·00
114	15 c. brt ultram (*ordinary paper*) (8.41)	1·75	13·00
115	25 c. dull purple and scarlet (12.39)	..	70·00	4·25
116	30 c. dull purple and orange (17.10.38)	9·50	3·00
117	40 c. scarlet and dull purple	..	50·00	2·00
118	50 c. black/*emerald* (17.10.38)	..	27·00	75
119	$1 black and red/*blue* (7.40)	..	£130	16·00
120	$2 green and scarlet (9.40)	..	£140	60·00
121	$5 green and red/*emerald* (1.41)	..	£200	£275
103/21			*Set of* 19	£650	£400
103/21 Perf "Specimen"	..	*Set of* 19	£300

No. 108 exists in coils constructed from normal sheets.

The stamps issued during 1941 were printed by Harrison and Sons following bomb damage to the De La Rue works on 29 December 1940.

During shortages in 1941 stamps of STRAITS SETTLE-MENTS (2 c.), SELANGOR (2 c., 3 c.) and PAHANG (8 c.) were issued in Perak.

1948 (1 Dec). *Royal Silver Wedding. As Nos.* 143/4 *of Jamaica.*

122	10 c. violet	..	..	..	15	10
123	$5 green	..	..	..	20·00	26·00

1949 (10 Oct). *75th Anniv of U.P.U. As Nos.* 145/8 *of Jamaica.*

124	10 c. purple	..	..	..	15	10
125	15 c. deep blue	..	..	1·00	1·25
126	25 c. orange	..	..	..	45	45
127	50 c. blue-black	..	..	1·75	3·00
124/7	..	..	..	*Set of* 4	3·00	4·50

52 Sultan Yussuf
'Izzuddin Shah

1950 (17 Aug)–**56.** *Chalk-surfaced paper. Wmk Mult Script CA. P* 17½×18.

128	52	1 c. black				10	10
129		2 c. orange				10	10
130		3 c. green				2·00	10
		a. Yellowish green (15.11.51)			5·00	4·50
131		4 c. brown				10	10
		a. Yellow-brown (20.6.56)			3·50	10
132		5 c. bright purple (1.9.52)			50	1·00
		a. Bright mauve (10.11.54)			1·25	1·00
133		6 c. grey				10	10
134		8 c. scarlet				30	1·00
135		8 c. green (1.9.52)				1·00	60
136		10 c. purple				10	10
		a. Brown-purple (20.6.56)			3·75	30
137		12 c. scarlet (1.9.52)				1·00	2·75
138		15 c. ultramarine				30	10
139		20 c. black and green				30	30
140		20 c. bright blue (1.9.52)				75	10
141		25 c. purple and orange				30	10
142		30 c. scarlet and purple (5.9.55)			1·25	20
143		35 c. scarlet and purple (1.9.52)			70	25
144		40 c. red and purple				1·50	4·25
145		50 c. black and blue				90	10
146		$1 blue and purple				7·00	40
147		$2 green and scarlet				13·00	4·50
148		$5 green and brown				38·00	11·00
128/48					Set of 21	60·00	23·00

STAMP BOOKLETS

1935.
SB1 $1 booklet containing twenty 5 c. (No. 91) in blocks of 10
SB2 $1.30, booklet containing 5 c. and 8 c. (Nos. 91, 93), each in block of 10

1938.
SB3 $1 booklet containing twenty 5 c. (No. 108) in blocks of 10
SB4 $1.30, booklet containing 5 c. and 8 c. (Nos. 108, 110), each in block of 10

PERLIS

1948 (1 Dec). *Royal Silver Wedding. As Nos. 143/4 of Jamaica.*
1	10 c. violet					30	2·00
2	$5 brown				28·00	42·00

1949 (10 Oct). *75th Anniv of U.P.U. As Nos. 145/8 of Jamaica.*
3	10 c. purple					30	60
4	15 c. deep blue				1·25	3·00
5	25 c. orange					65	2·00
6	50 c. blue-black				1·40	3·75
3/6					Set of 4	3·25	8·50

1 Raja Syed Putra

1951 (26 Mar)–**55.** *Chalk-surfaced paper. Wmk Mult Script CA. P* 17½ × 18.

7	1	1 c. black				10	80
8		2 c. orange				30	40
9		3 c. green				75	2·75
10		4 c. brown				90	30
11		5 c. bright purple (1.9.52)			30	2·75
12		6 c. grey				90	1·25
13		8 c. scarlet				1·75	4·50
14		8 c. green (1.9.52)				75	2·50
15		10 c. purple				30	20
16		12 c. scarlet (1.9.52)				75	2·50
17		15 c. ultramarine				1·75	3·00
18		20 c. black and green				90	5·00
19		20 c. bright blue (1.9.52)			85	65
20		25 c. purple and orange			1·25	1·25
21		30 c. scarlet and purple (5.9.55)			1·75	8·00
22		35 c. scarlet and purple (1.9.52)			75	3·25
23		40 c. red and purple				1·50	15·00
24		50 c. black and blue				2·75	3·75
25		$1 blue and purple				6·50	17·00
26		$2 green and scarlet				13·00	24·00
27		$5 green and brown				50·00	70·00
7/27					Set of 21	75·00	£150

SELANGOR

46 Mosque at Palace, Klang   47 Sultan Suleiman

(Des E. J. McNaughton)

1935 (2 Dec)–**41.** *Wmk Mult Script CA (sideways on T* 46*). Chalk-surfaced paper. P* 14 *or* 14×14½ *(No.* 70*).*

68	46	1 c. black (1.1.36)				30	10
69		2 c. green (1.1.36)				90	10
70		2 c. orange (ordinary paper) (p 14×14½) (21.8.41)			3·50	75
		a. Perf 14. Ordinary paper (9.41)		20·00	6·50
		ab. Chalk-surfaced paper		28·00	7·00
71		3 c. green (21.8.41)				15·00	2·75
		a. Ordinary paper				1·00	7·00
72		4 c. orange				30	10
73		5 c. brown (5.12.35)				70	10
74		6 c. scarlet (1.1.37)				5·50	10
75		8 c. grey				60	10
76		10 c. dull purple (1.1.36)				60	10
77		12 c. bright ultramarine (1.1.36)			1·00	10
78		15 c. brt ultram (ordinary paper) (1.10.41)		11·00	32·00
79		25 c. dull purple and scarlet (1.4.36)		1·00	60
80		30 c. dull purple and orange (1.1.36)		1·00	85
81		40 c. scarlet and dull purple			1·25	1·25
82		50 c. black/emerald (1.2.36)			1·00	15
83	47	$1 black and rose/blue (1.4.36)			7·00	80
84		$2 green and scarlet (16.5.36)			22·00	8·00
85		$5 green and red/emerald (16.5.36)		50·00	23·00
68/85					Set of 18	95·00	60·00
68/85 Perf "Specimen"				Set of 18	£250

The stamps issued during 1941 were printed by Harrison and Sons following bomb damage to the De La Rue works on 29 December 1940.

Supplies of an unissued 8 c. scarlet were diverted to Australia in 1941. Examples circulating result from leakages of this supply (*Price* £425).

48 Sultan Hisamud-din Alam Shah 49

1941. *Wmk Mult Script CA. Chalk-surfaced paper. P* 14.
86 **48** $1 black and red/*blue* (15.4.41) .. .. 12·00 6·00
87 $2 green and scarlet (7.7.41) (Perf S. £70) 48·00 27·00
A $5 green and red on emerald, T **48**, was issued overprinted during the Japanese occupation of Malaya. Unoverprinted examples are known, but were not issued (*Price* £100).

During shortages in 1941 stamps of STRAITS SETTLE-MENTS (2 c.) and PERAK (25 c.) were issued in Selangor.

1948 (1 Dec). *Royal Silver Wedding. As Nos.* 143/4 *of Jamaica.*
88 10 c. violet 20 10
89 $5 green .. .. 24·00 14·00

1949 (12 Sept)–**55.** *Wmk Mult Script CA. Chalk-surfaced paper. P* 17½×18.
90 **49** 1 c. black 10 20
91 2 c. orange 10 30
92 3 c. green .. .. .. 30 1·50
93 4 c. brown 10 10
94 5 c. bright purple (1.9.52) .. 30 1·10
 a. Bright mauve (17.9.53) .. 30 10
95 6 c. grey 10 10
96 8 c. scarlet 25 65
97 8 c. green (1.9.52) 65 80
98 10 c. purple 10 10
99 12 c. scarlet (1.9.52) .. .. 80 2·50
 w. Wmk inverted £150
100 15 c. ultramarine .. .. 2·00 10
101 20 c. black and green 65 10
102 20 c. bright blue (1.9.52) .. 80 10
103 25 c. purple and orange .. 1·00 10
104 30 c. scarlet and purple (5.9.55) 1·25 90
105 35 c. scarlet and purple (1.9.52) 70 1·00
106 40 c. scarlet and purple .. 4·00 3·75
107 50 c. black and blue 70 10
108 $1 blue and purple .. .. 2·75 30
109 $2 green and scarlet .. .. 9·50 30
110 $5 green and brown .. .. 45·00 1·75
90/110 .. .. .. *Set of 21* 60·00 12·00

1949 (10 Oct). *75th Anniv of U.P.U. As Nos.* 145/8 *of Jamaica.*
111 10 c. purple 30 10
112 15 c. deep blue .. .. .. 1·50 1·25
113 25 c. orange .. .. .. 50 2·50
114 50 c. blue-black .. .. .. 1·25 2·50
111/14 .. .. .. *Set of 4* 3·25 5·50

STAMP BOOKLETS

1935. *Stapled.*
SB1 $1 booklet containing twenty 5 c. (No. 73) in blocks of 10 .. ..
SB2 $1.30, booklet containing 5 c. and 8 c. (Nos. 73, 75), each in block of 10 .. ..

TRENGGANU

2 CENTS

4 Sultan Suleiman **5** **(6)**

1921–41. *Chalk-surfaced paper. P* 14. (*a*) *Wmk Mult Crown CA.*
23 **4** $1 purple and blue/*blue* .. .. 12·00 20·00
24 $3 green and red/*emerald* .. .. 85·00 £180
25 **5** $5 green and red/*pale yellow* .. 85·00 £250
23/5 .. .. .. *Set of 3* £170 £400
23/5 Optd "Specimen" .. .. *Set of 3* £100

(*b*) *Wmk Mult Script CA*
26 **4** 1 c. black (1926) .. .. 1·25 1·00
 a. Ordinary paper (1941) .. .. — 17·00
27 2 c. green .. .. .. 1·25 1·40
 a. Ordinary paper (1941) .. .. — 17·00
28 3 c. green (1926) .. .. 1·75 85
29 3 c. reddish brown (1938) .. 21·00 11·00
 a. Ordinary paper. *Chestnut* (1941) — 13·00
30 4 c. rose-red .. .. .. 1·25 50
 a. Ordinary paper. *Scarlet-verm* (1941) — 17·00
31 5 c. grey and deep brown .. 2·00 4·50
32 5 c. purple/*yellow* (1926) .. 1·75 1·00
 a. Deep reddish purple/brt yellow (1939)
33 6 c. orange (1924) .. .. 3·25 30
 a. Ordinary paper (1941) .. .. — 20·00
34 8 c. grey (1938) .. .. 22·00 4·25
 a. Ordinary paper (1941) .. .. — 15·00
35 10 c. bright blue .. .. .. 2·00 80
36 12 c. bright ultramarine (1926) .. 4·25 4·25
37 20 c. dull purple and orange .. 2·00 1·50
38 25 c. green and deep purple .. 2·25 2·75
39 30 c. dull purple and black .. 3·25 2·25
40 35 c. carmine/*yellow* (1926) .. 4·75 8·00
41 50 c. green and bright carmine .. 5·00 2·25
42 $1 purple and blue/*blue* (1929) 9·00 3·50
43 $3 green and lake/*green* (1926) .. 60·00 £120
 a. Green and brown-red/green (1938) .. £130
44 **5** $5 green and red/*yellow* (1938) .. £250 £1300
45 $25 purple and blue (S. £100) .. £650 £950
46 $50 green and yellow (S. £190) .. £1500 £2500
47 $100 green and scarlet (S. £400) .. £4750 £5500
26/44 .. .. .. *Set of 19* £350 £1400
26/44 Optd/Perf "Specimen" .. *Set of 19* £600
The used price quoted for No. 44 is for an example with an identifiable cancellation from 1938–41.
Printings of the 2 c. yellow-orange, 3 c. blue-green, 4 c. purple/*yellow*, 6 c. slate-grey, 8 c. rose, 15 c. ultramarine and $1 black and red/*blue* on ordinary paper were despatched to Malaya in late 1941, but did not arrive before the Japanese occupation. Unused examples are known of the 2, 3, 6, 8 and 15 c. (*Prices,* 3 c. £225, *others* £120 *each, unused*).

1941 (1 May). *Nos.* 32a *and* 35 *surch as T* **6**.
59 **4** 2 c. on 5 c. deep reddish purple/*brt yellow* 6·50 3·50
60 8 c. on 10 c. bright blue .. .. .. 7·00 3·50

1948 (2 Dec). *Royal Silver Wedding. As Nos.* 143/4 *of Jamaica.*
61 10 c. violet 15 90
62 $5 carmine .. .. 22·00 35·00

1949 (10 Oct). *75th Anniv of U.P.U. As Nos.* 145/8 *of Jamaica.*
63 10 c. purple 30 35
64 15 c. deep blue .. .. .. 1·10 2·25
65 25 c. orange .. .. 55 2·25
66 50 c. blue-black .. .. .. 1·40 3·00
63/6 .. .. *Set of 4* 3·00 7·00

7 Sultan Ismail

1949 (27 Dec)–**55.** *Wmk Mult Script CA. Chalk-surfaced paper. P* 17½×18.
67 **7** 1 c. black 10 30
68 2 c. orange 10 30
69 3 c. green .. .. 30 2·25
70 4 c. brown 10 30
71 5 c. bright purple (1.9.52) 30 90
72 6 c. grey 40 30
73 8 c. scarlet .. .. 20 1·75
74 8 c. green (1.9.52) .. .. .. 65 1·00
 a. Deep green (11.8.53) .. .. 4·50 5·50
75 10 c. purple 20 10
76 12 c. scarlet (1.9.52) .. .. .. 65 1·75
77 15 c. ultramarine 65 30
78 20 c. black and green .. .. .. 65 2·25

79 **7**	20 c. bright blue (1.9.52)	..	..	..	80	30
80	25 c. purple and orange	..	..	..	75	90
81	30 c. scarlet and purple (5.9.55)	..	..	1·25	1·25
82	35 c. scarlet and purple (1.9.52)	..	..	70	1·60
83	40 c. red and purple	..	..	..	3·25	12·00
84	50 c. black and blue	..	..	..	80	1·25
85	$1 blue and purple	..	..	..	4·25	5·50
86	$2 green and scarlet	..	..	.. 22·00	17·00
87	$5 green and brown	..	..	.. 50·00	48·00
67/87	..	..	..	*Set of* 21	80·00	90·00

POSTAGE DUE STAMPS

D 1

1937 (10 Aug). *Wmk Mult Script CA. P* 14.

D1	D **1**	1 c. scarlet	..	..	..	7·50	55·00
D2		4 c. green	..	..	..	9·00	60·00
D3		8 c. yellow	..	..	.. 55·00	60·00
D4		10 c. brown	..	..	.. £110	95·00
D1/4	..	..	..	..	*Set of* 4	£160	£450
D1/4 Perf "Specimen"		..	..	*Set of* 4	£130

JAPANESE OCCUPATION OF MALAYA

Japanese forces invaded Malaya on 8 December 1941 with the initial landings taking place at Kota Bharu on the east coast. Penang fell, to a force which crossed the border from Thailand, on 19 December, Kuala Lumpur on 11 January 1942 and the conquest of the Malay penisula was completed by the capture of Singapore on 15 February.

During the Japanese Occupation various small Dutch East Indies islands near Singapore were administered as part of Malaya. Stamps of the Japanese Occupation of Malaya were issued to the post offices of Dabo Singkep, Puloe Samboe, Tanjong Balei, Tanjong Batu, Tanjong Pinang and Terempa between 1942 and 1945. The overprinted issues were also used by a number of districts in Atjeh (Northern Sumatra) whose postal services were administered from Singapore until the end of March 1943.

Malayan post offices were also opened in October 1943 to serve camps of civilians working on railway construction and maintenance in Thailand. Overprinted stamps of the Japanese Occupation of Malaya were used at these offices between October 1943 and the end of the year after which mail from the camps was carried free. Their postmarks were inscribed in Japanese Katakana characters, and, uniquely, showed the Japanese postal symbol.

JOHORE

The postal service in Johore was reconstituted in mid-April 1942 using Nos. J146/60 and subsequently other general issues. Stamps of Johore overprinted "DAI NIPPON 2602" were, however, only used for fiscal purposes. Overprinted Johore postage due stamps were not issued for use elsewhere in Malaya.

POSTAGE DUE STAMPS

(1) (Upright)

(2)

Second character sideways (R.6/3)

1942 (Apr). *Nos. D1/5 of Johore optd as T* **1** *in brown.*

JD1	D **1**	1 c. carmine	..	..	.. 60·00	85·00
		a. Black opt	..	..	.. 25·00	70·00
JD2		4 c. green	..	..	.. 80·00	95·00
		a. Black opt	..	..	.. 65·00	80·00
JD3		8 c. orange	..	..	.. £110	£120
		a. Black opt	..	..	.. 75·00	90·00
JD4		10 c. brown	..	..	.. 40·00	65·00
		a. Black opt	..	..	.. 16·00	50·00
JD5		12 c. purple	..	..	.. 65·00	80·00
		a. Black opt	..	..	.. 29·00	50·00

1943. *Nos. D1/5 of Johore optd with T* **2**.

JD 6	D **1**	1 c. carmine	..	..	4·50	20·00
		a. Second character sideways	.. £160	£325
JD 7		4 c. green	..	..	4·75	21·00
		a. Second character sideways	.. £170	£325
JD 8		8 c. orange	..	..	5·00	22·00
		a. Second character sideways	.. £200	£375
JD 9		10 c. brown	..	..	4·50	26·00
		a. Second character sideways	.. £200	£400
JD10		12 c. purple	..	..	6·00	38·00
		a. Second character sideways	.. £225	£450

KEDAH

Postal services resumed by 31 January 1942 using unoverprinted Kedah values from 1 c. to 8 c. which were accepted for postage until 13 May 1942.

During the Japanese occupation Perlis was administered as part of Kedah.

DAI NIPPON   **DAI NIPPON**

2602   **2602**

(3)   (4)

1942 (13 May)–43. *Stamps of Kedah (Script wmk) optd with T* **3** *(1 c. to 8 c.) or* **4** *(10 c. to $5), both in red.*

J 1	**1**	1 c. black (No. 68a)	..	..	3·50	5·50
J 2		2 c. bright green (No. 69)	.. 24·00	30·00
J 3		4 c. violet	..	..	3·50	4·00
J 4		5 c. yellow	..	..	3·00	3·50
		a. Black opt (1943)	..	.. £200	£225
J 5		6 c. carmine (No. 56) (Blk.)	..	2·25	8·50
J 6		8 c. grey-black	..	..	2·75	1·75
J 7	**6**	10 c. ultramarine and sepia	..	8·00	8·00
J 8		12 c. black and violet	..	.. 22·00	28·00
J 9		25 c. ultramarine and purple	..	7·00	9·50
		a. Black opt (1943)	..	.. £250	£250
J10		30 c. green and scarlet	..	.. 65·00	75·00
J11		40 c. black and purple	..	.. 28·00	40·00
J12		50 c. brown and blue	..	.. 30·00	42·00
J13		$1 black and green	..	.. £140	£150
		a. Opt inverted	..	.. £600	£600
J14		$2 green and brown	..	.. £170	£170
J15		$5 black and scarlet	..	.. 65·00	75·00
		a. Black opt (1943)	..	.. £750	£750

Nos. J1/15 were gradually replaced by issues intended for use throughout Malaya. Kedah and Perlis were ceded to Thailand by the Japanese on 19 October 1943.

KELANTAN

Postal services resumed on 1 June 1942. Stamps used in Kelantan were overprinted with the personal seals of Sunagawa, the Japanese Governor, and of Handa, the Assistant Governor.

(5) Sunagawa Seal

(6) Handa Seal

40 CENTS
(7)

$1.00
■ ■
(8)

1   Cents

(9)

1942 (June).   *Stamps of Kelantan surch*

(a) As T **7** or **8** (*dollar values*). Optd with T **5** in red

J16	4	1 c. on 50 c. grey-olive and orange	£225	£180
J17		2 c. on 40 c. orange and blue-green	£450	£275
J18		4 c. on 30 c. violet and scarlet	£1700	£1200
J19		5 c. on 12 c. blue (R.)	£225	£180
J20		6 c. on 25 c. vermilion and violet	£275	£190
J21		8 c. on 5 c. red-brown (R.)	£325	£140
J22		10 c. on 6 c. lake	75·00	£120
		a. "CENST" for "CENTS"	£2500	
J23		12 c. on 8 c. grey-olive (R.)	48·00	£110
J24		25 c. on 10 c. purple (R.)	£1200	£1300
J25		30 c. on 4 c. scarlet	£1800	£2000
J26		40 c. on 2 c. green (R.)	55·00	85·00
		a. Surch double (B.+R.)	£1500	
J27		50 c. on 1 c. grey-olive and yellow	£1300	£1200
J28	1	$1 on 4 c. black and red (R., bars Blk.)	50·00	75·00
J29		$2 on 5 c. green and red/*yellow*	50·00	75·00
J30		$5 on 6 c. scarlet	50·00	75·00
		a. Surch double	£350	

(b) As T **7**. Optd with T **6** in red

J31	4	12 c. grey-olive	£140	£200
		a. Type **6** omitted (in horiz pair with normal)	£1500	

(c) As T **9**. Optd with T **5** in red.

J32	4	1 c. on 50 c. grey-olive and orange	£130	85·00
		a. "Cente" for "Cents" (R. 5/1)	£1000	£800
J33		2 c. on 40 c. orange and blue-green	£110	90·00
		a. "Cente" for "Cents" (R. 5/1)	£950	
J34		5 c. on 12 c. blue (R.)	£110	£110
		a. "Cente" for "Cents" (R. 5/1)	£900	
J35		8 c. on 5 c. red-brown (R.)	£100	70·00
		a. "Cente" for "Cents" (R. 5/1)	£850	£700
J36		10 c. on 6 c. lake ..	£250	£275
		a. "Cente" for "Cents" (R. 5/1)	£1700	
J37		12 c. on 8 c. grey-olive (R.)	£425	£450
		a. "Cente" for "Cents" (R. 5/1)	£2250	
J38		30 c. on 4 c. scarlet	£2000	£2250
		a. "Cente" for "Cents" (R. 5/1)		
J39		40 c. on 2 c. green (R.)	£450	£475
		a. "Cente" for "Cents" (R. 5/1)	£2250	
J40		50 c. on 1 c. grey-olive and yellow	£1100	£1100
		a. "Cente" for "Cents" (R. 5/1)		

(d) As T **9**. Optd with T **6** in red.

J41	4	1 c. on 50 c. grey-olive and orange	90·00	£130
		a. "Cente" for "Cents" (R. 5/1)	£850	
J42		2 c. on 40 c. orange and blue-green	95·00	£140
		a. "Cente" for "Cents" (R. 5/1)	£850	
J43		8 c. on 5 c. red-brown (R.)	65·00	£120
		a. "Cente" for "Cents" (R. 5/1)	£750	
J44		10 c. on 6 c. lake	85·00	£140
		a. "Cente" for "Cents" (R. 5/1)	£850	

As stamps of the above series became exhausted the equivalent stamps from the series intended for use throughout Malaya were introduced. Stamps as Nos. J28/30, J32/3 and J35/40, but without Type **5** or **6**, are from remainders sent to Singapore or Kuala Lumpur after the state had been ceded to Thailand (*Price from* £15 *each unused*). Nos. J19, J21, J23 and J25/6 have also been seen without Type **5** (*Price from* £50 *each unused*).

Kelantan was ceded to Thailand by the Japanese on 19 October 1943.

NEW INFORMATION

The editor is always interested to correspond with people who have new information that will improve or correct the Catalogue.

MALACCA

Postal services from Malacca resumed on 21 April 1942, but there were no stamps available for two days.

PRICES. Those quoted are for single stamps. Blocks of four showing the complete handstamp are worth from five times the price of a single stamp.

(10) "Military Administration
Malacca State Government Seal"

1942 (23 Apr).   *Stamps of Straits Settlements handstamped as T* **10**, *in red, each impression covering four stamps.*

			Single Un.	Used
J45	58	1 c. black	80·00	65·00
J46		2 c. orange	55·00	65·00
J47		3 c. green	55·00	65·00
J48		5 c. brown	£110	£110
J49		8 c. grey ..	£160	£100
J50		10 c. dull purple	70·00	75·00
J51		12 c. ultramarine	90·00	95·00
J52		15 c. ultramarine	65·00	75·00
J53		40 c. scarlet and dull purple	£550	£600
J54		50 c. black/*emerald*	£850	£850
J55		$1 black and red/*blue* ..	£900	£850

The 30 c., $2 and $5 also exist with this overprint, but these values were not available to the public. (*Price for set of 3* £3750 *unused*)

POSTAGE DUE STAMPS

1942 (23 Apr).   *Postage Due stamps of Malayan Postal Union handstamped as T* **10**, *in red, each impression covering four stamps.*

JD11	D 1	1 c. slate-purple	£180	£170
JD12		4 c. green	£225	£225
JD13		8 c. scarlet	£1700	£1400
JD14		10 c. yellow-orange	£350	£350
JD15		12 c. ultramarine	£550	£475
JD16		50 c. black	£1700	£1300

Nos. J45/55 and JD11/16 were replaced during May 1942 by the overprinted issues intended for use throughout Malaya.

PENANG

Postal services on Penang Island resumed on 30 March 1942 using Straits Settlements stamps overprinted by Japanese seals.

奥
川

(11) Okugawa
Seal

内
妊

(12) Ochiburi
Seal

DAI NIPPON

2602

PENANG

(13)

1942 (30 Mar).   *Straits Settlements stamps optd.*

(a) As T **11** (*three forms of the seal*)

J56	58	1 c. black	9·50	11·00
J57		2 c. orange	24·00	22·00
J58		3 c. green	20·00	22·00
J59		5 c. brown	24·00	24·00

J60	**58**	8 c. grey			26·00 27·00
J61		10 c. dull purple			50·00 50·00
J62		12 c. ultramarine			27·00 38·00
J63		15 c. ultramarine			38·00 45·00
J64		40 c. scarlet and dull purple			90·00 £100
J65		50 c. black/*emerald*			£190 £200
J66		$1 black and red/*blue*			£200 £225
J67		$2 green and scarlet			£500 £500
J68		$5 green and red/*emerald*			£1500 £1400

(b) With T 12

J69	**58**	1 c. black			£120 £110
J70		2 c. orange			£110 85·00
J71		3 c. green			90·00 95·00
J72		5 c. brown			£1400 £1400
J73		8 c. grey			65·00 80·00
J74		10 c. dull purple			95·00 £110
J75		12 c. ultramarine			90·00 £100
J76		15 c. ultramarine			90·00 £100

Straits Settlements stamps overprinted with a similar seal impression, but circular and containing four characters, are believed to be fiscal issues.

1942 (15 Apr). *Straits Settlements stamps optd with T 13.*

J77	**58**	1 c. black (R.)			2·50 2·00
		a. Opt inverted			£325 £325
		b. Opt double			£275 £275
J78		2 c. orange			4·25 3·00
		a. "PE" for "PENANG"			95·00 80·00
		b. Opt inverted			£150
		c. Opt double			£350
J79		3 c. green (R.)			3·75 2·25
		a. Opt double, one inverted			£325
J80		5 c. brown (R.)			2·25 4·00
		a. "N PPON"			£160
		b. Opt double			£325 £325
J81		8 c. grey (R.)			2·25 1·40
		a. "N PPON"			50·00 55·00
		b. Opt double, one inverted			£325
J82		10 c. dull purple (R.)			1·50 2·00
		a. Opt double			£350 £350
		b. Opt double, one inverted			£400 £400
J83		12 c. ultramarine (R.)			3·00 10·00
		a. "N PPON"			£400
		b. Opt double			£350
		c. Opt double, one inverted			£425 £450
J84		15 c. ultramarine (R.)			1·75 2·25
		a. "N PPON"			£100 £110
		b. Opt inverted			£400 £400
		c. Opt double			£450 £450
J85		40 c. scarlet and dull purple			4·25 10·00
J86		50 c. black/*emerald* (R.)			3·75 18·00
J87		$1 black and red/*blue*			6·00 25·00
		a. Opt inverted			£750
J88		$2 green and scarlet			42·00 75·00
J89		$5 green and red/*emerald*			£450 £550

Nos. J77/89 were replaced by the overprinted issues intended for use throughout Malaya.

SELANGOR

Postal services resumed in the Kuala Lumpur area on 3 April 1942 and gradually extended to the remainder of the state. Stamps of the general overprinted issue were used, but the following commemorative set was only available in Selangor.

SELANGOR
EXHIBITION
DAI NIPPON
2602
MALAYA

(14)

1942 (3 Nov). *Selangor Agri-horticultural Exhibition. Nos. 294 and 283 of Straits Settlements optd with T 14.*

J90	**58**	2 c. orange			12·00 24·00
		a. "C" for "G" in "SELANGOR" (R. 1/9)	£300 £350
		b. Opt inverted			£300 £400
J91		8 c. grey			13·00 24·00
		a. "C" for "G" in "SELANGOR" (R. 1/9)	£300 £350
		b. Opt inverted			£300 £400

SINGAPORE

The first post offices re-opened in Singapore on 16 March 1942.

(15) "Malaya Military Government Division Postal Services Bureau Seal"

(Handstamped at Singapore)

1942 (16 Mar). *Stamps of Straits Settlements optd with T 15 in red.*

J92	**58**	1 c. black			13·00 17·00
J93		2 c. orange			13·00 13·00
		a. Pair, one without handstamp		£1100
J94		3 c. green			50·00 70·00
J95		8 c. grey			22·00 18·00
J96		15 c. ultramarine			15·00 15·00

The overprint Type **15** has a double-lined frame, although the two lines are not always apparent, as in the illustration. Three chops were used, differing slightly in the shape of the characters, but forgeries also exist. It is distinguishable from Type **1**, except for the general issues, by its extra width, measuring approximately 14 mm against 12¹/₂ mm.

The 6, 10, 30, 40, 50 c., $2 and $5 also exist with this overprint, but were not sold to the public.

Nos. J92/6 were replaced on the 3 May 1942 by the stamps overprinted with Type **1** which were intended for use throughout Malaya.

TRENGGANU

Postal services resumed in Trengganu on 5 March 1942 using unoverprinted stamps up to the 35 c. value. These remained in use until September 1942.

1942 (Sept). *Stamps of Trengganu (Script wmk) optd as T 1 at Kuala Lumpur.*

J 97	**4**	1 c. black			95·00 90·00
		a. Red opt			£180 £200
		b. Brown opt			£450 £275
J 98		2 c. green (No. 27a)			£140 £140
		a. Red opt			£225 £250
		b. Brown opt			£475 £325
J 99		2 c. on 5 c. deep reddish purple/*bright yellow* (No. 59)	60·00 75·00
		a. Red opt			45·00 70·00
J100		3 c. chestnut (No. 29a)			80·00 80·00
		a. Red opt			£500 £500
J101		4 c. scarlet-vermilion (No. 30a)		£140 £140
J102		5 c. dp reddish purple/*brt yell* (No. 32a)	10·00 19·00
		a. Red opt			21·00
J103		6 c. orange (No. 33a)			8·50 25·00
		a. Red opt			90·00
		b. Brown opt			£450 £450
J104		8 c. grey (No. 34a)			9·00 13·00
		a. Brown to red opt			50·00 65·00
J105		8 c. on 10 c. bright blue (No. 60)	13·00 38·00
		a. Red opt			21·00
J106		10 c. bright blue			16·00 28·00
		a. Red opt			90·00
		b. Brown opt			£450 £450
J107		12 c. bright ultramarine			8·00 29·00
		a. Red opt			27·00
J108		20 c. dull purple and orange			8·50 26·00
		a. Red opt			21·00
J109		25 c. green and deep purple			7·50 32·00
		a. Red opt			22·00
		b. Brown opt			£475 £475
J110		30 c. dull purple and black			8·00 26·00
		a. Red opt			25·00
J111		35 c. carmine/*yellow*			22·00 38·00
		a. Red opt			24·00
J112		50 c. green and bright carmine			65·00 75·00

J113	4	$1 purple and blue/*blue*		.. £2500	£2500
J114		$3 green & brown-red/*green* (No. 43*a*)		50·00	85·00
		a. Red opt	..	..	60·00	
J115	5	$5 green and red/*yellow*	..	.. £130	£180
J116		$25 purple and blue	..	.. £1000	
		a. Red opt	..	..	.. £3250	
J117		$50 green and yellow	..	.. £8500	
J118		$100 green and scarlet	..	.. £1100	

DAI NIPPON

2602

MALAYA

(16)

1942 (Sept). *Stamps of Trengganu (Script wmk) optd with T* 16.

J119	4	1 c. black (No. 26*a*)	..	.. 12·00	10·00
J120		2 c. green (No. 27*a*)	..	.. £160	£180
J121		2 c. on 5 c. deep reddish purple/*bright yellow* (No. 59)	..	.. 6·00	8·00
J122		3 c. chestnut (No. 29*a*)	..	9·00	17·00
J123		4 c. scarlet-vermilion (No. 30*a*)	..	9·00	11·00
J124		5 c. dp reddish purple/*brt yell* (No. 32*a*)		5·50	12·00
J125		6 c. orange (No. 33*a*)	..	.. 5·00	12·00
J126		8 c. grey (No. 34*a*)	..	.. 70·00	25·00
J127		8 c. on 10 c. bright blue (No. 60)	..	5·50	10·00
J128		12 c. bright ultramarine	..	5·00	20·00
J129		20 c. dull purple and orange	..	10·00	13·00
J130		25 c. green and deep purple	..	7·00	27·00
J131		30 c. dull purple and black	..	7·50	24·00
J132		$3 green & brown-red/*green* (No. 43*a*)	60·00	£110

1943. *Stamps of Trengganu (Script wmk) optd with T* 2.

J133	4	1 c. black	..	.. 9·00	16·00
J134		2 c. green (No. 27*a*)	..	.. 8·00	24·00
J135		2 c. on 5 c. bright reddish purple/*bright yellow* (No. 59)	..	.. 6·00	18·00
J136		5 c. brt reddish purple/*brt yell* (No. 32*a*)	6·50	24·00
J137		6 c. orange (No. 33*a*)	..	8·00	27·00
J138		8 c. grey (No. 34*a*)	..	55·00	80·00
J139		8 c. on 10 c. bright blue (No. 60)	..	19·00	40·00
J140		10 c. bright blue	..	80·00	£180
J141		12 c. bright ultramarine	..	13·00	35·00
J142		20 c. dull purple and orange	..	15·00	35·00
J143		25 c. green and deep purple	..	13·00	38·00
J144		30 c. dull purple and black	..	16·00	40·00
J145		35 c. carmine/*yellow*	..	.. 16·00	42·00

POSTAGE DUE STAMPS

1942 (Sept). *Nos. D1/4 of Trengganu optd with T* 1 *sideways.*

JD17	D 1	1 c. scarlet	..	.. 50·00	80·00
JD18		4 c. green	..	.. 75·00	95·00
		a. Brown opt	..	.. 50·00	85·00
JD19		8 c. yellow	..	.. 14·00	50·00
JD20		10 c. brown	..	.. 14·00	50·00

The Trengganu 8 c. postage due also exists overprinted with Type **16**, but this was not issued (*Price* £400 *unused*).

Trengganu was ceded to Thailand by the Japanese on 19 October 1943.

GENERAL ISSUES

The following stamps were produced for use throughout Malaya, except for Trengganu.

1942 (3 Apr). *Stamps optd as T* 1. (*a*) *On Straits Settlements.*

J146	58	1 c. black (R.)	..	.. 3·25	3·25
		a. Black opt	..	.. £325	£325
		b. Violet opt	..	.. £550	£500
J147		2 c. green (V.)	..	.. £1700	£1700
J148		2 c. orange (R.)	..	3·00	2·25
		a. Black opt	..	.. £100	£110
		b. Violet opt	..	.. £180	£180
		c. Brown opt	..	.. £550	£550

J149	58	3 c. green (R.)	..	.. 2·75	2·25
		a. Black opt	..	.. £275	£300
		b. Violet opt	..	.. £550	£550
J150		5 c. brown (R.)	..	.. 22·00	28·00
		a. Black opt	..	.. £475	£475
J151		8 c. grey (R.)	..	.. 3·75	2·25
		a. Black opt	..	.. £225	£225
J152		10 c. dull purple (R.)	..	42·00	42·00
		a. Brown opt	..	.. £650	£650
J153		12 c. ultramarine (R.)	..	75·00	95·00
J154		15 c. ultramarine (R.)	..	3·50	3·75
		a. Violet opt	..	.. £550	£500
J155		30 c. dull purple and orange (R.)	..	£1500	£1600
J156		40 c. scarlet and dull purple (R.)	..	80·00	90·00
		a. Brown opt	..	.. £500	£375
J157		50 c. black/*emerald* (R.)	..	45·00	48·00
J158		$1 black and red/*blue* (R.)	..	75·00	75·00
J159		$2 green and scarlet (R.)	..	£130	£140
J160		$5 green and red/*emerald* (R.)	..	£170	£180

(*b*) *On Negri Sembilan*

J161	6	1 c. black (R.)	..	.. 19·00	13·00
		a. Violet opt	..	.. 22·00	20·00
		b. Brown opt	..	.. 15·00	16·00
		c. Black opt	..	.. 48·00	38·00
		d. Pair. Nos. J161/a	..	.. £275	
		e. Pair. Nos. J161 and J161*b*		
J162		2 c. orange (R.)	..	.. 20·00	16·00
		a. Violet opt	..	.. 40·00	27·00
		b. Black opt	..	.. 32·00	28·00
		c. Brown opt	..	.. 55·00	45·00
J163		3 c. green (R.)	..	.. 27·00	20·00
		a. Violet opt	..	.. 23·00	29·00
		c. Brown opt	..	.. 90·00	50·00
		d. Black opt	..	.. 45·00	42·00
J164		5 c. brown	..	.. 28·00	21·00
		a. Pair, one without opt	..	£1200	
		b. Brown opt	..	.. 17·00	15·00
		c. Red opt	..	.. 15·00	11·00
		d. Violet opt	..	.. 50·00	38·00
J165		6 c. grey	..	.. £140	£120
		a. Brown opt	..	.. £325	£325
J166		8 c. scarlet	..	.. 85·00	75·00
J167		10 c. dull purple	..	.. £130	£130
		a. Red opt	..	.. £200	£200
		b. Brown opt	..	.. £325	£300
J168		12 c. bright ultramarine (Br.)	..	£1100	£1100
J169		15 c. ultramarine (R.)	..	18·00	8·00
		a. Violet opt	..	.. 55·00	28·00
		b. Brown opt	..	.. 27·00	12·00
J170		25 c. dull purple and scarlet	..	28·00	38·00
		a. Red opt	..	.. 60·00	75·00
		b. Brown opt	..	.. £300	£275
J171		30 c. dull purple and orange	..	£180	£150
		a. Brown opt	..	.. £800	£750
J172		40 c. scarlet and dull purple	..	£850	£800
		a. Brown opt	..	.. £800	£800
J173		50 c. black/*emerald*	..	.. £550	£550
J174		$1 black and red/*blue*	..	£180	£190
		a. Red opt	..	.. £160	£180
		b. Brown opt	..	.. £450	£450
J175		$5 green and red/*emerald*	..	£450	£475
		a. Red opt	..	.. £650	£700

(*c*) *On Pahang*

J176	15	1 c. black	..	.. 45·00	40·00
		a. Red opt	..	.. 50·00	42·00
		b. Violet opt	..	.. £300	£250
		c. Brown opt	..	.. £200	£190
J177		3 c. green	..	.. £225	£225
		a. Red opt	..	.. £225	£225
		b. Violet opt	..	.. £600	£475
J178		5 c. brown	..	.. 12·00	9·00
		a. Red opt	..	.. £160	£110
		b. Brown opt	..	.. £180	£110
		c. Violet opt	..	.. £400	£250
J179		8 c. grey	..	.. £475	£425
J180		8 c. scarlet	..	.. 22·00	10·00
		a. Red opt	..	.. £100	60·00
		b. Violet opt	..	.. £100	65·00
		c. Brown opt	..	.. £110	85·00
J181		10 c. dull purple	..	.. £180	£120
		a. Red opt	..	.. £200	£200
		b. Brown opt	..	.. £325	£250
J182		12 c. bright ultramarine	..	£1400	£1400
		a. Red opt	..	.. £1200	£1200

J183 **15** 15 c. ultramarine £100 £100
    a. Red opt £225 £225
    b. Violet opt £550 £475
    c. Brown opt £450 £325
J184 25 c. dull purple and scarlet .. 19·00 29·00
J185 30 c. dull purple and orange .. 12·00 28·00
    a. Red opt £140 £170
J186 40 c. scarlet and dull purple .. 17·00 32·00
    a. Brown opt £275 £275
    b. Red opt .. .. 70·00 75·00
J187 50 c. black/*emerald* £550 £550
    a. Red opt £600 £600
J188 $1 black and red/*blue* (R.) .. £110 £130
    a. Black opt £300 £300
    b. Brown opt £550 £550
J189 $5 green and red/*emerald* .. £600 £700
    a. Red opt £900 £950

(d) On Perak

J190 **51** 1 c. black .. .. 50·00 32·00
    a. Violet opt £160 £100
    b. Brown opt .. .. 80·00 80·00
J191 2 c. orange .. .. 29·00 20·00
    a. Violet opt .. .. 70·00 70·00
    b. Red opt .. .. 50·00 40·00
    c. Brown opt .. .. 55·00 55·00
J192 3 c. green .. .. 26·00 28·00
    a. Violet opt £350 £300
    b. Brown opt £170 £150
    c. Red opt £300 £250
J193 5 c. brown .. .. 7·00 6·00
    a. Pair, one without opt .. £1000
    b. Brown opt .. .. 30·00 26·00
    c. Violet opt £180 £180
    d. Red opt £200 £200
J194 8 c. grey .. .. 50·00 42·00
    a. Red opt £325 £225
    b. Brown opt £325 £250
J195 8 c. scarlet .. .. 28·00 35·00
    a. Violet opt £425 £275
J196 10 c. dull purple .. .. 26·00 24·00
    a. Red opt £275 £225
J197 12 c. bright ultramarine .. £225 £225
J198 15 c. ultramarine .. .. 24·00 30·00
    a. Red opt £200 £200
    b. Violet opt £300 £250
    c. Brown opt £300 £250
J199 25 c. dull purple and scarlet .. 14·00 25·00
J200 30 c. dull purple and orange .. 17·00 32·00
    a. Pair, one without opt .. £1300
    b. Brown opt £400 £350
    c. Red opt .. .. 32·00 55·00
J201 40 c. scarlet and dull purple .. £325 £325
    a. Brown opt £500 £475
J202 50 c. black/*emerald* .. .. 38·00 50·00
    a. Red opt .. .. 48·00 60·00
    b. Brown opt £300 £325
J203 $1 black and red/*blue* £400 £400
    a. Brown opt £550 £450
J204 $2 green and scarlet £2000 £2000
J205 $5 green and red/*emerald* .. £475
    a. Brown opt £1500

(e) On Selangor

J206 **46** 1 c. black, S .. .. 12·00 22·00
    a. Red opt, SU .. .. 30·00 35·00
    b. Violet opt, SU .. .. 38·00 35·00
J207 2 c. green, SU £900 £900
    a. Violet opt, U £1100 £1100
J208 2 c. orange (*p* 14×14¹/₂), S .. 80·00 50·00
    a. Red opt, U £160 £150
    b. Violet opt, U £225 £150
    c. Brown opt, S .. .. 65·00 75·00
J209 2 c. orange (*p* 14), S .. £100 80·00
    a. Red opt, U £180 £160
    b. Violet opt, U £250 £160
J210 3 c. green, SU .. .. 23·00 17·00
    a. Red opt, SU .. .. 18·00 18·00
    b. Violet opt, SU .. .. 65·00 50·00
    c. Brown opt, SU .. .. 18·00 18·00
J211 5 c. brown, SU .. .. 6·00 5·50
    a. Red opt, SU .. .. 11·00 16·00
    b. Violet opt, SU .. .. 21·00 27·00
    c. Brown opt, SU .. .. 90·00 80·00
J212 6 c. scarlet, S £300 £300
    a. Red opt, S £200 £250
    b. Brown opt, S £550

J213 **46** 8 c. grey, S .. .. 17·00 17·00
    a. Red opt, SU .. .. 42·00 32·00
    b. Violet opt, U .. .. 35·00 32·00
    c. Brown opt, S .. .. £120 70·00
J214 10 c. dull purple, S .. 13·00 21·00
    a. Red opt, S .. .. 60·00 55·00
    b. Brown opt, S .. .. £120 75·00
J215 12 c. bright ultramarine, S .. 60·00 60·00
    a. Red opt, S £110 £110
    b. Brown opt, S £110 £110
J216 15 c. ultramarine, S .. 16·00 22·00
    a. Red opt, SU .. .. 48·00 48·00
    b. Violet opt, U .. .. £140 95·00
    c. Brown opt, S .. .. 80·00 60·00
J217 25 c. dull purple and scarlet, S .. 75·00 85·00
    a. Red opt, S .. .. 60·00 80·00
J218 30 c. dull purple and orange, S .. 11·00 24·00
    a. Brown opt, S £325 £250
J219 40 c. scarlet and dull purple, S .. £130 £130
    a. Brown opt, S £325 £225
J220 50 c. black/*emerald*, S £110 £110
    a. Red opt, S .. .. 85·00 90·00
    b. Brown opt, S £325 £325
J221 **48** $1 black and red/*blue* .. 30·00 42·00
    a. Red opt £120 £140
J222 $2 green and scarlet .. 35·00 60·00
    a. Pair, one without opt .. £1200
    b. Red opt £450 £475
J223 $5 green and red/*emerald* .. 65·00 85·00

Nos. J161a and J163a exist with the handstamped overprint sideways.

On T **46** the overprint is normally sideways (with "top" to either right or left), but on T **48** it is always upright.

S= Sideways

U= Upright

SU= Sideways or upright (our prices being for the cheaper).

Specialists recognise nine slightly different chops as Type **1**. Initial supplies with the overprint in red were produced at Singapore. Later overprintings took place at Kuala Lumpur in violet, red or brown and, finally, black. No. J155 was from the Kuala Lumpur printing only. Except where noted these overprints were used widely in Malaya and, in some instances, Sumatra.

The following stamps also exist with this overprint, but were not available to the public:

Straits Settlements (in red) 6, 25 c.

Kelantan (in black) 10 c.

Negri Sembilan 2 c. green (Blk. or Brn.), 4 c. (Blk.), 6 c. scarlet (Blk.), 8 c. grey (Blk.), 12 c. (Blk.), $2 (Blk. or Brn.)

Pahang (in black, 2 c. also in brown) 2, 4, 6 c., $2

Perak 2 c. green (R.), 6 c. (Blk.)

Selangor 4 c. (Blk.)

1942 (May). *Optd with T* **16**. *(a) On Straits Settlements.*

J224 **58** 2 c. orange 85 50
    a. Opt inverted .. .. 9·00 17·00
    b. Opt double, one inverted .. 48·00 60·00
J225 3 c. green .. .. .. 50·00 65·00
J226 8 c. grey .. .. .. 3·50 2·00
    a. Opt inverted .. .. 13·00 27·00
J227 15 c. blue .. .. .. 9·00 6·50

(b) On Negri Sembilan

J228 **6** 1 c. black .. .. .. 1·50 60
    a. Opt inverted .. .. 9·00 25·00
    b. Opt double, one inverted .. 35·00 50·00
J229 2 c. orange .. .. .. 4·00 50
J230 3 c. green .. .. .. 3·00 45
J231 5 c. brown .. .. .. 60 1·00
J232 6 c. grey .. .. .. 2·50 1·00
    a. Opt inverted .. .. —£1000
    b. Stop omitted at right (R. 10/4) .. 75·00 80·00
J233 8 c. scarlet .. .. .. 3·25 1·25
J234 10 c. dull purple .. .. 3·00 2·50
J235 15 c. ultramarine .. .. 10·00 2·50
J236 25 c. dull purple and scarlet .. 3·00 9·50
J237 30 c. dull purple and orange .. 5·00 3·00
J238 $1 black and red/*blue* .. £100 £110

(c) On Pahang

J239 **15** 1 c. black .. .. .. 1·50 1·50
    a. Opt omitted (in pair with normal) £500
J240 5 c. brown .. .. .. 1·00 70
J241 8 c. scarlet .. .. .. 25·00 2·50
    a. Opt omitted (in pair with normal) £1000
J242 10 c. dull purple .. .. 9·00 6·50
J243 12 c. bright ultramarine .. 1·25 8·00

J244	**15**	25 c. dull purple and scarlet	..	..	3·75 14·00
J245		30 c. dull purple and orange	..	..	1·90 7·00

(d) On Perak

J246	**51**	2 c. orange	..	..	1·75 1·00
		a. Opt inverted	..	..	29·00 29·00
J247		3 c. green	..	..	60 75
		a. Opt inverted	..	..	12·00 23·00
		b. Opt omitted (in pair with normal)			£500
J248		8 c. scarlet	..	..	60 40
		a. Opt inverted	..	..	4·50 7·00
		b. Opt double, one inverted	..		£200 £225
		c. Opt omitted (in horiz pair with normal)	..	..	£400
J249		10 c. dull purple	..	..	9·00 5·50
J250		15 c. ultramarine	..	..	4·00 2·00
J251		50 c. black/*emerald*	..	..	2·00 3·00
J252		$1 black and red/*blue*	..	..	£350 £400
J253		$5 green and red/*emerald*	..		32·00 65·00
		a. Opt inverted	..		£275 £325

(e) On Selangor

J254	**46**	3 c. green	..	..	60 2·00
J255		12 c. bright ultramarine ..			1·10 9·00
J256		15 c. ultramarine	..		3·50 1·50
J257		40 c. scarlet and dull purple	..		2·00 3·00
J258	**48**	$2 green and scarlet	..		10·00 30·00

On T **46** the overprint is sideways, with "top" to left or right.
The following stamps also exist with this overprint, but were not available to the public.
Perak 1, 5, 30 c. (*Price for set of 3 £350 unused*).
Selangor 1, 5, 10, 30 c., $1, $5 (*Price for set of 6 £600 unused*).

DAI NIPPON
2602
MALAYA

2 Cents
(17)

DAI NIPPON
YUBIN

2 Cents
(18)
"Japanese
Postal Service"

1942 (Nov). *No. 108 of Perak surch with T* 17.
J259 **51** 2 c. on 5 c. brown .. .. .. 1·25 1·75

1942 (Nov). *Perak stamps surch or opt only, as in T* 18.

J260	**51**	1 c. black	..	..	3·00 6·50
		a. Opt inverted	..	..	19·00 40·00
J261		2 c. on 5 c. brown	..	..	2·00 6·50
		a. "DAI NIPPON YUBIN" inverted			17·00 38·00
		b. Ditto and "2 Cents" omitted	..		45·00 65·00
J262		8 c. scarlet	..	..	3·50 2·25
		a. Opt inverted	..	..	11·00 24·00

A similar overprint exists on the Selangor 3 c. but this was not available to the public (*Price £325 unused*).

On 8 December 1942 contemporary Japanese 3, 5, 8 and 25 s. stamps were issued without overprint in Malaya and the 1, 2, 4, 6, 7, 10, 30 and 50 s. and 1 y. values followed on 15 February 1943.

大日本郵便
(19)

6 cts.
(20)

6 cts.
(21)

2 Cents
(22)

6 cts.
(23)

$1·00
(24)

1942 (4 Dec)–**44**. *Stamps of various Malayan territories optd "Japanese Postal Service" in Kanji characters as T* 2 *or* 19, *some additionally surch as T* 20 *to* 24.

(a) Stamps of Straits Settlements optd with T 2

J263	**58**	8 c. grey (Blk.) (1943)	..	..	1·40 50
		a. Opt inverted	..	..	38·00 48·00
		b. Opt omitted (in pair with normal)			£800
		c. Red opt	..		1·40 1·75

J264	**58**	12 c. ultramarine (1943)	..	..	65 6·50
J265		40 c. scarlet and dull purple (1943)	..		75 3·00

(b) Stamps of Negri Sembilan optd with T 2 *or such also*

J266	**6**	1 c. black	..	..	30 85
		a. Opt inverted	..	..	8·50 24·00
		b. Sideways second character	..		27·00 28·00
		ba. Opt inverted with sideways second character	..		£600
J267		2 c. on 5 c. brown (surch as T 20)	..		50 50
J268		6 c. on 5 c. brown (surch T 21) (1943)			40 95
		a. Opt Type 2 and surch as Type 21 both inverted	..		£225 £225
J269		25 c. dull purple and scarlet (1943)	..		1·10 9·50

(c) Stamp of Pahang optd with T 2 *and surch also*

J270	**15**	6 c. on 5 c. brown (surch T 20) (1943)		50 75
J271		6 c. on 5 c. brown (surch T 21) (1943)		1·00 1·50

(d) Stamps of Perak optd with T 2 *or surch also*

J272	**51**	1 c. black	..	80 60
		a. Sideways second character	..	£190 £200
J273		2 c. on 5 c. brown (surch as T 20)	..	50 50
		a. Opt Type 2 and surch Type 20 both inverted	..	18·00 32·00
		b. Opt Type 2 inverted	..	18·00 32·00
		c. Sideways second character	..	50·00 50·00
J274		2 c. on 5 c. brown (surch T 22)	..	45 45
		a. Surch Type 22 inverted	..	18·00 32·00
		b. Opt Type 2 and surch Type 22 both inverted	..	18·00 32·00
		c. Sideways second character	..	25·00 32·00
		ca. Surch Type 22 inverted	..	£950
		cb. Opt Type 2 with sideways second character and surch Type 22 both inverted	..	£950
		d. Inverted "s" in Type 22 (R. 3/5)	..	50·00
J275		5 c. brown	..	45 40
		a. Opt inverted	..	27·00 35·00
		b. Sideways second character	..	£400 £375
J276		8 c. scarlet	..	55 70
		a. Opt inverted	..	15·00 26·00
		b. Sideways second character	..	50·00 60·00
		ba. Opt inverted with sideways second character	..	£650
J277		10 c. dull purple (1943)	..	60 50
J278		30 c. dull purple and orange (1943)	..	1·75 3·00
J279		50 c. black/*emerald* (1943)	..	3·00 13·00
J280		$5 green and red/*emerald* (1943)	..	50·00 80·00

(e) Stamps of Selangor optd with T 2 *(sideways on T* 46*)*

J281	**46**	1 c. black (1943)	..	90 1·50
J282		3 c. green	..	40 45
		a. Sideways second character	..	17·00 25·00
J283		12 c. bright ultramarine	..	45 1·60
		a. Sideways second character	..	35·00 50·00
J284		15 c. ultramarine	..	2·75 3·00
		a. Sideways second character	..	45·00 50·00
J285	**48**	$1 black and red/*blue*	..	3·00 16·00
		a. Opt inverted	..	£225 £225
		b. Sideways second character	..	£300 £325
J286		$2 green and scarlet (1943)	..	10·00 38·00
J287		$5 green and red/*emerald* (1943)	..	22·00 70·00
		a. Opt inverted	..	£225 £225

(f) Stamps of Selangor optd with T 19 *or surch also*

J288	**46**	1 c. black (R.) (1943)	..	35 50
J289		2 c. on 5 c. brown (surch as T 21) (R.) (1943)	..	30 50
J290		3 c. on 5 c. brown (surch as T 21) (1943)		30 3·00
		a. "s" in "cts." inverted (R. 4/3)	..	28·00 50·00
		b. Comma after "cts" (R. 9/3)	..	28·00 50·00
J291		5 c. brown (R.) (1944) ..	..	50 3·00
J292		6 c. on 5 c. brown (surch T 21) (1944)		30 1·00
J293		6 c. on 5 c. brown (surch T 23) (1944)		30 70
		a. "6" inverted (R. 7/8)	..	£700
		b. Surch and opt double	..	£350
J294		15 c. ultramarine	..	4·00 4·00
J295		$1 on 10 c. dull purple (surch T 24) (18.12.1944)	..	30 1·00
J296		$1.50 on 30 c. dull purple and orange (surch T 24) (18.12.1944) ..		30 1·00

The error showing the second character in Type 2 sideways occurred on R. 6/3 in the first of four settings only.
The 2 c. orange, 3 c. and 8 c. grey of Perak also exist overprinted with Type 2, but these stamps were not available to the public (*Price for set of 3 £100 unused*).
Examples of No. J275 are known postally used from the Shan States (part of pre-war Burma).

25 Tapping Rubber   26 Fruit   27 Japanese Shrine, Singapore

(Litho Kolff & Co, Batavia)

1943 (29 Apr–30 Oct). *T 25/7 and similar designs. P 12½.*

J297	25	1 c. grey-green (30 Oct)		30	55
J298	26	2 c. pale emerald (1 June)		30	15
J299	25	3 c. drab (30 Oct)		15	15
J300	–	4 c. carmine-rose		65	15
J301	–	8 c. dull blue		15	15
J302	–	10 c. brown-purple (30 Oct)		15	15
J303	27	15 c. violet (30 Oct)		35	2·25
J304	–	30 c. olive-green (30 Oct)		35	35
J305	–	50 c. blue (30 Oct)		1·75	2·25
J306	–	70 c. blue (30 Oct)		16·00	10·00
J297/306				*Set of* 10	18·00	14·50

Designs: *Vert*—4 c. Tin dredger; 8 c. War Memorial, Bukit Batok, Singapore; 10 c. Fishing village; 30 c. Sago palms; 50 c. Straits of Johore. *Horiz*—70 c. Malay Mosque, Kuala Lumpur.

The 2 c. and 4 c. values exist, printed by typography, in paler shades either imperforate or rouletted. It is suggested that these may have been available in Singapore at the very end of the Japanese Occupation.

28 Ploughman   29 Rice-planting

1943 (1 Sept). *Savings Campaign. Litho. P 12½.*

J307	28	8 c. violet		7·50	2·75
J308		15 c. scarlet		6·00	2·75

(Des Hon Chin. Litho)

1944 (15 Feb). *"Re-birth" of Malaya. P 12½.*

J309	29	8 c. rose-red		10·00	2·75
J310		15 c. magenta		4·00	3·00

大日本   大日本   大日本

マライ郵便   マライ郵便   マライ郵便

50 セント   1½ドル

         1ドル

(30)   (31)   (32)

1944 (16 Dec). *Stamps intended for use on Red Cross letters. Surch with T 30/2 in red. (a) On Straits Settlements.*

J311	58	50 c. on 50 c. black/*emerald*		11·00	24·00
J312		$1 on $1 black and red/*blue*		20·00	35·00
J313		$1.50 on $2 green and scarlet		32·00	70·00

(b) On Johore

J314	29	50 c. on 50 c. dull purple and red		8·00	20·00
J315		$1.50 on $2 green and carmine		5·50	14·00

(c) On Selangor

J316	48	$1 on $1 black and red/*blue*		4·00	14·00
J317		$1.50 on $2 green and scarlet		6·50	20·00

Nos. J311/17 were issued in Singapore but were withdrawn after one day, probably because supplies of Nos. J295/6 were received and issued on the 18 December.

A similar 6 c. surcharge exists on the Straits Settlements 5 c. but this was not available to the public (*Price* £400 *unused*).

STAMP BOOKLETS

1942. *Nos. SB3/4 of Perak and SB2 of Selangor with covers optd with T* **1**.

SB1	$1 booklet containing twenty 5 c. (No. J193) in blocks of 10			£20Q0
SB2	$1.30, booklet containing 5 c. and 8 c. (Nos. J193/4), each in block of 10			£2000
SB3	$1.30, booklet containing 5 c. and 8 c. (Nos. J211 and J213), each in block of 10			£2000

POSTAGE DUE STAMPS

Postage Due stamps of the Malayan Postal Union overprinted.

1942 (3 Apr). *Handstamped as T* **1** *in black.*

JD21	D 1	1 c. slate-purple			12·00	20·00
		a. Red opt			85·00	85·00
		b. Brown opt			90·00	95·00
JD22		3 c. green			48·00	50·00
		a. Red opt			£130	£140
JD23		4 c. green			32·00	26·00
		a. Red opt			45·00	42·00
		b. Brown opt			£100	£100
JD24		8 c. scarlet			65·00	55·00
		a. Red opt			95·00	90·00
		b. Brown opt			£120	£120
JD25		10 c. yellow-orange			20·00	30·00
		a. Red opt			90·00	90·00
		b. Brown opt			50·00	55·00
JD26		12 c. ultramarine			20·00	38·00
		a. Red opt			£120	£120
JD27		50 c. black			50·00	65·00
		a. Red opt			£275	£300

1942. *Optd with T* **16**.

JD28	D 1	1 c. slate-purple			1·60	8·00
JD29		3 c. green			9·50	15·00
JD30		4 c. green			8·50	10·00
JD31		8 c. scarlet			12·00	14·00
JD32		10 c. yellow-orange			1·60	10·00
JD33		12 c. ultramarine			1·60	12·00

The 9 c. and 15 c. also exist with this overprint, but these were not issued (*Price* £425 *each unused*).

1943–45. *Optd with T* **2**.

JD34	D 1	1 c. slate-purple			80	2·75
JD35		3 c. green			80	2·75
		a. Opt omitted (in pair with normal)			£650	
JD36		4 c. green			38·00	38·00
JD37		5 c. scarlet			70	3·25
JD38		9 c. yellow-orange			60	4·75
		a. Opt inverted			20·00	28·00
JD39		10 c. yellow-orange			70	4·50
		a. Opt inverted			50·00	50·00
JD40		12 c. ultramarine			90	9·50
JD41		15 c. ultramarine			90	9·50

THAI OCCUPATION OF MALAYA

Stamps issued for use in the Malay States of Kedah (renamed Syburi), Kelantan, Perlis and Trengganu, ceded by Japan to Thailand on 19 October 1943. British rule was restored on 9 (Kelantan), 18 (Perlis), 22 (Kedah) and 24 September 1945 (Trengganu). Nos. TM1/6 continued to be used for postage until replaced by the overprinted B.M.A. Malaya issues on 10 October 1945.

KELANTAN

TK 1

(Typo Kelantan Ptg Dept, Khota Baru)

1943 (15 Nov). *Handstamped with State arms in violet. No gum. P* 11.

TK1	TK 1	1 c. black					£190	£275
TK2		2 c. black	..			..	£225	£225
		a. Handstamp omitted		..		..	£700	
TK3		4 c. black				..	£225	£275
		a. Handstamp omitted				..	£850	
TK4		8 c. black	..			..	£225	£225
		a. Handstamp omitted		..		..	£550	
TK5		10 c. black	..			..	£275	£375

Nos. TK1/5 were printed in sheets of 84 (12×7) and have sheet watermarks in the form of "STANDARD" in block capitals with curved "CROWN" above and "AGENTS" below in double-lined capitals. This watermark occurs four times in the sheet.

Sheets were imperforate at top and left so that stamps exist imperforate at top, left or at top and left.

Genuine examples have a solid star at the top centre of the arms, as shown in Type TK **1**. Examples with a hollow outline star in this position are forgeries.

Similar stamps, but with red handstamps, were for fiscal use.

GENERAL ISSUE

TM 1 War Memorial

(Litho Defence Ministry, Bangkok)

1944 (15 Jan–4 Mar). *Thick opaque, or thin semi-transparent paper. Gummed or ungummed. P* 12½.

TM1	TM 1	1 c. yellow (4 Mar)	..		..	30·00	32·00
TM2		2 c. red-brown		..	..	12·00	20·00
		a. Imperf (pair)	..		..	£850	
		b. Perf 12½×11	..		..	20·00	20·00
TM3		3 c. green (4 Mar)		..	..	20·00	38·00
		a. Perf 12½×11	..		..	30·00	42·00
TM4		4 c. purple (4 Mar)			..	14·00	28·00
		a. Perf 12½×11	..		..	20·00	35·00
TM5		8 c. carmine (4 Mar)			..	14·00	20·00
		a. Perf 12½×11	..		..	20·00	20·00
TM6		15 c. blue (4 Mar)			..	38·00	60·00
		a. Perf 12½×11	..		..	42·00	60·00

5 c. and 10 c. stamps in this design were prepared, but never issued.

TRENGGANU

TRENGGANU

(TT 1)

(Overprinted at Trengganu Survey Office)

1944 (1 Dec). *Various stamps optd with Type* TT **1**.

(a) On Trengganu without Japanese opt

TT 1	4	1 c. black (26a)		..		
TT 2		30 c. dull purple and black (39)		..		

(b) On Trengganu stamp optd as T **1** *of Japanese Occupation*

TT 3	4	8 c. grey (J104)	..	..	..	£375	£275

(c) On stamps optd with T **16** *of Japanese Occupation.*
(i) *Pahang*

TT 4	15	12 c. bright ultramarine (J243)	..	£275	£120

(ii) *Trengganu*

TT 5	4	2 c. on 5 c. deep reddish purple/bright yellow (J121)*	..	..	£375	£375
TT 6		8 c. on 10 c. brt blue (J127) (inverted)		£300	£300
TT 7		12 c. brt ultramarine (J128) (inverted)		£300	£300

"This is spelt "TRENGANU" with one "G".

(d) On stamps optd with T **2** *of Japanese Occupation.*
(i) *Straits Settlements*

TT 8	58	12 c. ultramarine (J264)	..	..	£350	£350
TT 9		40 c. scarlet and dull purple (J265)	..	£350	£350

(ii) *Pahang*

TT10	15	6 c. on 5 c. brown (J271)	..	..	

(iii) *Perak*

TT11	51	1 c. black (J272)	..	..	
TT12		10 c. dull purple (J277)	..	..	
TT13		30 c. dull purple and orange (J278)	..	£600	£350

(iv) *Selangor*

TT14	46	3 c. green (J282)	..	..	£250	£250
TT15		12 c. brt ultramarine (J283) (L. to R.)	£150	£150
TT16		12 c. brt ultramarine (J283) (R. to L.)	£150	£110
		a. Sideways second character	..	£1700	£1700

(e) On Selangor stamps optd with T **19** *of Japanese Occupation*

TT17	46	2 c. on 5 c. brown (J289)	..	£350	£350
TT18		3 c. on 5 c. brown (J290)	..	£350	£350

(f) On pictorials of 1943 (Nos. J297/306)

TT19	25	1 c. grey-green	..	..	..	£275	£275
TT20	26	2 c. pale emerald	..	..	..	£275	£150
TT21	25	3 c. drab	..	..	..	£180	£120
TT22	–	4 c. carmine-rose	..	..	..	£250	£150
TT23	–	8 c. dull blue	..	..	..	£400	£400
TT24	–	10 c. brown-purple	..	..	£800	£600
TT25	27	15 c. violet	..	..	..	£250	£150
TT26	–	30 c. olive-green	..	..	..	£300	£130
TT27	–	50 c. blue	..	..	..	£350	£250
TT28	–	70 c. blue	..	..	..	£750	£600

(g) On Savings Campaign stamps (Nos. J307/8)

TT29	28	8 c. violet	..	..	..	£400	£400
TT30		15 c. scarlet	..	..	..	£275	£160

(h) On stamps of Japan

TT31	–	3 s. green (No. 319)	..		..	
TT32	–	5 s. claret (No. 396)	..	£325	£325
TT33	–	25 c. brown and chocolate (No. 329)	£170	£110
TT34	–	30 c. blue-green (No. 330)	..	£325	£160

(i) On Trengganu Postage Due stamp optd with T **1** *of Japanese Occupation*

TT35	D 1	1 c. scarlet (JD17)	..	..	..	£1300	£1300

Maldive Islands

100 larees = 1 rupee

1950 (24 Dec). *P* 13.

21	5	2 l. olive-green	..	..	..	..	1·50	40
22		3 l. blue ..	..	..	..	..	8·50	40
23		5 l. emerald-green	..	..	..	..	8·50	50
24		6 l. red-brown	..	..	..	..	70	30
25		10 l. scarlet	..	..	..	..	70	30
26		15 l. orange	..	..	..	..	70	30
27		25 l. purple	..	..	..	..	70	30
28		50 l. violet	..	..	..	..	70	30
29		1 r. chocolate	..	..	..	..	8·50	25·00
21/9	..	..	..	..	..	*Set of* 9	27·00	25·00

1952. *P* 13.

30	7	3 l. blue ..	..	..	..	..	1·00	30
31	8	5 l. emerald	..	..	..	..	50	1·40

Malta

12 pence (d) = 1 shilling; 20 shillings = 1 pound

CROWN COLONY

1937 (12 May). *Coronation. As Nos. 118/20 of Jamaica.*

214	½d. green	..	..	..	10	10
215	1½d. scarlet	..	..	..	50	20
	a. *Brown-lake*	..	..	£550	£550
216	2½d. bright blue	..	..		50	40
214/16		..	..	*Set of 3*	1·00	60
214/16 Perf "Specimen"	..	..	*Set of 3*	60·00	

37 Grand Harbour, Valletta   **38** H.M.S. *St. Angelo*

39 Verdala Palace   **40** Hypogeum, Hal Saflieni

Broken cross
(Right pane R. 5/7)

Extra windows (R. 2/7)
(corrected in 1945)

Damaged value
tablet (R. 4/9)

Semaphore flaw
(R. 2/7)

(Recess Waterlow)

1938 (17 Feb*)–**43.** *T* **37/40** *and similar designs. Wmk Mult Script CA (sideways on No. 217). P* 12½.

217	**37**	¼d. brown	..	..	10	10
218	**38**	½d. green	..	..	1·75	30
218a		½d. red-brown (8.3.43)	..	55	30
219	**39**	1d. red-brown	..	4·25	30
219a		1d. green (8.3.43)	..	60	10
220	**40**	1½d. scarlet	..	..	1·00	30
		a. Broken cross	..	70·00	
220b		1½d. slate-black (8.3.43)	..	30	15
		ba. Broken cross	..	50·00	
221	–	2d. slate-black	..	40	1·75
		a. Extra windows	..	35·00	
221b	–	2d. scarlet (8.3.43)	..	40	20
		ba. Extra windows	..	35·00	
222	–	2½d. greyish blue	..	75	45
222a	–	2½d. dull violet (8.3.43)	..	60	10
223	–	3d. dull violet	..	45	80
223a	–	3d. blue (8.3.43)	..	30	10
224	–	4½d. olive-green and yellow-brown	50	10
225	–	6d. olive-green and scarlet	..	75	30
226	–	1s. black	..	75	30
227	–	1s. 6d. black and olive-green	7·00	3·75
228	–	2s. green and deep blue	..	4·00	3·75
229	–	2s. 6d. black and scarlet	..	7·50	5·00
		a. Damaged value tablet	..	£150	
230	–	5s. black and green	..	4·50	5·50
		a. Semaphore flaw	..	65·00	
231	–	10s. black and carmine	..	15·00	15·00
217/31		..	..	*Set of 21*	45·00	32·00
217/31 Perf "Specimen"	..	*Set of 21*	£350	

Designs: *Horiz (as T* **39**)—2d. Victoria and citadel, Gozo; 2½d. De l'Isle Adam entering Mdina; 4½d. Ruins at Mnajdra; 1s. 6d. St. Publius; 2s. Mdina Cathedral; 2s. 6d. Statue of Neptune, *Vert (as T* **40**)—3d. St. John's Co-Cathedral; 6d. Statue of Manoel de Vilhena; 1s. Maltese girl wearing faldetta; 5s. Palace Square, Valletta; 10s. St. Paul.

*This is the local date of issue but the stamps were released in London on 15 February.

1946 (3 Dec). *Victory. As Nos. 141/2 of Jamaica, but inscr* "MALTA" *between Maltese Cross and George Cross.*

232	1d. green	..	..	..	15	10
233	3d. blue	..	..	..	20	40
232/3 Perf "Specimen"	..	..	*Set of 2*	50·00	

SELF-GOVERNMENT

(52)   "NT" joined
(R. 4/10)

NEW INFORMATION

The editor is always interested to correspond with people who have new information that will improve or correct the Catalogue.

Halation flaw (Pl 2 R. 2/5)
(ptg of 8 Jan 1953)

Cracked plate (Pl 2
R. 5/1) (ptg of 8 Jan 1953)

(Optd by Waterlow)

1948 (25 Nov)–53. *New Constitution. As Nos.* 217/31 *but optd as T* **52**; *reading up on* ¹/₂d. *and* 5s., *down on other values, and smaller on* ¹/₄d. *value.*

234	37	¹/₄d. brown	..		..	20	20
235	38	¹/₂d. red-brown		..	..	20	10
		a. "NT" joined	..		..	17·00	
236	39	1d. green	..		..	20	10
236a		1d. grey (R.) (8.1.53)		..	..	20	10
237	40	1¹/₂d. blue-black (R.) ..			..	75	10
		a. Broken cross	..		..	60·00	
237b		1¹/₂d. green (8.1.53)	..		..	30	10
		ba. Albino opt	..		..	†£10000	
238	–	2d. scarlet ..			..	85	10
		a. Extra windows ..		..	..	38·00	
238b	–	2d. yellow-ochre (8.1.53)		..	..	30	10
		ba. Halation flaw	..		..	£110	
		bc. Cracked plate	..		..	£100	
239	–	2¹/₂d. dull violet (R.) ..			..	80	10
239a		2¹/₂d. scarlet-vermilion (8.1.53)			..	30	85
240	–	3d. blue (R.)	..		..	45	15
240a		3d. dull violet (R.) (8.1.53) ..			..	35	15
241	–	4¹/₂d. olive-green and yellow-brown		..		2·00	1·50
241a		4¹/₂d. olive-grn & dp ultram (R.) (8.1.53)			..	50	90
242	–	6d. olive-green and scarlet ..			..	1·75	15
243	–	1s. black	..		..	2·25	45
244	–	1s. 6d. black and olive-green			..	2·50	45
245	–	2s. green and deep blue (R.)			..	5·00	1·50
246	–	2s. 6d. black and scarlet		..		12·00	2·50
		a. Damaged value tablet		..		£325	
247	–	5s. black and green (R.)		..		17·00	3·50
		a. "NT" joined	..		..	£170	£100
		b. Semaphore flaw ..			..	—	£1600
248	–	10s. black and carmine		..		17·00	21·00
234/48		..	..	..	*Set of* 21	55·00	30·00

1949 (4 Jan). *Royal Silver Wedding. As Nos.* 143/4 *of Jamaica, but inscr* "MALTA" *between Maltese Cross and George Cross and with* £1 *ptd in recess.*

249		1d. green	..	..	..	..	50	10
250		£1 indigo	..	..	..	..	38·00	35·00

1949 (10 Oct). *75th Anniv of U.P.U. As Nos.* 145/8 *of Jamaica, but inscr* "MALTA" *in recess.*

251		2¹/₂d. violet	..	..	..	..	30	10
252		3d. deep blue	..	..	..	..	3·25	50
253		6d. carmine-red	..	..	..	..	1·00	50
254		1s. blue-black	..	..	..	..	1·00	1·75
251/4	..	..	..	..	*Set of* 4	5·00	2·50

53 Queen Elizabeth II when Princess

54 "Our Lady of Mount Carmel" (attrib Palladino)

(T **53**/4. Recess B.W.)

1950 (1 Dec). *Visit of Princess Elizabeth to Malta. Wmk Mult Script CA. P* 12 × 11¹/₂.

255	**53**	1d. green	..	..	..	10	10
256		3d. blue ..		..	..	20	10
257		1s. black	..	..	..	55	60
255/7	..	..	..	*Set of* 3	70	70

1951 (12 July). *Seventh Centenary of the Scapular. Wmk Mult Script CA. P* 12 × 11¹/₂.

258	**54**	1d. green	..	..	..	10	10
259		3d. violet	..	..	..	20	10
260		1s. black	..	..	..	60	40
258/60	..	..	..	*Set of* 3	80	50

Mauritius

100 cents = 1 rupee

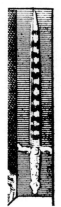
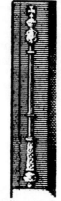

Line through sword (R. 2/2)   Line by sceptre (R. 5/3)

1937 (12 May). *Coronation. As Nos. 118/20 of Jamaica.*

249	5 c. violet..	..	..	40	10
250	12 c. scarlet	..	..	40	1·50
251	20 c. bright blue	..	..	40	10
	a. Line through sword	..	..	55·00	
	b. Line by sceptre	..	..	55·00	
249/51	..	..	*Set of 3*	1·10	1·50
249/51	Perf "Specimen"	..	*Set of 3*	55·00	

51

Sliced "S" at right (R. 2/2, 3/2, right pane)

Sliced "S" at top (R. 4/1, left pane and R. 8/4, right pane)

Broken frame under "A" of "MAURITIUS" (R. 9/3 left pane, Key Plate 2)

"IJ" flaw (R. 3/6 of right pane)   Battered "A" (R. 6/1 of right pane)

(Typo D.L.R.)

1938–49. *T* **51** *and similar types. Wmk Mult Script CA. Chalk-surfaced paper (25 c. to 10 r.). P* 14.

252	2 c. olive-grey (9.3.38)	..	..	30	10
	a. Perf 15×14 (1942)	..	..	1·00	10
253	3 c. reddish purple and scarlet (27.10.38)		2·00	1·75
	a. Sliced "S" at right	..	..	70·00	
	b. *Reddish lilac and red* (4.43)	..	2·75	2·75
	ba. Sliced "S" at right	..	..	8·00	
254	4 c. dull green (26.2.38)	..	..	2·50	1·75
	a. Open "C"	..	..	80·00	
	b. *Deep dull green* (4.43)	..	..	1·00	1·75
	ba. Open "C"	..	..	55·00	
255	5 c. slate-lilac (23.2.38)	..	..	7·50	70
	a. *Pale lilac* (*shades*) (4.43)	..	2·25	20
	b. Perf 15×14 (1942)	..	..	45·00	10
256	10 c. rose-red (9.3.38)	..	..	2·25	20
	a. Sliced "S" at top	..	..	85·00	
	b. *Deep reddish rose* (*shades*) (4.43)		2·25	10
	ba. Sliced "S" at top	..	..	85·00	
	c. Perf 15×14. *Pale reddish rose* (1942)		27·00	90
	ca. Sliced "S" at top	..	..	£275	
257	12 c. salmon (*shades*) (26.2.38)	..	1·00	20
	a. Perf 15×14 (1942)	..	..	50·00	75
258	20 c. blue (26.2.38)..	..	..	1·00	10
	a. Broken frame	..	..	£130	
259	25 c. brown-purple (2.3.38)	..	8·00	20
	a. "IJ" flaw	..	..	£190	
	b. Ordinary paper (8.4.43)	..	5·00	10
	ba. "IJ" flaw	..	..	£130	
260	1 r. grey-brown (2.3.38)	..	..	22·00	1·50
	a. Battered "A" ..	..	..	£300	
	b. Ordinary paper (8.4.43)	..	16·00	90
	ba. Battered "A"	..	..	£225	
	c. *Drab* (4.49) ..	..	..	24·00	4·00
	ca. Battered "A" ..	..	..	£300	
261	2 r. 50, pale violet (2.3.38)	..	38·00	11·00
	a. Ordinary paper (8.4.43)	..	27·00	10·00
	b. *Slate-violet* (4.48)	..	45·00	24·00
262	5 r. olive-green (2.3.38)	..	48·00	22·00
	a. Ordinary paper. *Sage-green* (8.4.43)		27·00	22·00
263	10 r. reddish purple (*shades*) (2.3.38)		42·00	28·00
	a. Ordinary paper (8.4.43)	..	11·00	22·00
252/63a	..	..	*Set of 12*	85·00	50·00
252/63	Perf "Specimen"	..	*Set of 12*	£180	

The stamps perf 15 × 14 were printed by Bradbury, Wilkinson from De La Rue plates and issued only in the colony in 1942. De La Rue printings of the 2 c. to 20 c. in 1943–45 were on thin, whiter paper. 1943–45 printings of the 25 c. to 10 r. were on unsurfaced paper.

1946 (20 Nov). *Victory. As Nos. 141/2 of Jamaica.*

264	5 c. lilac	..	..	10	10
265	20 c. blue	..	..	10	10
264/5	Perf "Specimen"	..	*Set of 2*	50·00	

52 1d. "Post Office" Mauritius and King George VI

(Recess B.W.)

1948 (22 Mar). *Centenary of First British Colonial Postage Stamp. Wmk Mult Script CA. P* 11½×11.

266	**52**	5 c. orange and magenta			10	30
267		12 c. orange and green			10	10
268	–	20 c. blue and light blue			10	10
269	–	1 r. blue and red-brown			15	30
266/9				*Set of* 4	40	60
266/9	Perf "Specimen"			*Set of* 4	95·00	

Design:—20 c., 1 r. As T **52** but showing 2d. "Post Office" Mauritius.

1948 (25 Oct). *Royal Silver Wedding. As Nos.* 143/4 *of Jamaica.*

270		5 c. violet			10	10
271		10 r. magenta			9·50	22·00

1949 (10 Oct). *75th Anniv of U.P.U. As Nos.* 145/8 *of Jamaica.*

272		12 c. carmine			40	65
273		20 c. deep blue			1·75	1·50
274		35 c. purple			40	65
275		1 r. sepia			40	20
272/5				*Set of* 4	2·75	2·75

53 Labourdonnais Sugar Factory

55 Aloe Plant

(Photo Harrison)

1950 (1 July). *T* **53, 55** *and similar designs. Wmk Mult Script CA. Chalk surfaced paper. P* 13½ × 14½ (*horiz*), 14½ × 13½ (*vert*).

276		1 c. bright purple			10	50
277		2 c. rose-carmine			15	10
278		3 c. yellow-green			60	2·50
279		4 c. green			20	1·25
280		5 c. blue			15	10
281		10 c. scarlet			30	75
282		12 c. olive-green			1·25	2·00
283		20 c. ultramarine			60	15
284		25 c. brown-purple			1·25	40

285		35 c. violet				30	1(
286		50 c. emerald-green				2·00	5(
287		1 r. sepia				4·25	1(
288		2 r. 50, orange				12·00	6·5(
289		5 r. red-brown				14·00	14·0(
290		10 r. dull blue				14·00	18·0(
276/290				*Set of* 15	45·00	40·0(

Designs: *Horiz*—2 c. Grand Port; 5 c. Rempart Mountain; 10 c. Transporting cane; 12 c. Mauritius Dodo and map; 35 c Government House, Reduit; 1 r. Timor Deer; 2 r. 50, Port Louis 5 r. Beach scene; 10 r. Arms of Mauritius. *Vert*—4 c. Tamarind Falls; 20 c. Legend of Paul and Virginie (inscr "VIRGINIA") 25 c. Labourdonnais statue; 50 c. Pieter Both Mountain.

The latitude is incorrectly shown on No. 282. This was corrected before the same design was used for No. 302a.

STAMP BOOKLETS

1953 (10 Oct). *Black on white cover. Stapled.*

SB1   5 r. booklet containing four 5 c., eight 10 c. and 50 c. (Nos. 280, 286, 291) in blocks of 4 and one pane of 4 air mail labels   ..   ..   £18(

POSTAGE DUE STAMPS

D 1

(Typo Waterlow)

1933–54. *Wmk Mult Script CA. P* 15 × 14.

D1	D 1	2 c. black				1·25	5(
D2		4 c. violet				40	6(
D3		6 c. scarlet				40	8(
D4		10 c. green				60	7(
D5		20 c. bright blue				50	1·0(
D6		50 c. deep magenta (1.3.54)				55	15·0(
D7		1 r. orange (1.3.54)				70	15·0(
D1/7					*Set of* 7	4·00	30·0(
D1/5	Perf "Specimen"				*Set of* 5	65·00	

Montserrat

1937. 12 pence (d) = 1 shilling; 20 shillings = 1 pound
1951. 100 cents = 1 West Indian dollar

PRESIDENCY

1937 (12 May). *Coronation. As Nos. 118/20 of Jamaica.*

98	1d. scarlet	..	..	..	30	50
99	1½d. yellow-brown	..	..	..	40	30
100	2½d. bright blue	..	..	..	40	75
98/100	..	..	*Set of 3*	1·00	1·40
98/100 Perf "Specimen"	..	*Set of 3*	50·00	

11 Carr's Bay   **12** Sea Island Cotton

13 Botanic Station

(Recess D.L.R.)

1938 (2 Aug)–**48**. *Wmk Mult Script CA. P 12 (10s., £1) or 13 (others).*

101	11	½d. blue-green	..	..	2·50	1·50
		a. Perf 14 (1942)	..	..	15	20
102	12	1d. carmine	..	..	2·00	40
		a. Perf 14 (1943)	..	..	30	30
103		1½d. purple	..	..	10·00	50
		a. Perf 14 (1942)	..	..	30	50
		ab. "A" of "CA" missing from wmk				
104	13	2d. orange	..	..	10·00	60
		a. Perf 14 (1942)	..	..	85	70
105	12	2½d. ultramarine	..	..	65	60
		a. Perf 14 (1943)	..	..	40	30
106	11	3d. brown	..	..	1·75	40
		a. Perf 14. *Red-brown* (1942)	..	1·75	40
		ab. *Deep brown* (1943)	..	1·75	4·25
107	13	6d. violet	..	..	8·00	80
		a. Perf 14 (1943)	..	..	2·50	60
108	11	1s. lake	..	..	10·00	70
		a. Perf 14 (1942)	..	..	2·00	30
109	13	2s. 6d. slate-blue	..	..	20·00	80
		a. Perf 14 (1943)	..	..	17·00	2·50
110	11	5s. rose-carmine	..	..	27·00	8·00
		a. Perf 14 (1942)	..	..	21·00	3·00
111	13	10s. pale blue (1.4.48)	..	13·00	17·00
112	11	£1 black (1.4.48)	..	13·00	27·00
101a/12	..	..	*Set of 12*	65·00	45·00
101/12 Perf "Specimen"	..	*Set of 12*	£250	

Nos. 101/2 exist in coils constructed from normal sheets.

1946 (1 Nov). *Victory. As Nos. 141/2 of Jamaica.*

113	1½d. purple	..	..	..	10	10
114	3d. chocolate	..	..	..	10	10
113/14 Perf "Specimen"	..	*Set of 2*	55·00	

1949 (3 Jan). *Royal Silver Wedding. As Nos. 143/4 of Jamaica.*

115	2½d. ultramarine	..	..	..	10	10
116	5s. carmine ..	..	..	..	4·75	6·50

1949 (10 Oct). *75th Anniv of U.P.U. As Nos. 145/8 of Jamaica.*

117	2½d. ultramarine	..	..	..	20	30
118	3d. brown	..	..	..	1·75	30
119	6d. purple	..	..	..	40	30
120	1s. purple	..	..	..	40	30
117/20	..	..	..	*Set of 4*	2·50	1·10

(New Currency. 100 cents = 1 West Indies, later Eastern Caribbean dollar)

1951 (16 Feb). *Inauguration of B.W.I. University College. As Nos. 149/50 of Jamaica.*

121	3 c. black and purple	..	..	..	20	60
122	12 c. black and violet	..	..	..	20	60

14 Government House   **18** Badge of Presidency

(Recess B.W.)

1951 (17 Sept). *T 14, 18 and similar horiz designs. Wmk Mult Script CA. P 11½ × 11.*

123	14	1 c. black	..	..	10	1·50
124	–	2 c. green	..	..	15	70
125	–	3 c. orange-brown	..	..	30	70
126	–	4 c. carmine	..	..	30	50
127	–	5 c. reddish violet	..	..	30	70
128	18	6 c. olive-brown ..	..	..	30	30
129	–	8 c. deep blue	..	..	35	20
130	–	12 c. blue and chocolate ..	..	35	30
131	–	24 c. carmine and yellow-green ..	..	95	30
132	–	60 c. black and carmine ..	..	6·00	2·50
133	–	$1.20, yellow-green and blue	..	6·00	4·50
134	–	$2.40, black and green ..	..	5·00	12·00
135	18	$4.80, black and purple	..	16·00	16·00
123/135	..	..	*Set of 13*	32·00	35·00

Designs:—2 c., $1.20, Sea Island cotton: cultivation; 3 c. Map of colony; 4, 24 c. Picking tomatoes; 5, 12 c. St. Anthony's Church; 8, 60 c. Sea Island cotton: ginning; $2.40, Government House.

Morocco Agencies

BRITISH CURRENCY

From 3 June 1937 unoverprinted stamps of Great Britain were supplied to the post offices at Tangier and Tetuan (Spanish Zone) as local stocks of issues overprinted "MOROCCO AGENCIES" were exhausted.

Type G

Stamps of GREAT BRITAIN cancelled as Type G at Tetuan.

1937–39. *King George VI (Nos. 465/75)*
Z211	2d. orange					
Z212	2½d. ultramarine					
Z213	3d. violet					15·00
Z214	4d. grey-green					
Z215	6d. purple					15·00
Z216	9d. deep olive-green					10·00
Z217	1s. bistre-brown					10·00

1939–42. *King George VI (Nos. 476/7).*
Z218	2s. 6d. brown ..					
Z219	2s. 6d. yellow-green					32·00
Z220	5s. red					42·00

1941. *King George VI pale colours (Nos. 485/90).*
Z221	½d. pale green					
Z222	2d. pale orange					
Z223	2½d. light ultramarine ..					
Z224	3d. pale violet					10·00

Other unoverprinted stamps of Great Britain are known with Morocco Agencies postmarks during this period, but it is believed that only Nos. Z170/224 were sold by the local post offices.

The use of unoverprinted stamps in Tangier ceased with the issue of Nos. 261/75 on 1 January 1949. Stamps overprinted "MOROCCO AGENCIES" replaced the unoverprinted values at Tetuan on 16 August 1949.

Type E

Type F

Stamps of GREAT BRITAIN cancelled as Types E or F at Tangier.

1937–39. *King George VI (Nos. 462/75).*
Z178	½d. green	..		..		12·00
Z179	1d. scarlet					12·00
Z180	1½d. red-brown			..		10·00
Z181	2d. orange			..		10·00
Z182	2½d. ultramarine			..		8·00
Z183	3d. violet ..					8·00
Z184	4d. grey-green			..		8·00
Z185	5d. brown ..					10·00
Z186	6d. purple ..			..		5·00
Z187	7d. emerald-green			..		8·00
Z188	8d. bright carmine					15·00
Z189	9d. deep olive-green ..					10·00
Z190	10d. turquoise-blue			..		15·00
Z191	1s. bistre-brown			..		5·00

1939–42. *King George VI (Nos. 476/8a).*
Z192	2s. 6d. brown ..	..		..		40·00
Z193	2s. 6d. yellow-green		..			12·00
Z194	5s. red		..			18·00
Z195	10s. dark blue ..		..			75·00
Z196	10s. ultramarine		..			32·00

1941–42. *King George VI pale colours (Nos. 485/90).*
Z197	½d. pale green		..			8·00
Z198	1d. pale scarlet					8·00
Z199	1½d. pale red-brown		..			8·00
Z200	2d. pale orange		..			8·00
Z201	2½d. light ultramarine ..					7·00
Z202	3d. pale violet		..			5·00

1946. *Victory (Nos. 491/2).*
Z203	2½d. ultramarine			..		7·00
Z204	3d. violet ..		..			7·00

NEW INFORMATION

The editor is always interested to correspond with people who have new information that will improve or correct the Catalogue.

MOROCCO	MOROCCO
AGENCIES	AGENCIES
(9)	(10)

1949 (16 Aug). *King George VI, optd with T 9 or 10 (2s. 6d. 5s.).*
77	½d. pale green	..		..		1·75	7·00
78	1d. pale scarlet		..			2·75	9·00
79	1½d. pale red-brown		..			2·75	8·50
80	2d. pale orange	..				3·00	9·00
81	2½d. light ultramarine					3·25	10·00
82	3d. pale violet ..		..			1·50	1·60
83	4d. grey-green		..			45	90
84	5d. brown ..	..				3·00	15·00
85	6d. purple	..				1·50	1·00
86	7d. emerald-green	..				40	16·00
87	8d. bright carmine	..				3·00	6·50
88	9d. deep olive-green	..				40	11·00
89	10d. turquoise-blue	..				40	6·00
90	11d. plum ..					70	6·00
91	1s. bistre-brown ..					2·75	6·00
92	2s. 6d. yellow-green					12·00	29·00
93	5s. red ..	..			..	28·00	55·00
77/93	..	..		..	Set of 17	60·00	£170

1951 (3 May). *King George VI (Nos. 503/7, 509/10), optd with T* **9** *or* **10** *(2s. 6d., 5s.).*
94	¹/₂d. pale orange ..	..	..	..	1·75	50
95	1d. light ultramarine	..	..	..	1·75	65
96	1¹/₂d. pale green	..	..	..	1·75	1·75
97	2d. pale red-brown	..	..	..	1·75	3·25
98	2¹/₂d. pale scarlet ..	..	..	..	1·75	3·00
99	2s. 6d. yellow-green (H.M.S. *Victory*)	..		12·00	18·00
100	5s. red (Dover) ..	..	..	..	12·00	19·00
94/100	..	..	..	*Set of* 7	29·00	42·00

SPANISH CURRENCY

(19)

1937 (13 May). *Coronation (No. 461), surch as T* **19**.
164	15 c. on 1¹/₂d. maroon (B.) ..	..	..	50	30

MOROCCO AGENCIES   **MOROCCO AGENCIES**

10 CENTIMOS **10 CENTIMOS**

(20)   (21)

1937 (June)–**52**. *King George VI (Nos. 462/4, 466, 468, 471 and 474), surch as T* **20**.
165	5 c. on ¹/₂d. green (B.)	..	..	..	55	15
166	10 c. on 1d. scarlet	..	..	..	50	10
167	15 c. on 1¹/₂d. red-brown (B.) (4.8.37)	..	55	25
168	25 c. on 2¹/₂d. ultramarine	..	..	60	50
169	40 c. on 4d. grey-green (9.40)	..	..	28·00	10·00
170	70 c. on 7d. emerald-green (9.40) ..	..	60	9·00
171	1 p. on 10d. turquoise-blue (16.6.52)	..	1·00	3·50
165/71	..	..	..	*Set of* 7	29·00	21·00

1940 (6 May). *Centenary of First Adhesive Postage Stamps (Nos. 479/81 and 483), surch as T* **21**.
172	5 c. on ¹/₂d. green (B.)	..	..	..	30	1·75
173	10 c. on 1d. scarlet	..	..	..	2·75	2·00
174	15 c. on 1¹/₂d. red-brown (B.)	..	..	40	2·00
175	25 c. on 2¹/₂d. ultramarine	..	..	40	60
172/5	..	..	..	*Set of* 4	3·50	5·50

25 CENTIMOS

45 PESETAS MOROCCO AGENCIES

MOROCCO AGENCIES ≡

(22)   (23)

1948 (26 Apr). *Silver Wedding (Nos. 493/4), surch with T* **22** *or* **23**.
176	25 c. on 2¹/₂d. ultramarine	..	..	40	15
177	45 p. on £1 blue	..	..	..	17·00	22·00

1948 (29 July). *Olympic Games (Nos. 495/8), variously surch as T* **22**.
178	25 c. on 2¹/₂d. ultramarine	..	..	40	60
179	30 c. on 3d. violet ..	..	..	40	60
180	60 c. on 6d. bright purple ..	..	40	60
181	1 p. 20 c. on 1s. brown	..	..	55	60
	a. Surch double ..	..	..	£700	
178/81	..	..	..	*Set of* 4	1·60	2·25

1951 (3 May)–**52**. *King George VI (Nos. 503/5 and 507/8), surch as T* **20**.
182	5 c. on ¹/₂d. pale orange	..	..	2·00	2·25
183	10 c. on 1d. light ultramarine	..	3·25	4·00
184	15 c. on 1¹/₂d. pale green	..	..	1·75	12·00
185	25 c. on 2¹/₂d. pale scarlet ..	..	1·75	4·00
186	40 c. on 4d. light ultramarine (26.5.52)	..	60	9·00
182/6	..	..	..	*Set of* 5	8·50	28·00

FRENCH CURRENCY

1937 (13 May). *Coronation (No. 461), surch as T* **19**, *but in French currency.*
229	15 c. on 1¹/₂d. maroon (B.) ..	..	..	30	20

1937 (June). *King George VI, surch as T* **20**, *but in French currency.*
230	5 c. on ¹/₂d. green (B.)	..	..	1·25	1·40

Stamps surcharged in French currency were withdrawn from sale on 8 January 1938.

TANGIER INTERNATIONAL ZONE

TANGIER   **TANGIER**   **TANGIER**

(28)   (29)

1937 (13 May). *Coronation (No. 461), optd with T* **28**.
244	1¹/₂d. maroon (B.) ..	..	..	..	40	30

1937. *King George VI (Nos. 462/4), optd with T* **29**.
245	¹/₂d. green (B.) (June)	..	..	1·25	40
246	1d. scarlet (June)	..	..	3·75	30
247	1¹/₂d. red-brown (B.) (4 Aug)	..	1·00	10
245/7	..	..	..	*Set of* 3	5·50	70

TANGIER   **TANGIER**

(30)   (31)

1940 (6 May). *Centenary of First Adhesive Postage Stamps (Nos. 479/81), optd with T* **30**.
248	¹/₂d. green (B.)	..	..	..	30	3·25
249	1d. scarlet	..	..	..	45	50
250	1¹/₂d. red-brown (B.)	..	..	2·00	2·75
248/50	..	..	..	*Set of* 3	2·50	6·00

1944. *King George VI pale colours (Nos. 485/6), optd with T* **29**.
251	¹/₂d. pale green (B.)	..	..	7·00	2·50
252	1d. pale scarlet	..	..	..	7·00	2·25

1946 (11 June). *Victory (Nos. 491/2), optd as T* **31**.
253	2¹/₂d. ultramarine	..	..	..	30	20
254	3d. violet ..	..	..	..	30	55

The opt on No. 254 is smaller (23×2¹/₂ mm).

1948 (26 Apr). *Royal Silver Wedding (Nos. 493/4), optd with T* **30.**

255	2½d. ultramarine	..	..	..	30	15

   a. Opt omitted (in vert pair with stamp
     optd at top) £3000

256	£1 blue	..	..	..	25·00	25·00

No. 255a comes from a sheet on which the overprint is misplaced downwards resulting in the complete absence of the opt from the six stamps of the top row. On the rest of the sheet the opt falls at the top of each stamp instead of at the foot (*Price* £250, *unused*).

1948 (29 July). *Olympic Games (Nos. 495/8), optd with T* **30.**

257	2½d. ultramarine	..	..	..	75	1·25
258	3d. violet	..	..	..	75	1·25
259	6d. bright purple	..	..	..	75	1·25
260	1s. brown	..	..	..	75	60
257/60	..	..	..	*Set of* 4	2·75	4·00

1949 (1 Jan). *King George VI, optd with T* **29.**

261	2d. pale orange	..	..	..	4·00	4·00
262	2½d. light ultramarine	..	..	..	60	2·75
263	3d. pale violet	..	..	..	35	65
264	4d. grey-green	..	..	..	7·50	10·00
265	5d. brown	..	..	..	3·50	11·00
266	6d. purple	..	..	..	35	30
267	7d. emerald-green	..	..	..	90	10·00
268	8d. bright carmine	..	..	..	3·50	8·50
269	9d. deep olive-green	..	..	..	70	11·00

270	10d. turquoise-blue	..	..	..	70	11·00
271	11d. plum	..	..	..	70	8·50
272	1s. bistre-brown	..	..	..	70	1·75
273	2s. 6d. yellow-green	..	..	..	4·25	11·00
274	5s. red	..	..	..	13·00	38·00
275	10s. ultramarine	..	..	..	38·00	95·00
261/75	..	..	..	*Set of* 15	70·00	£200

1949 (10 Oct). *75th Anniv of U.P.U. (Nos. 499/502), optd with T* **30.**

276	2½d. ultramarine	..	..	..	50	1·25
277	3d. violet	..	..	..	50	85
278	6d. bright purple	..	..	..	50	85
279	1s. brown	..	..	..	50	1·75
276/9	..	..	..	*Set of* 4	1·75	4·25

1950 (2 Oct)–**51.** *King George VI, optd with T* **29** *or* **30** (*shilling values*).

280	½d. pale orange (3.5.51)	..	..	..	60	1·00
281	1d. light ultramarine (3.5.51)	..	..	70	2·50
282	1½d. pale green (3.5.51)	..	..	70	14·00
283	2d. pale red-brown (3.5.51)	..	..	70	2·00
284	2½d. pale scarlet (3.5.51)	..	..	70	3·25
285	4d. light ultramarine	..	..	..	1·50	2·50
286	2s. 6d. yell-grn (H.M.S. *Victory*) (3.5.51)	8·00	4·50
287	5s. red (Dover) (3.5.51)	..	..	14·00	15·00
288	10s. ultramarine (St. George) (3.5.51)	..	19·00	15·00
280/8	..	..	..	*Set of* 9	42·00	55·00

Muscat

12 pies = 1 anna; 16 annas = 1 rupee

INDIAN POSTAL ADMINISTRATION

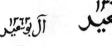
(1)

(2)

1944 (20 Nov). *Bicentenary of Al-Busaid Dynasty. Nos. 259/60, 265/8 and 269a/77 (King George VI) of India optd ("AL BUSAID 1363" in Arabic script) as T 1 or 2 (rupee values).*

1	3 p. slate	..	..	..	..	30	5·00
	w. Wmk inverted		..	..	..	15·00	
2	½ a. purple	..	..	..	..	30	5·00
3	9 p. green	..	..	..	..	30	5·00
4	1 a. carmine	..	..	..	..	30	5·00
5	1½ a. dull violet	..	..	..	..	30	5·00
6	2 a. vermilion	..	..	..	..	30	5·00
7	3 a. bright violet	..	..	..	..	50	5·00
	w. Wmk inverted		..	..	..	20·00	
8	3½ a. bright blue	..	..	..	..	50	5·00
9	4 a. brown	..	..	..	..	50	5·00
10	6 a. turquoise-green	..	..	..	..	65	5·00
11	8 a. slate-violet	..	..	..	..	65	5·00
12	12 a. lake	..	..	..	..	80	5·00
13	14 a. purple	..	..	..	..	2·00	7·00
14	1 r. grey and red-brown	..	..	..	50	9·00
15	2 r. purple and brown	..	..	1·50	15·00
1/15	..	..	..	*Set of* 15	8·50	80·00

OFFICIAL STAMPS

1944 (20 Nov). *Bicentenary of Al-Busaid Dynasty. Nos. O138, O143, O144a/6 and 146b/50 of India optd as T 1 or 2 (1 r.).*

O 1	3 p. slate	..	..	..	..	50	9·50
O 2	½ a. purple	..	..	..	..	50	9·50
O 3	9 p. green	..	..	..	..	50	9·50
O 4	1 a. carmine	..	..	..	..	50	9·50
O 5	1½ a. dull violet	..	..	..	50	9·50
O 6	2 a. vermilion	..	..	..	..	50	9·50
O 7	2½ a. bright violet		..	..	..	1·50	9·50
O 8	4 a. brown	..	..	..	..	1·00	9·50
O 9	8 a. slate-violet	..	..	..	2·00	11·00
O10	1 r. grey and red-brown	..	..	2·25	19·00
O1/10	..	..	..	..	*Set of* 10	8·75	95·00

From December 1947 there was a Pakistani postal administration and stamps of Pakistan were used until 31 March 1948. The subsequent British administration operated from 1 April 1948 to 29 April 1966 when the stamps of the BRITISH POSTAL AGENCIES IN EASTERN ARABIA were used.

Newfoundland

100 cents = 1 dollar

---

107 Atlantic Cod

108 King George V

110 Duke of Windsor when Prince of Wales

111 Caribou

113 Atlantic Salmon

114 Newfoundland Dog

115 Harp Seal

116 Cape Race

117 Sealing Fleet

118 Fishing Fleet

120 Queen Mother, when Duchess of York

121 Corner Brook Paper Mills

122 Loading Iron Ore, Bell Island

(Recess P.B.)

1932 (15 Aug)–**38.** *W* **106** (*sideways* on vert designs*). P 13½ (*comb*).

222	107	1 c. grey	..	..	90	10
		a. Imperf (pair)	..	..	40·00	
		c. Perf 14 (line)	..	..	6·00	9·00
		d. Perf 14 (line). Small holes	..	15·00	24·00
		e. Pair, with and without wmk	..	40·00	
		w. Wmk top of shield to right	..	50·00	
223	108	2 c. green	..	..	40	10
		a. Imperf (pair)	..	..	35·00	
		c. Perf 14 (line)	..	..	7·00	9·00
		ca. Imperf between (horiz pair)	..	£250	
		d. Perf 14 (line). Small holes	..	18·00	24·00
		e. Pair, with and without wmk	..	42·00	
		w. Wmk top of shield to right	..	35·00	
224	110	4 c. carmine (21.7.34)	..	..	1·75	40
		a. Imperf (pair)	..	..	50·00	
		b. Perf 14 (line)	..	..	3·25	4·75
		ba. Imperf between (horiz or vert pair)	..	..	£120	
		w. Wmk top of shield to right	..	50·00	
225	111	5 c. violet (Die I)	..	..	2·00	1·75
		a. Imperf (pair)	..	..	55·00	
		b. Perf 14 (line). Small holes	..	24·00	22·00
		c. Die II	..	..	70	30
		ca. Imperf (pair)	..	..	60·00	
		cb. Perf 14 (line)	..	..	22·00	19·00
		cbw. Wmk top of shield to right			
		cc. Imperf between (horiz pair)	..	£190	
		cd. Pair, with and without wmk	..	£120	
226	120	7 c. red-brown	..	..	2·75	3·25
		b. Perf 14 (line)	..	..	£130	
		ba. Imperf between (horiz pair)	..	£450	
		c. Imperf (pair)	..	..	£140	
		w. Wmk top of shield to right			
227	121	8 c. brownish red	..	..	3·00	2·00
		a. Imperf (pair)	..	..	85·00	
		w. Wmk inverted	..	..		
228	122	24 c. bright blue	..	..	85	3·00
		a. Imperf (pair)	..	..	£180	
		b. Doubly printed	..	..	£750	
		w. Wmk inverted	..	..	25·00	
228c	i18	48 c. red-brown (1.1.38)	..	..	5·00	10·00
		ca. Imperf (pair)	..	..	85·00	
222/8c	..	..	..	..	*Set of* 8	13·50	17·00

*The normal sideways watermark shows the top of the shield to left, *as seen from the back of the stamp.*

No. 223. Two dies exist of the 2 c. Die I was used for No. 210 and both dies for No. 223. The differences, though numerous, are very slight.

No. 225. There are also two dies of the 5 c., Die I only being used for No. 213 and both dies for the violet stamp. In Die II the antler pointing to the "T" of "POSTAGE" is taller than the one pointing to the "S" and the individual hairs on the underside of the caribou's tail are distinct.

For similar stamps in a slightly larger size and perforated 12½ or 13½ (5 c.) see Nos. 276/89.

1937 (12 May). *Coronation Issue. As Nos. 95/7 of Antigua, but name and value uncoloured on coloured background.* P 11×11½.

254	2 c. green	..	..	..	1·00	2·25
255	4 c. carmine		..	..	1·60	2·75
256	5 c. purple		..	..	3·00	2·75
254/6		..	..	Set of 3	5·00	7·00
254/6 Perf "Specimen"		..	..	Set of 3	75·00	

144 Atlantic Cod

Die I   Die II

No. 258. In Die II the shading of the King's face is heavier and dots have been added down the ridge of the nose. The top frame line is thicker and more uniform.

Fish-hook flaw   Re-entry to right
(R. 1/7 or 3/3)   of design (inscr
                 oval, tree and
                 value) (R.4/8)

Extra chimney (R. 6/5)

(Recess P.B.)

1937 (12 May). *Additional Coronation Issue.* T **144** *and similar horiz designs.* W **106**. P 14–13½ (*line*)*.

257	1 c. grey	..	..	..	2·25	20
	a. Pair, with and without wmk			..	22·00	
	b. Fish-hook flaw		..	..	21·00	
	c. Perf 13 (comb)		..	..	23·00	45·00
	ca. Pair, with and without wmk					
	cb. Fish-hook flaw		..	..	£170	
258	3 c. orange-brown (I)		..	..	6·00	3·00
	a. Pair, with and without wmk			..	55·00	
	b. Imperf between (horiz or vert pair)		..	£350		
	c. Perf 13 (comb)		..	..	4·25	3·00
	d. Die II		..	..	3·50	3·00
	da. Pair, with and without wmk			..	85·00	
	db. Imperf between (horiz or vert pair)		..	£450		
	dc. Perf 13 (comb)		..	..	5·00	2·50
	dca. Pair, with and without wmk			..	90·00	
259	7 c. bright ultramarine		..	..	2·25	90
	a. Pair, with and without wmk					
	b. Re-entry at right		..	..	45·00	
	c. Perf 13 (comb)		..	..	£275	£350
	cb. Re-entry at right		..	..	£1200	
260	8 c. scarlet		..	..	1·75	2·50
	a. Pair, with and without wmk			..	55·00	
	b. Imperf between (horiz or vert pair)		..	£550		
	c. Imperf (pair)	..		..	£275	
	d. Perf 13 (comb)		..	..	6·50	8·50
261	10 c. blackish brown		..	..	3·75	7·00
	a. Pair, with and without wmk			..	60·00	
	b. Perf 13 (comb)		..	..	3·25	9·50
	bw. Wmk inverted		..	..	75·00	
262	14 c. black	..		..	1·40	2·00
	a. Pair, with and without wmk			..	50·00	
	b. Perf 13 (comb)		..	..	£4750	£2750
263	15 c. claret	..		..	9·00	4·00
	a. Pair, with and without wmk			..	60·00	
	b. Imperf between (vert pair)		..	£375		
	cw. Wmk inverted		..	..	75·00	
	d. Perf 13 (comb)		..	..	17·00	19·00
	da. Pair, with and without wmk			..	95·00	
264	20 c. green	..		..	2·25	6·00
	a. Pair, with and without wmk			..	£120	
	b. Imperf between (vert pair)		..	£600		
	c. Extra chimney		..	..	40·00	
	dw. Wmk inverted		..	..	85·00	
	e. Perf 13 (comb)		..	..	2·50	7·00
	ec. Extra chimney		..	..	42·00	
265	24 c. light blue		..	..	2·25	2·50
	a. Pair, with and without wmk			..	£120	
	b. Imperf between (vert pair)		..	£600		
	c. Perf 13 (comb)		..	..	20·00	21·00
266	25 c. slate	..		..	2·75	1·75
	a. Pair, with and without wmk			..	£110	
	b. Perf 13 (comb)		..	..	22·00	42·00
267	48 c. slate-purple	..		..	8·50	4·50
	a. Pair, with and without wmk			..	£150	
	b. Imperf between (vert pair)		..	£600		
	c. Perf 13 (comb)		..	..	29·00	55·00
257/67	..	..	..	Set of 11	32·00	30·00

Designs:—3 c. Map of Newfoundland; 7 c. Reindeer; 8 c. Corner Brook paper mills; 10 c. Atlantic Salmon; 14 c. Newfoundland dog; 15 c. Harp Seal, 20 c. Cape Race; 24 c. Bell Island; 25 c. Sealing fleet; 48 c. The Banks fishing fleet.

*The line perforation was produced by two machines measuring respectively 13.7 and 14.1. The comb perforation measures 13.3×13.2.

Four used examples of No. 259c have now been identified on separate covers.

The paper used had the watermarks spaced for smaller format stamps. In consequence the individual watermarks are out of alignment so that stamps from the second vertical row were sometimes without watermark.

155 King George VI   156 Queen Mother

Damaged "A" (R. 5/9)

(Recess P.B.)

1938 (12 May). *T* **155/6** *and similar vert designs.* **W 106**
(sideways). *P* 13½ *(comb).*

268	2 c. green ..	..	..	1·50	60
	a. Pair, with and without wmk		£130	
	b. Imperf (pair) ..	..	..	75·00	
269	3 c. carmine	..	..	1·00	70
	a. Perf 14 (line) ..	..	..	£375	£225
	b. Pair, with and without wmk		£180	
	c. Imperf (pair) ..	..	..	75·00	
	d. Damaged "A"	..	..	38·00	
270	4 c. light blue	..	..	1·75	20
	a. Pair, with and without wmk		85·00	
	b. Imperf (pair) ..	..	..	70·00	
	w. Wmk inverted	..	..	65·00	
271	7 c. deep ultramarine	..	..	75	3·75
	a. Imperf (pair) ..	..	..	£100	
268/71	..	..	..	*Set of* 4	4·50	4·75

Designs:— 4 c. Queen Elizabeth II as princess; 7 c. Queen Mary.
For similar designs, perf 12½, see Nos. 277/281.

159 King George VI and Queen Elizabeth

(Recess B.W.)

1939 (17 June). *Royal Visit. No wmk. P* 13½.
272 **159** 5 c. deep ultramarine .. .. .. 2·00 40

(160)

1939 (20 Nov). *No. 272 surch as T* **160**, *at St. John's.*
273 **159** 2 c. on 5 c. deep ultramarine (Br.) .. 2·00 30
274 4 c. on 5 c. deep ultramarine (C.) .. 1·25 60

161 Grenfell on the *Strathcona*   **162** Memorial University
(after painting by Gribble)   College

(Recess C.B.N.)

1941 (1 Dec). *50th Anniv of Sir Wilfred Grenfell's Labrador
Mission. P* 12.
275 **161** 5 c. blue 30 55

(Recess Waterlow)

1941–44. *W* **106** (*sideways* on vert designs*). *P* 12½ (*line*).

276	107	1 c. grey	..	..	..	..	20	30
277	155	2 c. green	..	..	..	30	20
		w. Wmk top of shield to right	..	35·00	
278	156	3 c. carmine ..	..	..	30	10
		a. Pair, with and without wmk	..	75·00	
		w. Wmk top of shield to right	..	35·00	
279	–	4 c. blue (As No. 270)	..	..	2·25	20
		a. Pair, with and without wmk	..	£140	
		w. Wmk top of shield to right	..	35·00	
280	111	5 c. violet (Die I) (*p* 13½ *comb*)	..	90·00	
		a. Perf 12½ (line) (6.42)	..	2·75	30
		ab. Pair, with and without wmk	..	£120	
		ac. Printed double ..	..	..	£300	
		ad. Imperf vert (horiz pair)	..	£325	
		b. Imperf (pair)	..	..	£120	
281	–	7 c. deep ultramarine (As No. 271)	..	6·00	9·50
		a. Pair, with and without wmk	..	£150	
282	121	8 c. rose-red ..	..	..	1·50	1·75
		a. Pair, with and without wmk	..	£140	
283	113	10 c. black-brown	..	..	1·75	1·00
284	114	14 c. black	..	..	..	3·00	5·50
285	115	15 c. claret	..	..	..	5·50	7·50
286	116	20 c. green	..	..	..	5·50	5·50
287	122	24 c. blue	..	..	..	3·25	12·00
		w. Wmk top of shield to right	..	55·00	
288	117	25 c. slate	..	..	..	6·50	7·50
289	118	48 c. red-brown (1944)	..	..	6·50	5·50
276/89		..	..	..	*Set of* 14	35·00	50·00

*The normal sideways watermark shows the top of the shield
to left, *as seen from the back of the stamp.*
Nos. 276/89 are redrawn versions of previous designs with
slightly larger dimensions; the 5 c. for example, measures
21 mm in width as opposed to the 20.4 mm of the Perkins Bacon
printings.
No. 280. For Die I see note relating to No. 225.

(Recess C.B.N.)

1943 (1 Jan). *P* 12.
290 **162** 30 c. carmine .. .. .. 1·00 1·60

163 St. John's

TWO

CENTS

(164)

(Recess C.B.N.)

1943 (1 June). *Air. P* 12.
291 **163** 7 c. ultramarine 40 65

1946 (21 Mar). *No. 290 surch locally with T* **164**.
292 **162** 2 c. on 30 c. carmine 30 75

165 Queen Elizabeth II   **166** Cabot off Cape Bonavista
when Princess

(Recess Waterlow)

1947 (21 Apr). *Princess Elizabeth's 21st Birthday. W* **106** (*sideways*). *P* 12½.
293 **165** 4 c. light blue 30 75
| | a. Imperf vert (horiz pair) .. .. £275 | |

(Recess Waterlow)

1947 (24 June). *450th Anniv of Cabot's Discovery of Newfoundland.* W **106** (*sideways*). *P* 12½.

294	**166**	5 c. mauve	..	..	20	80
		a. Imperf between (horiz pair)		.. £1200	

POSTAGE DUE STAMPS

D 1   D **6ac**

(Litho John Dickinson & Co, Ltd)

1939 (1 May)–**49.** *P* 10.

D1	D **1**	1 c. green	..	..	..	2·25	8·50
		a. Perf 11 (1949)	..	..	..	3·25	10·00
D2		2 c. vermilion	..	..	..	13·00	7·50
		a. Perf 11 × 9 (1946) ..		..	13·00	19·00
D3		3 c. ultramarine	..	..	..	5·00	19·00
		a. Perf 11 × 9 (1949) ..		..	11·00	30·00
		b. Perf 9	..	..	..	£500	
D4		4 c. orange	..	..	..	9·00	17·00
		a. Perf 11 × 9 (May 1948)		..	12·00	45·00
D5		5 c. brown	..	..	..	5·50	24·00
D6		10 c. violet	..	..	..	6·00	17·00
		a. Perf 11 (W **106**) (1949)	..	..	22·00	75·00
		ab. Ditto. Imperf between (vert pair) ..			£650	
		ac. "POSTAGE LUE" (R 3/3 or 3/8) ..			£100	£275
D1/6 ...		..	..	..	..	*Set of* 6	38·00	85·00

Newfoundland joined the Dominion of Canada on 31 March 1949.

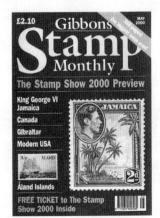

New Hebrides

100 gold centimes = 1 gold franc

ANGLO-FRENCH CONDOMINIUM

STAMPS INSCRIBED IN ENGLISH

6 Lopevi Is and Outrigger
Canoe

(Des J. Kerhor. Eng J. G. Hall. Recess B.W.)

1938 (1 June). *Gold Currency. Wmk Mult Script CA. P 12.*
52	**6**	5 c. blue-green	..	..	..	2·50	3·00
53		10 c. orange		..	..	1·25	1·50
54		15 c. bright violet ..		..	..	3·00	3·25
55		20 c. scarlet		..	..	1·60	2·00
56		25 c. reddish brown		..	..	1·60	2·00
57		30 c. blue ..		..	..	1·90	1·50
58		40 c. grey-olive	..	..	..	4·50	4·25
59		50 c. purple		..	..	1·60	1·50
60		1 f. red/*green*		..	..	4·00	7·50
61		2 f. blue/*green*	..	..	..	30·00	17·00
62		5 f. red/*yellow*		..	..	70·00	48·00
63		10 f. violet/*blue*	..	..	..	£200	75·00
52/63 ..			..	*Set of 12*	£300	£150
52/63 Perf "Specimen"			..	*Set of 12*	£225	

(Recess Waterlow)

1949 (10 Oct). *75th Anniv of U.P.U. As No. 148 of Jamaica.*
Wmk Mult Script CA. P 13½×14.
64	**6**	10 c. red-orange	..	..	..	30	40
65		15 c. violet	..	..	..	30	40
66		30 c. ultramarine	..	..	..	30	40
67		50 c. purple	..	..	..	40	40
64/7 ..			..	..	*Set of 4*	1·10	1·40

POSTAGE DUE STAMPS

POSTAGE DUE

(D 2)

1938 (1 June). *Optd with Type D 2, by B.W.*
D 6	**6**	5 c. blue-green	..	..	..	22·00	29·00
D 7		10 c. orange	..	..	..	22·00	29·00
D 8		20 c. scarlet	..	..	..	28·00	45·00
D 9		40 c. grey-olive	..	..	..	35·00	60·00
D10		1 f. red/*green*	..	..	..	45·00	70·00
D6/10 ..			..	..	*Set of 5*	£140	£200
D6/10 Perf "Specimen"			..	*Set of 5*	£120	

STAMPS INSCRIBED IN FRENCH

(New Currency. 100 gold centimes = 1 gold franc)

1938 (1 June). *Gold Currency. Wmk "R F" in sheet or without*
wmk. P 12.
F53	**6**	5 c. blue-green ..		..	..	1·60	3·25
F54		10 c. orange	..	..	..	1·60	2·75
F55		15 c. bright violet	..	..	..	1·25	3·25
F56		20 c. scarlet	..	..	..	1·60	2·75

F57	**6**	25 c. reddish brown	..	..	..	4·00	3·25
F58		30 c. blue ..		..	..	4·00	2·50
F59		40 c. grey-olive	..	..	..	1·25	6·50
F60		50 c. purple	..	..	..	1·25	2·25
F61		1 f. lake/*pale green* (shades)	..		1·60	3·75
F62		2 f. blue/*pale green* (shades)	..		26·00	28·00
F63		5 f. red/*yellow* ..		..	..	50·00	45·00
F64		10 f. violet/*blue* ..		..	..	£120	90·00
F53/64 ..			..	..	*Set of 12*	£190	£170
F53/64 Perf "Specimen" ..			..	*Set of 12*	£300	

France Libre

(F 6)

1941 (15 Apr). *Adherence to General de Gaulle. Optd with Type*
F 6, at Nouméa, New Caledonia.
F65	**6**	5 c. blue-green ..		..	..	2·50	22·00
F66		10 c. orange	..	..	..	4·00	21·00
F67		15 c. bright violet	..	..	..	6·00	30·00
F68		20 c. scarlet	..	..	..	14·00	27·00
F69		25 c. reddish brown	..	..	..	14·00	35·00
F70		30 c. blue ..		..	..	14·00	28·00
F71		40 c. grey-olive	..	..	..	14·00	32·00
F72		50 c. purple	..	..	..	14·00	27·00
F73		1 f. lake/*pale green*	..	..	..	14·00	27·00
F74		2 f. blue/*pale green*	..	..	..	14·00	32·00
F75		5 f. red/*yellow* ..		..	..	14·00	32·00
F76		10 f. violet/*blue* ..		..	..	14·00	32·00
F65/76 ..			..	..	*Set of 12*	£120	£300

1949 (10 Oct). *75th Anniv of U.P.U. As Nos. 64/7. Wmk "R F" in*
sheet or without wmk. P 13½.
F77		10 c. red-orange	..	..	..	2·25	4·25
F78		15 c. violet	..	..	..	3·50	7·00
F79		30 c. ultramarine	..	..	..	5·00	10·00
F80		50 c. purple	..	..	..	6·00	10·00
F77/80 ..			..	..	*Set of 4*	15·00	28·00

POSTAGE DUE STAMPS

CHIFFRE TAXE

(FD 2)

1938 (1 June). *Optd with Type FD 2, by Bradbury, Wilkinson.*
FD65	**6**	5 c. blue-green	..	..	..	14·00	38·00
FD66		10 c. orange ..		..	..	17·00	38·00
FD67		20 c. scarlet	..	..	..	23·00	48·00
FD68		40 c. grey-olive	..	..	..	45·00	£100
FD69		1 f. lake/*pale green* ..		..	..	48·00	£110
FD65/9 ..			..	..	*Set of 5*	£130	£300
FD65/9 Perf "Specimen" ..			..	*Set of 5*	£200	

1941 (15 Apr). *Nos. FD65/9 optd with Type F 6 at Nouméa, New*
Caledonia.
FD77	**6**	5 c. blue-green ..		..	..	8·75	38·00
FD78		10 c. orange	..	..	..	8·75	38·00
FD79		20 c. scarlet	..	..	..	8·75	38·00
FD80		40 c. grey-olive ..		..	..	8·75	38·00
FD81		1 f. lake/*pale green*	..	..	..	17·00	38·00
FD77/81 ..			..	..	*Set of 5*	48·00	£170

New Zealand

12 pence (d) = 1 shilling; 20 shillings = 1 pound

DOMINION

43 "Single" Wmk

81 Collared Grey Fantail

82 Brown Kiwi

83 Maori Woman

84 Maori Carved House

85 Mt Cook

86 Maori Girl

87 Mitre Peak

88 Striped Marlin

89 Harvesting

90 Tuatara Lizard

91 Maori Panel

92 Tui

93 Capt. Cook at Poverty Bay

94 Mt Egmont

Die I   Die II

"Captain Coqk"
(R. 1/4)

98 "Multiple Wmk"

NEW INFORMATION

The editor is always interested to correspond with people who have new information that will improve or correct the Catalogue.

(Litho Govt Ptg Office, Wellington (9d). Recess Waterlow or D.L.R. (others))

1936–42. *W* 98.

577	81	¹/₂d. bright green, *p* 14×13¹/₂	..	2·75	10
		w. Wmk inverted	.. ..	5·00	1·50
578	82	1d. scarlet (Die II), *p* 14×13¹/₂ (4.36)		2·25	10
		w. Wmk inverted	..	7·00	2·50
579	83	1¹/₂d. red-brown, *p* 14×13¹/₂ (6.36)	..	9·00	5·50
580	84	2d. orange, *p* 14×13¹/₂ (3.36)	..	30	10
		aw. Wmk inverted	.. ..	80·00	27·00
		b. Perf 12¹/₂† (6.41)	.. ..	3·75	10
		bw. Wmk inverted	..		
		c. Perf 14 (6.41)	.. ..	25·00	90
		d. Perf 14×15 (6.41)	.. ..	38·00	18·00
581	85	2¹/₂d. chocolate and slate, *p* 13–14×13¹/₂	3·75	14·00
		aw. Wmk inverted	.. ..	20·00	30·00
		b. Perf 14 (11.36)	.. ..	4·00	1·50
		bw. Wmk inverted	.. ..	13·00	16·00
		c. Perf 14×13¹/₂ (11.42)	..	50	4·00
582	86	3d. brown, *p* 14×13¹/₂	..	35·00	55
		w. Wmk inverted	..	60·00	27·00
583	87	4d. black and sepia, *p* 14×13¹/₂	..	4·75	40
		aw. Wmk inverted	.. ..	14·00	7·50
		b. Perf 12¹/₂* (1941)	..	27·00	9·50
		bw. Wmk inverted	..	†	—
		c. Perf 14, line (1941)	..	65·00	95·00
		d. Perf 14×14¹/₂ comb (7.42)	..	90	10
		dw. Wmk inverted	..	90·00	
584	88	5d. ultramarine, *p* 13–14×13¹/₂ (8.36)	15·00	1·90
		aw. Wmk inverted	.. ..	30·00	13·00
		b. Perf 12¹/₂*† (7.41)	..	20·00	3·00
		c. Perf 14×13¹/₂ (11.42)	..	3·00	75
		cw. Wmk inverted	..	90·00	70·00
585	89	6d. scarlet, *p* 13¹/₂×14 (8.36)	..	11·00	80
		aw. Wmk inverted	.. ..	35·00	5·00
		b. Perf 12¹/₂* (10.41)	..	3·00	3·50
		c. Perf 14¹/₂×14 (6.42)	..	11·00	10
		cw. Wmk inverted	..	£225	65·00
586	90	8d. choc, *p* 14×13¹/₂ (*wmk sideways*)	10·00	3·00
		aw. Wmk sideways inverted ..	..	25·00	9·00
		b. Wmk upright (7.39)	..	4·00	3·00
		bw. Wmk inverted	..		
		c. Perf 12¹/₂* (*wmk sideways*) (7.41)	3·75	1·50
		d. Perf 14×14¹/₂ (*wmk sideways*) (7.42)	.. ..	3·75	70
		dw. Wmk sideways inverted ..	—	35·00
587	91	9d. red and grey, *p* 14×15 (*wmk sideways*)	..	40·00	3·25
		ay. Wmk sideways inverted and reversed ..	.. ..	—	75·00
		b. Wmk upright. *Red and grey-black, p* 13¹/₂×14 (1.3.38)	..	65·00	3·25
		bw. Wmk inverted	..	90·00	24·00
588	92	1s. deep green, *p* 14×13¹/₂	..	2·50	60
		aw. Wmk inverted	..	55·00	10·00
		b. Perf 12¹/₂* (11.41)	..	65·00	15·00
589	93	2s. olive-green, *p* 13–14×13¹/₂ (8.36)	35·00	5·00
		a. "CAPTAIN COQK"	..	60·00	
		bw. Wmk inverted	..	£100	28·00
		c. Perf 13¹/₂×14 (3.39)	..	£275	3·00
		ca. "CAPTAIN COQK"	..	£275	
		d. Perf 12¹/₂*† (7.41)	..	26·00	6·00
		da. "CAPTAIN COQK"	..	60·00	
		e. Perf 14×13¹/₂ (10.42)	..	10·00	1·50
		ea. "CAPTAIN COQK"	..	80·00	
		ew. Wmk inverted	..	—	85·00
590	94	3s. chocolate & yell-brn, *p* 13–14×13¹/₂	42·00	6·00
		aw. Wmk inverted	.. ..	65·00	16·00
		b. Perf 12¹/₂* (1941)	..	80·00	48·00
		c. Perf 14×13¹/₂ (1942)	..	5·00	2·25
577/90c	..	.. .. ..	*Set of* 14	£100	14·00

*†Stamps indicated with an asterisk were printed and perforated by Waterlow; those having a dagger were printed by D.L.R. and perforated by Waterlow. No. 580d was printed by D.L.R. and perforated by Harrison and No. 583c was printed by Waterlow and perforated by D.L.R. These are all known as "Blitz perfs" because De La Rue were unable to maintain supplies after their works were damaged by enemy action. All the rest, except the 9d., were printed and perforated by D.L.R.

On stamps printed and perforated by De La Rue the perf 14×13¹/₂ varies in the sheet and is sometimes nearer 13¹/₂. 2d. perf 14×15 is sometimes nearer 14×14¹/₂.

2¹/₂d., 5d., 2s. and 3s. In perf 13–14×13¹/₂ one half the length of each horizontal perforation measures 13 and the other 14. In perf 14×13¹/₂ the horizontal perforation is regular.

4d. No. 583c. is line-perf measuring 14 exactly and has a

blackish sepia frame. No. 583d is a comb-perf measuring 14×14.3 or 14×14.2 and the frame is a warmer shade. 2s. No. 589c is comb-perf and measures 13.5×13.75. For 9d. typographed, see Nos. 630/1.

106 King George VI and Queen Elizabeth

(Recess B.W.)

1937 (13 May). *Coronation. W* 98. *P* 14 × 13¹/₂.

599	106	1d. carmine	..	..	30	10
600		2¹/₂d. Prussian blue	..	..	1·00	2·25
601		6d. red-orange ..	..	..	1·50	2·00
599/601		.. .. ..	*Set of* 3	2·50	3·75

107 Rock climbing

108   King George VI

108a

(Des G. Bull and J. Berry. Recess John Ash, Melbourne)

1937 (1 Oct). *Health Stamp. W* 43. *P* 11.

602	107	1d. + 1d. scarlet	..	..	2·25	3·25

Broken ribbon flaw (R. 6/6 of Pl 8)

(Des W. J. Cooch. Recess B.W.)

1938–44. *W* 98. *P* 14×13¹/₂.

603	108	¹/₂d. green (1.3.38)	..	..	6·50	10
604		¹/₂d. orange-brown (10.7.41)	..	12·00	2·50
		w. Wmk inverted ..	..	20	10
605		1d. scarlet (1.7.38)	..	5·00	10
		a. Broken ribbon ..	..	50·00	
		w. Wmk inverted	..	12·00	2·50
606		1d. green (21.7.41)	..	20	10
		w. Wmk inverted ..	..	30·00	18·00
607	108a	1¹/₂d. purple-brown (26.7.38)	..	26·00	2·00
		w. Wmk inverted ..	..	38·00	3·75
608		1¹/₂d. scarlet (1.2.44)	..	20	30
		w. Wmk inverted ..	..	—	60·00
609		3d. blue (26.9.41)	..	20	10
		w. Wmk inverted ..	..	—	45·00
603/9		.. .. ..	*Set of* 7	35·00	2·25

For other values see Nos. 680/9.

109 Children playing   110 Beach Ball

(Des J. Berry. Recess B.W.)

1938 (1 Oct). *Health Stamp.* W **98**. P 14 × 13½.
610 109   1d. + 1d. scarlet   .. .. .. 4·00 2·50

(Des S. Hall. Recess Note Printing Branch, Commonwealth Bank
of Australia, Melbourne)

1939 (16 Oct). *Health Stamps. Surcharged with new value.* W **43**.
P 11.
611 110   1d. on ½d. + ½d. green   .. .. 3·75 4·00
612   2d. on 1d. + 1d. scarlet..   .. .. 3·75 4·00

111 Arrival of the Maoris, 1350   115 Signing Treaty of
Waitangi, 1840

(Des L. C. Mitchell (½d., 3d., 4d.); J. Berry (others). Recess B.W.)

1940 (2 Jan–8 Mar). *Centenary of Proclamation of British Sovereignty.* T **111, 115** *and similar designs.* W **98**. P 14 × 13½ (2½d.),
13½ × 14 (5d.) *or* 13½ (*others*).
613   ½d. blue-green   30   10
614   1d. chocolate and scarlet .. ..   .. 2·75   10
615   1½d. light blue and mauve 30   30
616   2d. blue-green and chocolate ..   .. 1·50   10
617   2½d. blue-green and blue   .. ..   .. 1·75   75
618   3d. purple and carmine   .. ..   .. 3·50   75
619   4d. chocolate and lake   .. ..   .. 16·00 1·25
620   5d. pale blue and brown   .. ..   .. 7·00 3·50
621   6d. emerald-green and violet ..   .. 13·00   90
622   7d. black and red   ..   ..   .. 1·50 3·75
623   8d. black and red (8.3)   ..   .. 13·00 2·75
624   9d. olive-green and orange ..   .. 7·50 1·75
625   1s. sage-green and deep green ..   .. 17·00 3·50
613/25   ..   ..   ..   *Set of* 13 75·00 17·00
Designs: *Horiz* (*as* T **111**)—1d. *Endeavour*, Chart of N.Z., and
Capt. Cook; 1½d. British Monarchs; 2d. Tasman with his ship
and chart; 3d. Landing of immigrants, 1840; 4d. Road, Rail, Sea
and Air Transport; 6d. *Dunedin* and "Frozen Mutton Route" to
London; 7d., 8d. Maori council; 9d. Gold mining in 1861 and 1940.
(*As* T **115**)—5d. H.M.S. *Britomar* at Akaroa, 1840. *Vert* (*as* T
111)—1s. Giant Kauri tree.

1940 (1 Oct). *Health Stamps. As* T **110**, *but without extra
surcharge.* W **43**. P 11.
626 110   1d. + ½d. blue-green ..   ..   .. 13·00 14·00
627   2d. + 1d. brown-orange   ..   .. 13·00 14·00

1ᴰ **1**ᴰ

■ ■

2ᴰ

1941

(123)   Inserted "2"   (124)

1941. *Nos.* 603 *and* 607 *surch as* T **123**.
628 108   1d. on ½d. green (1.5.41)   90   10
629 108a   2d. on 1½d. purple-brown (4.41) .. 90   10
         a. Inserted "2" £550 £300
The surcharge on No. 629 has only one figure, at top left, and
there is only one square to obliterate the original value at bottom
right.
The variety "Inserted 2" occurs on the 10th stamp, 10th row. It is
identified by the presence of remnants of the damaged "2", and by
the spacing of "2" and "D" which is variable and different from the
normal.

(Typo Govt Printing Office, Wellington)

1941. *As* T **91**, *but smaller* (17½×20½ *mm*). *Chalk-surfaced
paper.* P 14×15. (*a*) W **43**.
630 91   9d. scarlet and black (5.41) ..   .. 95·00 25·00
         w. Wmk inverted   ..   ..   .. † £200
            (*b*) W **98**
631 91   9d. scarlet and black (29.9.41) .. 3·25 2·25
         w. Wmk inverted   ..   ..   .. £120 75·00

1941 (4 Oct). *Health Stamps. Nos.* 626/7 *optd with* T **124**.
632 110   1d. + ½d. blue-green 30   2·00
633   2d. + 1d. brown-orange   30   2·00

125 Boy and Girl   126 Princess Margaret
on Swing

(Des S. Hall. Recess Note Printing Branch, Commonwealth Bank
of Australia, Melbourne)

1942 (1 Oct). *Health Stamps.* W **43**. P 11.
634 125   1d. + ½d. blue-green 30   90
635   2d. + 1d. orange-red 30   90

(Des J. Berry. Recess B.W.)

1943 (1 Oct). *Health Stamps.* T **126** *and similar triangular design.*
W **98**. P 12.
636   1d. + ½d. green   20   1·10
         a. Imperf between (vert pair) £6500
637   2d. + 1d. red-brown..   20   20
         a. Imperf between (vert pair) .. £8000 £8000
Design:—2d. Queen Elizabeth II as Princess.

✚ **TENPENCE** ✚
(128)

1944 (1 May). *No.* 615 *surch with* T **128**.
662 10d. on 1½d. light blue and mauve 15   20

MINIMUM PRICE

The minimum price quote is 10p which represents
a handling charge rather than a basis for valuing
common stamps. For further notes about prices
see introductory pages.

129 Queen Elizabeth II as Princess and Princess Margaret

130 Statue of Peter Pan, Kensington Gardens

(Recess B.W.)

1944 (9 Oct). *Health Stamps. W **98**. P* 13½.
663 **129** 1d. + ½d. green 25 40
664 2d. + 1d. blue 25 30

(Des J. Berry. Recess B.W.)

1945 (1 Oct). *Health Stamps. W **98**. P* 13½.
665 **130** 1d. + ½d. green and buff 15 20
w. Wmk inverted .. .. 50·00 35·00
666 2d. + 1d. carmine and buff 15 20
w. Wmk inverted .. .. 60·00 45·00

(Des J. Berry. Photo Harrison (1½d. and 1s.). Recess B.W. (1d. and 2d.) and Waterlow (others))

1946 (1 Apr). *Peace issue. T* **131/3**, **139** *and similar designs. W* **98** (*sideways on* 1½d.). *P* 13 (1d., 2d.), 14×14½ (1½d., 1s.), 13½ (*others*).
667 ½d. green and brown 20 40
a. Printer's guide mark .. .. 7·50
w. Wmk inverted .. .. 55·00 40·00
668 1d. green 10 10
w. Wmk inverted .. .. 38·00 23·00
669 1½d. scarlet 10 30
w. Wmk sideways inverted .. 10 10
670 2d. purple 15 10
671 3d. ultramarine and grey 30 15
a. Completed rudder .. .. 6·50
672 4d. bronze-green and orange 20 20
w. Wmk inverted .. .. 90·00 42·00
673 5d. green and ultramarine 40 60
674 6d. chocolate and vermilion 15 30
675 8d. black and carmine 15 20
676 9d. blue and black 15 20
677 1s. grey-black 15 20
667/77 .. .. *Set of* 11 1·75 2·40
Designs: *Horiz* (as *T* **132**)—2d. The Royal Family. (As *T* **131**)—3d. R.N.Z.A.F. badge and airplanes; 4d. Army badge, tank and plough; 5d. Navy badge, H.M.N.Z.S. *Achilles* (cruiser) and *Dominion Monarch* (liner); 6d. N.Z. coat of arms, foundry and farm; 9d. Southern Alps and Franz Josef Glacier. *Vert* (as *T* **139**)—1s. National Memorial Campanile.

131 Lake Matheson

132 King George VI and Parliament House, Wellington

142 Soldier helping Child over Stile

(Des J. Berry. Recess Waterlow)

1946 (24 Oct). *Health Stamps. W **98**. P* 13½.
678 **142** 1d. + ½d. green and orange-brown .. 15 15
a. *Yellow-green and orange-brown* .. 4·50 5·00
w. Wmk inverted .. .. 13·00 13·00
679 2d. + 1d. chocolate and orange-brown 15 15

133 St. Paul's Cathedral

139 "St. George" (Wellington College War Memorial Window)

144 King George VI

145 Statue of Eros

Printer's guide mark (R. 12/3)

Completed rudder (R. 2/4 of Pl 42883 and R. 3/2 of Pl 42796)

Plate 1   Plate 2

(Des W. J. Cooch. Recess T **108**a, B.W.; T **144**, D.L.R.)

1947–52. *W* **98** (*sideways on "shilling" values*). (*a*) *P* 14×13½.
680	**108**a	2d. orange	..	..	15	10
		w. Wmk inverted	..	..	80·00	
681		4d. bright purple	..	..	70	30
682		5d. slate	..	..	50	70
683		6d. carmine	..	..	40	10
		w. Wmk inverted	..	..	75·00	16·00
684		8d. violet	..	..	65	30
685		9d. purple-brown	..	..	1·75	30
		w. Wmk inverted	..	..	38·00	12·00

(*b*) *P* 14
686	**144**	1s. red-brown and carmine (Plate 1)		1·40	80
		aw. Wmk sideways inverted		13·00	8·50
		b. Wmk upright (Plate 1)	..	50	70
		c. Wmk upright (Plate 2)	..	2·25	80
		cw. Wmk inverted	..	60·00	23·00
687		1s. 3d. red-brown and blue (Plate 2)	1·25	80
		aw. Wmk sideways inverted		7·50	5·50
		b. Wmk upright (14.1.52)	..	2·25	4·00
		bw. Wmk inverted	..		
688		2s. brown-orange and green (Plate 1)	3·00	2·00
		aw. Wmk sideways inverted		15·00	11·00
		b. Wmk upright (Plate 1)	..	4·00	6·50
689		3s. red-brown and grey (Plate 2)	3·25	3·25
		w. Wmk sideways inverted	..	29·00	14·00
680/9		.. .. ..	*Set of* 10	11·00	7·50

In head-plate 2 the diagonal lines of the background have been strengthened and result in the upper corners and sides appearing more deeply shaded.

(Des J. Berry. Recess Waterlow)

1947 (1 Oct). *Health Stamps. W* **98** (*sideways*). *P* 13½.
690	**145**	1d. + ½d. green	..	..	15	15
		w. Wmk sideways inverted	..	25·00	25·00
691		2d. + 1d. carmine	..	..	15	15
		w. Wmk sideways inverted	..	38·00	38·00

146 Port Chalmers, 1848   148 First Church, Dunedin

(Des J. Berry. Recess B.W.)

1948 (23 Feb). *Centennial of Otago. T* **146**, **148** *and similar designs. W* **98** (*sideways on 3d.*). *P* 13½.
692		1d. blue and green	..	..	20	20
		w. Wmk inverted	..	..	30·00	30·00
693		2d. green and brown	..	..	20	20
694		3d. purple	..	..	20	40
695		6d. black and rose	..	..	20	40
		w. Wmk inverted	..	..	—	£170
692/5		.. .. ..	*Set of* 4	70	1·10

Designs: *Horiz*—2d. Cromwell, Otago; 6d. University of Otago.

150 Boy Sunbathing and Children Playing

151 Nurse and Child

(Des E. Linzell. Recess B.W.)

1948 (1 Oct). *Health Stamps. W* **98**. *P* 13½.
696	**150**	1d. + ½d. blue and green	..	15	15
		w. Wmk inverted	..	..	20·00	20·00
697		2d. + 1d. purple and scarlet	..	15	15

1949 ROYAL VISIT ISSUE. Four stamps were prepared to commemorate this event: 2d. Treaty House, Waitangi; 3d. H.M.S. *Vanguard*; 5d. Royal portraits; 6d. Crown and sceptre. The visit did not take place and the stamps were destroyed, although a few examples of the 3d. later appeared on the market. A similar set was prepared in 1952, but was, likewise, not issued.

(Des J. Berry. Photo Harrison)

1949 (3 Oct). *Health Stamps. W* **98**. *P* 14 × 14½.
698	**151**	1d. + ½d. green	..	..	20	20
699		2d. + 1d. ultramarine	..	..	20	20
		a. No stop below "D" of "1D." (R.1/2)	6·50	15·00

1½d.

POSTAGE

(152)

153 Queen Elizabeth II and Prince Charles

1950 (28 July). *As Type* F **6**, *but without value, surch with T* **152**. *W* **98** (*inverted*). *Chalk-surfaced paper. P* 14.
700	F **6**	1½d. carmine	..	..	30	30
		w. Wmk upright	..	..	2·50	3·00

(Des J. Berry and R. S. Phillips. Photo Harrison)

1950 (2 Oct). *Health Stamps. W* **98**. *P* 14×14½.
701	**153**	1d. +½d. green	..	..	15	15
		w. Wmk inverted	..	..	4·75	4·75
702		2d. +1d. plum	..	..	15	15
		w. Wmk inverted	..	..	16·00	16·00

154 Christchurch Cathedral   155 Cairn on Lyttelton Hills

(Des L. C. Mitchell (2d.), J. A. Johnstone (3d.) and J. Berry (others). Recess B.W.)

1950 (20 Nov). *Centennial of Canterbury, N.Z. T* **154**/5 *and similar designs. W* **98** (*sideways on* 1d. *and* 3d.). *P* 13½.
703		1d. green and blue	..	..	20	40
704		2d. carmine and orange	..	..	20	40
705		3d. dark blue and blue	..	..	20	60
706		6d. brown and blue	..	..	20	60
707		1s. reddish purple and blue	..	20	80
703/7		.. .. ..	*Set of* 5	90	2·50

Designs: *Vert* (*as T* **154**)—3d. John Robert Godley. *Horiz* (*as T* **155**)—6d. Canterbury University College; 1s. Aerial view of Timaru.

159 "Takapuna" class Yachts

(Des J. Berry and R. S. Phillips. Recess B.W.)

1951 (1 Nov).   *Health Stamps.* W **98.** *P* 13½.
708   **159**   1½d. + ½d. scarlet and yellow   ..   15   70
709   2d. + 1d. deep green and yellow   ..   15   10
          w. Wmk inverted ..   ..   ..   45·00 45·00

STAMP BOOKLETS

B 1

1938 (Nov).   *Cream (No.* SB18) *or blue (No.* SB19) *covers as
Type* B **1.**
SB18   2s. booklet containing twelve ½d. and eighteen
        1d. (Nos. 603, 605) in blocks of 6   ..   ..   £350
SB19   2s. 3d. booklet containing eighteen 1½d. (No.
        607) in blocks of 6   ..   ..   £325

EXPRESS DELIVERY STAMPS

E 1

1937–39.   *Thin, hard, chalk-surfaced "Wiggins Teape" paper.*
          (a) P 14 × 14½
E4   E **1**   6d. carmine and bright violet ..   ..   85·00 48·00
          (b) P 14 × 15 (1939)
E5   E **1**   6d. vermilion and bright violet   ..   £140   £200

E **2** Express Mail Delivery Van

(Des J. Berry. Eng Stamp Ptg Office, Melbourne Recess Govt Ptg
Office, Wellington)
1939 (16 Aug).   W **43.** *P.* 14.
E6   E **2**   6d. violet   ..   ..   1·50   1·75
          w. Wmk inverted   ..   ..   ..   70·00

POSTAGE DUE STAMPS

D 2   **D 3**

1937–38.   *"Wiggins Teape" thin, hard chalky paper.* W **43.**
P 14 × 15.
D37   D **2**   ½d. carmine and yellow-green (2.38)..   18·00 32·00
D38   1d. carmine and yellow-green (1.37)..   11·00   3·75
D39   2d. carmine and yellow-green (6.37)..   30·00 13·00
D40   3d. carmine and yellow-green (11.37)   85·00 55·00
D37/40   ..   ..   *Set of* 4 £130 95·00

(Des J. Berry. Typo Govt Printing Office, Wellington)
1939–49.   *P* 15×14. *(a)* W **43** *(sideways inverted)* (16.8.39).
D41   D **3**   ½d. turquoise-green   ..   ..   5·00   5·00
D42   1d. carmine   ..   ..   ..   2·75   30
          w. Wmk sideways   ..   ..   £100   1·50
D43   2d. bright blue   ..   ..   ..   6·00   2·75
D44   3d. orange-brown   ..   ..   ..   23·00 25·00
          w. Wmk sideways
D41/4   ..   ..   *Set of* 4 32·00 30·00

          (b) W **98** *(sideways* (1*d.*), *sideways inverted* (2*d.*) *or upright*
          (3*d.*)
D45   D **3**   1d. carmine (4.49) ..   ..   ..   16·00   5·50*
D46   2d. bright blue (12.46)   ..   ..   7·50   1·40
          w. Wmk sideways (4.49)   ..   ..   2·75   8·00
D47   3d. orange-brown (1943)   ..   ..   42·00 32·00
          a. Wmk sideways inverted (6.45)   17·00   5·00
          aw. Wmk sideways (28.11.49)   ..   9·00   8·00
D45/7   ..   ..   *Set of* 3 25·00 10·00*
*The use of Postage Due stamps ceased on 30 September
1951, our used price for No. D45 being for stamps postmarked
after this date *(price for examples clearly cancelled* 1949–51,
£27).

OFFICIAL STAMPS

Official   Official
     (O **4**)   (O **5**)

1936–61.   W **98** *(Mult* "N Z" *and Star).* Optd with Type O **4.**
O120   **81**   ½d. bright green, *p* 14×13½ (7.37)   6·50   4·50
O121   **82**   1d. scar (Die II), *p* 14×13½ (11.36)   3·75   50
          w. Wmk inverted   ..   ..   ..   7·50   4·50
O122   **83**   1½d. red-brown, *p* 14×13½ (7.36)   ..   16·00   4·25
O123   **84**   2d. orange, *p* 14×13½ (1.38)   ..   2·25   10
          aw. Wmk inverted ..   ..   ..   —   £110
          b. Perf 12½ (1942)   ..   ..   £190 55·00
          c. Perf 14 (1942)   ..   ..   48·00 15·00
O124   **85**   2½d. chocolate & slate, *p* 13–14×13½
          (26.7.38)   ..   ..   ..   48·00 75·00
          a. Perf 14 (1938)   ..   ..   14·00 21·00
O125   **86**   3d. brown, *p* 14×13½ (1.3.38)   ..   48·00 25·00
          w. Wmk inverted   ..   ..   ..   — 27·00
O126   **87**   4d. black and sepia, *p* 14×13½ (8.36)   8·50   1·10
          a. Perf 14 (8.41)   ..   ..   ..   7·50   4·00
          b. Perf 12½ (1941)   ..   ..   5·00   5·00
          c. Perf 14×14½ (10.42)   ..   ..   3·75   85
          cw. Wmk inverted   ..   ..   ..   — 45·00
O127   **89**   6d. scarlet, *p* 13½×14 (12.37)   ..   15·00   70
          aw. Wmk inverted   ..
          b. Perf 12½ (1941)   ..   ..   15·00   50
          c. Perf 14½×14 (7.42)   ..   ..   8·00   30
O128   **90**   8d. chocolate, *p* 12½ (*wmk sideways*)
          (1942)   ..   ..   14·00 17·00
          a. Perf 14×14½ (*wmk sideways*)
          (1945)   ..   ..   ..   8·00 16·00
          b. Perf 14×13½   ..   ..   ..   †£1600
O129   **91**   9d. red & grey-black (G.) (No. 587*a*)*b*
          p 13½×14 (1.3.38)   ..   60·00 38·00
O130   9d. scar & blk (*chalk-surfaced paper*)
          (Blk.) (No. 631), *p* 14×15 (1943) 20·00 22·00

O131	92	1s. deep green, *p* 14×13¹/₂ (2.37)			45·00	1·50
		aw. Wmk inverted ..			—	85·00
		b. Perf 12¹/₂ (1942)	..	..	22·00	1·00
O132	93	2s. olive-green, *p* 13–14×13¹/₂ (5.37)		80·00	30·00
		a. "CAPTAIN COQK"	..	..	95·00	
		b. Perf 13¹/₂×14 (1939)	..	..	£170	6·50
		ba. "CAPTAIN COQK"	..	..	£180	
		c. Perf 12¹/₂ (1942)	..	..	90·00	27·00
		ca. "CAPTAIN COQK"	..	..	£110	
		d. Perf 14×13¹/₂ (1944)	..	..	42·00	7·00
		da. "CAPTAIN COQK"	..	..	£225	
O133	F 6	5s. green (*chalk-surfaced paper*),				
		p 14 (3.43)	..	..	38·00	5·00
		aw. Wmk inverted ..	..	..	38·00	5·00
		b. Perf 14×13¹/₂. *Yellow-green*				
		(*ordinary paper*) (10.61)	..	17·00	32·00
O120/33		.. ..	*Set of* 14	£250	£110

The opt on No. O127a was sometimes applied at the top of the stamp, instead of always at the bottom, as on No. O127.

All examples of No. O128b were used by a government office in Whangerei.

The 5s. value on ordinary paper perforated 14×13¹/₂ does not exist without the "Official" overprint.

See notes on perforations after No. 590b.

1938–51. *Nos.* 603 *etc.*, *optd with Type* O 4.

O134	108	¹/₂d. green (1.3.38) ..	..	..	16·00	2·25
O135		¹/₂d. brown-orange (1946)	..	..	1·60	3·00
O136		1d. scarlet (1.7.38) ..	..	..	16·00	15
O137		1d. green (10.7.41)	..	..	2·25	10
O138	108a	1¹/₂d. purple-brown (26.7.38) ..	..	75·00	18·00
O139		1¹/₂d. scarlet (2.4.51) ..	..	..	9·00	5·00
O140		3d. blue (16.10.41) ..	..	..	2·25	10
O134/40		.. ..	*Set of* 7	£110	25·00

1940 (2 Jan–8 Mar). *Centennial. Nos.* 613, *etc.*, *optd with Type* O 5.

O141	¹/₂d. blue-green (R.)	..	..	1·75	35
	a. "ff" joined, as Type O 4	..	50·00	60·00
O142	1d. chocolate and scarlet ..	..	4·00	10
	a. "ff" joined, as Type O 4	..	50·00	60·00
O143	1¹/₂d. light blue and mauve ..	..	2·75	2·00
O144	2d. blue-green and chocolate	..	4·00	10
	a. "ff" joined, as Type O 4	..	60·00	60·00
O145	2¹/₂d. blue-green and ultramarine ..		4·00	2·75
	a. "ff" joined, as Type O 4	..	50·00	65·00
O146	3d. purple and carmine (R.)	..	8·00	90
	a. "ff" joined, as Type O 4	..	42·00	48·00
O147	4d. chocolate and lake	..	..	40·00	2·00
	a. "ff" joined, as Type O 4	..	£120	80·00
O148	6d. emerald-green and violet	..	25·00	2·00
	a. "ff" joined, as Type O 4	..	70·00	70·00
O149	8d. black and red (8.3)	..	..	30·00	17·00
	a. "ff" joined, as Type O 4	..	70·00	£100
O150	9d. olive-green and vermilion	..	11·00	7·00
O151	1s. sage-green and deep green	..	48·00	4·00
O141/51	.. ..	*Set of* 11	£160	35·00

For this issue the Type O 4 overprint occurs on R.4/3 of the 2¹/₂d. and on R.1/10 of the other values.

1947–49. *Nos.* 680, *etc.*, *optd with Type* O 4.

O152	108a	2d. orange ..	..	..	1·75	10
O153		4d. bright purple	..	..	4·25	1·75
O154		6d. carmine ..	..	..	11·00	40
O155		8d. violet	..	..	8·00	6·50
O156		9d. purple-brown ..	..	..	9·00	6·50
O157	144	1s. red-brown and carmine (*wmk*			
		upright) (Plate 1)	..	17·00	95
		a. Wmk sideways (Plate 1) (1949)	8·50	9·00
		aw. Wmk sideways inverted	..	35·00	
		b. Wmk upright (Plate 2)	..	24·00	7·00
		bw. Wmk inverted ..	..	65·00	28·00
O158		2s. brown-orange and green (*wmk*			
		sideways) (Plate 1)	..	23·00	16·00
		a. Wmk upright (Plate 1)	..	32·00	40·00
O152/8		.. .. ..	*Set of* 7	60·00	28·00

LIFE INSURANCE DEPARTMENT

L 2   Lighthouse

1944–47. W 98. *P* 14×15.

L37	L 2	¹/₂d. yellow-green (7.47)	..	..	4·50	9·00
L38		1d. scarlet (6.44)	..	..	3·25	2·00
L39		2d. yellow (1946) ..	..	..	10·00	13·00
L40		3d. brown-lake (10.46)	..	..	15·00	35·00
L41		6d. pink (7.47)	..	..	11·00	32·00
L37/41		.. .. ..	*Set of* 5	40·00	80·00

L 3 Castlepoint Lighthouse   L 6 Cape Campbell
                                          Lighthouse

(Des J. Berry. Recess B.W.).

1947 (1 Aug)–**65.** *Type* L 3, L 6 *and similar designs.* W 98 (*sideways on* 1d., 2d., 2¹/₂d.). *P* 13¹/₂.

L42	¹/₂d. grey-green and orange-red	..	..	1·00	60
L43	1d. olive-green and pale blue	..	..	1·00	65
L44	2d. deep blue and grey-black	..	..	70	50
L45	2¹/₂d. black and bright blue (*white opaque*			
	paper) (4.11.63) ..	..	..	9·50	13·00
L46	3d. mauve and pale blue	..	..	2·50	35
L47	4d. brown and yellow-orange	..	..	3·25	1·25
	a. Wmk sideways (*white opaque paper*)			
	(13.10.65)	..	..	5·00	13·00
L48	6d. chocolate and blue	..	..	3·50	1·75
L49	1s. red-brown and blue	..	..	3·50	2·75
L42/49	.. .. ..	*Set of* 8	22·00	19·00

Designs: *Horiz* (*as Type* L 3)–1d Taiaroa lighthouse; 2d. Cape Palliser lighthouse; 6d. The Brothers lighthouse. *Vert* (*as Type* L 6)–3d. Eddystone lighthouse; 4d. Stephens Island lighthouse; 1s. Cape Brett lighthouse.

POSTAL FISCAL STAMPS

F 6   (F 7)

(Des H. L. Richardson. Typo Govt Ptg Office)

1931–40. *As Type* F 6 (*various frames*). W 43. *P* 14.

(i) *Thick, opaque, chalk-surfaced "Cowan" paper, with horizontal mesh* (1931–35)

F145	1s. 3d. lemon (4.31)	..	..	..	8·00	35·00
F146	1s. 3d. orange-yellow	..	..	..	5·50	5·50
F147	2s. 6d. deep brown	..	..	..	13·00	4·00
F148	4s. red ..	..	..	..	14·00	4·75

F149	5s. green ..	17·00	7·50
F150	6s. carmine-rose ..	32·00	12·00
F151	7s. blue ..	27·00	20·00
F152	7s. 6d. olive-grey ..	60·00	80·00
F153	8s. slate-violet ..	28·00	28·00
F154	9s. brown-orange ..	30·00	28·00
F155	10s. carmine-lake ..	24·00	8·00
F156	12s. 6d. deep plum (9.35) ..	£140	£140
F157	15s. sage-green ..	60·00	35·00
F158	£1 pink ..	60·00	19·00
F159	25s. greenish blue ..	£250	£375
F160	30s. brown (1935) ..	£250	£140
F161	35s. orange-yellow ..	£2500	£2750
F162	£2 bright purple ..	£300	60·00
F163	£2 10s. red ..	£250	£300
F164	£3 green ..	£325	£170
F165	£3 10s. rose (1935) ..	£1300	£1000
F166	£4 light blue (1935) ..	£325	£130
F167	£4 10s. deep olive-grey (1935) ..	£1000	£1100
F168	£5 indigo-blue ..	£325	90·00

(ii) *Thin, hard "Wiggins Teape" paper with vertical mesh* (1936–40)

(a) Chalk-surfaced (1936–39)

F169	1s. 3d. pale orange-yellow ..	13·00	3·25
F170	2s. dull brown ..	48·00	3·25
F171	4s. pale red-brown ..	55·00	6·00
F172	5s. green ..	65·00	7·00
	w. Wmk inverted ..		
F173	6s. carmine-rose ..	70·00	25·00
F174	7s. pale blue ..	80·00	28·00
F175	8s. slate-violet ..	£100	45·00
F176	9s. brown-orange ..	£110	65·00
F177	10s. pale carmine-lake ..	£120	6·50
F178	15s. sage-green ..	£170	50·00
F179	£1 pink ..	£130	24·00
F180	30s. brown (1.39) ..	£350	£140
F181	35s. orange-yellow ..	£3000	£3000
F182	£2 bright purple (1937) ..	£475	80·00
	w. Wmk inverted ..		
F183	£3 green (1937) ..	£500	£200
F184	£5 indigo-blue (1937) ..	£700	£160

(b) Unsurfaced (1940)

F185	7s. 6d. olive-grey ..	£150	90·00

Not all values listed above were stocked at ordinary post offices as some of them were primarily required for fiscal purposes but all were valid for postage.

1939. *No.* F161 *surch with Type* F **7.**

F186	35/- on 35s. orange-yellow ..	£400	£225

Because the 35s. orange-yellow could so easily be confused with the 1s. 3d. in the same colour it was surcharged.

1940 (June). *New values surch as Type* F **7.** *W* 43. *"Wiggins Teape" chalk-surfaced paper. P* 14.

F187	3/6 on 3s. 6d. grey-green ..	50·00	16·00
F188	5/6 on 5s. 6d. lilac ..	80·00	45·00
F189	11/- on 11s. yellow ..	£140	£110
F190	22/- on 22s. scarlet ..	£350	£250
F187/90	.. .. *Set of* 4	£550	£375

These values were primarily needed for fiscal use.

1940–58. *As Type* F **6** *(various frames). W* 98.

(i) *P* 14. *"Wiggins Teape" chalk-surfaced paper with vertical mesh* (1940–56)

F191	1s. 3d. orange-yellow ..	8·00	1·50
	w. Wmk inverted ..		
F192	1s. 3d. yellow and black (*wmk inverted*) (14.6.55) ..	1·50	80
	aw. Wmk upright (9.9.55) ..	27·00	27·00
	b. Error. Yellow and blue (*wmk inverted*) (7.56) ..	4·00	5·50
F193	2s. 6d. deep brown ..	8·00	60
	w. Wmk inverted (3.49) ..	8·00	30
F194	4s. red-brown ..	12·00	90
	w. Wmk inverted (3.49) ..	14·00	70
F195	5s. green ..	17·00	80
	w. Wmk inverted (1.5.50) ..	22·00	80
F196	6s. carmine-rose ..	30·00	3·25
	w. Wmk inverted (1948) ..	32·00	2·75
F197	7s. pale blue ..	30·00	4·75
F198	7s. 6d. ol-grey (*wmk inverted*) (21.12.50) ..	60·00	50·00
F199	8s. slate-violet ..	48·00	17·00
	w. Wmk inverted (6.12.50) ..	45·00	17·00

F200	9s. brown-orange (1.46) ..	22·00	38·00
	w. Wmk inverted (9.1.51) ..	45·00	38·00
F201	10s. carmine-lake ..	28·00	2·25
	w. Wmk inverted (4.50) ..	28·00	2·50
F202	15s. sage-green ..	42·00	18·00
	w. Wmk inverted (8.12.50) ..	55·00	25·00
F203	£1 pink ..	27·00	3·75
	w. Wmk inverted (1.2.50) ..	38·00	4·25
F204	25s. greenish blue (1946) ..	£325	£350
	w. Wmk inverted (7.53) ..	£375	£400
F205	30s. brown (1946) ..	£225	£100
	w. Wmk inverted (9.49) ..	£200	£100
F206	£2 bright purple (1946) ..	80·00	20·00
	w. Wmk inverted (17.6.52) ..	80·00	20·00
F207	£2 10s. red (*wmk inverted*) (9.8.51) ..	£250	£250
F208	£3 green (1946) ..	£110	48·00
	w. Wmk inverted (17.6.52) ..	£100	45·00
F209	£3 10s. rose (11.48) ..	£1500	£1000
	w. Wmk inverted (5.52) ..	£1600	£1000
F210	£4 light blue (*wmk inverted*) (12.2.52) ..	£130	95·00
	w. Wmk upright ..	†	—
F211	£5 indigo-blue ..	£225	48·00
	w. Wmk inverted (11.9.50) ..	£160	45·00
F191/211 ..	.. .. *Set of* 21	£2500	£1700

THREE SHILLINGS I.

THREE SHILLINGS II.

3s. 6d.

Type I. Broad serifed capitals

Type II. Taller capitals, without serifs

Surcharged as Type F **7**

F212	3/6 on 3s. 6d. grey-green (I) (1942) ..	20·00	7·00
	w. Wmk inverted (12.10.50) ..	32·00	8·00
F213	3/6 on 3s. 6d. grey-green (II) (6.53) ..	13·00	38·00
	w. Wmk inverted (6.53) ..	35·00	40·00
F214	5/6 on 5s. 6d. lilac (1944) ..	48·00	18·00
	w. Wmk inverted (13.9.50) ..	48·00	18·00
F215	11/- on 11s. yellow (1942) ..	75·00	48·00
F216	22/- on 22s. scarlet (1945) ..	£250	£130
	w. Wmk inverted (1.3.50) ..	£250	£130
F212/16 ..	.. .. *Set of* 5	£350	£200

(ii) *P* 14×13½. *"Wiggins Teape" unsurfaced paper with horizontal mesh* (1956–58)

F217	1s. 3d. yellow and black (11.56) ..	1·75	1·75
	w. Wmk inverted ..	18·00	17·00
F218	£1 pink (20.10.58) ..	32·00	12·00

No. F192b had the inscription printed in blue in error but as many as 378,000 were printed.

From 1949–53 inferior paper had to be used and for technical reasons it was necessary to feed the paper into the machine in a certain way which resulted in whole printings with the watermark inverted for most values.

COOK ISLANDS

COOK ISLANDS.

(19)

20 Capt. Cook landing

21 Capt. Cook

22 Double Maori Canoe   23 Natives working
                                Cargo

24 Port of Avarua   25 R.M.S. *Monowai*

1936 (15 July)–**44.** *Stamps of New Zealand optd with T* **19.**
W **43.** *P* 14.

(a) *T* **72.** *Cowan thick, opaque chalk-surfaced paper*
116   2s. light blue (No. 469) ..   ..   .. 12·00 45·00
117   3s. pale mauve (No. 470)   ..   .. 13·00 65·00

(b) *Type F* **6.** *Cowan thick, opaque chalk-surfaced paper*
118   2s. 6d. deep brown (No. F147) ..   .. 17·00 60·00
119   5s. green (No. F149) (R.)   ..   .. 20·00 80·00
120   10s. carmine-lake (No. F155)   .. 40·00 £130
121   £1 pink (No. F158)   ..   .. 60·00 £160
118/21   ..   .. *Set of* 4 £120 £375

(c) *Type F* **6.** *Thin, hard, chalk-surfaced Wiggins, Teape paper*
122   2s. 6d. dull brown (No. F170) (12.40) .. 85·00 95·00
123   5s. green (No. F172) (R.) (10.40)   .. £325 £350
123a   10s. pale carmine-lake (No. F177) (11.44) £120 £170
123b   £3 green (No. F183) (R.) (date?)   .. £325 £550
122/3b   ..   ..   ..   *Set of* 4 £750 £1000

COOK
IS'DS.
(28)

IS'DS.
Small second "S"
(R. 1/2)

1937 (1 June).   *Coronation. Nos.* 599/601 *of New Zealand* (inscr
"12th MAY 1937") *optd with T* **28.**
124   1d. carmine   40   30
      a. Small second "S"   ..   .. 11·00
125   2½d. Prussian blue..   80   30
      a. Small second "S"   ..   .. 20·00
126   6d. red-orange   80   30
      a. Small second "S"   ..   .. 20·00
124/6   ..   ..   .. *Set of* 3   1·75   80

29 King George VI   30 Native Village

31 Native Canoe   32 Tropical Landscape

(Des J. Berry (2s., 3s., and frame of 1s.). Eng B.W. Recess Govt Ptg.
Office, Wellington)
1938 (2 May).   *W* **43** *of New Zealand. P* 14.
127   **29**   1s. black and violet   ..   ..   .. 8·00 10·00
128   **30**   2s. black and red-brown   ..   .. 18·00 11·00
      w. Wmk inverted   ..   ..   ..
129   **31**   3s. light blue and emerald-green   .. 42·00 32·00
127/9   ..   .. *Set of* 3 60·00 48·00

(Recess B.W.)
1940 (2 Sept).   *Surch as in T* **32.** *W* **98** *of New Zealand.*
P 13½ × 14.
130   **32**   3d. on 1½d. black and purple   50   50
Type **32** was not issued without surcharge.

1943–54. *Postal Fiscal stamps as Type F* **6** *of New Zealand*
optd with T **19.** *W* **98.** *Wiggins, Teape chalk-surfaced paper.*
P 14.
131   2s. dull brown (No. F193) (3.46)   .. 38·00 50·00
      w. Wmk inverted (2.4.51)   .. 14·00 18·00
132   5s. green (No. F195) (R.) (11.43)   .. 8·50 18·00
      w. Wmk inverted (5.54) ..   .. 17·00 20·00
133   10s. pale carmine-lake (No. F201) (10.48) 55·00 75·00
      w. Wmk inverted (10.51)   .. 42·00 70·00
134   £1 pink (No. F203) (11.47)   .. 50·00 75·00
      w. Wmk inverted (19.5.54)   .. 48·00 75·00
135   £3 green (No. F208) (R.) (1946?)   .. £450 £650
      w. Wmk inverted (28.5.53)   .. 55·00 £160
136   £5 indigo-blue (No. F211) (R.) (25.10.50) £225 £350
      w. Wmk inverted (19.5.54)   .. £250 £375
131/6   ..   ..   ..   *Set of* 6 £350 £600
The £3 and £5 were mainly used for fiscal purposes.

(Recess Govt Ptg Office, Wellington)
1944–46. *W* **98** *of New Zealand* (*sideways on* ½d. 1d., 1s., *and* 2s.).
P 14.
137   **20**   ½d. black and deep green (11.44)   .. 1·50 3·50
      w. Wmk sideways inverted ..   .. 7·00
138   **21**   1d. black and scarlet (3.45)   ..   .. 2·00   35
      w. Wmk sideways inverted ..   .. 10·00
139   **22**   2d. black and brown (2.46)   ..   .. 1·25 4·25
140   **23**   2½d. black and deep blue (5.45)   ..   65 1·75
141   **24**   4d. black and blue (4.44)   ..   .. 3·50 8·00
      y. Wmk inverted and reversed   .. 40·00 40·00
142   **25**   6d. black and orange (6.44) ..   .. 1·50 1·75
143   **29**   1s. black and violet (9.44)   ..   .. 1·50 2·25
144   **30**   2s. black and red-brown (8.45)   .. 32·00 30·00
145   **31**   3s. light blue & emerald-green (6.45) 30·00 28·00
137/45   ..   ..   *Set of* 9 65·00 70·00

COOK
ISLANDS
(33)

1946 (4 June).   *Peace. Nos.* 668, 670, 674/5 *of New Zealand optd*
with T **33** (*reading up and down at sides on* 2d.).
146   1d. green (Parliament House)   30   10
147   2d. purple (Royal family) (B.)   30   40
148   6d. chocolate and vermilion (Coat of arms,
            foundry and farm)   30   40
149   8d. black and carmine ("St. George") (B.)   30   40
146/9   ..   ..   *Set of* 4   1·10   1·10

34 Ngatangiia Channel,   41 Map and Statue
      Rarotonga   of Capt. Cook

(Des J. Berry. Recess Waterlow)

1949 (1 Aug)–**61**. *T* **34, 41** *and similar designs. W* **98** *of New Zealand (sideways on shilling values). P* 13½ × 13 *(horiz) or* 13 × 13½ *(vert).*

150	½d. violet and brown			10	1·00
151	1d. chestnut and green			3·50	2·00
152	2d. reddish brown and scarlet			1·25	2·00
153	3d. green and ultramarine			1·25	2·00
	aw. Wmk inverted			£100	
	b. Wmk sideways (white opaque paper) (22.5.61)			3·50	2·50
154	5d. emerald-green and violet			4·25	1·50
155	6d. black and carmine			4·50	2·75
156	8d. olive-green and orange			55	3·75
	w. Wmk inverted			85·00	50·00
157	1s. light blue and chocolate			4·25	3·75
158	2s. yellow-brown and carmine			3·00	12·00
	w. Wmk sideways inverted				
159	3s. light blue and bluish green			8·50	19·00
150/9			*Set of* 10	28·00	45·00

Designs: *Horiz*—1d. Capt. Cook and map of Hervey Islands; 2d. Rarotonga and Revd. John Williams; 3d. Aitutaki and palm trees; 5d. Rarotonga Airfield; 6d. Penrhyn village; 8d. Native hut. *Vert*—2s. Native hut and palms; 3s. *Matua* (inter-island freighter).

See note on white opaque paper below No. 736 of New Zealand.

NIUE

(14)   **15** King George VI   **16** Tropical Landscape

1937 (13 May). *Coronation. Nos. 599/601 of New Zealand optd with T* **14**.

72	1d. carmine			30	10
73	2½d. Prussian blue			40	50
74	6d. red-orange			40	20
72/4			*Set of* 3	1·00	70

1938 (2 May). *T* **15** *and similar designs inscr* "NIUE COOK ISLANDS". *W* **43** *of New Zealand. P* 14.

75	1s. black and violet			7·00	7·00
76	2s. black and red-brown			12·00	16·00
77	3s. light blue and emerald-green			32·00	16·00
75/7			*Set of* 3	45·00	35·00

Designs: *Vert*—2s. Island village. *Horiz*—3s. Cook Islands canoe.

1940 (2 Sept). *Unissued stamp surch as in T* **16**. *W* **98** *of New Zealand. P* 13½×14.

78	3d. on 1½d. black and purple			50	20

NIUE.

(17)

1941–67. *Postal Fiscal stamps as Type* F **6** *of New Zealand with thin opt, T* **17**. *P* 14.

(i) *Thin, hard, chalk-surfaced "Wiggins Teape" paper with vertical mesh (1941–43)*. (a) *W* **43** *of New Zealand*

79	2s. 6d. deep brown (B.) (4.41)			60·00	70·00
80	5s. green (R.) (4.41)			£250	£180
81	10s. pale carmine-lake (B.) (6.42)			£120	£180
82	£1 pink (B.) (2.43?)			£180	£275
79/82			*Set of* 4	£550	£650

(b) *W* **98** *of New Zealand* (1944–54)

83	2s. 6d. deep brown (B.) (3.45)			3·50	9·00
	w. Wmk inverted (11.51)			9·00	12·00
84	5s. green (R.) (11.44)			7·50	11·00
	w. Wmk inverted (19.5.54)			7·50	11·00

85	10s. carmine-lake (B.) (11.45)			55·00	90·00
	w. Wmk inverted			55·00	90·00
86	£1 pink (B.) (6.42)			42·00	55·00
83/6			*Set of* 4	95·00	£150

(ii) *Unsurfaced "Wiggins Teape" paper with horizontal mesh. W* **98** *of New Zealand* (1957–67)

87	2s. 6d. deep brown (p 14 × 13½) (1.11.57)		7·50	10·00
88	5s. pale yellowish green (wmk sideways) (6.67)			28·00	75·00

No. 88 came from a late printing made to fill demands from Wellington, but no supplies were sent to Niue. It exists in both line and comb perf.

1944–46. *As Nos. 62/7 and 75/7, but W* **98** *of New Zealand (sideways on* ½d., 1d., 1s. *and* 2s.).

89	**12**	½d. black and emerald		50	1·75
90	—	1d. black and deep lake		50	80
91	—	2d. black and red-brown		5·50	6·50
92	—	2½d. black and slate-blue (1946)		60	95
93	—	4d. black and greenish blue		3·50	90
		w. Wmk inverted and reversed		16·00	
94	—	6d. black and red-orange		1·50	1·40
95	**15**	1s. black and violet		1·25	85
96	—	2s. black and red-brown (1945)		8·50	2·75
97	—	3s. light blue and emerald-green (1945)	15·00	7·00
89/97			*Set of* 9	32·00	21·00

1946 (4 June). *Peace. Nos. 668, 670, 674/5 of New Zealand optd as T* **17** *without stop (twice, reading up and down on* 2d.).

98	1d. green (Blk.)			20	10
99	2d. purple (B.)			20	10
100	6d. chocolate and vermilion (Blk.)		20	40
	a. Opt double, one albino			£200	
101	8d. black and carmine (B.)			30	40
98/101			*Set of* 4	80	80

Nos. 102/112 are no longer used.

18 Map of Niue   **19** H.M.S. *Resolution*

23 Bananas   **24** Matapa Chasm

(Des J. Berry. Recess B.W.)

1950 (3 July). *T* **18/19, 23/24** *and similar designs. W* **98** *of New Zealand (sideways inverted on* 1d., 2d., 3d., 4d., 6d. *and* 1s.). *P* 13½×14 *(horiz) or* 14×13½ *(vert).*

113	½d. orange and blue			10	50
114	1d. brown and blue-green			2·25	1·50
115	2d. black and carmine			60	60
116	3d. blue and violet-blue			10	15
117	4d. olive-green and purple-brown		10	15
118	6d. green and brown-orange			60	60
119	9d. orange and brown			10	60
120	1s. purple and black			10	15
121	2s. brown-orange and dull green		1·00	3·75
122	3s. blue and black			4·50	4·00
113/22			*Set of* 10	8·00	10·50

Designs: *Horiz (as T* **19**)—2d. Alofi landing; 3d. Native hut; 4d. Arch at Hikutavake; 6d. Alofi bay; 1s. Cave, Makefu. *Vert (as T* **18**)—9d. Spearing fish.

TOKELAU ISLANDS

32 Samoan Chief   **33** Apia Post Office

1 Atafu Village and Map

(Des J. Berry from photographs by T. T. C. Humphrey. Recess B.W.)

1948 (22 June). *T* **1** *and similar horiz designs. Wmk T* **98** *of New Zealand (Mult* N Z *and Star). P* 13½.

1	½d. red-brown and purple	..	..	..	15	40
2	1d. chestnut and green	..	..	..	15	30
	w. Wmk inverted	..	..	..	£275	
3	2d. green and ultramarine	..	..	..	15	30
1/3	..	..	..	*Set of* 3	40	90

Designs:—1d. Nukunono hut and map; 2d. Fakaofo village and map.

Covers are known postmarked 16 June 1948, but this was in error for 16 July.

(Recess B.W.)

1940 (2 Sept). *W* **98** *of New Zealand (Mult* "N Z" *and Star). P* 14 × 13½.

199	**32**	3d. on 1½d. brown	..	..	20	10

T **32** was not issued without surcharge.

WESTERN SAMOA

NEW ZEALAND MANDATE

WESTERN SAMOA.

(27)

(T **33**. Des L. C. Mitchell. Recess B.W.)

1944–49. *T* **33** *and similar designs. W* **98** *of New Zealand (Mult* "N Z" *and Star) (sideways on* 2½d.*). P* 14 *or* 13½×14 (5d.).

200	½d. green	..	..	..	30	14·00
202	2d. black and orange	..	..	..	2·50	5·50
203	2½d. black and blue (1948)	..	..	4·25	24·00
205	5d. sepia and blue (8.6.49)	..	..	1·00	50
200/5	..	..	..	*Set of* 4	7·25	40·00

Designs: *Vert*—½d. Samoan girl; 2½d. Chief and wife. *Horiz*—2d. River scene.

1935–42. *Postal Fiscal stamps as Type F* **6** *of New Zealand optd with T* **43** *of New Zealand. P* 14.

(a) *Thick, opaque chalk-surfaced "Cowan" paper* (7.8.35)

189	2s. 6d. deep brown (B.)	..	..	..	6·00	16·00
190	5s. green (B.)	..	..	..	11·00	20·00
191	10s. carmine-lake (B.)	..	..	45·00	60·00
192	£1 pink (B.)	..	..	..	60·00	95·00
193	£2 bright purple (R.)	..	..	£140	£300
194	£5 indigo-blue (R.)	..	..	..	£250	£550

(b) *Thin, hard chalk-surfaced "Wiggins, Teape" paper* (1941–42)

194a	5s. green (B.) (6.42)	..	..	80·00	90·00
194b	10s. pale carmine-lake (B.) (6.41)	..	£130	£130
194c	£2 bright purple (R.) (2.42)	..	£500	£700
194d	£5 indigo-blue (R.) (2.42)	..	..	£850	£1000

The £2 and £5 values were primarily for fiscal use. See also Nos. 207/14.

1945–53. *Postal Fiscal stamps as Type F* **6** *of New Zealand optd with T* **27**. *W* **98** *of New Zealand. Thin hard, chalk-surfaced "Wiggins Teape" paper. P* 14.

207	2s. 6d. deep brown (B.) (6.45)	..	..	5·00	13·00
	w. Wmk inverted	..	..	..	6·50	10·00
208	5s. green (B.) (5.45)	..	..	12·00	12·00
	w. Wmk inverted	..	..	..	13·00	13·00
209	10s. carmine-lake (B.) (4.46)	..	..	20·00	17·00
	w. Wmk inverted	..	..	..	26·00	27·00
210	£1 pink (B.) (6.48)	..	..	..	90·00	£160
	w. Wmk inverted	..	..	..		
211	30s. brown (8.48)	..	..	..	£150	£300
	w. Wmk inverted	..	..	..	£275	£400
212	£2 bright purple (R.) (11.47)	..	..	£150	£275
	w. Wmk inverted	..	..	..	£200	£300
213	£3 green (8.48)	..	..	..	£180	£375
	w. Wmk inverted	..	..	..	£300	£475
214	£5 indigo-blue (R.) (1946)	..	..	£325	£450
	w. Wmk inverted (5.53)	..	..	£325	£450
207/10	..	..	*Set of* 4	£110	£180

The £2 to £5 values were mainly used for fiscal purposes. See also Nos. 232/5.

28 Coastal Scene   **31** Robert Louis Stevenson

(Des J. Berry (1d. and 1½d.). L. C. Mitchell (2½d. and 7d.). Recess B.W.)

1939 (29 Aug). *25th Anniv of New Zealand Control. T* **28**, **31** *and similar horiz designs. W* **98** *of New Zealand. P* 13½ × 14 *or* 14 × 13½ (7d.).

195	1d. olive-green and scarlet	..	..	..	30	10
196	1½d. light blue and red-brown	..	..	45	30
197	2½d. red-brown and blue	..	..	..	90	65
198	7d. violet and slate-green	..	..	6·50	2·75
195/8	..	..	..	*Set of* 4	7·50	3·25

Designs:—1½d. Map of Western Samoa; 2½d. Samoan dancing party.

WESTERN SAMOA

(34)

1946 (4 June). *Peace Issue. Nos.* 668, 670 *and* 674/5 *of New Zealand optd with T* **34** *(reading up and down at sides on* 2d.*).*

215	1d. green	..	..	..	10	10
	w. Wmk inverted	..	..	..	£130	
216	2d. purple (B.)	..	..	..	10	10
217	6d. chocolate and vermilion	..	..	20	10
218	8d. black and carmine (B.)	..	..	20	10
215/18	..	..	..	*Set of* 4	50	30

Nigeria

12 pence (d) = 1 shilling; 20 shillings = 1 pound

CROWN COLONY

1937 (12 May). *Coronation. As Nos. 118/20 of Jamaica, but ptd by B.W. & Co. P 11×11½.*

46	1d. carmine					30	1·50
47	1½d. brown					1·25	2·25
48	3d. blue					1·40	2·25
46/8				Set of 3		2·75	5·50
46/8 Perf "Specimen"			Set of 3	55·00

15 King George VI

16 Victoria-Buea Road

(Recess B.W. (T **15**), D.L.R. (others))

1938 (1 May)–**51**. *Designs as T* **15/16**. *Wmk Mult Script CA. P* 12 (*T* **15**) *or* 13×11½ (*others*).

49	**15**	½d. green				10	10
		a. Perf 11½ (15.2.50)			60	20
50		1d. carmine				19·00	2·50
		a. *Rose-red* (*shades*) (1940)		75	30
50b		1d. bright purple (1.12.44)		10	20
		ba. Perf 11½ (15.2.50)			30	50
		bw. Wmk inverted (*p* 12)			
51		1½d. brown				20	10
		a. Perf 11½ (15.11.50)			10	10
52		2d. black				10	1·00
52a		2d. rose-red (1.12.44)			10	80
		ab. Perf 11½ (15.2.50)			10	40
52b		2½d. orange (4.41)			10	70
53		3d. blue				10	10
		a. Wmk sideways			† £3000
53b		3d. black (1.12.44)			15	40
54		4d. orange				48·00	2·75
54a		4d. blue (1.12.44)			15	1·75

55	**15**	6d. blackish purple				40	10
		a. Perf 11½ (17.4.51)			60	60
56		1s. sage-green				60	10
		a. Perf 11½ (15.2.50)			15	10
57		1s. 3d. light blue (1940)			90	30
		a. Perf 11½ (14.6.50)			80	70
		ab. Wmk sideways			† £2750
58	**16**	2s. 6d. black and blue			60·00	13·00
		a. Perf 13½ (6.42)			3·75	4·25
		ab. *Black and deep blue* (1947)		55·00	50·00
		b. Perf 14 (1942)			2·25	3·00
		c. Perf 12 (15.8.51)			1·75	3·50
59	—	5s. black and orange			£110	12·00
		a. Perf 13½ (8.42)			5·50	4·50
		b. Perf 14 (1948)			6·00	3·00
		c. Perf 12 (19.5.49)			5·50	4·00
49/59c				Set of 16	50·00	12·00
49/52a, 53/9 Perf "Specimen"		Set of 15	£200

Design: *Horiz as T* **16**—5s. R. Niger at Jebba.
The 1d., No. 50ba, exists in coils constructed from normal sheets.

1946 (21 Oct). *Victory. As Nos. 141/2 of Jamaica.*

60	1½d. chocolate				25	10
61	4d. blue				25	1·25
60/1 Perf "Specimen"		Set of 2	55·00

1948 (20 Dec). *Royal Silver Wedding. As Nos.* 143/4 *of Jamaica.*

62	1d. bright purple				35	30
63	5s. brown-orange				5·00	8·00

1949 (10 Oct). *75th Anniv of U.P.U. As Nos.* 145/8 *of Jamaica.*

64	1d. bright reddish purple			20	10
65	3d. deep blue				1·25	2·50
66	6d. purple				70	2·25
67	1s. olive				80	1·75
64/7				Set of 4	2·75	6·00

North Borneo

100 cents = 1 Malayan dollar

BRITISH NORTH BORNEO COMPANY ADMINISTRATION

81 Buffalo Transport	82 Palm Cockatoo

(Eng J. A. C. Harrison. Recess Waterlow)

1939 (1 Jan).   *T 81/2 and similar designs. P 12½.*

303	1 c. green and red-brown	..	..	..	1·25	1·00
304	2 c. purple and greenish blue		..	..	5·00	1·00
305	3 c. slate-blue and green	..	..	..	2·00	2·00
306	4 c. bronze-green and violet ..		..	..	4·00	50
307	6 c. deep blue and claret	..	..	..	3·25	5·50
308	8 c. scarlet	..	..	..	7·50	1·50
309	10 c. violet and bronze-green ..		..	..	38·00	6·00
310	12 c. green and royal blue	..	..	..	18·00	5·00
	a. Green and blue ..			..	32·00	6·00
311	15 c. blue-green and brown	..	..	..	17·00	7·50
312	20 c. violet and slate-blue	..	..	..	10·00	3·25
313	25 c. green and chocolate	..	..	..	13·00	9·00
314	50 c. chocolate and violet	..	..	..	16·00	7·00
315	$1 brown and carmine	..	..	..	65·00	19·00
316	$2 violet and olive-green	..	..	..	£100	85·00
317	$5 indigo and pale blue	..	..	..	£300	£225
303/17	..	..	..	*Set of* 15	£550	£325
303/17 Perf "Specimen"				*Set of* 15	£275	

Designs: *Vert*—3 c. Native; 4 c. Proboscis Monkey; 6 c. Mounted Bajaus; 10 c. Orang-Utan; 15 c. Dyak; $1, $2 Badge of the Company. *Horiz*—8 c. Eastern Archipelago; 12 c. Murut with blow-pipe; 20 c. River scene; 25 c. Native boat; 50 c. Mt Kinabalu; $5 Arms of the Company.

WAR TAX	**WAR TAX**
(96)	**(97)**

1941 (24 Feb).   *Nos. 303/4 optd at Sandakan with T 96/7.*

318	1 c. green and red-brown	..	..	90	2·00
	a. Optd front and back ..		..	£300	
319	2 c. purple and greenish blue	..	..	4·75	3·50

The 1 c. was for compulsory use on internal mail and the 2 c. on overseas mail, both in addition to normal postage.

BRITISH MILITARY ADMINISTRATION

North Borneo, including Labuan, was occupied by the Japanese in January 1942. Australian forces landed on Labuan on 10 June 1945 and by the end of the war against Japan on 14 August had liberated much of western North Borneo. The territory was placed under British Military Administration on 5 January 1946.

BMA	
(98)	**(99)**

1945 (17 Dec).   *Nos. 303/17 optd with T 98.*

320	1 c. green and red-brown	..	..	4·25	1·75
321	2 c. purple and greenish blue	..	..	12·00	1·75
	a. Opt double	..	..	£5000	

322	3 c. slate-blue and green	..	..	..	1·25	1·25
323	4 c. bronze-green and violet ..		..	..	16·00	14·00
324	6 c. deep blue and claret	..	..	..	1·25	75
325	8 c. scarlet	..	..	..	3·00	75
326	10 c. violet and bronze-green ..		..	..	3·00	40
327	12 c. green and blue	..	..	..	4·75	2·50
	a. Green and royal blue		..	..	7·00	1·00
328	15 c. blue-green and brown	..	..	..	1·50	1·00
329	20 c. violet and slate-blue	..	..	..	3·50	1·25
330	25 c. green and chocolate	..	..	..	5·00	1·50
331	50 c. chocolate and violet	..	..	..	3·00	1·50
332	$1 brown and carmine	..	..	..	45·00	30·00
333	$2 violet and olive-green	..	..	..	38·00	24·00
	a. Opt double		..	..	£2750	
334	$5 indigo and pale blue	..	..	..	16·00	11·00
320/34	..	..	..	*Set of* 15	£140	80·00

These stamps and the similarly overprinted stamps of Sarawak were obtainable at all post offices throughout British Borneo (Brunei, Labuan, North Borneo and Sarawak), for use on local and overseas mail.

CROWN COLONY

North Borneo became a Crown Colony on 15 July 1946.

Lower bar broken at right (R. 8/3)	Lower bar broken at left (R. 8/4)

1947 (1 Sept–22 Dec).   *Nos. 303 to 317 optd with T 99 and bars obliterating words "THE STATE OF" and "BRITISH PROTECTORATE".*

335	1 c. green and red-brown (15.12) ..		..	15	1·00
	b. Lower bar broken at right	..	..	17·00	
	c. Lower bar broken at left		..	17·00	
336	2 c. purple and greenish blue (22.12)		..	1·75	90
337	3 c. slate-blue and green (R.) (22.12)		..	15	90
338	4 c. bronze-green and violet		..	70	40
339	6 c. deep blue and claret (R.) (22.12)		..	15	20
340	8 c. scarlet		..	20	20
	b. Lower bar broken at right	..	..	17·00	
341	10 c. violet and bronze-green (15.12)		..	75	40
342	12 c. green and royal blue (22.12) ..		..	2·00	2·25
	a. Green and blue		..	3·00	3·25
343	15 c. blue-green and brown (22.12)		..	2·25	30
344	20 c. violet and slate-blue (22.12) ..		..	1·50	85
	b. Lower bar broken at right		..	28·00	
345	25 c. green and chocolate (22.12) ..		..	2·50	45
	b. Lower bar broken at right		..	45·00	
346	50 c. chocolate and violet (22.12) ..		..	1·50	85
	b. Lower bar broken at right		..	45·00	
	c. Lower bar broken at left	..		45·00	
347	$1 brown and carmine (22.12)		..	2·50	1·25
348	$2 violet and olive-green (22.12)		..	7·50	12·00
349	$5 indigo and pale blue (R.) (22.12)		..	16·00	12·00
	b. Lower bar broken at right		..	£110	
335/49	..	..	..	*Set of* 15	35·00	30·00
335/49 Perf "Specimen" ..		..	*Set of* 15	£250	

1948 (1 Nov).   *Royal Silver Wedding. As Nos. 143/4 of Jamaica.*

350	8 c. scarlet	..	..	..	..	30	80
351	$10 mauve	..	..	..	..	20·00	35·00

1949 (10 Oct). *75th Anniv of U.P.U. As Nos. 145/8 of Jamaica.*
352   8 c. carmine 40   30
353   10 c. brown .. .. 2·75   1·00
354   30 c. orange-brown 90   1·75
355   55 c. blue 90   2·25
352/5   .. .. *Set of* 4   4·50   4·75

100 Mount Kinabalu

102 Coconut Grove

(Photo Harrison)

1950 (1 July)–**52**. *T* **100, 102** *and similar designs. Wmk Mult
Script CA. Chalk-surfaced paper. P* 13½ × 14½ *(horiz),*
14½ × 13½ *(vert).*
356   1 c. red-brown 15   70
357   2 c. blue 15   50
358   3 c. green 15   15
359   4 c. bright purple 15   10
360   5 c. violet 15   10
361   8 c. scarlet 75   85
362   10 c. maroon 60   15
363   15 c. ultramarine .. .. .. 2·00   65
364   20 c. brown .. .. 1·00   10
365   30 c. olive-brown .. .. .. 2·50   20
366   50 c. rose-carmine ("JESSLETON") .. 85   3·00
366*a* 50 c. rose-carmine ("JESSELTON") (1.5.52) .. 6·50   2·00
367    $1 red-orange .. .. .. 2·50   1·00
368    $2 grey-green .. .. 2·50   9·00
369    $5 emerald-green .. .. .. 12·00 16·00
370    $10 dull blue .. .. 35·00 45·00
356/70   .. .. .. *Set of* 16 60·00 70·00
Designs: *Horiz*—2 c. Native musical instrument; 8 c. Map; 10 c.
Log pond; 15 c. Malay prau, Sandakan; 20 c. Bajau Chief; $2
Murut with blowpipe; $5 Net-fishing; $10 Arms of North Borneo.
Vert—4 c. Hemp drying; 5 c. Cattle at Kota Belud; 30 c. Suluk
river canoe, Lahad Datu; 50 c. Clock tower, Jesselton; $1 Bajau
horsemen.

POSTAGE DUE STAMPS

D 2 Crest of the Company

(Recess Waterlow)

1939 (1 Jan). *P* 12½.
D66   D **2**   2 c. brown .. .. .. 6·50 70·00
D67   4 c. scarlet .. .. .. 6·50 95·00
D68   6 c. violet .. .. 22·00 £120
D69   8 c. green .. .. 22·00 £200
D70   10 c. blue .. .. 45·00 £350
D66/70   .. .. .. *Set of* 5 90·00 £750
D66/70 Perf "Specimen" .. .. *Set of* 5 £140

JAPANESE OCCUPATION OF NORTH BORNEO

Japanese forces landed in Northern Borneo on 15 December
1941 and the whole of North Borneo had been occupied by 19
January 1942.
    Brunei, North Borneo, Sarawak and, after a short period,
Labuan, were administered as a single territory by the
Japanese. Until September–October 1942, previous stamp
issues, without overprint, continued to be used in conjunction

with existing postmarks. From October 1942 onwards
unoverprinted stamps of Japan were made available and
examples can be found used from the area for much of the
remainder of the War. Japanese Occupation issues for Brunei,
North Borneo and Sarawak were equally valid throughout the
combined territory but not, in practice, equally available.

(1)   2 Mt Kinabalu

3 Borneo Scene

1942 (30 Sept). *Stamps of North Borneo handstamped with
T* 1.
(*a*) *In violet on Nos. 303/17*
J 1   1 c. green and red-brown £140 £190
    a. Black opt £190 £190
    ab. Pair, one without opt £1400
J 2   2 c. purple and greenish blue £140 £190
    a. Black opt £200 £190
J 3   3 c. slate-blue and green £120 £190
    a. Black opt £225 £200
J 4   4 c. bronze-green and violet £120 £190
    a. Black opt .. .. .. 50·00 £110
J 5   6 c. deep blue and claret £130 £190
    a. Black opt £225 £200
J 6   8 c. scarlet £130 £170
    a. Pair, one without opt £1500
J 7   10 c. violet and bronze-green £140 £190
    a. Black opt £200 £190
J 8   12 c. green and bright blue £160 £325
    a. Black opt £375 £325
J 9   15 c. blue-green and brown £160 £325
    a. Pair, one without opt £1600
    b. Black opt £375 £325
J10   20 c. violet and slate-blue £190 £375
    a. Black opt £425 £375
J11   25 c. green and chocolate £190 £375
    a. Black opt £425 £375
J12   50 c. chocolate and violet £275 £425
    a. Black opt £475 £425
J13 $1 brown and carmine £275 £500
    a. Black opt £600 £500
J14 $2 violet and olive-green £375 £700
    a. Pair, one without opt £2500
    b. Black opt £800 £700
J15 $5 indigo and pale blue £450 £800
    a. Black opt £900 £800
(*b*) *In black on Nos. 318/19* ("WAR TAX")
J16   1 c. green and red-brown £400 £250
    a. Pair, one without opt .. .. † £2500
    b. Violet opt .. .. .. — £425
J17   2 c. purple and greenish blue £1100 £350
    a. Violet opt .. .. .. — £550

(Litho Kolff & Co., Batavia)
1943 (29 Apr). *P* 12½.
J18   **2**   4 c. red .. .. .. 14·00 32·00
J19   **3**   8 c. blue .. .. .. 14·00 32·00

(4)   (5)

("Imperial Japanese Postal Service North Borneo")

1944 (30 Sept). *Nos. 303/15 of North Borneo optd as T* **4**.

J20	1 c. green and red-brown	..		4·50	9·50
J21	2 c. purple and greenish blue	..	..	7·50	8·50
	a. Optd on No. J2	..	..	£425	
J22	3 c. slate-blue and green ..	..		4·25	7·50
	a. Optd on No. J3	..	..	£425	
J23	4 c. bronze-green and violet	..		4·50	11·00
J24	6 c. deep blue and claret ..	..		3·75	6·50
J25	8 c. scarlet	..	..	5·50	17·00
	a. Optd on No. J6	..	..	£425	
J26	10 c. violet and bronze-green	..		8·50	13·00
	a. Optd on No. J7	..	..	£425	
	b. Optd on No. J7a	..	..	£180	£350
J27	12 c. green and bright blue	..		7·00	13·00
	a. Optd on No. J8	..	..	£425	
J28	15 c. blue-green and brown	..		7·00	15·00
	a. Optd on No. J9	..	..	£425	
J29	20 c. violet and slate-blue ..	..		17·00	40·00
	a. Optd on No. J10	..	..	£1000	
J30	25 c. green and chocolate ..	..		17·00	40·00
	a. Optd on No. J11	..	..	£1000	
J31	50 c. chocolate and violet ..	..		55·00	£110
	a. Optd on No. J12	..	..	£1500	
J32	$1 brown and carmine	..		85·00	£150
J20/32	..	..	..	*Set of* 13	£200 £400

The spacing between the second and third lines of the overprint is 12 mm on the horizontal stamps, and 15 mm on the upright.

1944 (11 May). *No. J1 surch with T* **5**.

J33	81	$2 on 1 c. green and red-brown	.. £4500 £3750

(6)

7 Girl War-worker

オネル ボ北

(8) ("North Borneo")

本 月 大

五 弗

花 邦 国 帝

1944 (11 May). *North Borneo No.* 315 *surch with T* **6**.

J34	$5 on $1 brown and carmine	..	..	£4000 £2750
	a. Surch on No. J13	..	..	— £4000

1944 (2 Oct)–**45**. *Contemporary stamps of Japan as T* **7** (*various subjects*) *optd with T* **8** *at Chinese Press, Kuching.*

J35	1 s. red-brown (No. 391) (2.45)	..	6·00	15·00
J36	2 s. scarlet (No. 318) (10.44)	..	6·00	14·00
J37	3 s. emerald-green (No. 319) (8.45)	..	5·00	15·00
J38	4 s. yellow-green (No. 395) (12.44)	..	6·00	13·00
J39	5 s. claret (No. 396) (1.45)	..	7·00	16·00
J40	6 s. orange (No. 322) (8.45)	..	8·00	17·00
	a. Opt double, one inverted	..	£350	£350
J41	8 s. violet (No. 324) (2.45)	..	5·50	17·00
J42	10 s. carmine and pink (No. 399) (11.44)	..	5·50	17·00
J43	15 s. blue (No. 401) (11.44)	..	7·50	17·00
J44	20 s. blue-slate (No. 328) (11.44)	..	90·00	85·00
J45	25 s. brown and chocolate (No. 329) (2.45)	55·00	70·00
J46	30 s. turquoise-blue (No. 330)	..	£160	95·00
J47	50 s. olive and bistre (No. 331) (8.45)	..	60·00	60·00
J48	1 y. red-brown & chocolate (No. 332) (5.45)	60·00	80·00
J35/48	..	..	..	*Set of* 14 £425 £475

Designs:—2 s. General Nogi; 3 s. Hydro-electric Works; 4 s. Hyuga Monument and Mt Fuji; 5 s. Admiral Togo; 6 s. Garambi Lighthouse, Formosa; 8 s. Meiji Shrine; 10 s. Palms and map of S.E. Asia; 15 s. Airman; 20 s. Mt Fuji and cherry blossoms; 25 s. Horyu Temple; 30 s. Torii, Itsukushima Shrine at Miyajima; 50 s. Kinkaku Temple; 1 y. Great Buddha, Kamakura.

Examples of some values have been found with hand-painted forged overprints.

POSTAGE DUE STAMPS

1942 (30 Sept). *Nos. D66/7 and D69 of North Borneo hand-stamped with T* **1** *in black.*

JD1	D 2	2 c. brown	..	..	..	— £2250
JD2		4 c. scarlet	..	..	..	— £2250
JD3		8 c. green	..	..	..	— £2250

Northern Rhodesia

12 pence (d) = 1 shilling; 20 shillings = 1 pound

THERN_RHODE

Hyphen between
"NORTHERN" AND "RHODESIA"
(R. 9/6)

1937 (12 May). *Coronation. As Nos. 118/20 of Jamaica, but ptd by B.W. P* 11×11½.

22	1½d. carmine	..	..	..	..	30	35
23	2d. buff	..	..	..	..	40	35
24	3d. blue	..	..	..	..	60	1·25
	a. Hyphen flaw	..	..	..	£140	
22/4	..	..	..	..	*Set of 3*	1·10	1·75
22/4 Perf "Specimen"	..	..	*Set of 3*	65·00	

3   4

"Tick bird" flaw (R. 7/1 of ptgs
from Sept 1938 onwards)

(Recess Waterlow)

1938 (1 Mar)–**52**. *Wmk Mult Script CA. P* 12½.

25	3	½d. green	..	..	..	10	10
		a. "C" of "CA" missing from wmk	..		
26		½d. chocolate (15.11.51)	..	..	10	80
		a. Perf 12½×14 (22.10.52)	..	..	1·40	5·00
27		1d. brown	..	..	..	10	10
		a. Chocolate (1948)	..	..	1·60	60
28		1d. green (15.11.51)	..	..	60	90
29		1½d. carmine-red	..	..	45·00	40
		a. Imperf between (horiz pair)	..	£12000	
		b. "Tick bird" flaw	..	..	£2250	£170
30		1½d. yellow-brown (10.1.41)	..	30	10
		b. "Tick bird" flaw	..	..	50·00	23·00
31		2d. yellow-brown	..	..	45·00	1·25
32		2d. carmine-red (10.1.41)	..	..	30	30
33		2d. purple (1.12.51)	..	..	45	90
34		3d. ultramarine	..	..	..	30	10
35		3d. scarlet (1.12.51)	..	..	50	2·00
36		4d. dull violet	..	..	..	30	40

37	3	4½d. blue (5.5.52)	..	..	..	40	4·50
38		6d. grey	..	..	..	30	10
39		9d. violet (5.5.52)	..	..	40	2·25
40	4	1s. yellow-brown and black	..	..	2·25	40
41		2s. 6d. black and green	..	..	7·00	2·25
42		3s. violet and blue	..	..	13·00	4·00
43		5s. grey and dull violet	..	..	9·00	6·00
44		10s. green and black	..	..	12·00	12·00
45		20s. carmine-red and rose-purple	..	38·00	45·00
25/45		..	..	..	*Set of 21*	£160	70·00
25/45 Perf "Specimen"	..	..	*Set of 15*	£275	

Nos. 26a and 28 exist in coils, constructed from normal sheets.

1946 (26 Nov). *Victory. As Nos. 141/2 of Jamaica. P* 13½×14.

46	1½d. red-orange	..	..	..	10	10
	a. Perf 13½	..	..	..	11·00	12·00
47	2d. carmine	..	..	..	10	40
46/7 Perf "Specimen"	..	..	*Set of 2*	55·00	

The decimal perforation gauge for Nos. 46/7 is 13.7×14.1 and
for No. 46a 13.7×13.4.

1948 (1 Dec). *Royal Silver Wedding. As Nos. 143/4 of Jamaica, but* 20s. *ptd in recess.*

48	1½d. orange	..	..	..	..	30	10
49	20s. brown-lake	..	..	..	42·00	45·00

1949 (10 Oct). *75th Anniv of U.P.U. As Nos. 145/8 of Jamaica.*

50	2d. carmine	..	..	..	..	30	30
51	3d. deep blue	..	..	..	1·90	1·25
52	6d. grey	..	..	..	..	1·00	1·25
53	1s. red-orange	..	..	..	1·00	1·00
50/3	..	..	..	..	*Set of 4*	3·75	3·50

POSTAGE DUE STAMPS

D 1

(Typo D.L.R.)

1929–52. *Wmk Mult Script CA. Ordinary paper. P* 14.

D1	D 1	1d. grey-black	..	..	..	2·50	2·50
		a. Chalk-surfaced paper. *Blk* (22.1.52)	20·00	75·00
		ab. Error. St. Edward's Crown, W9*b*	..	£1400	
D2		2d. grey-black	..	..	..	3·00	3·00
D3		3d. grey-black	..	..	..	3·00	24·00
		a. Chalk-surfaced paper. *Blk* (22.1.52)	7·00	65·00
		ab. Error. Crown missing, W9*a*	..	£225	
		ac. Error. St. Edward's Crown, W9*b*	£150	
D4		4d. grey-black	..	..	..	50·00	28·00
D1/4		..	..	..	..	*Set of 4*	16·00	50·00
D1/4 Perf "Specimen"	..	..	*Set of 4*	85·00	

The 2d. is known bisected and used as a 1d. at Luanshya or
Nkana on various dates between 1937 and 1951 and on
understamped letters from South Africa at Chingola in May
1950 (*Price on cover £425*).

Nyasaland

12 pence (d) = 1 shilling; 20 shillings = 1 pound

1937 (12 May). *Coronation. As Nos.* 118/20 *of Jamaica, but ptd by B.W. P* 11×11½.

127	½d. green ..			30	60
128	1d. brown			50	40
129	2d. grey-black			50	1·50
127/9			*Set of 3*	1·10	2·25
127/9 Perf "Specimen"			*Set of 3*	60·00	

18 Symbol of the Protectorate **19**

(T **18** recess Waterlow; T **19** typo D.L.R.)

1938 (1 Jan)–44. *Chalk-surfaced paper (2s. to £1). P* 12½ (T **18**) *or* 14 (T **19**). (*a*) *Wmk Mult Script CA*

130	**18**	½d. green			30	1·00
130*a*		½d. brown (12.12.42) ..			10	1·50
131		1d. brown			70	20
131*a*		1d. green (12.12.42)			30	60
132		1½d. carmine ..			2·00	4·50
132*a*		1½d. grey (12.12.42)			30	4·00
133		2d. grey			4·00	1·00
133*a*		2d. carmine (12.12.42)			30	1·25
134		3d. blue			60	40
135		4d. bright magenta ..			2·25	1·25
136		6d. violet			2·50	1·25
137		9d. olive-bistre			2·50	2·50
138		1s. black and orange			3·00	1·25
139	**19**	2s. purple and blue/*blue*			10·00	8·50
140		2s. 6d. black and red/*blue* ..			12·00	8·50
141		5s. pale green and red/*yellow*			40·00	18·00
		a. Ordinary paper. *Green and red/ pale yellow* (3.44)			85·00	85·00
142		10s. emerald and deep red/*pale green*			55·00	26·00
		a. Ordinary paper. *Bluish green and brown-red/pale green* (1.38)			£325	£225

(*b*) *Wmk Mult Crown CA*

143	**19**	£1 purple and black/*red*			30·00	26·00
		c. Serif on "G"			£475	£425
130/43		..		*Set of 18*	£150	95·00
130/43 Perf "Specimen" ..			*Set of 18*	£600	

No. 141a has a yellow surfacing often applied in horizontal lines giving the appearance of laid paper.

The printer's archives record the despatch of No. 142a to Nyasaland in January 1938, but no examples have been reported used before 1945. The paper coating on this printing varied considerably across the sheet. It is reported that some examples show a faint reaction to the silver test.

STANLEY GIBBONS
STAMP COLLECTING SERIES

Introductory booklets on *How to Start, How to Identify Stamps* and *Collecting by Theme.* A series of well illustrated guides at a low price.
Write for details.

20 Lake Nyasa **21** King's African Rifles

(Recess B.W.)

1945 (1 Sept). *T* **20**/1 *and similar designs. Wmk Mult Script CA* (*sideways on horiz designs). P* 12.

144		½d. black and chocolate			30	10
145		1d. black and emerald			40	70
146		1½d. black and grey-green			20	50
147		2d. black and scarlet			50	50
148		3d. black and light blue			20	30
149		4d. black and claret..			1·25	45
150		6d. black and violet..			1·25	40
151		9d. black and olive ..			1·50	2·50
152		1s. indigo and deep green			1·25	20
153		2s. emerald and maroon			3·75	4·25
154		2s. 6d. emerald and blue			7·50	4·25
155		5s. purple and blue ..			4·50	6·00
156		10s. claret and emerald			12·00	13·00
157		20s. scarlet and black			17·00	24·00
144/57				*Set of 14*	45·00	50·00
144/57 Perf "Specimen"			*Set of 14*	£275	

Designs: *Horiz*—1½d., black and emerald; 2d., 1s., 10s. Map of Nyasaland; 4d., 2s. 6d. Tobacco; 9d. Type **20** ; 5s., 20s. Badge of Nyasaland. *Vert*—3d., 2s. Fishing Village.

1946 (16 Dec). *Victory. As Nos.* 141/2 *of Jamaica.*

158		1d. green			10	10
159		2d. red-orange			30	10
158/9 Perf "Specimen"			*Set of 2*	55·00	

26 Symbol of the **27** Arms in 1891 and 1951
Protectorate

(Recess B.W.)

1947 (20 Oct). *Wmk Mult Script CA. P* 12.

160	**26**	1d. red-brown and yellow-green ..			50	20
160 Perf "Specimen"		..			45·00	

1948 (15 Dec). *Royal Silver Wedding. As Nos.* 143/4 *of Jamaica.*

161		1d. green			15	10
162		10s. mauve			15·00	25·00

1949 (21 Nov). *75th Anniv of U.P.U. As Nos. 145/8 of Jamaica.*

163	1d. blue-green	..	..	..	..	50	20
164	3d. greenish blue	..	..	..	..	2·25	2·50
165	6d. purple	..	..	..	..	1·00	50
166	1s. ultramarine	..	..	..	..	50	50
163/6	..	..	..	..	*Set of* 4	3·75	3·25

(Des C. Twynam. Recess B.W.)

1951 (15 May). *Diamond Jubilee of Protectorate. Wmk Mult Script CA. P 11 × 12.*

167	27	2d. black and scarlet	..	..	1·00	1·00
168		3d. black and turquoise-blue	..	..	1·00	1·00
169		6d. black and violet	..	..	1·00	1·50
170		5s. black and indigo	..	..	2·00	7·00
167/70	..	..	..	*Set of* 4	4·50	9·50

POSTAGE DUE STAMPS

D 1

(Typo D.L.R.)

1950 (1 July). *Wmk Mult Script CA. P 14.*

D1	D 1	1d. scarlet	..	..	..	3·75	18·00
D2		2d. ultramarine	..	..	..	9·00	22·00
D3		3d. green	..	..	..	9·50	6·00
D4		4d. purple	..	..	..	17·00	40·00
D5		6d. yellow-orange	..	..	..	23·00	95·00
D1/5	..	..	..	*Set of* 5	55·00	£160

Pakistan

12 pies = 1 anna; 16 annas = 1 rupee

7 Scales of Justice 8 Star and Crescent 9 Lloyds Barrage

DOMINION

PAKISTAN
(1)

PAKISTAN
(2)

1947 (1 Oct). *Nos. 259/68 and 269a/77 (King George VI) of India optd by litho at Nasik, as T* **1** *(3 p. to 12 a.) or* **2** *(14 a. and rupee values).*

1	3 p. slate	..	..	10	10
2	½ a. purple			10	10
3	9 p. green	..		10	10
4	1 a. carmine	..		10	10
5	1½ a. dull violet	..		10	10
	w. Wmk inverted	..			
6	2 a. vermilion	..		10	20
7	3 a. bright violet	..		10	20
8	3½ a. bright blue	..		65	2·25
9	4 a. brown	..		20	10
10	6 a. turquoise-green			1·00	75
11	8 a. slate-violet			30	60
12	12 a. lake	..		1·00	20
13	14 a. purple			2·50	1·25
14	1 r. grey and red-brown	..		1·75	70
15	2 r. purple and brown			3·25	1·25
16	5 r. green and blue			4·00	3·75
17	10 r. purple and claret			4·00	2·50
18	15 r. brown and green			48·00	75·00
19	25 r. slate-violet and purple			55·00	42·00
1/19	..		*Set of* 19	£110	£110

Numerous provisional "PAKISTAN" overprints, both hand-stamped and machine-printed, in various sizes and colours, on Postage and Official stamps, also exist.

These were made under authority of Provincial Governments, District Head Postmasters or Local Postmasters and are of considerable philatelic interest.

The 1 a. 3 p. (India No. 269) exists only as a local issue (*Price*, Karachi opt 90p. *unused;* £1.75 *used*).

The 12 a., as No. 12 but overprinted at Karachi, exists with overprint inverted (*Price* £60 *unused*).

The 1 r. value with local overprint exists with overprint inverted (*Price* £150 *unused*) or as a pair with one stamp without overprint (*Price* £600 *unused*).

10 Karachi Airport

13 Khyber Pass

(Des M. Suharwardi (T **8**). Recess Pakistan Security Ptg Corp Ltd, Karachi (P 13 and 13½), D.L.R. (others))

1948 (14 Aug)–**56?** *T* **7/10, 13** *and similar designs. P* 13½×14 *or* 11½ (1 r.).

24	7	3 p. red (*p* 12½?)		..	10	10
		a. Perf 13½ (1954?)	..		20	50
25		6 p. violet (*p* 12½)		..	80	10
		a. Perf 13½ (1954?)	..		2·00	1·75
26		9 p. green (*p* 12½)		..	50	10
		a. Perf 13½ (1954?)	..		75	75
27	8	1 a. blue (*p* 12½)		..	10	50
28		1½ a. grey-green (*p* 12½)			10	10
29		2 a. red (*p* 12½)		..	40	50
30	9	2½ a. green (*p* 14×13½)			2·75	6·00
31	10	3 a. green (*p* 14)			7·50	65
32	9	3½ a. bright blue (*p* 14×13½)			3·50	5·00
33		4 a. reddish brown (*p* 12½)			50	10
34	—	6 a. blue (*p* 14×13½)			50	50
35	—	8 a. black (*p* 12½)			50	50
36	10	10 a. scarlet (*p* 14)			4·50	7·00
37	—	12 a. scarlet (*p* 14×13½)			6·50	80
38	—	1 r. ultramarine (*p* 14)			5·50	10
		a. Perf 13½ (1954?)	..		14·00	2·75
39	—	2 r. chocolate (*p* 14)			20·00	30
		a. Perf 13½ (1954?)	..		24·00	1·50
40	—	5 r. carmine (*p* 14)			15·00	60
		a. Perf 13½ (7.53)	..		9·00	20
41	13	10 r. magenta (*p* 14)			9·00	15·00
		a. Perf 12			70·00	5·00
		b. Perf 13 (1951)			18·00	30
42		15 r. blue-green (*p* 12)			17·00	12·00
		a. Perf 14			15·00	32·00
		b. Perf 13 (1956?)			18·00	12·00
43		25 r. violet (*p* 14)			55·00	80·00
		a. Perf 12			27·00	30·00
		b. Perf 13 (1954)			40·00	20·00
24/43		..	..	*Set of* 20	£100	48·00

Designs: *Vert (as T* **7**)—6 a., 8 a., 12 a. Karachi Port Trust. (*As T* **10**)—1 r., 2 r., 5 r. Salimullah Hostel, Dacca.

For 25 r. with W **98**, see No. 210.

3 Constituent Assembly Building, Karachi

6 Crescent and Stars

(Des A. Chughtai (1 r.). Recess D.L.R.)

1948 (9 July). *Independence. T* **3, 6** *and similar horiz designs. P* 13½ × 14 *or* 11½ (1 r.).

20	1½ a. ultramarine	..	..	70	50
21	2½ a. green	..	..	70	10
22	3 a. purple-brown	..	..	70	20
23	1 r. scarlet	..	..	70	50
	a. Perf 14 × 13½	..	..	4·50	13·00
20/3	..	..	*Set of* 4	2·50	1·10

Designs:—2½ a. Karachi Airport entrance; 3 a. Gateway to Lahore Fort.

14 Star and Crescent 15 Karachi Airport

(Recess Pakistan Security Ptg Corp (P 13½), D.L.R. (others).

1949 (Feb)–53? *Redrawn. Crescent moon with points to left as*
T 14/15.

44	14	1 a. blue (p 12½)	..	..	.. 4·00	70
		a. Perf 13½ (1953?)	..	..	.. 3·50	10
45		1½ a. grey-green (p 12½)		..	.. 3·75	70
		a. Perf 13½ (1952?)	..		.. 3·00	10
		ab. Printed on the gummed side			.. 50·00	
46		2 a. red (p 12½)	..	..	.. 4·00	10
		a. Perf 13½ (1953?)	..	..	.. 3·50	10
47	15	3 a. green (p 14)	..	..	.. 8·50	65
48	–	6 a. blue (as No. 34) (p 14×13½)			.. 8·50	60
49	–	8 a. black (as No. 35) (p 12½)	..		.. 4·50	1·00
50	15	10 a. scarlet (p 14)		..	.. 15·00	1·50
51	–	12 a. scarlet (as No. 37) (p 14×13½)			.. 18·00	30
44/51		..	..	..	Set of 8 55·00	3·50

16

(Recess D.L.R.)

1949 (11 Sept). *First Death Anniv of Mohammed Ali Jinnah.*
T 16 and similar design. P 14.

52	16	1½ a. brown	..	..	.. 1·25	90
53		3 a. green		..	.. 1·25	90
54	–	10 a. black	..	..	.. 4·00	6·50
52/4		..	..	Set of 3	6·00	7·50

Design:—10 a. Similar inscription reading "QUAID-I-AZAM/
MOHAMMAD ALI JINNAH" etc.

17 Pottery    18 Aeroplane and Hour-glass

Two Types of 3½ a.:

I     II

19 Saracenic Leaf Pattern   20 Archway and Lamp

(Des A. Chughtai. Recess D.L.R., later printings, Pakistan
Security Ptg Corp)

1951 (14 Aug)–56. *Fourth Anniv of Independence. P 13.*

55	17	2½ a. carmine	..	..	.. 1·00	50
56	18	3 a. purple		..	.. 50	10
57	17	3½ a. blue (I)		..	.. 75	3·25
57a		3½ a. blue (II)(12.56)		..	.. 3·25	3·00
58	19	4 a. green	..	..	.. 35	10
59		6 a. brown-orange	..	..	.. 45	10

60	20	8 a. sepia	..	..	..	.. 4·00	10
61		10 a. violet				80	80
62	18	12 a. slate	..	..	..	90	10
55/62	..				Set of 9	11·00	7·00

The above and the stamps issued on the 14 August 1954, 1955
and 1956, are basically definitive issues, although issued on the
Anniversary date of Independence.

OFFICIAL STAMPS

PAKISTAN

(O 1)

1947. *Nos. O138/41 and O143/50 (King George VI) of India,*
optd as Type O 1 (Nos. O1/9) or as T 2 (Nos. O10/13) both in
litho by Nasik.

O 1	3 p. slate	..	..	..	.. 80	10
O 2	½ a. purple	..	..	..	30	10
O 3	9 p. green	..	..	..	.. 4·00	2·50
O 4	1 a. carmine	..	..	..	30	10
O 5	1½ a. dull violet	..	..	..	30	10
	w. Wmk inverted	..	..	.. 20·00	
O 6	2 a. vermilion	..	..	..	30	10
O 7	2½ a. bright violet	..	..	.. 6·00	7·50
O 8	4 a. brown	..	..	..	1·25	30
O 9	8 a. slate-violet	..	..	.. 1·50	1·25
O10	1 r. grey and red-brown	..		.. 80	85
O11	2 r. purple and brown	..		.. 3·50	3·00
O12	5 r. green and blue	..		.. 15·00	26·00
O13	10 r. purple and claret	..		.. 40·00	85·00
O1/13			Set of 13	65·00	£110

See note after No. 19. The 1 a. 3 p. (India No. O146a) exists as
a local issue (*Price, Karachi opt, £4.25 mint, £12 used*).

SERVICE   **SERVICE**

(O 2)   (O 3)

NOTE. Apart from a slight difference in size, Types O 2 and O 3
can easily be distinguished by the difference in the shape of the
"c".

PRINTERS. Type O 2 was overprinted by De La Rue and Type
O 3 by the Pakistan Security Ptg Corp.

1948 (14 Aug)–54? *Optd with Type O 2.*

O14	7	3 p. red (No. 24)	..		.. 10	10
O15		6 p. violet (No. 25) (R.)	..		.. 10	10
O16		9 p. green (No. 26) (R.)	..		.. 10	10
O17	8	1 a. blue (No. 27) (R.)	..		.. 3·75	10
O18		1½ a. grey-green (No. 28) (R.)		.. 3·50	10
O19		2 a. red (No. 29)	..		.. 1·50	10
O20	10	3 a. green (No. 31)	..		.. 24·00	6·00
O21	9	4 a. reddish brown (No. 33)		.. 80	10
O22	–	8 a. black (No. 35) (R.)	..		.. 1·50	6·00
O23	–	1 r. ultramarine (No. 38)	..		.. 1·00	10
O24	–	2 r. chocolate (No. 39)	..		.. 13·00	6·50
O25	–	5 r. carmine (No. 40)	..		.. 26·00	6·50
O26	13	10 r. magenta (No. 41)	..		.. 14·00	40·00
		a. Perf 12 (10.10.51)	..		.. 15·00	40·00
		b. Perf 13 (1954?)	..		.. 13·00	48·00
O14/26		..	..		Set of 13	80·00	60·00

1949. *Optd with Type O 2.*

O27		1 a. blue (No. 44) (R.)	..		.. 1·25	
O28		1½ a. grey-green (No. 45) (R.)	..	.. 40	
		a. Opt inverted	..	..	£250	40·00
O29		2 a. red (No. 46)	..	..	.. 1·25	
		a. Opt omitted (in pair with normal)	..	—	£12
O30		3 a. green (No. 47)	..	..	.. 20·00	4·50
O31		8 a. black (No. 49) (R.)	..		.. 29·00	14·00
O27/31		..	..		Set of 5	48·00	17·00

1951 (14 Aug). *4th Anniv of Independence. As Nos. 56, 58 and 60*
but inscr "SERVICE" *instead of* "PAKISTAN POSTAGE".

O32	18	3 a. purple	..	..	.. 6·00	8·00
O33	19	4 a. green	..	..	.. 1·50	10
O34	20	8 a. sepia	..	..	.. 7·00	2·50
O32/4	..	..	..	..	Set of 3	13·00	9·50

1953. *Optd with Type* O 3.

O35	3 p. red (No. 24a)	..	..	10	10
O36	6 p. violet (No. 25a) (R.)	..	..	10	10
O37	9 p. green (No. 26a) (R.)	..	..	10	10
O38	1 a. blue (No. 44a) (R.)	..	..	10	10
O39	1½ a. grey-green (No. 45a) (R.)		..	10	10
O40	2 a. red (No. 46a) (1953?)	..	..	15	10
O41	1 r. ultramarine (No. 38a)	..	..	9·00	3·00
O42	2 r. chocolate (No. 39a)	..	..	3·50	10
O43	5 r. carmine (No. 40a)	..	..	26·00	12·00
O44	10 r. magenta (No. 41b) (date?)	..	..	21·00	48·00
O35/44		..	*Set of* 10	55·00	55·00

BAHAWALPUR

Bahawalpur, a former feudatory state situated to the west of the Punjab, was briefly independent following the partition of India on 15 August 1947 before acceding to Pakistan on 3 October of the same year.

East India Company and later Indian Empire post offices operated in Bahawalpur from 1854. By a postal agreement of 1879 internal mail from the state administration was carried unstamped, but this arrangement was superseded by the issue of Official stamps in 1945.

These had been preceded by a series of pictorial stamps prepared in 1933–34 on unwatermarked paper. It was intended that these would be used as state postage stamps, but permission for such use was withheld by the Indian Government so they were used for revenue purposes. The same designs were utilised for the 1945 Official series, Nos. O1/6, on paper watermarked Star and Crescent. Residual stocks of the unwatermarked 1 a., 8 a., 1 r. and 2 r. were used for the provisional Officials, Nos. O7 and O11/13.

A commemorative 1 a. Receipt stamp was produced to mark the centenary of the alliance with Great Britain. This may not have been ready until 1935, but an example of this stamp is known used on cover from Deh Rawal to Sadiq Garh and postmarked 14 August 1933. Both this 1 a. and the same value from the unwatermarked set also exist with Official Arabic overprint in black. These were not issued for postal purposes although one used example of the latter has been recorded postmarked 22 February 1933 also from Deh Rawal.

Stamps of India were overprinted in the interim period between 15 August and 3 October 1947. After the state joined Pakistan postage stamps were issued for internal use until 1953.

Nawab (from 1947 Amir) Sadiq Mohammad Khan Abbasi V, 1907–1966

(1)

1947 (15 Aug). *Nos. 265/8, 269a/77 and 259/62 (King George VI) of India optd locally with T 1.*

1	3 p. slate (R.)	..	..	..	..	14·00
2	½ a. purple	..			..	14·00
3	9 p. green (R.)	..	..	..	..	14·00
4	1 a. carmine				..	14·00
5	1½ a. dull violet (R.)	..			..	14·00
6	2 a. vermilion				..	14·00
	a. Opt double	..	..	..	..	£850
7	3 a. bright violet (R.)				..	14·00
8	3½ a. bright blue (R.)				..	14·00
9	4 a. brown	..	..	..	..	14·00
10	6 a. turquoise-green (R.)	..	..	..	14·00
	a. Opt double	..	..	..	..	£850
11	8 a. slate-violet (R.)	..	..	..	14·00
12	12 a. lake	..	..	..	..	14·00
13	14 a. purple	..	..	..	..	48·00
14	1 r. grey and red-brown	..	..	..	19·00
15	2 r. purple and brown (R.)	..	..	..	£900
16	5 r. green and blue (R.)	..	..	..	£900
17	10 r. purple and claret	..	..	..	£900
1/17			..	*Set of* 17	£2500

Nos. 1/17 were issued during the interim period, following the implementation of the Indian Independence Act, during which time Bahawalpur was part of neither of the two Dominions created.

The Amir acceded to the Dominion of Pakistan on 3 October 1947 and these overprinted stamps of India were then withdrawn.

The stamps of Bahawalpur only had validity for use within the state. For external mail Pakistan stamps were used.

PRINTERS. All the following issues were recess-printed by De La Rue & Co, Ltd, London.

2 Amir Muhammad Bahawal Khan I Abbasi

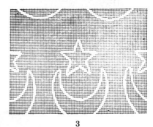

3

1947 (1 Dec). *Bicentenary Commemoration. W* **3** *(sideways).*
P 12½ × 11½.

18	2	½ a. black and carmine	..	..	..	1·25	1·25

4 H.H. the Amir of Bahawalpur

5 The Tombs of the Amirs

6 Mosque in Sadiq-Garh

7 Fort Derawar from the Lake

8 Nur-Mahal Palace

9 The Palace, Sadiq-Garh

10 H.H. the Amir of Bahawalpur
11 Three Generations of Rulers; H.H. the Amir in centre

1948 (1 Apr). *W 3* (*sideways on vert designs*). *P 12½* (*T 4*), 11½ × 12½ (*T 5, 7, 8 and 9*), 12½ × 11½ (*T 6 and 10*) or 13½ × 14 (*T 11*).

19	4	3 p. black and blue	..	..	75	15·00
20		½ a. black and claret	..	..	75	15·00
21		9 p. black and green	..	..	75	15·00
22		1 a. black and carmine	..	..	75	15·00
23		1½ a. black and violet	..	..	75	12·00
24	5	2 a. green and carmine	..	..	1·00	16·00
25	6	4 a. orange and brown	..	..	1·25	16·00
26	7	6 a. violet and blue	..	..	1·25	16·00
27	8	8 a. carmine and violet	..	..	1·25	16·00
28	9	12 a. green and carmine	..	..	1·50	22·00
29	10	1 r. violet and brown	..	..	16·00	32·00
30		2 r. green and claret	..	..	32·00	50·00
31		5 r. black and violet	..	..	32·00	65·00
32	11	10 r. scarlet and black	..	..	32·00	80·00
19/32	..	..	..	..	*Set of* 14	£110 £350

12 H.H. The Amir of Bahawalpur and Mohammed Ali Jinnah
13 Soldiers of 1848 and 1948

1948 (3 Oct). *First Anniv of Union of Bahawalpur with Pakistan. W 3. P 13.*

33	12	1½ a. carmine and blue-green	..	..	60	1·25

1948 (15 Oct). *Multan Campaign Centenary. W 3. P 11½.*

34	13	1½ a. black and lake	..	..	70	7·50

1948. *As Nos.* 29/32, *but colours changed.*

35	10	1 r. deep green and orange	..	70	15·00
36		2 r. black and carmine	..	..	1·00	18·00
37		5 r. chocolate and ultramarine	..	1·10	32·00
38	11	10 r. red-brown and green	..	1·25	38·00
35/8	..	..	..	..	*Set of* 4	3·50 90·00

14 Irrigation
17 U.P.U. Monument, Berne

1949 (3 Mar). *Silver Jubilee of Accession of H.H. the Amir of Bahawalpur. T* **14** *and similar horiz designs. W 3. P 14.*

39		3 p. black and ultramarine	..	..	10	8·00
40		½ a. black and brown-orange	..	..	10	8·00
41		9 p. black and green	..	..	10	8·00
42		1 a. black and carmine	..	..	10	8·00
39/42	..	..	..	..	*Set of* 4	30 29·00

Designs:—½ a. Wheat; 9 p. Cotton; 1 a. Sahiwal bull.
Nos. 39/42 exist imperforate (*Prices, £15 per pair, unused*).

1949 (10 Oct). *75th Anniv of Universal Postal Union. W 3. P 13.*

43	17	9 p. black and green	..	..	20	2·00
		a. Perf 17½ × 17	..	..	2·50	14·00
44		1 a. black and magenta	..	..	20	2·00
		a. Perf 17½ × 17	..	..	2·50	14·00
45		1½ a. black and orange	..	..	20	2·00
		a. Perf 17½ × 17	..	..	2·50	14·00
46		2½ a. black and blue	..	..	20	2·00
		a. Perf 17½ × 17	..	..	2·50	14·00
43/6	..	..	..	..	*Set of* 4	70	7·00
43a/6a	..	..	..	*Set of* 4	9·00 50·00

Nos. 43/6 exist imperforate (*Prices, £10 per pair, unused*).

OFFICIAL STAMPS

O 1 Panjnad Weir
O 2 Dromedary and Calf

O 3 Blackbuck
O 4 Eastern White Pelicans

O 5 Friday Mosque, Fort Derawar
O 6 Temple at Pattan Munara

1945 (1 Mar). *Various horizontal pictorial designs, with red Arabic opt. W 3. P 14.*

O1	O 1	½ a. black and green	..	..	2·75	10·00
O2	O 2	1 a. black and carmine	..	..	3·75	6·00
		a. Opt omitted	..	..	†	£750
O3	O 3	2 a. black and violet	..	..	3·25	9·50
O4	O 4	4 a. black and olive-green	..	7·50	22·00
O5	O 5	8 a. black and brown	..	..	18·00	12·00
O6	O 6	1 r. black and orange	..	..	18·00	12·00
O1/6	..	..	..	..	*Set of* 6	48·00 65·00

Permission for the introduction of Nos. O1/6 was granted by the Imperial Government as from 1 January 1945, but the stamps were not used until 1 March. First Day covers exist showing the January date.

Examples of No. O2a come from a sheet used at Rahimya Khan.

It is believed that examples of Nos. O1/2 in different shades and with white gum appeared in 1949 and were included in the Silver Jubilee Presentation Booklet.

O 7 Baggage Camels   (O 8)

O 11 Allied Banners

1945 (10 Mar). *Revenue stamp with red Arabic opt. No wmk.*
P 14.
O7 O 7 1 a. black and brown .. .. .. 29·00 48·00

1945 (Mar–June). *Surch as Type O 8 (at Security Printing Press, Nasik) instead of red Arabic opt. No wmk. P* 14.
O11 O 5 ½ a. on 8 a. black and purple .. .. 4·25 3·50
O12 O 6 1½ a. on 1 r. black and orange .. .. 32·00 9·00
O13 O 1 1½ a. on 2 r. black and blue (1 June) .. £120 10·00
O11/13 .. .. *Set of* 3 £140 20·00
The stamps used as a basis for Nos. O7 and O11/13 were part
of the Revenue series issued in 1933–34.

SERVICE

(O 9)   O 10 H.H. the Amir of
Bahawalpur

1945. *Optd with Type* O **9** *(by D.L.R.) instead of red Arabic opt. No
wmk. P* 14.
O14 O 1 ½ a. black and carmine.. .. .. 1·25 10·00
O15 O 2 1 a. black and carmine.. .. .. 2·00 13·00
O16 O 3 2 a. black and orange .. .. .. 3·25 38·00
O14/16 .. .. *Set of* 3 6·00 55·00

1945. *P* 14.
O17 O 10 3 p. black and blue .. .. .. 2·50 7·00
O18 1½ a. black and violet.. .. .. 14·00 7·00

(Des E. Meronti. Recess, background litho)

1946 (1 May). *Victory. P* 14.
O19 O 11 1½ a. green and grey .. .. .. 2·00 3·00

1948. *Nos.* 19, 22, 24/5 *and* 35/8 *optd as Nos.* O1/6.
O20 **4** 3 p. black and blue (R.) .. .. 60 10·00
O21 1 a. black and carmine (Blk.) .. .. 60 9·00
O22 **5** 2 a. green and carmine (Blk.) .. .. 60 10·00
O23 **6** 4 a. orange and brown (Blk.) .. .. 60 14·00
O24 **10** 1 r. deep green and orange (R.) .. 60 16·00
O25 2 r. black and carmine (R.) .. .. 60 22·00
O26 5 r. chocolate and ultramarine (R.) .. 60 35·00
O27 **11** 10 r. red-brown and green (R.) .. 60 35·00
O20/7 .. .. *Set of* 8 4·25 £130

1949 (10 Oct). *75th Anniv of Universal Postal Union. Nos.* 43/6
optd as Nos. O1/6.
O28 **17** 9 p. black and green .. .. .. 15 4·50
  aw. Wmk inverted .. .. .. † £100
  b. Perf 17½×17 .. .. 2·00 25·00
O29 1 a. black and magenta .. .. .. 15 4·50
  b. Perf 17½×17 .. .. 2·00 25·00
O30 1½ a. black and orange .. .. .. 15 4·50
  b. Perf 17½×17 .. .. 2·00 25·00
O31 2½ a. black and blue .. .. .. 15 4·50
  b. Perf 17½×17 .. .. 2·00 25·00
O28/31 .. .. *Set of* 4 55 16·00
O28b/31b .. .. *Set of* 4 7·50 90·00
Nos. O28/31 exist imperforate (*Prices,* £10 *per pair, unused*)

From 1947 stamps of Pakistan were used on all external mail.
Bahawalpur issues continued to be used on internal mail until
1953.

Palestine

1000 mils = 1 Palestine pound

BRITISH MANDATE

9 Rachel's Tomb

10 Dome of the Rock

11 Citadel, Jerusalem

12 Sea of Galilee

(Des F. Taylor. Typo Harrison)

1927 (1 June)–**45**. *Wmk Mult Script CA. P* 13½ × 14½ (2 *m. to* 20 *m.) or* 14.

90	9	2 m. greenish blue (14.8.27)		30	10
		w. Wmk inverted		—	£400
91		3 m. yellow-green		40	10
		w. Wmk inverted		—	£200
92	10	4 m. rose-pink (14.8.27)		3·25	1·25
93	11	5 m. orange (14.8.27)		65	10
		a. From coils. Perf 14½×14 (1935)		14·00	18·00
		b. *Yellow* (12.44)		65	15
		c. *Yellow. From coils. Perf* 14½×14 (1945)		30·00	27·00
		w. Wmk inverted		15·00	18·00
94	10	6 m. pale green (14.8.27)		3·00	1·75
		a. *Deep green*		50	20
95	11	7 m. scarlet (14.8.27)		4·00	60
96	10	8 m. yellow-brown (14.8.27)		12·00	6·00
97	9	10 m. slate (14.8.27)		40	10
		a. *Grey. From coils. Perf* 14½×14 (11.38)		20·00	24·00
		aw. Wmk inverted			
		b. *Grey* (1944)		75	10
98	10	13 m. ultramarine		4·00	30
99	11	20 m. dull olive-green (14.8.27)		1·00	15
		a. *Bright olive-green* (12.44)		1·00	15
		w. Wmk inverted		—	£275
100	12	50 m. deep dull purple (14.8.27)		1·00	30
		a. *Bright purple* (12.44)		1·25	30
		w. Wmk inverted			
101		90 m. bistre (14.8.27)		55·00	60·00
102		100 m. turquoise-blue (14.8.27)		2·00	70
103		200 m. deep violet (14.8.27)		8·00	5·00
		a. *Bright violet* (1928)		27·00	16·00
		b. *Blackish violet* (12.44)		6·00	3·50
90/103*b*			Set of 14	80·00	65·00
90/103 H/S "Specimen"			Set of 14	£325	

Three stamps may be made of the above issue; one on thin paper, one on thicker paper with a ribbed appearance, and another on thick white paper without ribbing.

2 m. stamps in the grey colour of the 10 m., including an example postmarked in 1935, exist as do 50 m. stamps in blue, but it has not been established whether they were issued.

Nos. 90/1 and 93 exist in coils, constructed from normal sheets.

1932 (1 June)–**44**. *New values and colours. Wmk Mult Script CA. P* 13½ × 14½ (4 *m. to* 15 *m.) or* 14.

104	10	4 m. purple (1.11.32)		65	10
		w. Wmk inverted		—	£400
105	11	7 m. deep violet		45	10
106	10	8 m. scarlet		60	20
		w. Wmk inverted		—	£500
107		13 m. bistre (1.8.32)		70	10
108		15 m. ultramarine (1.8.32)		1·75	10
		a. *Grey-blue* (12.44)		1·00	40
		b. *Greenish blue*		1·10	40
		w. Wmk inverted		—	£500
109	12	250 m. brown (15.1.42)		3·75	1·75
110		500 m. scarlet (15.1.42)		4·50	3·00
111		£P1 black (15.1.42)		5·00	3·50
104/11			Set of 8	15·00	8·00
104/11 Perf "Specimen"			Set of 8	£375	

No. 108 exists in coils, constructed from normal sheets.

STAMP BOOKLETS

1929. *Blue cover inscr* "PALESTINE POSTAGE STAMP BOOKLET" *and contents in English. Without advertisements on front. Stitched.*
SB1   150 m. booklet containing twelve 2 m., 3 m. and eighteen 5 m. (Nos. 90/1, 93) in blocks of 6 .. .. .. £2000
        a. As No. SB1, but stapled £1600

1930. *Blue cover inscr* "PALESTINE POSTS & TELEGRAPHS POSTAGE STAMP BOOKLET" *and contents all in English, Arabic and Hebrew. Without advertisements on front. Stapled.*
SB2   150 m. booklet. Contents as No. SB1   .. ..

1937–38. *Red cover inscr* "POSTAGE STAMP BOOKLET" *and contents in English, Hebrew and Arabic. With advertisements on front. Stapled.*
SB3   150 m. booklet containing 2 m., 3 m., 5 m. and 15 m. (Nos. 90/1, 93, 108) in blocks of 6   £1600
        a. Blue cover (1938) £1600

1939. *Pink cover inscr* "POSTAGE STAMP BOOKLET" *and contents in English, Hebrew and Arabic. With advertisements on front. Stapled.*
SB4   120 m. booklet containing six 10 m. and twelve 5 m. (Nos. 93, 97) in blocks of 6 .. .. £1500

POSTAGE DUE STAMPS

D 3 (MIL)

1928 (1 Feb)–**45**. *Wmk Mult Script CA. P* 14.

D12	D 3	1 m. brown		45	85
		a. Perf 15×14 (1944)		32·00	60·00
D13		2 m. yellow		55	60
		w. Wmk inverted		†	£400
D14		4 m. green		80	1·60
		a. Perf 15×14 (1945)		55·00	75·00
D15		6 m. orange-brown (10.33)		12·00	8·50

D16	D 3	8 m. carmine	..	..	..	1·75	90
D17		10 m. pale grey	..	..	..	1·25	60
D18		13 m. ultramarine	..	..	..	1·50	1·75
D19		20 m. pale olive-green		..	..	1·60	1·25
D20		50 m. violet	..	..	..	2·50	1·25
D12/20	..	..	..	..	Set of 9	20·00	16·00

D12/20 Perf (D15) or Optd (others) "Specimen"
Set of 9   £300

Nos. D12a and D14a were printed and perforated by Harrison and Sons following bomb damage to the De La Rue works on 29 December 1940.

The British Mandate terminated on 14 May 1948. Later issues of stamps and occupation issues will be found listed under Gaza, Israel and Jordan in Part 19 (*Middle East*) of this catalogue.

Pitcairn Islands

12 pence (d) = 1 shilling; 20 shillings = 1 pound

CROWN COLONY

Stamps of New Zealand were used on Pitcairn Islands from 7 June 1927 until 14 October 1940.

PRICES. Those quoted for Nos. Z54/72 are for examples showing a virtually complete strike of Type Z 1. Due to the size of the cancellation such examples will usually be on piece.

Z 1

Stamps of New Zealand cancelled with Type Z 1.

1937. *Coronation (Nos. 599/601).*

Z54	1d. carmine	..	..	..	..	.. 27·00
Z55	2¹/₂d. Prussian blue		..	..	..	.. 29·00
Z56	6d. red-orange	..	..	..	..	.. 29·00

1937. *Health (No. 602).*

Z57	1d. + 1d. scarlet	..	..	.. 55·00

1938. *King George VI (Nos. 603, 605, 607).*

Z58	¹/₂d. green	..	..	..	.. 55·00
Z59	1d. scarlet	..	..	..	.. 55·00
Z60	1¹/₂d. purple-brown	..	..	.. 65·00

1940. *Centenary of British Sovereignty (Nos. 613/22, 624/5).*

Z61	¹/₂d. blue-green	..		..	.. 28·00
Z62	1d. chocolate and scarlet			..	.. 32·00
Z63	1¹/₂d. light blue and mauve		..	.. 35·00
Z64	2d. blue-green and chocolate	..		.. 35·00
Z65	2¹/₂d. blue-green and blue			..	.. 38·00
Z66	3d. purple and carmine		..	..	.. 38·00
Z67	4d. chocolate and lake	..		..	.. 55·00
Z68	5d. pale blue and brown		..	..	.. 60·00
Z69	6d. emerald-green and violet	..		.. 60·00
Z70	7d. black and red	..		..	.. 80·00
Z71	9d. olive-green and orange	..		.. 80·00
Z72	1s. sage-green and deep green			.. 80·00

1 Cluster of Oranges

2 Christian on *Bounty* and Pitcairn Island

(Recess B.W. (1d., 3d., 4d., 8d. and 2s. 6d.), and Waterlow (others))

1940 (15 Oct)–**51.** *T 1/2 and similar horiz designs. Wmk Mult Script CA.* P 11¹/₂×11 (1d., 3d., 4d., 8d. and 2s. 6d.) or 12¹/₂ (others).

1	¹/₂d. orange and green	..		..	40	60
2	1d. mauve and magenta	..		..	55	70
3	1¹/₂d. grey and carmine	..		..	55	50
4	2d. green and brown	..		..	1·75	1·40
5	3d. yellow-green and blue		..		1·25	1·40
	aw. Wmk inverted		..		.. £3250	
5b	4d. black and emerald-green (1.9.51)		.. 15·00	10·00
6	6d. brown and grey-blue	..		..	5·00	1·50
6a	8d. olive-green and magenta (1.9.51)		.. 16·00	7·00
7	1s. violet and grey		..		3·00	1·50
8	2s. 6d. green and brown	..		..	7·50	3·75
1/8	..	..	..	..	*Set of* 10 45·00	25·00

1/5, 6, 7/8 Perf "Specimen" .. *Set of* 8 £800

Designs:—1¹/₂d. John Adams and his house: 2d. Lt. Bligh and H.M.S. *Bounty*; 3d. Pitcairn Islands and Pacific Ocean; 4d. *Bounty* Bible; 6d. H.M.S. *Bounty*; 8d. School, 1949; 1s. Fletcher Christian and Pitcairn Island; 2s. 6d. Christian on H.M.S. *Bounty* and Pitcairn Coast.

Flagstaff flaw (R. 8/2)

1946 (2 Dec). *Victory. As Nos. 141/2 of Jamaica.*

9	2d. brown	..	..	..	60	15
10	3d. blue	..		..	60	15
	a. Flagstaff flaw	..		..	27·00	

9/10 Perf "Specimen" .. .. *Set of* 2 £140

1949 (1 Aug). *Royal Silver Wedding. As Nos. 143/4 of Jamaica.*

11	1¹/₂d. scarlet	..	..	..	..	2·00	1·00
12	10s. mauve	..	..	..	..	48·00	50·00

1949 (10 Oct). *75th Anniv of U.P.U. As Nos. 145/8 of Jamaica.*

13	2¹/₂d. red-brown	..	..	..	..	1·00	3·50
14	3d. deep blue	..	..	..	..	11·00	4·00
15	6d. deep blue-green	..	..	..	7·00	5·00
16	1s. purple	..	..	..	..	7·00	5·00
13/16	..	..	..	..	..	*Set of* 4 23·00	5·00

STAMP BOOKLETS

1940 (15 Oct). *Black on deep green cover. Stapled.*
SB1 4s. 8d. booklet containing one each ¹/₂d., 1d., 1¹/₂d., 2d., 3d., 6d., 1s. and 2s. 6d. (Nos. 1/5, 6, 7/8) £2750

Genuine examples of No. SB1 are interleaved with ordinary kitchen wax-paper, which frequently tones the stamps, and are secured with staples 17 mm long.

The status of other booklets using different size staples and paper fasteners is uncertain although it is believed that some empty booklet covers were available on the island.

St. Helena

12 pence (d) = 1 shilling; 20 shillings = 1 pound

CROWN COLONY

1937 (19 May). *Coronation. As Nos. 118/20 of Jamaica.*

128	1d. green ..	..	..	..	40	30
129	2d. orange	..	..	..	55	30
130	3d. bright blue	..	..	..	80	30
128/30	..	..	..	*Set of 3* 1·60	80
128/30 Perf "Specimen"	..	..	*Set of 3* 60·00		

33 Badge of St. Helena

(Recess Waterlow)

1938 (12 May)**–44.** *Wmk Mult Script CA. P* 12½.

131	**33**	½d. violet	..	..	10	40
132		1d. green	..	..	12·00	2·25
132a		1d. yellow-orange (8.7.40)	..	..	20	30
133		1½d. scarlet	..	..	20	40
134		2d. red-orange ..	..	..	20	15
135		3d. ultramarine	..	..	90·00	18·00
135a		3d. grey (8.7.40)	..	..	30	30
135b		4d. ultramarine (8.7.40)	..	..	2·00	45
136		6d. light blue	..	..	2·00	30
136a		8d. sage-green (8.7.40) ..	..	..	3·25	90
		b. Olive-green (24.5.44)	..	..	4·50	4·00

137	**33**	1s. sepia	..	..	..	90	30
138		2s. 6d. maroon ..	..	..	..	17·00	4·50
139		5s. chocolate	..	..	..	18·00	11·00
140		10s. purple	..	..	..	18·00	18·00
131/140		..	..	*Set of 14*	£150	50·00
131/40 Perf "Specimen"		..	..	*Set of 14*	£300	

See also Nos. 149/51.

1946 (21 Oct). *Victory. As Nos. 141/2 of Jamaica.*

141	2d. red-orange	..	..	..	15	10
142	4d. blue	..	..	..	15	10
141/2 Perf "Specimen"	..	..	*Set of 2* 60·00		

1948 (20 Oct). *Royal Silver Wedding. As Nos. 143/4 of Jamaica.*

143	3d. black	..	..	..	30	20
144	10s. violet-blue	..	..	..	23·00	28·00

1949 (10 Oct). *75th Anniv of U.P.U. As Nos. 145/8 of Jamaica.*

145	3d. carmine	..	..	..	50	30
146	4d. deep blue	..	..	..	3·25	90
147	6d. olive	..	..	..	90	90
148	1s. blue-black	..	..	..	65	1·10
145/8	..	..	..	*Set of 4*	4·75	3·00

1949 (1 Nov). *Wmk Mult Script CA. P* 12½.

149	**33**	1d. black and green	..	..	60	80
150		1½d. black and carmine ..	..	..	60	80
151		2d. black and scarlet	..	..	60	80
149/51		..	..	*Set of 3*	1·60	2·25

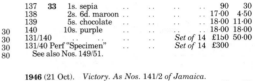
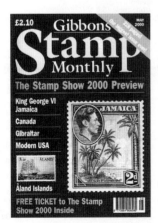

St. Kitts–Nevis

1937. 12 pence (d) = 1 shilling; 20 shillings = 1 pound
1951. 100 cents = 1 West Indian dollar

CROWN COLONY

1937 (12 May). *Coronation. As Nos. 118/20 of Jamaica.*
65	1d. scarlet					30	20
66	1½d. buff	..	..	..	..	40	10
67	2½d. bright blue	..	..	..	..	60	45
65/7	..	..	..		*Set of* 3	1·10	65
65/7 Perf "Specimen"			..		*Set of* 3	55·00	

Nos. 61/7 are inscribed "ST. CHRISTOPHER AND NEVIS".

7 King George VI

8 King George VI and
Medicinal Spring

9 King George VI and
Christopher Columbus

10 King George VI and
Anguilla Island

Break in value tablet (R.
12/5) (1947 ptg only)

Break in oval (R. 12/1)
(1938 ptg only)

Break in value tablet
frame (R.3/2)

Break in value tablet
frame (R. 12/3) (ptgs
between 1941 and 1945)

Break in frame above ornament
(R. 2/4) (ptgs between 1941 and
1950)

Break in oval at foot (R. 12/5)
(ptgs between 1941 and 1945
only). Sometimes touched-in by
hand painting)

Break in oval at left
(R. 7/1) (ptgs between
1941 and 1945 only)

(Typo; centre litho (T **10**). D.L.R.)

1938 (15 Aug)–**50**. *Wmk Mult Script CA (sideways on T **8** and
9). Chalk-surfaced paper* (10s., £1). P 14 (T **7** *and* **10**) *or* 13×1?
(T **8/9**).

68	**7**	½d. green	..		..	..	3·00	2?
		a. *Blue-green* (5.4.43)		..		..	10	1?
69		1d. scarlet	..		..	..	4·50	7?
		a. *Carmine* (5.43)		..		..	80	5?
		b. *Carmine-pink* (4.47)		..		60·00	16·0?
		c. *Rose-red* (7.47)			..	..	80	8?
70		1½d. orange	..		..	..	20	3?
71	**8**	2d. scarlet and grey	..		..	17·00	2·5?
		a. Chalk-surfaced paper. *Carmine and deep grey* (5.41*)				55·00	10·0?
		b. Perf 14. *Scarlet & pale grey* (6.43*)				70	1·2?
		ba. *Scarlet and deep grey* (6.42*)				20·00	5·0?
		c. Perf 14. Chalk-surfaced paper. *Scarlet and pale grey* (2.50*)				1·50	2·5?
72	**7**	2½d. ultramarine	..		..	3·50	3?
		a. *Bright ultramarine* (5.4.43)				30	3?
73	**8**	3d. dull reddish purple and scarlet			..	14·00	3·7?
		a. Chalk-surfaced paper. *Brown-purple and carmine-red* (1940)				18·00	4·5?
		b. Perf 14. Chalk-surfaced paper. *Dull reddish purple & carm-red* (6.43*)				30·00	3·7?
		c. Perf 14. Ordinary paper. *Reddish lilac and scarlet* (8.46*)				2·50	12·0?
		d. Perf 14. Ordinary paper. *Purple and bright scarlet* (1.46*)				6·50	6·5?
		da. Break in value tablet	..			70·00	
		e. Perf 14. Chalk-surfaced paper. *Deep purple and scarlet* (12.47*)				75·00	18·0?
		f. Perf 14. Ordinary paper. *Rose-lilac and bright scarlet* (1.49*)				6·50	7·0?
		g. Perf 14. Chalk-surfaced paper. *Deep reddish purple & brt scarlet* (8.50*)				3·75	4·5?

74	9	6d. green and bright purple	6·50	2·25
		a. Break in oval .. .. .. 85·00		
		b. Perf 14. Chalk-surfaced paper.		
		Green and deep claret (6.43*) .. 55·00	11·00
		c. Perf 14. Ordinary paper. Green and		
		purple (10.44*)	4·75	1·50
		d. Perf 14. Chalk-surfaced paper.		
		Green and purple (11.48*) ..	4·25	3·00
75	8	1s. black and green	12·00	1·25
		a. Break in value tablet frame .. £120		
		b. Perf 14 (8.43*)	3·75	85
		ba. Break in value tablet frame .. 70·00		
		c. Perf 14. Chalk-surfaced paper		
		(7.50*)	3·25	3·50
		ca. Break in value tablet frame .. 60·00		
76		2s. black and scarlet .. .. 32·00	9·00
		a. Perf 14. Chalk-surfaced paper		
		(12.43*)	13·00	6·00
		ab. Ordinary paper (5.45*) ..	12·00	3·75
77	9	5s. grey-green and scarlet .. 65·00	18·00
		a. Perf 14. Chalk-surfaced paper		
		(12.43*) £130	28·00
		ab. Break in value tablet frame .. £375		
		ac. Break in frame above ornament .. £375		
		ad. Break in oval at foot .. £375		
		ae. Break in oval at left .. £375		
		b. Perf 14. Ordinary paper. Bluish		
		green and scarlet (7.11.45*) ..	24·00	12·00
		ba. Break in value tablet frame .. £170		
		bb. Break in frame above ornament .. £180		
		bc. Break in oval at foot .. £160		
		bd. Break in oval at left .. £170		
		c. Perf 14. Chalk-surfaced paper.		
		Green & scarlet-vermilion (10.50*) .. 32·00	30·00
		cb. Break in frame above ornament .. £190		
77d	10	10s. black and ultramarine (1.9.48) .. 10·00	19·00
77e		£1 black and brown (1.9.48) .. .. 10·00	23·00
38/77		.. .. Set of 12 60·00	55·00
38/77		Perf "Specimen" Set of 10 £180	

*Earliest postmark date. Many printings were supplied to St.
Kitts-Nevis considerably earlier. Details of earliest dates are
taken, with permission, from *A Study of the King George VI
Stamps of St. Kitts-Nevis* by P. L. Baldwin (2nd edition 1997).

1946 (1 Nov). *Victory. As Nos. 141/2 of Jamaica.*

78		1½d. red-orange	10	10
79		3d. carmine	10	10
78/9		Perf "Specimen" .. .. Set of 2 60·00	

1949 (3 Jan). *Royal Silver Wedding. As Nos. 143/4 of Jamaica.*

30		2½d. ultramarine	10	10
31		5s. carmine .. .. .. 6·00	2·50

1949 (10 Oct). *75th Anniv of U.P.U. As Nos. 145/8 of Jamaica.*

32		2½d. ultramarine	35	20
33		3d. carmine-red .. .. 1·00	60
34		6d. magenta	40	30
35		1s. blue-green	40	30
32/5		.. .. Set of 4 1·90	1·25

ANGUILLA

ANGUILLA

TERCENTENARY
1650-1950

(11)

TERCENTENARY
1650—1950

(12)

1950 (10 Nov). *Tercentenary of British Settlement in Anguilla.
Nos. 69c, 70 and 72a (perf 14) optd as T 11 and new ptgs of
T 8/9 on chalk-surfaced paper perf 13×12½ optd as T 12.*

86	7	1d. rose-red	10	20
87		1½d. orange	10	20
		a. Error. Crown missing, W 9a .. £1500		
		b. Error. St. Edward's Crown, W 9b .. £850		
88		2½d. bright ultramarine	10	20
89	8	3d. dull purple and scarlet ..	10	40
90	9	6d. green and bright purple ..	10	20
91	8	1s. black and green (R.) ..	30	20
		a. Break in value tablet frame .. 9·50		
86/91		.. .. Set of 6 60	1·25

Nos. 87a/b occur on a row in the watermark, in which the crowns
and letters "CA" alternate.

**(New Currency. 100 cents = 1 West Indian, later East
Caribbean, dollar)**

1951 (16 Feb). *Inauguration of B.W.I. University College. As
Nos. 149/50 of Jamaica.*

92		3c. black and yellow-orange ..	30	15
93		12c. turquoise-green and magenta	30	85

13 Bath House and Spa, Nevis	**14** Map of the Islands

(Recess Waterlow)

1952 (14 June). *Vert designs as T 14 (3, 12 c.) or horiz as 13
(others). Wmk Mult Script CA. P 12½.*

94		1 c. deep green and ochre	15	90
95		2 c. green	75	90
96		3 c. carmine-red and violet	30	80
97		4 c. scarlet	20	20
98		5 c. bright blue and grey	30	10
99		6 c. ultramarine	30	15
100		12 c. deep blue and reddish brown ..	50	10
101		24 c. black and carmine-red ..	30	10
102		48 c. olive and chocolate	1·75	1·75
103		60 c. ochre and deep green	1·50	2·00
104		$1.20, deep green and ultramarine ..	5·50	2·25
105		$4.80, green and carmine	13·00	18·00
94/105		.. .. Set of 12 22·00	24·00

Designs:—2 c. Warner Park; 4 c. Brimstone Hill; 5 c. Nevis
from the sea, North; 6 c. Pinney's Beach, Nevis; 12 c. Sir Thomas
Warner's Tomb; 24 c. Old Road Bay; 48 c. Sea Island cotton,
Nevis; 60 c. The Treasury; $1.20, Salt pond, Anguilla; $4.80,
Sugar factory.

St. Lucia

1937. 12 pence (d) = 1 shilling; 20 shillings = 1 pound
1949. 100 cents = 1 West Indian dollar

CROWN COLONY

1937 (12 May). *Coronation. As Nos. 118/20 of Jamaica, but ptd by B.W. P 11×11½.*

125	1d. violet				30	30
126	1½d. carmine				55	20
127	2½d. blue				55	50
125/7				Set of 3	1·25	90
125/7 Perf "Specimen"			Set of 3	55·00	

26 King George VI

27 Columbus Square

28 Government House

31 Device of St. Lucia

(Des E. Crafer (T **26**), H. Fleury (5s.). Recess Waterlow (½d. to 3½d., 8d., 3s., 5s., £1), D.L.R. (6d., 1s.) and B.W. (2s., 10s.))

1938 (22 Sept)–**48**. T **26/8, 31** *and similar designs.* Wmk Mult Script CA *(sideways on 2s.).*

128	**26**	½d. green (p 14½ × 14)		75	10
		a. Perf 12½ (1943)		10	10
129		1d. violet (p 14½ × 14)		90	75
		a. Perf 12½ (1938)		10	15
129b		1d. scarlet (p 12½) (1947)		10	10
		c. Perf 14½ × 14 (1948)		10	10
130		1½d. scarlet (p 14½ × 14)		1·25	40
		a. Perf 12½ (1943)		30	70
131		2d. grey (p 14½ × 14)		90	1·25
		a. Perf 12½ (1943)		10	10
132		2½d. ultramarine (p 14½ × 14)		1·75	15
		a. Perf 12½ (1943)		10	10
132b		2½d. violet (p 12½) (1947)		30	30
133		3d. orange (p 14½ × 14)		15	10
		a. Perf 12½ (1943)		10	10
133b		3½d. ultramarine (p 12½) (1947)		30	15
134	**27**	6d. claret (p 13½)		3·00	50
		a. Carmine-lake (p 13½) (1945)		1·75	35
		b. Perf 12. Claret (1948)		1·00	70
134c	**26**	8d. brown (p 12½) (1946)		2·75	30
135	**28**	1s. brown (p 13½)		55	30
		a. Perf 12 (1948)		40	20
136	–	2s. blue and purple (p 12)		3·50	1·25
136a	**26**	3s. bright purple (p 12½) (1946)		8·00	2·25
137	–	5s. black and mauve (p 12½)		14·00	6·00
138	**31**	10s. black/yellow (p 12)		4·50	9·00
141	**26**	£1 sepia (p 12½) (1946)		11·00	8·00
128a/141			Set of 17	40·00	26·00
128/41 Perf "Specimen"		Set of 17	£300	

Designs: *Horiz (as T* **28***)*—2s. The Pitons; 5s. *Lady Hawkins* loading bananas.

1946 (8 Oct). *Victory. As Nos. 141/2 of Jamaica.*

142	1d. lilac				10	10
143	3½d. blue				10	10
142/3 Perf "Specimen"			Set of 2	50·00	

1948 (26 Nov). *Royal Silver Wedding. As Nos. 143/4 of Jamaica.*

144	1d. scarlet				15	10
145	£1 purple-brown				13·00	35·00

(New Currency. 100 cents = 1 West Indian, later Eastern Caribbean dollar)

32 King George VI

33 Device of St. Lucia

(Recess Waterlow (**32**), B.W. (**33**))

1949 (1 Oct)–**50**. *Value in cents or dollars. Wmk Mult Script CA. P 12½ (1 c. to 16 c.), 11 × 11½ (others).*

146	**32**	1 c. green			10	10
		a. Perf 14 (1949)			1·50	40
147		2 c. magenta			10	10
		a. Perf 14½ × 14 (1949)			1·50	1·00
148		3 c. scarlet			10	90
149		4 c. grey			10	10
		a. Perf 14½ × 14			† £550	
150		5 c. violet			10	10
151		6 c. orange			15	90
152		7 c. ultramarine			1·50	1·70
153		12 c. claret			4·50	1·25
		a. Perf 14½ × 14 (1950)			£475	£350
154		16 c. brown			2·00	20
155	**33**	24 c. light blue			30	10
156		48 c. olive-green			1·50	90
157		$1.20, purple			2·25	7·00
158		$2.40, blue-green			3·00	17·00
159		$4.80, rose-carmine			6·00	18·00
146/159				Set of 14	19·00	42·00

Most examples of Nos. 146a and 147a were produced as coils but a few sheets in these perforations were distributed and blocks of four are scarce.

1949 (10 Oct). *75th Anniv of U.P.U. As Nos. 145/8 of Jamaica.*

160	5 c. violet				20	20
161	6 c. orange				1·40	90
162	12 c. magenta				30	20
163	24 c. blue-green				65	20
160/3				Set of 4	2·25	1·40

1951 (16 Feb). *Inauguration of B.W.I. University College. As Nos. 149/50 of Jamaica.*

164	3 c. black and scarlet				45	50
165	12 c. black and deep carmine				55	50

N	1
E	9
W	5
	1

CONSTITUTION

34 Phoenix rising from Burning Buildings

(35)

(Flames typo, rest recess B.W.)

1951 (19 June). *Reconstruction of Castries. Wmk Mult Script CA. P 13½ × 13.*

| 166 | **34** | 12 c. red and blue | .. | .. | .. | 15 | 70 |

1951 (25 Sept). *New Constitution. Nos. 147, 149/50 and 153 optd with T 35 by Waterlow. P 12½.*

167	**32**	2 c. magenta	..	..	..	..	15	50
168		4 c. grey	..	..	..	..	15	50
169		5 c. violet	..	..	..	..	15	30
170		12 c. claret	..	..	..	..	15	50
167/70		..	..	..	Set of 4	55	1·60

POSTAGE DUE STAMPS

D 2

D 3

(Typo D.L.R.)

1933–47. *Wmk Mult Script CA. P 14.*

D3	D 2	1d. black	..	..	..	..	4·50	6·00
D4		2d. black	..	..	..	..	16·00	8·00
D5		4d. black (28.6.47)	..	..	..	5·50	32·00
D6		8d. black (28.6.47)	..	..	..	5·50	42·00
D3/6	..	..	..	..	..	Set of 4	28·00	80·00
D3/6 Perf "Specimen"		..	..	Set of 4	£130

1949 (1 Oct)–**52.** *Value in cents. Wmk Mult Script CA. Typo. P 14.*

D 7	D 3	2 c. black	..	..	..	..	1·75	24·00
		a. Chalk-surfaced paper (27.11.52)			10	7·50
		ab. Error. Crown missing, W **9**a	..	95·00
		ac. Error. St. Edward's Crown, W **9**b	30·00
D 8		4 c. black	..	..	..	..	3·50	17·00
		a. Chalk-surfaced paper (27.11.52)..		40	9·00
		ab. Error. Crown missing, W **9**a	..	£130
		ac. Error. St. Edward's Crown, W **9**b	42·00
D 9		8 c. black	..	..	..	..	3·25	21·00
		a. Chalk-surfaced paper (27.11.52)..		3·00	28·00
		ac. Error. St. Edward's Crown, W **9**b	£225
D10		16 c. black	..	..	..	..	15·00	65·00
		a. Chalk-surfaced paper (27.11.52)..		4·00	48·00
		ac. Error. St. Edward's Crown, W **9**b	£325
D7/10	..	..	..	..	Set of 4	21·00	£110
D7a/10a	..	..	..	..	Set of 4	6·75	85·00

St. Vincent

1937. 12 pence (d) = 1 shilling; 20 shillings = 1 pound
1949. 100 cents = 1 West Indian dollar

CROWN COLONY

1937 (12 May). *Coronation. As Nos. 118/20 of Jamaica, but ptd by B.W. P* 11×11½.

146	1d. violet					35	40
147	1½d. carmine					40	30
148	2½d. blue					45	1·50
146/8					*Set of 3*	1·10	2·00
146/8 Perf "Specimen"			*Set of 3* 50·00				

25

26 Young's Island and Fort Duvernette

27 Kingstown and Fort Charlotte

28 Bathing Beach at Villa

29 Victoria Park, Kingstown

NEW CONSTITUTION 1951

(29a)

(Recess B.W.)

1938 (11 Mar)–**47**. *Wmk Mult Script CA. P* 12.

149	25	½d. blue and green			10	10
150	26	1d. blue and lake-brown			10	10
151	27	1½d. green and scarlet			20	10
152	25	2d. green and black			40	35
153	28	2½d. blue-black and blue-green			20	40
153a	29	2½d. green and purple-brown (1947)			40	20
154	25	3d. orange and purple			20	10
154a	28	3½d. blue-black and blue-green (1947)			40	1·75
155	25	6d. black and lake			1·00	40
156	29	1s. purple and green			1·00	80
157	25	2s. blue and purple			6·00	75
157a		2s. 6d. red-brown and blue (1947)			1·25	3·50
158		5s. scarlet and deep green			10·00	2·50

158a	25	10s. violet and brown (1947)			3·75	8·50
		aw. Wmk inverted				— £1300
159		£1 purple and black			16·00	15·00
149/59				*Set of 15* 35·00 30·00		
149/59 Perf "Specimen"			*Set of 15* £250			

1946 (15 Oct). *Victory. As Nos. 141/2 of Jamaica.*

160		1½d. carmine			10	10
161		3½d. blue			10	10
160/1 Perf "Specimen"			*Set of 2* 50·00			

1948 (30 Nov). *Royal Silver Wedding. As Nos. 143/4 of Jamaica.*

162	1½d. scarlet			10	10
163	£1 bright purple			15·00	17·00

No. 163 was originally printed in black, but the supply of these was stolen in transit. A few archive examples exist, some perforated "Specimen".

(New Currency. 100 cents = 1 West Indian, later East Caribbean dollar)

1949 (26 Mar)–**52**. *Value in cents and dollars. Wmk Mult Script CA. P* 12.

164	25	1 c. blue and green			20	1·00
164a		1 c. green and black (10.6.52)			30	2·00
165	26	2 c. blue and lake-brown			15	40
166	27	3 c. green and scarlet			40	50
166a	25	3 c. orange and purple (10.6.52)			30	2·00
167		4 c. green and black			35	20
167a		4 c. blue and green (10.6.52)			30	15
168	29	5 c. green and purple-brown			15	10
169	25	6 c. orange and purple			40	75
169a	27	6 c. green and scarlet (10.6.52)			30	2·00
170	28	7 c. blue-black and blue-green			3·50	80
170a		10 c. blue-black and blue-green (10.6.52)			50	20
171	25	12 c. black and lake			35	15
172	29	24 c. purple and green			35	45
173	25	48 c. blue and purple			2·00	2·00
174		60 c. red-brown and blue			1·75	3·00
175		$1.20, scarlet and deep green			4·25	4·00
176		$2.40, violet and brown			6·00	9·00
177		$4.80, purple and black			11·00	19·00
164/77				*Set of 19* 29·00 40·00		

1949 (10 Oct). *75th Anniv of U.P.U. As Nos. 145/8 of Jamaica.*

178		5 c. blue			25	15
179		6 c. purple			55	1·40
180		12 c. magenta			30	1·40
181		24 c. blue-green			50	25
178/81				*Set of 4* 1·40 2·75		

1951 (16 Feb). *Inauguration of B.W.I. University College. As Nos. 149/50 of Jamaica.*

182	3 c. deep green and scarlet			30	30
183	12 c. black and purple			30	50

1951 (21 Sept). *New Constitution. Optd with T 29a by B.W.*

184	27	3 c. green and scarlet			15	90
185	25	4 c. green and black			15	30
186	29	5 c. green and purple-brown			15	30
187	25	12 c. black and lake			60	30
184/7				*Set of 4* 95		1·60

Sarawak

100 cents = 1 Malayan dollar

BROOKE FAMILY ADMINISTRATION

21 Sir Charles Vyner
Brooke

B M A

(22)

(Recess B.W.)

1934 (1 May)–**41.** *No wmk. P* 12.

106	**21**	1 c. purple	..	..	30	10
107		2 c. green	..	..	40	10
107a		2 c. black (1.3.41)	..	..	1·50	1·60
108		3 c. black	..		30	10
108a		3 c. green (1.3.41)	..	..	3·50	4·50
109		4 c. bright purple	..	..	30	15
110		5 c. violet	..	..	60	10
111		6 c. carmine	..	..	1·00	60
111a		6 c. lake-brown (1.3.41)	..	..	4·75	8·00
112		8 c. red-brown	..	..	1·40	10
112a		8 c. carmine (1.3.41)	..	..	4·50	10
113		10 c. scarlet	..	..	1·25	40
114		12 c. blue	..	..	2·00	25
114a		12 c. orange (1.3.41)	..	..	2·50	4·75
115		15 c. orange	..	..	2·25	6·00
115a		15 c. blue (1.3.41)	..	..	4·50	15·00
116		20 c. olive-green and carmine	..	..	2·25	70
117		25 c. violet and orange	..	..	2·25	1·50
118		30 c. red-brown and violet	..	..	2·25	2·50
119		50 c. violet and scarlet	..	..	2·25	75
120		$1 scarlet and sepia	..	..	60	75
121		$2 bright purple and violet	..	..	8·50	8·50
122		$3 carmine and green	..	..	25·00	25·00
123		$4 blue and scarlet	..	..	25·00	32·00
124		$5 scarlet and red-brown	..	..	25·00	32·00
125		$10 black and yellow	..	..	19·00	42·00
106/25				*Set of* 26	£130	£170
106/25 Perf "Specimen"				*Set of* 26	£450	

For the 3 c. green, wmkd Mult Script CA, see No. 152a.

BRITISH MILITARY ADMINISTRATION

Following the Japanese surrender elements of the British Military Administration reached Kuching on 11 September 1945. From 5 November 1945 current Australian 1d., 3d., 6d. and 1s. stamps were made available for civilian use until replaced by Nos. 126/45. Other Australian stamps were also accepted as valid for postage during this period.

1945 (17 Dec). *Optd with T* **22.**

126	**21**	1 c. purple	..	..	40	60
127		2 c. black (R.)	..	..	40	50
		a. Opt double			† £4000	
128		3 c. green	..	..	40	40
129		4 c. bright purple	..	..	40	30
130		5 c. violet (R.)	..	..	60	90
131		6 c. lake-brown	..	..	1·00	75
132		8 c. carmine	..	..	11·00	9·00
133		10 c. scarlet	..	..	60	70
134		12 c. orange	..	..	90	3·75
135		15 c. blue	..	..	1·75	40
136		20 c. olive-green and carmine	..		2·25	1·40
137		25 c. violet and orange (R.)	..		2·25	2·75
138		30 c. red-brown and violet	..		5·50	2·75
139		50 c. violet and scarlet	..		1·25	35
140		$1 scarlet and sepia	..		2·50	1·25
141		$2 bright purple and violet	..		9·00	8·00

142	**21**	$3 carmine and green	..	..	17·00	38·00
143		$4 blue and scarlet	..	..	25·00	30·00
144		$5 scarlet and red-brown	..	..	£120	£140
145		$10 black and yellow (R.)	..	..	£120	£160
126/45				*Set of* 20	£275	£350

These stamps, and the similarly overprinted stamps of North Borneo, were obtainable at all post offices throughout British Borneo (Brunei, Labuan, North Borneo and Sarawak), for use on local and overseas mail.

The administration of Sarawak was returned to the Brooke family on 15 April 1946, but the Rajah, after consulting the inhabitants, ceded the territory to Great Britain on 1 June 1946. Values from the 1934–41 issue were used until replaced by Nos. 150/64.

23 Sir James Brooke, Sir Charles Vyner
Brooke and Sir Charles Brooke

(24)

(Recess B.W.)

1946 (18 May). *Centenary Issue. P* 12.

146	**23**	8 c. lake	..	..	1·10	30
147		15 c. blue	..	..	1·10	1·75
148		50 c. black and scarlet	..	..	1·25	1·75
149		$1 black and sepia	..	..	1·50	14·00
146/9				*Set of* 4	4·50	16·00
146/9 Perf "Specimen"				*Set of* 4	90·00	

CROWN COLONY

1947 (16 Apr). *Optd with T* **24,** *typo by B.W. in blue-black or red. Wmk Mult Script CA. P* 12.

150	**21**	1 c. purple	..	..	15	30
151		2 c. black (R.)	..	..	15	15
152		3 c. green (R.)	..	..	15	15
		a. Albino opt	..	..	£4000	
153		4 c. bright purple	·	..	15	15
154		6 c. lake-brown	..	..	20	90
155		8 c. carmine	..	..	40	10
156		10 c. scarlet	..	..	20	20
157		12 c. orange	..	..	20	90
158		15 c. blue (R.)	..	..	20	40
159		20 c. olive-green and carmine (R.)	..		1·00	50
160		25 c. violet and orange (R.)	..		40	30
161		50 c. violet and scarlet (R.)	..		40	40
162		$1 scarlet and sepia	..	..	75	90
163		$2 bright purple and violet	..		1·40	3·25
164		$5 scarlet and red-brown	..		3·00	3·25
150/64				*Set of* 15	7·50	10·50
150/64 Perf "Specimen"				*Set of* 15	£250	

No. 152a shows an uninked impression of T **24.**

1948 (25 Oct). *Royal Silver Wedding. As Nos. 143/4 of Jamaica.*

165		8 c. scarlet	..	..	30	30
166		$5 brown	..	..	30·00	32·00

1949 (10 Oct). *75th Anniv of U.P.U. As Nos. 145/8 of Jamaica.*

167		8 c. carmine	..	..	1·25	50
168		15 c. deep blue	..	..	2·50	2·25
169		25 c. deep blue-green	..	..	2·00	1·50
170		50 c. violet	..	..	2·00	4·00
167/70			..	*Set of* 4	7·00	7·50

25 *Trogonoptera brookiana*   **26** Western Tarsier

(Recess; Arms typo B.W.)

1950 (3 Jan).   *T* **25/6** *and similar designs. Wmk Mult Script CA.*
P 11½ × 11 *(horiz) or* 11 × 11½ *(vert).*

171	1 c. black			..	30	30
172	2 c. red-orange		..	..	20	40
173	3 c. green	..			20	60
174	4 c. chocolate ..				20	20
175	6 c. turquoise-blue	..			20	15
176	8 c. scarlet	..			20	30
177	10 c. orange				50	3·50
178	12 c. violet	..			2·25	1·50
179	15 c. blue				1·00	15
180	20 c. purple-brown and red-orange			60	30
181	25 c. green and scarlet..			1·50	30
182	50 c. brown and violet..			1·75	15
183	$1 green and chocolate			14·00	2·75
184	$2 blue and carmine			23·00	12·00
185	$5 black, yellow, red and purple		19·00	12·00
171/85			Set of 15	55·00	30·00

Designs: *Horiz*—8 c. Dayak dancer; 10 c. Malayan Pangolin;
12 c. Kenyah boys; 15 c. Fire-making; 20 c. Kelemantan rice
barn; 25 c. Pepper vines; $1 Kelabit smithy; $2 Map of Sarawak;
$5 Arms of Sarawak. *Vert*—3 c. Kayan tomb; 4 c. Kayan girl and
boy; 6 c. Bead work; 50 c. Iban woman.

40 Map of Sarawak

(Recess B.W.)

1952 (1 Feb).   *Wmk Mult Script CA. P* 11½ × 11.
186   **40**   10 c. orange   85   40

JAPANESE OCCUPATION OF SARAWAK

Japanese forces landed in North Borneo on 16 December 1941
and Sarawak was attacked on 23 December 1941.

Brunei, North Borneo, Sarawak and after a short period
Labuan, were administered as a single territory by the
Japanese. Until September–October 1942, previous stamp
issues, without overprint, continued to be used in conjunction
with existing postmarks. From 1 October 1942 onwards
unoverprinted stamps of Japan were made available and
examples can be found used from the area for much of the
remainder of the War. Japanese Occupation issues for Brunei,
North Borneo and Sarawak were equally valid throughout the
combined territory but not, in practice, equally available.

南 方 国 泉 本 日 大

(1)
("Imperial Japanese Government")

1942 (Oct).   *Stamps of Sarawak handstamped with T* **1** *in
violet.*

J 1	**21**	1 c. purple	..	..	..	32·00	60·00
		a. Pair, one without opt	..	·· £1100
J 2		2 c. green	..	..	..	80·00	£140
		a. Black opt ..		..	·· 80·00
J 3		2 c. black		..	..	75·00	85·00
		a. Black opt ..		..	·· 95·00	£110
J 4		3 c. black	..	..	..	£250	£250
J 5		3 c. green	..	..	..	42·00	70·00
		a. Black opt ..		..	·· 75·00
J 6		4 c. bright purple	..	..	50·00	70·00
		a. Black opt ..		..	·· 75·00
J 7		5 c. violet	..	..	..	60·00	70·00
		a. Black opt ..		..	·· 75·00
J 8		6 c. carmine	..	..	..	90·00	95·00
J 9		6 c. lake-brown	..	..	60·00	70·00
		a. Black opt ..		..	·· 75·00	85·00
J10		8 c. red-brown	..	..	..	£200	£225
		a. Black opt ..		..	·· £325
J11		8 c. carmine	..	..	..	75·00	£110
		a. Black opt ..		..	·· £160	£180
J12		10 c. scarlet	..	..	..	55·00	75·00
		a. Black opt ..		..	·· 75·00
J13		12 c. blue	..	..	..	£120	£130
		a. Black opt ..		..	·· £160
J14		12 c. orange	..	..	..	£120	£140
J15		15 c. orange	..	..	..	£250	£250
		a. Black opt ..		..	·· £275
J16		15 c. blue	..	..	..	80·00	85·00
J17		20 c. olive-green and carmine	..	45·00	75·00
		a. Black opt ..		..	·· 75·00
J18		25 c. violet and orange	..	..	75·00	75·00
		a. Black opt ..		..	·· 85·00
J19		30 c. red-brown and violet	..	50·00	80·00
		a. Black opt ..		..	·· 75·00
J20		50 c. violet and scarlet	..	..	60·00	80·00
		a. Black opt ..		..	·· £160
		b. Blue opt ..		..	·· £275
J21		$1 scarlet and sepia	..	..	75·00	95·00
		a. Blue opt ..		..	·· £170
J22		$2 bright purple and violet	..	..	£160	£190
		a. Blue opt ..		..	·· £225
J23		$3 carmine and green	..	..	£850	£950
		a. Black opt ..		..	·· £1300
J24		$4 blue and scarlet	..	..	£180	£250
J25		$5 scarlet and red-brown	..	£180	£250
J26		$10 black and yellow	..	..	£180	£250

The overprint, being handstamped, exists inverted or double
on some values.

Stamps of T **21** optd with Japanese symbols within an oval
frame are revenue stamps, while the same stamps overprinted
with three Japanese characters between two vertical double
rules, were used as seals.

Nos. J1/26 have been extensively forged. Recent research
indicates that complete or part sets on cover cancelled by
Japanese circular postmarks in violet dated "17 11 21" (21 Nov
1942) or "18 3 1" (1 Mar 1943) have forged overprints.

Seychelles

100 cents = 1 Mauritius rupee

CROWN COLONY

1937 (12 May). *Coronation. As Nos. 118/20 of Jamaica, but ptd by B.W. P* 11×11½.

132	6 c. sage-green			35	15
133	12 c. orange			50	30
134	20 c. blue			70	65
132/4			Set of 3	1·40	1·00
132/4 Perf "Specimen"		Set of 3	55·00	

14 Coco-de-mer Palm

15 Giant Tortoise

16 Fishing Pirogue

"Handkerchief" on oar flaw (R. 6/2)

(Photo Harrison)

1938 (1 Jan)–**49.** *Wmk Mult Script CA. Chalk-surfaced paper. P* 14½×13½ (*vert*) *or* 13½×14½ (*horiz*).

135	14	2 c. purple-brown (10.2.38)			1·00	40
		a. Ordinary paper (18.11.42)			30	90
136	15	3 c. green			7·00	1·25
136a		3 c. orange (8.8.41)			1·25	50
		ab. Ordinary paper (18.11.42)		55	1·50
137	16	6 c. orange			7·00	2·50
137a		6 c. greyish green (8.8.41)		3·50	70
		aw. Wmk inverted			£450	
		b. Ordinary paper. *Green* (18.11.42)	55	1·25
		c. *Green* (5.4.49)		2·75	75
138	14	9 c. scarlet (10.2.38)			10·00	2·00

138a	14	9 c. grey-blue (8.8.41)			5·00	40
		ab. Ordinary paper (18.11.42)		6·50	1·25
		ac. Ordinary paper. *Dull bl* (19.11.45)	4·00	1·75
		ad. *Dull blue* (5.4.49)		10·00	6·00
		aw. Wmk inverted			
139	15	12 c. reddish violet			38·00	1·25
139a		15 c. brown-carmine (8.8.41)		6·00	30
		ab. Ordinary paper. *Brn-red* (18.11.42)	3·75	1·75
139c	14	18 c. carmine-lake (8.8.41)		6·00	60
		ca. Ordinary paper (18.11.42)		3·25	1·50
		cb. *Rose-carmine* (5.4.49)		10·00	9·00
140	16	20 c. blue			42·00	5·00
140a		20 c. brown-ochre (8.8.41)		4·75	45
		ab. Ordinary paper (18.11.42)		2·50	1·75
		ac. "Handkerchief" flaw		£100	
141	14	25 c. brown-ochre			60·00	14·00
142	15	30 c. carmine (10.2.38)		60·00	9·00
142a		30 c. blue (8.8.41)			4·75	50
		ab. Ordinary paper (18.11.42)		1·75	2·50
143	16	45 c. chocolate (10.2.38)		10·00	1·25
		a. Ordinary paper. *Pur-brn* (18.11.42)	1·75	1·75
		b. *Purple-brown* (5.4.49)		11·00	9·50
144	14	50 c. deep reddish violet (10.2.38)	4·25	60
		a. Ordinary paper (18.11.42)		1·00	2·25
144b		50 c. bright lilac (13.6.49)		80	1·50
145	15	75 c. slate-blue (10.2.38)		85·00	38·00
145a		75 c. deep slate-lilac (8.8.41)		6·50	1·50
		ab. Ordinary paper (18.11.42)		1·25	2·25
146	16	1 r. yellow-green (10.2.38)		£100	48·00
146a		1 r. grey-black (8.8.41)		8·00	85
		ab. Ordinary paper (18.11.42)		1·25	2·25
147	14	1 r. 50, ultramarine (10.2.38)		15·00	1·50
		a. Ordinary paper (18.11.42)		4·50	5·00
		aw. Wmk inverted			£1200	
148	15	2 r. 25, olive (10.2.38)		19·00	4·00
		a. Ordinary paper (18.11.42)		10·00	12·00
149	16	5 r. red (10.2.38)			8·00	3·25
		a. Ordinary paper (18.11.42)		12·00	16·00
135/49			Set of 25	£400	£120
135/49 (*excl* No. 144b) Perf "Specimen"	Set of 24	£375	

Lamp on mast flaw (R. 1/5)

1946 (23 Sept). *Victory. As Nos. 141/2 of Jamaica.*

150	9 c. light blue				10	10
151	30 c. deep blue				10	10
	a. Lamp on mast flaw			18·00	
150/1 Perf "Specimen"		Set of 2	50·00	

Line by crown (R. 1/3)

1948 (5 Nov). *Royal Silver Wedding. As Nos.* 143/4 *of Jamaica.*
152	9 c. ultramarine	..	..	..	..	15	25
	a. Line by crown		..	..	.. 18·00		
153	5 r. carmine	..	..	..	.. 11·00	22·00	

1949 (10 Oct). *75th Anniv of U.P.U. As Nos.* 145/8 *of Jamaica, but inscribed* "SEYCHELLES" *in recess.*
154	18 c. bright reddish purple	..	..	..	30	15
155	50 c. purple	..	..	..	.. 1·50	50
156	1 r. grey	..	..	·.	.. 40	15
157	2 r. 25, olive	..		..	.. 50	60
154/7	..	..	..	.. *Set of* 4	2·50	1·25

17 Sailfish   18 Map of Indian Ocean

(Photo Harrison)

1952 (3 Mar). *Various designs as T* **14/16** *but with new portrait and crown as in T* **17/18**. *Chalk-surfaced paper. Wmk Mult Script CA. P* 14½ × 13½ *(vert) or* 13½ × 14½ *(horiz).*
158	17	2 c. lilac	..		..	50	70
		a. Error. Crown missing, W 9a		..	£400	
		b. Error. St. Edward's Crown, W 9b	..	£110	
159	15	3 c. orange	..	..	..	50	30
		a. Error. Crown missing, W 9a		..	£350	
		b. Error. St. Edward's Crown, W 9b	..	£110	
160	14	9 c. chalky blue	..	..	..	50	1·25
		a. Error. Crown missing, W 9a		..	£550	
		b. Error. St. Edward's Crown, W 9b	..	£190	
161	16	15 c. deep yellow-green	..	..	40	75
		a. Error. Crown missing, W 9a		..	£450	
		b. Error. St. Edward's Crown, W 9b	..	£190	
162	18	18 c. carmine-lake	..	..	..	85	20
		a. Error. Crown missing, W 9a		..	£550	
		b. Error. St. Edward's Crown, W 9b	..	£275	
163	16	20 c. orange-yellow	..	..	90	60
		a. Error. Crown missing, W 9a		..	£600	
		b. Error. St. Edward's Crown, W 9b	..	£325	

164	15	25 c. vermilion	..	..	..	70	80
		a. Error. Crown missing, W 9a		..	£700	
		b. Error. St. Edward's Crown, W 9b	..	£300	
165	17	40 c. ultramarine	..	..	..	70	90
		a. Error. Crown missing, W 9a		..	£700	
		b. Error. St. Edward's Crown, W 9b	..	£375	
166	16	45 c. purple-brown	..	..	70	30
		a. Error. Crown missing, W 9a		..	£800	
		b. Error. St. Edward's Crown, W 9b	..	£400	
167	14	50 c. reddish violet	..	..	1·25	60
		a. Error. Crown missing, W 9a		..	£850	
		b. Error. St. Edward's Crown, W 9b	..	£400	
168	18	1 r. grey-black	..	..	..	2·50	2·00
		b. Error. St. Edward's Crown, W 9b	..	£700	
169	14	1 r. 50, blue	..	..	..	5·50	10·00
		b. Error. St. Edward's Crown, W 9b	..	£950	
170	15	2 r. 25, brown-olive	..	..	8·00	10·00
		b. Error. St. Edward's Crown, W 9b	..	£800	
171	18	5 r. red	..	..	..	8·50	12·00
		b. Error. St. Edward's Crown, W 9b	..	£700	
172	17	10 r. green	..	..	..	16·00	26·00
158/72		..	..	..	.. *Set of* 15	42·00	60·00

See *Introduction* re the watermark errors.

POSTAGE DUE STAMPS

D 1

(Frame recess, value typo B.W.)

1951 (1 Mar). *Wmk Mult Script CA. P* 11½.
D1	D 1	2 c. scarlet and carmine	..	..	80	1·50
D2		3 c. scarlet and green	..	..	2·00	1·50
D3		6 c. scarlet and bistre	..	..	2·00	1·25
D4		9 c. scarlet and orange	..	..	2·00	1·75
D5		15 c. scarlet and violet	..	..	1·75	11·00
D6		18 c. scarlet and blue	..	..	1·75	11·00
D7		20 c. scarlet and brown	..	..	1·75	11·00
D8		30 c. scarlet and claret	..	..	1·75	7·50
D1/8	..	..	..	..	*Set of* 8	12·50	42·00

Sierra Leone

12 pence (d) = 1 shilling; 20 shillings = 1 pound

CROWN COLONY

1937 (12 May). *Coronation. As Nos.* 118/20 *of Jamaica, but ptd by B.W.*

185	1d. orange				70	50
186	2d. purple				90	50
187	3d. blue				1·50	3·25
185/7				*Set of 3*	2·75	3·75
185/7 Perf "Specimen"			*Set of 3*	55·00	

30 Freetown from the Harbour

31 Rice Harvesting

(Recess Waterlow)

1938 (1 May)**–44.** *Wmk Mult Script CA (sideways). P* 12½.

188	**30**	½d. black and blue-green		15	30
189		1d. black and lake		40	40
		a. Imperf between (vert pair)		†	—

190	**31**	1½d. scarlet			20·00	70
190a		1½d. mauve (1.2.41)			30	60
191		2d. mauve			40·00	1·75
191a		2d. scarlet (1.2.41)			30	1·00
192	**30**	3d. black and ultramarine			40	40
193		4d. black and red-brown (20.6.38)		80	2·75
194	**31**	5d. olive-green (20.6.38)		5·00	3·50
195		6d. grey (20.6.38)			75	40
196	**30**	1s. black and olive-green (20.6.38)	1·50	50
196a	**31**	1s. 3d. yellow-orange (1.7.44)		40	40
197	**30**	2s. black and sepia (20.6.38)		4·50	2·00
198	**31**	5s. red-brown (20.6.38)		10·00	5·00
199		10s. emerald-green (20.6.38)		16·00	7·50
200	**30**	£1 deep blue (20.6.38)		17·00	18·00
188/200			*Set of* 16	£100	38·00
188/200 Perf "Specimen"		*Set of* 16	£250	

1946 (1 Oct). *Victory. As Nos.* 141/2 *of Jamaica.*

201	1½d. lilac				20	10
202	3d. ultramarine				20	10
201/2 Perf "Specimen"			*Set of* 2	55·00	

1948 (1 Dec). *Royal Silver Wedding. As Nos.* 143/4 *of Jamaica.*

203	1½d. bright purple				15	15
204	£1 indigo				16·00	16·00

1949 (10 Oct). *75th Anniv of U.P.U. As Nos.* 145/8 *of Jamaica.*

205	1½d. purple				20	50
206	3d. deep blue				1·25	2·50
207	6d. grey				35	2·75
208	1s. olive				35	1·00
205/8				*Set of* 4	1·90	6·00

Singapore

100 cents = 1 Malayan dollar

CROWN COLONY

Stamps in the Crown Colony Victory design with face values of 8 c. and 15 c. were prepared for Singapore in 1946, but were not issued.

(Typo D.L.R.)

1948 (1 Sept)–**52**. *As T* **58** *of Malaysia* (*Straits Settlements*), *but inscribed* "SINGAPORE" *at foot. Wmk Mult Script CA. Chalk-surfaced paper.* (*a*) *P* 14.

1	1 c. black	..	..	..	15	60
2	2 c. orange	..	..	..	15	30
3	3 c. green	..	..	..	50	50
4	4 c. brown	..	..	..	20	75
5	6 c. grey	..	..	..	40	50
6	8 c. scarlet (1.10.48)	..	..	..	30	50
7	10 c. purple	..	..	..	20	10
8	15 c. ultramarine (1.10.48)	..	..	8·50	10
9	20 c. black and green (1.10.48)	..	..	3·50	20
10	25 c. purple and orange (1.10.48)	..	..	4·25	15
11	40 c. red and purple (1.10.48) ..	..	..	8·00	5·00
12	50 c. black and blue (1.10.48) ..	..	..	3·25	10
13	$1 blue and purple (1.10.48)	..	..	10·00	2·00
14	$2 green and scarlet (25.10.48)	..	..	48·00	3·25
15	$5 green and brown (1.10.48)	..	..	£120	4·50
1/15	.. ..	*Set of* 15	£180	16·00

(*b*) *P* 17½×18

16	1 c. black (21.5.52)	..	..	..	60	2·75
17	2 c. orange (31.10.49)	..	..	..	70	80
19	4 c. brown (1.7.49)	..	..	..	80	10
19a	5 c. bright purple (1.9.52)	..	..	2·50	90
21	6 c. grey (10.12.52)	..	..	1·25	75
21a	8 c. scarlet (1.9.52)	..	..	4·00	3·00
22	10 c. purple (9.2.50)	..	..	50	10
22a	12 c. scarlet (1.9.52)	..	..	4·50	6·50
23	15 c. ultramarine (9.2.50) ..	..	..	12·00	10
24	20 c. black and green (31.10.49)	..	..	3·25	2·50

24a	20 c. bright blue (1.9.52)	..	..	..	4·00	10
25	25 c. purple and orange (9.2.50)	..	..	80	10
25a	35 c. scarlet and purple (1.9.52)	..	..	4·00	90
26	40 c. red and purple (4.5.51*)	..	..	30·00	11·00
27	50 c. black and blue (9.2.50)	..	..	7·50	10
28	$1 blue and purple (31.10.49)	..	..	13·00	20
	a. Error. St. Edward's Crown, W **9***b*	..	£4750	
29	$2 green and scarlet (24.5.51)	..	..	90·00	1·75
	a. Error. St. Edward's Crown. W **9***b*	..	£4750	
	w. Wmk inverted	..	..		
30	$5 green and brown (19.12.51)	..	..	£180	1·75
	w. Wmk inverted	..	..		
16/30	.. ..	*Set of* 18	£325	29·00

*Earliest known postmark date.

Single-colour values were from single plate printings (Die I) and all bi-colour, except the 25 c., from separate head and duty plates (Die I). For differences between the Dies see after Nos. 278/98 of Malaysia (Straits Settlements). The 25 c. is unique in this series in that it combines a Die II frame with a separate head plate.

Nos. 28a and 29a occur on rows in the watermark in which the crowns and letters "CA" alternate.

Postal forgeries of the 50 c., $1 and $2 exist on unwatermarked paper and perforated 14×14½.

1948 (25 Oct). *Royal Silver Wedding. As Nos.* 143/4 *of Jamaica.*

31	10 c. violet	..	..	..	75	50
32	$5 brown	..	..	..	£110	30·00

1949 (10 Oct). *75th Anniv of U.P.U. As Nos.* 145/8 *of Jamaica.*

33	10 c. purple	..	..	..	75	30
34	15 c. deep blue ..	..	..	..	6·00	2·25
35	25 c. orange	..	..	..	4·50	2·25
36	50 c. blue-black	..	..	..	6·00	3·00
33/6	.. ..	*Set of* 4	17·00	7·00

Somaliland Protectorate

1937. 12 pies = 1 anna; 16 annas = 1 rupee
1951. 100 cents = 1 shilling

PROTECTORATE

1937 (13 May).   *Coronation. As Nos.* 118/20 *of Jamaica.*
90	1 a. scarlet		15	20
91	2 a. grey-black		55	1·25
92	3 a. bright blue		70	55
90/2		*Set of* 3	1·25	1·75
90/2 Perf "Specimen"		*Set of* 3	55·00	

6 Berbera Blackhead
Sheep

7 Lesser Kudu

8 Somaliland Protectorate

(Des H. W. Claxton. Recess Waterlow)

1938 (10 May).   *Portrait to left. Wmk Mult Script CA. P* 12½.
93	**6**	½ a. green	30	4·00
94		1 a. scarlet	30	1·00
95		2 a. maroon	70	1·00
96		3 a. bright blue	7·00	8·50
97	**7**	4 a. sepia	4·00	6·00
98		6 a. violet	4·75	11·00
99		8 a. grey	1·00	11·00
100		12 a. red-orange	4·00	12·00
101	**8**	1 r. green	8·50	38·00
102		2 r. purple	14·00	38·00
103		3 r. bright blue	18·00	26·00
104		5 r. black	18·00	26·00
		a. Imperf between (horiz pair)	£12000	
93/104		*Set of* 12	70·00	£160
93/104 Perf "Specimen"		*Set of* 12	£150	

Examples of most values are known showing a forged Berbera
postmark dated "15 AU 38".

> Following the Italian Occupation, from 19 August 1940
> until 16 March 1941, the stamps of ADEN were used at
> Berbera from 1 July 1941 until 26 April 1942.

9 Berbera
Blackhead Sheep

5 Cents
(10)

1 Shilling
(11)

(Recess Waterlow)

1942 (27 Apr).   *As T* **6/8** *but with full-face portrait of King George*
VI, as in T **9**. *Wmk Mult Script CA. P* 12½.
105	**9**	½ a. green	20	30
106		1 a. scarlet	20	10
107		2 a. maroon	40	20
108		3 a. bright blue	1·25	20
109	**7**	4 a. sepia	2·00	20
110		6 a. violet	2·25	20
111		8 a. grey	1·75	20
112		12 a. red-orange	2·75	30
113	**8**	1 r. green	1·25	40
114		2 r. purple	1·25	4·00
115		3 r. bright blue	1·75	7·00
116		5 r. black	6·00	5·00
105/16		*Set of* 12	19·00	16·00
105/16 Perf "Specimen"		*Set of* 12	£150	

1946 (15 Oct).   *Victory. As Nos.* 141/2 *of Jamaica. P* 13½×14.
117	1 a. carmine		10	10
	a. Perf 13½		10·00	45·00
118	3 a. blue		10	10
117/18 Perf "Specimen"		*Set of* 2	48·00	

1949 (28 Jan).   *Royal Silver Wedding. As Nos.* 143/4 *of*
Jamaica.
119	1 a. scarlet		10	10
120	5 r. black		3·50	3·25

1949 (10 Oct).   *75th Anniv of U.P.U. As Nos.* 145/8 *of Jamaica.*
Surch with face values in annas.
121	1 a. on 10 c. carmine		30	15
122	3 a. on 30 c. deep blue (R.)		75	50
123	6 a. on 50 c. purple		40	50
124	12 a. on 1s. red-orange		55	50
121/4		*Set of* 4	1·75	1·50

(New Currency. 100 cents = 1 shilling)

1951 (1 Apr).   *1942 issue surch as T* **10/11**.
125	5 c. on ½ a. green		20	50
126	10 c. on 2 a. maroon		20	30
127	15 c. on 3 a. bright blue		60	30
128	20 c. on 4 a. sepia		80	20
129	30 c. on 6 a. violet		90	30
130	50 c. on 8 a. grey		90	20
131	70 c. on 12 a. red-orange		1·50	2·75
132	1 s. on 1 r. green		60	20
133	2 s. on 2 r. purple		3·50	9·00
134	2 s. on 3 r. bright blue		3·75	2·50
135	5 s. on 5 r. black (R.)		4·50	4·25
125/35		*Set of* 11	15·00	19·00

South Africa

12 pence = 1 shilling; 20 shillings = 1 pound

PRICES for Nos. 54/135 are for unused horizontal pairs, used horizontal pairs and used singles (either inscription), *unless otherwise indicated.* Vertical pairs are worth 50% of those prices quoted for horizontal pairs.

22 Gold Mine

22*a* Groot Schuur

6 Springbok

7 *Dromedaris*
(Van Riebeeck's ship)

Dies of 6d.

I

II

III

8 Orange Tree   **9**

23 Groot Constantia

11 Union Buildings, Pretoria

12*a* A Native Kraal

13 Black and Blue Wildebeest

"Falling ladder" flaw (R. 5/10)

14 Ox-wagon inspanned

15 Ox-wagon outspanned

1933–48. "SUID-AFRIKA" (*hyphenated*) *on Afrikaans stamps.* *W* **9.** *P* 15×14 (¹/₂*d.*, 1*d.* and 6*d.*) *or* 14 (*others*).

54	**6**	¹/₂d. grey and green (*wmk inverted*) (9.35)	. .	3·25	1·50	10
		aw. Wmk upright (1936)	. .	7·00	1·60	10
		b. Coil stamp. Perf 13¹/₂×14 (1935)	. .	30·00	50·00	1·00
		bw. Wmk upright	. .	30·00	50·00	1·00
		c. Booklet pane of 6 (with adverts on margins) (*wmk upright*)	. .	20·00		

56	7	1d. grey & car (*shades*) (19.4.34)	50	75	10
		a. Imperf (pair)	£140		
		b. Frame omitted (*single stamp*)	£250		
		cw. Wmk inverted	40	75	10
		d. Coil stamp. Perf 13½×14 (1935)	32·00	55·00	1·40
		dw. Wmk inverted	32·00	55·00	1·40
		e. Booklet pane of 6 (with adverts on margins) (1935)	11·00		
		f. Booklet pane of 6 (with blank margins) (1937) ..	12·00		
		h. Booklet pane of 6 (with postal slogans on margins) (1948)	4·00		
		i. *Grey & brt rose-carm* (7.48)	55	1·00	10
57	22	1½d. green & brt gold (12.11.36)	2·50	2·00	10
		a. Shading omitted from mine dump (in pair with normal)	£160	£140	
		bw. Wmk inverted	1·50	1·50	10
		c. *Blue-grn & dull gold* (8.40)	6·50	3·00	10
58	11	2d. blue and violet (11.38) ..	65·00	32·00	75
58a		2d. grey and dull purple (5.41)	40·00	65·00	1·25
59	22a	3d. ultramarine (2.40) ..	6·00	1·75	10
61	8	6d. green & vermilion (I) (10.37)	70·00	20·00	70
		a. "Falling ladder" flaw ..	£180		
61b		6d. green & vermilion (II) (6.38)	30·00	1·00	10
61c		6d. grn & red-orge (III) (11.46)	14·00	75	10
62	13	1s. brown & chalky blue (2.39)	42·00	8·50	10
		a. Frame omitted (*single stamp*)	£1900		
64	15	5s. black and green (10.33) ..	55·00	55·00	1·75
		aw. Wmk inverted	£110	£100	3·00
		b. *Black and blue-green* (9.44)	33·00	15·00	35
64c	23	10s. blue and sepia (8.39) ..	65·00	14·00	70
		ca. *Blue & blackish brn* (8.39)	42·00	5·50	30
54/9, 61c/64ca		*Set of* 10	£225	£110	2·50

The ½d. and 1d. coil stamps may be found in blocks emanating from the residue of the large rolls which were cut into sheets and distributed to Post Offices.

Nos. 54 and 56 also exist in coils.

1d. Is printed from Type II. Frames of different sizes exist due to reductions made from time to time for the purpose of providing more space for the perforations.

3d. In No. 59 the frame is unscreened and composed of solid lines. Centre is diagonally screened. Scrolls above "3d." are clear lined, light in the middle and dark at sides.

6d. Die I. Green background lines faint. "SUID-AFRIKA" 16¼ mm long.
Die II. Green background lines heavy. "SUID-AFRIKA" 17 mm long. "S" near end of tablet. Scroll open.
Die III. Scroll closed up and design smaller (18 × 22 mm).

Single specimens of the 1933–48 issue inscribed in English may be distinguished from those of 1930–45 as follows:—
½d. and 1d. Centres in grey instead of varying intensities of black.
2d. The letters of "SOUTH AFRICA" are narrower and thinner.
3d. The trees are taller and the sky is without lines.
6d. The frame is vermilion.
1s. The frame is chalky blue.
For similar designs, but printed in screened rotogravure, see Nos. 114 to 122a.

BOOKLET PANES. Booklets issued in 1935 contained ½d. and 1d. stamps with advertisements in the top and bottom margins and no margin at right (Nos. 54b and 56d). These were replaced in 1937 by editions showing blank margins on all four sides (Nos. 56e and 75ba). Following a period when the booklet panes were without margins, a further 3s. booklet was issued in 1948 which had four margins on the panes and postal slogans at top and bottom (Nos. 56h, 87b and 114a).

25

25a

"Mouse" flaw (R. 4/1)

(Des J. Prentice)

1937 (12 May). *Coronation.* W **9** (*sideways**). P 14.

71	25	½d. grey-black and blue-green ..	50	70	10
		w. Wmk horns pointing to left	50	70	10
72		1d. grey-black and carmine ..	50	50	10
		w. Wmk horns pointing to left	50	50	10
73		1½d. orange and greenish blue ..	50	50	10
		a. "Mouse" flaw	5·00		
		w. Wmk horns pointing to left	50	50	10
74		3d. ultramarine	2·00	2·25	10
		w. Wmk horns pointing to left	2·00	2·25	10
75		1s. red-brown and turquoise-blue	3·50	4·25	15
		a. Hyphen on Afrikaans stamp omitted (R. 2/13) ..	45·00		
		w. Wmk horns pointing to left	3·50	4·25	15
71/5		.. .. .. *Set of* 5	6·00	7·50	40

*The normal sideways watermark shows the horns of the springbok pointing to the right, *as seen from the back of the stamp.*

No. 75a shows the hyphen completely omitted and the top of the "K" damaged. A less distinct flaw, on which part of the hyphen is still visible and with no damage to the "K", occurs on R. 4/17.

"Tick" flaw on ear and spot on nose (multipositive flaw occurring in 1947) (R. 3/4, or 3/1 on some ptgs of No. 114)

1937–40. W **9**. P 15×14.

75b	25a	½d. grey and green	7·50	90	10
		ba. Booklet pane of 6 (with blank margins) (1937)	42·00		
		bd. *Grey and blue-green* (1940)	5·50	90	10
		be. "Tick" flaw and spot on nose	50·00		

The lines of shading in T **25a** are all horizontal and thicker than in T **6**. In Nos. 75b and 75bd the design is composed of solid lines. For stamps with designs composed of dotted lines, see No. 114. Later printings of No. 75bd have a smaller design.

26 Voortrekker Ploughing

27 Wagon crossing Drakensberg

28 Signing of Dingaan–Retief Treaty

32 Old Vicarage, Paarl,   33 Symbol of the Reformation
now a museum

29 Voortrekker Monument

(Des W. Coetzer and J. Prentice)

1938 (14 Dec).   *Voortrekker Centenary Memorial Fund. W* **9.** *P* 14
(*Nos.* 76/7) *or* 15 × 14 (*others*).
76 **26**   ¹/₂d. + ¹/₂d. blue and green   .. 10·00   4·00   30
77 **27**   1d. + 1d. blue and carmine   .. 11·00   5·00   40
78 **28**   1¹/₂d. + 1¹/₂d. chocolate & blue-grn 15·00   9·50   80
79 **29**   3d. + 3d. bright blue   ..   .. 17·00 11·00   1·00
76/9   ..   ..   ..   *Set of* 4 48·00 27·00   2·25

34 Huguenot Dwelling, Drakenstein
Mountain Valley

(Des J. Prentice)

1939 (17 July).   *250th Anniv of Huguenot Landing in South Africa
and Huguenot Commemoration Fund. W* **9.** *P* 14 (*Nos.* 82/3) *or*
15 × 14 (*No.* 84).
82 **32**   ¹/₂d. + ¹/₂d. brown and green   .. 4·75   6·00   30
83 **33**   1d. + 1d. green and carmine   .. 11·00   6·50   30
84 **34**   1¹/₂d. + 1¹/₂d. blue-green and purple 26·00 13·00   1·00
82/4   ..   ..   ..   *Set of* 3 38·00 23·00   1·40

30 Wagon Wheel

34a Gold Mine

31 Voortrekker Family

1941 (Aug)–**48.**   *W* **9** (*sideways*). *P* 14 × 15.
87 **34a** 1¹/₂d. blue-grn   and   yellow-buff
             (*shades*)   80   40   10
          a. Yellow-buff (centre) omitted £1500
          b. Booklet   pane   of   6   (with
             postal   slogans   on   margins)
             (1948)   ..   ..   .. 3·50

Three bolts in wheel rim (R. 15/5)

(Des W. Coetzer and J. Prentice)

1938 (14 Dec).   *Voortrekker Commemoration. W* **9.** *P* 15×14.
80 **30**   1d. blue and carmine   .. 4·50   4·25   30
          a. Three bolts in wheel rim   .. 27·00
81 **31**   1¹/₂d. greenish blue and brown .. 6·50   4·25   30

35 Infantry   36 Nurse and   37 Airman
               Ambulance

38 Sailor, Destroyer   39 Women's Auxiliary Services
and Lifebelts

40 Artillery

41 Electric Welding

43 Infantry

44 Nurse

45 Airman

46 Sailor

42 Tank Corps

42a Signaller

47 Women's Auxiliary Services

48 Electric Welding

49 Heavy Gun in Concrete Turret

50 Tank Corps

"Stain" on uniform (R. 14/11)

Unit (*pair*)

Unit (*triplet*)

"Cigarette" flaw (R. 18/2)

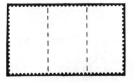

Apostrophe flaw (R. 19/1) (later corrected)

"Bursting Shell" (R. 11/20)

1941–46. *War Effort.* W **9** (*sideways on* 2*d.*, 4*d.*, 6*d.*). *P* 14 (2*d.*, 4*d.*, 6*d.*) *or* 15 × 14 (*others*). (*a*) *Inscr alternately.*

88	35	½d. green (19.11.41)	..	1·50	1·75	10
		a. Blue-green (7.42) ..	..	3·50	2·25	10
89	36	1d. carmine (3.10.41) ..	..	2·00	1·75	10
		a. "Stain" on uniform flaw	..	20·00		
90	37	1½d. myrtle-green (12.1.42)	..	1·50	1·25	10
91	39	3d. blue (1.8.41)	..	20·00	25·00	50
		a. "Cigarette" flaw	..	70·00		
92	40	4d. orange-brown (20.8.41)	..	19·00	14·00	15
		a. Red-brown (6.42) ..	..	35·00	32·00	1·25
93	41	6d. red-orange (3.9.41)	..	12·00	9·00	15
94	42a	1s. 3d. olive-brown (2.1.43)	..	12·00	6·50	20
		a. Blackish brown (5.46)	..	4·00	6·50	20

(*b*) *Inscr bilingually*

					Un	Us
					single	single
95	38	2d. violet (15.9.41) ..	..	..	90	30
96	42	1s. brown (27.10.41)	..	..	3·25	50
88/96	..	..	..	*Set of 7 pairs and 2 singles*	55·00	50·00

1942–44. *War Effort. Reduced sizes. In pairs perf* 14 (P) *or strips of three, perf* 15 × 14 (T), *subdivided by roulette* 6½. W **9** (*sideways* on* 3*d.*, 4*d. and* 1*s.*). (*a*) *Inscr alternately.*

				Un unit	Us unit	Us single
97	43	½d. blue-green (T) (10.42)	..	90	1·50	10
		a. Green (3.43) ..	..	2·75	2·00	10
		b. Greenish blue (7.44)	..	2·00	1·50	10
		c. Roulette omitted ..		£500		
98	44	1d. carmine-red (T) (5.1.43)	..	1·50	1·25	10
		a. Bright carmine (3.44)	..	1·00	1·00	10
		b. Both roulettes omitted	..	£425		
		ba. Left-hand roulette omitted		£550		

99	**45**	1½d. red-brown (P) (9.42)	..	65	1·50	10
		a. Roulette 13 (8.42) ..	..	1·50	4·00	15
		b. Roulette omitted ..	..	£225	£250	
100	**46**	2d. violet (P) (2.43) ..	..	90	1·75	10
		a. Reddish violet (6.43)	..	1·50	65	10
		b. Roulette omitted ..	..	£400		
		c. Apostrophe flaw ..	..	50·00		
101	**47**	3d. blue (T) (10.42) ..	..	7·00	15·00	10
102	**48**	6d. red-orange (P) (10.42)	..	2·00	1·60	10

(b) *Inscr bilingually*

103	**49**	4d. slate-green (T) (10.42)	..	18·00	6·50	10
104	**50**	1s. brown (P) (11.42) ..	..	15·00	3·25	10
		a. "Bursting shell" ..	..	60·00		
97/104		.. .. ..	*Set of* 8	40·00	27·00	65

*The sideways watermark shows springbok horns pointing to left on the 3d. and 1s., and to right on the 4d., *all as seen from the back of the stamp.*

52

53

1943. *Coil stamps. Redrawn. In single colours with plain back-ground.* W **9.** P 15 × 14.

				Un	Used	Used
				pair	pair	single
105	**52**	½d. blue-green (18.2.43)	..	1·25	3·75	20
106	**53**	1d. carmine (9.43) ..	..	2·25	3·00	15

Quoted prices are for *vertical* pairs.

54 Union Buildings, Pretoria

1945–46. *Redrawn.* W **9.** P 14.

107	**54**	2d. slate and violet (3.45)	..	10·00	2·50	10
		a. Slate & brt vio (shades) (10.46)	2·50	7·50	15

In Nos. 107 and 107a the Union Buildings are shown at a different angle from Nos. 58 and 58a. Only the centre is screened i.e., composed of very small square dots of colour arranged in straight diagonal lines. For whole design screened and colours changed, see No. 116. No. 107a also shows "2" of "2d." clear of white circle at top.

55 "Victory"

56 "Peace"

57 "Hope"

1945 (3 Dec). *Victory.* W **9.** P 14.

108	**55**	1d. brown and carmine..	..	20	80	10
109	**56**	2d. slate-blue and violet	..	20	85	10
110	**57**	3d. deep blue and blue ..	..	20	1·25	10
108/10		.. .. ..	*Set of* 3	55	2·75	25

58 King George VI

59 King George VI and Queen Elizabeth

60 Queen Elizabeth II as Princess, and Princess Margaret

"Bird" on "2" (Cyl 6912 R. 10/6)

(Des J. Prentice)

1947 (17 Feb). *Royal Visit.* W **9.** P 15 × 14.

111	**58**	1d. black and carmine	..	..	10	10	10
112	**59**	2d. violet..	..	..	15	30	10
		a. "Bird" on "2" flaw	..	..	2·50		
113	**60**	3d. blue ..	..	..	15	30	10
111/13		.. .. ..	*Set of* 3	35	60	20

"Flying saucer" flaw (Cyl 17 R. 17/2)

I
II
5s.

1947–54. "SUID-AFRIKA" *hyphenated on Afrikaans stamps.*
Printed from new cylinders with design in screened
rotogravure. W 9. P 15×14 (¹/₂d., 1d. and 6d.) *or* 14 (*others*).

114	**25**a	¹/₂d. grey and green (frame only screened) (1947)	90	2·00	10
		a. Booklet pane of 6 (with postal slogans on margins) (1948)	3·00		
		b. "Tick" flaw and spot on nose	30·00		
		c. Entire design screened (2.49)	90	2·00	10
		ca. Booklet pane of 6 (with margin at right) (1951)	3·50		
115	**7**	1d. grey and carmine (1.9.50)	70	1·75	10
		a. Booklet pane of 6 (with margin at right) (1951)	4·00		
116	**54**	2d. slate-blue & purple (3.50)	1·00	5·00	10
117	**22**a	3d. dull blue (4.49)	2·00	4·25	10
117a		3d. blue (3.51)	2·50	3·50	10
		ab. "Flying saucer" flaw	22·00		
		b. *Deep blue* (1954)	60·00	55·00	3·50
118	**12**a	4d. brown (22.8.52)	1·50	6·00	10
119	**8**	6d. grn & red-orge (III) (1.50)	1·75	50	10
		a. *Grn & brn-orge* (III) (1951)	1·50	40	10
120	**13**	1s. brown & chalky blue (1.50)	10·00	6·00	10
		a. *Blackish brown & ultram* (4.52)	18·00	9·00	15
121	**14**	2s. 6d. green and brown (8.49)	10·00	26·00	85
122	**15**	5s. blk & pale bl-grn (I) (9.49)	45·00	55·00	1·00
122a		5s. blk & dp yell-grn (II) (1.54)	70·00	80·00	2·50
114/22		Set of 9	65·00	95·00	1·75

In screened rotogravure the design is composed of very small
squares of colour arranged in straight diagonal lines.

¹/₂d. Size 17³/₄ × 21³/₄ mm. Early printings have only the frame
screened.

1d. Size 18 × 22 mm. For smaller, redrawn design, see No. 135.

2d. For earlier issue with centre only screened, and in different
colours, see Nos. 107/a.

3d. No. 117. Whole stamp screened with irregular grain. Scrolls
above "3d." solid and toneless. Printed from two cylinders.

No. 117a/b. Whole stamp diagonally screened. Printed from one
cylinder. Clouds more pronounced.

4d. Two groups of white leaves below name tablet and a clear
white line down left and right sides of stamp.

61 Gold Mine

63 *Wanderer* (emigrant
ship) entering Durban

Extended rigging on mainmast (R. 14/2)

(Des J. Prentice)

1949 (2 May). *Centenary of Arrival of British Settlers in Natal.*
W 9. P 15 × 14.

127	**63**	1¹/₂d. claret	50	50	10
		a. Extended rigging	6·00		

64 Hermes

65 Wagons approaching
Bingham's Berg

62 King George VI and
Queen Elizabeth

1948 (1 Apr). W 9 (*sideways*). *In pair, perf* 14, *sub-divided by*
roulette 6¹/₂.

			Un unit of 4	Us unit single	Used
124	**61**	1¹/₂d. blue-green and yellow-buff	1·75	3·00	10

Serif on "C" (R. 1/1)

(Des J. Booysen and J. Prentice)

1948 (26 Apr). *Silver Wedding.* W 9. P 14.

			Un pair	Used pair	Used single
125	**62**	3d. blue and silver	50	50	10

"Lake" in East Africa (R. 2/19)

(Typo Government Printer, Pretoria)

1948 (July). W 9. P 14¹/₂ × 14.

126	**6**	¹/₂d. pale grey and blue-green	85	8·00	65

This was an economy printing made from the old plates of the
1926 issue for the purpose of using up a stock of cut paper. For the
original printing in black and green, see No. 30.

(Des J. Booysen and J. Prentice)

1949 (1 Oct). *75th Anniv of Universal Postal Union. As T* **64** *inscr*
"UNIVERSAL POSTAL UNION" *and* "WERELDPOSUNIE"
alternately. W 9 (*sideways*). P 14 × 15.

128	**64**	¹/₂d. blue-green	60	85	10
129		1¹/₂d. brown-red	60	85	10

130	64	3d. bright blue				1·00	1·40	10
		a. Serif on "C"				22·00		
		b. "Lake" in East Africa			22·00			
128/30				Set of 3	2·00	2·75		25

(Des W. Coetzer and J. Prentice)

1949 (1 Dec). *Inauguration of Voortrekker Monument, Pretoria.*
T 65 and similar horiz designs. W 9. P 15 × 14.

						Un single	Us single
131	1d. magenta					10	10
132	1½d. blue-green					10	10
133	3d. blue					15	15
131/3				Set of 3		30	30

Designs:—1½d. Voortrekker Monument, Pretoria; 3d. Bible, candle and Voortrekkers.

68 Union Buildings, Pretoria

1950 (Apr)–51. *W 9 (sideways). P 14 × 15.*

					Un pair	Used pair	Used single
134	68	2d. blue and violet			30	50	10
		a. Booklet panes of 6 (with margin at right) (1951)			4·00		

1951 (22 Feb). *As No. 115, but redrawn with the horizon clearly defined. Size reduced to 17¼ × 21¼ mm.*

135	7	1d. grey and carmine			95	1·75	10

STAMP BOOKLETS

1935. *Black on lemon cover. Advertisement on front cover. Stitched.*
SB9 2s. 6d. booklet containing two panes of six ½d. (No. 54c) and four panes of six 1d. (No. 56e), all with adverts on margins £100

1937. *Black on lemon cover. Advertisement on front cover. Stitched.*
SB10 2s. 6d. booklet containing two panes of six ½d. (No. 75ba) and four panes of six 1d. (No. 56f), all with blank margins £200

1937. *Machine vended booklets. Red cover. Stitched.*
SB11 6d. booklet containing four ½d. and 1d. (Nos. 75b, 56) in pairs .. .. 7·00

1938. *Machine vended booklets. Blue cover. Stitched.*
SB12 3d. booklet containing ½d. and 1d. (Nos. 75b, 56), each in pair .. .. 30·00

1938. *Black on buff cover. Union arms at top left with advertisement at foot. Stitched.*
SB13 2s. 6d. booklet containing twelve ½d. and twenty-four 1d. (Nos. 75b, 56) in blocks of 6 £300

1939. *Black on buff cover. Union arms centred at top with advertisement at foot. Stitched.*
SB14 2s. 6d. booklet containing twelve ½d. and twenty-four 1d. (Nos. 75b, 56) in blocks of 6 £150

1939–40. *Green on buff cover. Union arms centred at top with large advertisement at bottom left. Stitched.*
SB15 2s. 6d. booklet containing twelve ½d. and twenty-four 1d. (Nos. 75b, 56) in blocks of 6 £2500
  a. Blue on buff cover (1940) .. .. .. 70·00

1941. *Blue on buff cover as No. SB15. Stitched.*
SB17 2s. 6d. booklet containing twelve ½d. and 1d. (Nos. 75b, 56) in blocks of 6 and 1½d. (No. 57) in block of 4 .. .. £110

1948. *Black on buff cover. With advertisement. Stitched.*
SB18 3s. booklet containing two panes of six ½d., 1d. and 1½d. (Nos. 114a, 56h, 87b), all with postal slogans on margins, and pane of air mail labels .. .. 24·00

1951. *Black on buff cover. Stitched.*
SB19 3s. 6d. booklet containing two panes of six ½d., 1d. and 2d. (Nos. 114ca, 115a, 134a), each with margins at right .. .. .. 15·00

POSTAGE DUE STAMPS

D 2 D 3 D 4

2

Blunt "2" (R. 3/6, 8/6)

1932–42. *Type D 2 redrawn. W 9. P 15×14.*

		(a) Frame roto, value typo		
D22	½d. black and blue-green (1934)		2·75	1·75
	w. Wmk inverted		2·25	1·60
D23	2d. black and deep purple (10.4.33)		7·50	1·75
	w. Wmk inverted		8·50	1·75

		(b) Whole stamp roto		
D25	1d. black & carmine (wmk inverted) (3.34)	2·25	10
D26	2d. black and deep purple (1940)	..	22·00	10
	a. Thick double "2d." (R. 5/6, R. 18/2)	£190	20·00
	w. Wmk inverted		22·00	10
D27	3d. black and Prussian blue (3.8.32)	..	22·00	14·00
D28	3d. dp blue & black (wmk inverted) (1935)	7·00	30
	a. Indigo and milky blue (wmk inverted) (1942)	55·00	2·75
	w. Wmk upright		32·00	
D29	6d. green and brown-ochre (wmk inverted) (7.6.33)	25·00	9·00
	a. Green & brt orge (wmk inverted) (1938)	11·00	4·00
D22/9a			Set of 7	70·00	19·00

In No. D26 the value, when magnified, has the meshed appearance of a photogravure screen, whereas in No. D23 the black of the value is solid.

1943–44. *Inscr bilingually. Roto. W 9. In units of three, perf 15 × 14 subdivided by roulette 6½.*

				Un unit	Us unit	Us single
D30	D 3	½d. blue-green (1944) ..		10·00	35·00	30
D31		1d. carmine	..	9·50	5·50	10
D32		2d. dull violet	..	6·50	11·00	15
		a. Bright violet	..	16·00	42·00	65
D33		3d. indigo (1943)	..	48·00	80·00	1·25
D30/3 ..			Set of 4	65·00	£120	1·90

Split "D" (R. 7/5 on every fourth sheet)

1948–49. *New figure of value and capital "D". Whole stamp roto.*
*W **9**. P 15 × 14.*

D34	D **4**	¹/₂d. black and blue-green	6·00	10·00
D35		1d. black and carmine	10·00	5·50
D36		2d. black and violet (1949)	10·00	5·50
		a. Thick (double) "2D." (R. 15/5–6,		
		R. 16/5–6)	50·00	26·00
D37		3d. deep blue and blue	15·00	17·00
		a. Split "D"	£140	
D38		6d. green and bright orange (1949)	25·00	8·00
D34/8		*Set of 5*	60·00	42·00

1950–58. *As Type D **4**, but "SUID-AFRIKA" hyphenated. Whole stamp roto. W **9**. P 15 × 14.*

D39	1d. black and carmine (5.50)	70	30
D40	2d. black and violet (4.51)	50	20
	a. Thick (double) "2D." (R. 15/5–6,		
	R. 16/5–6)	8·00	7·00
	b. Black and reddish violet (12.52)	70	20
	ba. Thick (double) "2D."	8·00	7·00
	bb. Black (value) omitted	£1700	
D41	3d. deep blue and blue (5.50)	4·50	2·00
	a. Split "D"	80·00	
D42	4d. deep myrtle-green and emerald (2.58)	12·00	15·00
D43	6d. green and bright orange (3.50)	9·00	9·00
D44	1s. black-brown and purple-brown (2.58)	12·00	15·00
D39/44	*Set of 6*	32·00	38·00

No. D40bb occurs in horizontal pair with a normal.

OFFICIAL STAMPS

(O 2)

(Approximate measurements of the space between the two lines of overprint are quoted in millimetres, either in the set headings or after individual listings)

1930–47. *Nos. 42/4 and 47/9 ("SUIDAFRIKA" in one word) optd with Type O **2**.*

O12	**6**	¹/₂d. black and green (9¹/₂–12¹/₂ mm) (1931)	2·25	4·25	40
		a. Stop after "OFFISIEEL" on English inscr stamp	38·00	45·00	4·00
		b. Ditto, but on Afrikaans inscr stamp	32·00	40·00	3·50
		w. Wmk inverted (1934)	5·00	7·50	60
O13	**7**	1d. black & carm (I) (12¹/₂ mm)	4·50	4·50	55
		a. Stop after "OFFISIEEL" on English inscr stamp	42·00	48·00	4·00
		b. Ditto, but on Afrikaans inscr stamp	35·00	40·00	3·50
		cw. Wmk inverted (1931)	4·50	4·50	55
		d. On Type II (No. 43d) (12¹/₂–13¹/₂ mm) (1933)	12·00	9·00	90
		da. Opt double	£275	£300	
O14	**11**	2d. slate-grey and lilac (20¹/₂–22¹/₂ mm) (1931)	6·00	11·00	1·50
		w. Wmk inverted (1934)	50·00	85·00	8·00
O15		2d. blue and violet (20¹/₂–22¹/₂ mm) (1938)	£100	£100	9·00
O16	**8**	6d. green & orange (12¹/₂–13¹/₂ mm) (wmk inverted) (1931)	7·00	8·50	85
		a. Stop after "OFFISIEEL" on English inscr stamp	65·00	70·00	6·50
		b. Ditto, but on Afrikaans inscr stamp	55·00	60·00	5·50
		c. "OFFISIEEL" reading upwards (R. 17/12, 18/12, 19/12, 20/12) (1933)	£425		
		w. Wmk upright (1935)	50·00	75·00	7·00

O17	**13**	1s. brown and deep blue (19 mm) (wmk inverted) (1932)	45·00	80·00	8·50
		a. Lines of opt 21 mm apart (wmk inverted) (1933)	48·00	70·00	7·50
		ab. Twisted horn flaw	£225		
		aw. Wmk upright (1936)	60·00	£100	10·00
O18	**14**	2s. 6d. green and brown (17¹/₂–18¹/₂ mm) (1933)	75·00	£130	15·00
		a. Lines of opt 21 mm apart (1934)	48·00	75·00	8·50
		aw. Wmk inverted (1937)	£200		
O19		2s. 6d. blue and brown (19¹/₂–20 mm) (11.47)	32·00	70·00	6·50
		a. Diaeresis over second "E" of "OFFISIEEL" on Afrikaans inscr stamp (R. 6/2)	£750	£850	
		b. Ditto, but on English inscr stamp (R. 6/3)	£750	£850	

The stop varieties for the ¹/₂d., 1d. and 6d. occur on R. 9/10, 9/12, 19/10, 19/12 with English inscriptions and R. 5/3, 5/11, 8/12, 15/3, 15/11, 18/12 with Afrikaans on the 1930 and 1931 overprintings only.

(O 3)   (O 4)

1935–49. *Nos. 54, 56/8, 61/2 and 64a/b ("SUID-AFRIKA" hyphenated) optd.*

*(a) With Type O **2** (reading downwards with "OFFICIAL" at right)*

O20	**6**	¹/₂d. grey and green (12¹/₂ mm) (wmk inverted) (1936)	4·25	20·00	1·75
		w. Wmk upright (1937)	4·25	20·00	1·25
O21	**7**	1d. grey and carmine (11¹/₂–13 mm) (wmk inverted)	3·00	3·00	35
		aw. Wmk upright (1937)	1·75	2·00	20
		b. Bright & deep rose-carmine (No. 56i) (1949)	2·50	3·25	30
O22	**22**	1¹/₂d. green and bright gold (20 mm) (wmk inverted) (1937)	32·00	24·00	1·75
		aw. Wmk upright (1939)	22·00	16·00	80
		b. Blue-green and dull gold (No. 57c) (1941)	45·00	11·00	1·10
O23	**11**	2d. blue & violet (20 mm) (1939)	£100	23·00	2·25
O24	**8**	6d. green and vermilion (I) (11¹/₂–13 mm) (1937)	80·00	45·00	3·75
		a. "Falling ladder" flaw	£300		
		b. Die II (No. 61b) (1938)	10·00	12·00	1·25
		c. Die III. Green & red-orange (No. 61c) (11.47)	4·00	8·50	85
O25	**13**	1s. brown and chalky blue (20 mm) (1939)	75·00	30·00	2·25
		a. Diaeresis over second "E" of "OFFISIEEL" on both English and Afrikaans inscr stamps (1941)	£1200	£850	
		b. Ditto, but on English inscr stamp only (11.47)	£1100	£750	
O26	**15**	5s. black and blue-green (20 mm) (6.48)	55·00	£130	13·00
O27	**23**	10s. blue and blackish brown (No. 64ba) (20 mm) (6.48)	85·00	£190	23·00

*(b) With Type O **3** (reading downwards with "OFFICIAL" at left and 18–19 mm between lines of opt)*

O28	**15**	5s. black and blue-green (1940)	85·00	£110	12·00
O29	**23**	10s. blue and sepia (1940)	£350	£350	38·00

*(c) With Type O **4** (reading upwards with "OFFICIAL" at right and 18¹/₂ mm between lines of opt)*

O30	**11**	2d. grey and dull purple (No. 58a) (1941)	8·00	24·00	2·25

No. O25a first appeared in the 1941 overprinting where the variety occurs on stamps 5 and 6 of an unidentified row. The variety reappears in the November 1947 overprinting where the stamps involved are R. 6/1 and 2. No. 25b occurs on R. 6/3 of the same overprinting.

Horizontal rows of 6 of the 1s. exist with "OFFICIAL" twice on the first stamp and "OFFISIEEL" twice on the last stamp. Such rows are believed to come from two half sheets which were overprinted in 1947, but not placed into normal stock.

OFFICIAL	OFFISIEEL	OFFICIAL	OFFISIEEL
(O 5)		(O 6)	

1937–44. No. 75b (redrawn design) optd. (a) With Type O 2 (reading downwards with "OFFICIAL" at right and 11–12½ mm between lines of opt)

O31 **25a** ½d. grey and green .. .. 12·00 13·00 1·25
    a. Grey and blue-green (No. 75bd) (1944) .. .. 1·25 6·50 60

(b) With Type O 5 (reading up and down with "OFFICIAL" at left and diaeresis over the second "E" of "OFFISIEEL". 10 mm between lines of opt)

O32 **25a** ½d. grey and blue-green (No. 75bd) (1944) .. .. 22·00 21·00 2·00

1944–50. Nos. 87 and 134 optd. (a) With Type O 2 (reading downwards with "OFFICIAL" at right)

O33 **34a** 1½d. blue-green and yellow-buff (14½ mm) .. .. 2·50 9·00 80
    a. With diaeresis over second "E" of "OFFISIEEL" .. £350 £190
    b. Lines of opt 16½ mm apart (6.48) .. .. 2·25 7·50 50

(b) With Type O 6 (reading upwards with "OFFICIAL" at left and 16 mm between lines of opt)

O34 **34a** 1½d. bl-green & yell-buff (1949) 35·00 45·00 4·00
O35 **68** 2d. blue and violet (1950) .. £1600 £1900 £170

Two different formes were used to overprint Type 34a between 1944 and 1946. The first, applied to the left halves of sheets only, had a diaeresis over the second "E" of "OFFISIEEL" on all positions of the setting, except for R. 1/2, 2/2 and 3/2. The second form, from which the majority of the stamps came, was applied twice to overprint complete sheets, had no diaeresis.

1947 (Nov)–**49.** No. 107 optd with Type O 2 (reading downwards with "OFFICIAL" at right and 20 mm between lines of opt).

O36 **54** 2d. slate and violet .. .. 3·00 19·00 1·75
    a. With diaeresis over second "E" of "OFFISIEEL" (R. 1/5-6, 11/5-6) .. £300 £475
    b. Slate-purple and bright violet (No. 107a) (1949) .. .. 5·50 14·00 1·60

1949–50. Nos. 114 and 120 optd with Type O 2 (reading downwards with "OFFICIAL" at right).

O37 **25a** ½d. grey and green (11 mm) .. 1·60 7·50 70
O38 **13** 1s. brown and chalky blue (17½–18½ mm) (1950) .. 9·00 28·00 2·50

OFFISIEEL	OFFICIAL
	(O 7)

1950 (June)–**54.** Optd as Type O 7 using stereo blocks measuring either 10 (½d., 1d., 6d.), 14½ (1½d., 2d.) or 19 mm (others) between the lines of opt.

O39 **25a** ½d. grey and green (No. 114c) (6.51) .. .. 70 1·50 15
O41 **7** 1d. grey & bright rose-carmine (No. 56i) .. .. .. 1·00 5·50 50
O42 1d. grey & car (No. 115) (3.51) 1·00 3·00 20
O43 1d. grey & car (No. 135) (6.52) 90 2·00 20
O44 **34a** 1½d. blue-green and yellow-buff (No. 87) (3.51) .. .. 1·40 4·00 30
O45 **68** 2d. blue and violet (No. 134) 1·00 2·00 20
    a. Opt inverted .. £1200
O46 **8** 6d. green & red-orge (No. 119) 1·00 3·50 35
    a. Green and brown-orange (No. 119a) (6.51) .. 1·50 3·50 35
O47 **13** 1s. brn & chalky bl (No. 120) 5·50 18·00 2·00
    a. Blackish brown and ultram (No. 120a) (1.54) .. £150 £160 18·00
O48 **14** 2s. 6d. green & brn (No. 121) 8·50 35·00 3·50
O49 **15** 5s. black and blue-green (No. 64a) (3.51) .. £180 90·00 9·00
O50 5s. black and pale blue-green (I) (No. 122) (2.53) .. 60·00 75·00 6·50
    a. Black & deep yellow-green (II) (No. 122a) (1.54) .. 70·00 90·00 9·00
O51 **23** 10s. blue and blackish brown (No. 64ba) .. .. 70·00 £170 22·00

Southern Rhodesia

12 pence (d) = 1 shilling; 20 shillings = 1 pound

SELF-GOVERNING COLONY

4

10 Cecil John Rhodes
(after S. P. Kendrick)

15 Lobengula's Kraal and Govt
House, Salisbury

1935–41. *Inscr* "POSTAGE AND REVENUE".
35	**4**	2d. green and chocolate (*p* 12½) ..	..	2·50	8·50
		a. Perf 14 (1941)..	..	1·50	10
35b		3d. deep blue (*p* 14) (1938)	..	3·00	10

6 Victoria Falls and Railway
Bridge

7 King George VI

1937 (12 May). *Coronation. P* 12½.
36	**6**	1d. olive and rose-carmine	..	80	60
37		2d. emerald and sepia	..	80	1·50
38		3d. violet and blue	..	3·75	7·00
39		6d. black and purple	..	2·25	3·25
36/9	..	.. ..	*Set of* 4	7·00	11·00

1937 (25 Nov). *P* 14.
40	**7**	½d. green	..	50	10
41		1d. scarlet	..	40	10
42		1½d. red-brown	..	1·00	20
43		4d. red-orange	..	1·50	10
44		6d. grey-black	..	1·50	40
45		8d. emerald-green	..	2·00	1·50
46		9d. pale blue	..	1·50	50
47		10d. purple	..	2·25	2·00
48		1s. black and blue-green	..	1·75	10
		a. Double print of frame	..	£1100	
49		1s. 6d. black and orange-yellow	..	10·00	2·00
50		2s. black and brown	..	14·00	55
51		2s. 6d. ultramarine and purple	..	9·00	4·75
52		5s. blue and blue-green	..	26·00	2·00
40/52	..	.. ..	*Set of* 13	60·00	12·50

Nos. 40/1 exist in coils, constructed from normal sheets.

8 British South Africa Co's Arms

Recut shirt collar
(R. 6/1)

"Cave" flaw (R. 6/6)

(Des Mrs. L. E. Curtis (½d., 1d., 1½d., 3d.), Mrs I. Mount
(others))

1940 (3 June). *British South Africa Company's Golden
Jubilee. T* **8/10**, **15** *and similar designs. P* 14.
53	½d. slate-violet and green ..		..	10	55
54	1d. violet-blue and scarlet		..	10	10
55	1½d. black and red-brown	..	..	15	80
	a. Recut shirt collar	..	..	20·00	
56	2d. green and bright violet		..	30	70
57	3d. black and blue	..	..	30	1·50
	a. Cave flaw	..	..	30·00	
58	4d. green and brown	..	..	2·00	2·50
59	6d. chocolate and green	..	..	50	2·00
60	1s. blue and green	..	..	50	2·00
53/60	.. ..	..	*Set of* 8	3·50	9·00

Designs: *Horiz* (*as T* **8**)—2d. Fort Victoria; 3d. Rhodes makes
peace. *Vert* (*as T* **10**)—4d. Victoria Falls Bridge; 6d. Statue of Sir
Charles Coghlan.

9 Fort Salisbury, 1890

16 Mounted Pioneer   Hat brim retouch (P1 1B R. 1/8)

(Roto South African Govt Printer, Pretoria)

1943 (1 Nov). *50th Anniv of Occupation of Matabeleland. W 9 of South Africa (Mult Springbok) sideways. P* 14.
61 **16** 2d. brown and green   20   50
　　a. Hat brim retouch   ..   ..   .. 17·00

17 Queen Elizabeth II when Princess
and Princess Margaret

1947 (1 Apr). *Royal Visit. T* **17** *and similar horiz design. P* 14.
62   ½d. black and green..   15   60
63   1d. black and scarlet..   15   60
　Design:—1d. King George VI and Queen Elizabeth.

19 Queen Elizabeth **20** King George VI **21** Queen Elizabeth II
when Princess

22 Princess Margaret   Damage to
right-hand frame
(R.1/10)

1947 (8 May). *Victory. P* 14.
64 **19** 1d. carmine   10   10
65 **20** 2d. slate   10   10
　　a. Double print £1000
　　b. Damaged frame   ..   ..   .. 20·00
66 **21** 3d. blue   55   50
67 **22** 6d. orange   30   90
64/7   ..   ..   *Set of* 4   90   1·40

(Recess B.W.)

1949 (10 Oct). *75th Anniv of U.P.U. As Nos.* 146/7 *of Jamaica.*
68   2d. slate-green   80   20
69   3d. blue   ..   .. 1·10   3·25

23 Queen Victoria, Arms and King George VI

1950 (12 Sept). *Diamond Jubilee of Southern Rhodesia. P* 14.
70   **23** 2d. green and brown   40   80

STAMP BOOKLETS

1938 (31 Mar). *Black on yellow cover. Stitched.*
SB4   2s. 6d. booklet containing twenty-four ½d. and
　　　eighteen 1d. (Nos. 40/1) in blocks of 6   .. £225

POSTAGE DUE STAMPS

SOUTHERN

RHODESIA
(D 1)

1951 (1 Oct). *Postage Due stamps of Great Britain optd with Type* D 1.
D1 **D 1** ½d. emerald (No. D27)   ..   .. 3·25 14·00
D2   1d. violet-blue (No. D36)   ..   .. 3·00   2·75
D3   2d. agate (No. D29)   ..   ..   .. 4·00   1·75
D4   3d. violet (No. D30)   ..   ..   .. 2·75   2·25
D5   4d. blue (No. D38)   ..   ..   .. 1·75   3·50
D6   4d. dull grey-green (No. D31)   .. £180 £550
D7   1s. deep blue (No. D33)   ..   .. 3·00   2·75
D1/5, 7   ..   ..   *Set of* 6 16·00 24·00
　No. D6 is reported to have been issued to Fort Victoria and
Gwelo main post offices only.

South West Africa

12 pence (d) = 1 shilling; 20 shillings = 1 pound

SOUTH AFRICAN ADMINISTRATION

PRICES for Nos. 96/140 are for unused horizontal pairs, used horizontal pairs or used singles (either inscr), *unless otherwise stated.*

27 Mail Train    **28**

(Recess B.W.)

1937 (1 Mar). *W 9 of South Africa. P* 14 × 13½.
96 **27** 1½d. purple-brown   .. .. 19·00 3·00   25

(Recess B.W.)

1937 (12 May). *Coronation. W 9 of South Africa (sideways).*
P 13½ × 14.

No.		Description			Un	Us	
97	28	½d. black and emerald	..	..	50	15	10
98		1d. black and scarlet	..	..	50	15	10
99		1½d. black and orange	..	..	50	15	10
100		2d. black and brown	..	..	50	15	10
101		3d. black and blue	..	..	50	15	10
102		4d. black and purple	..	..	50	20	10
103		6d. black and yellow	..	..	60	2·00	20
104		1s. black and grey-black	..		80	2·50	25
97/104		..	..	*Set of 8*	4·00	5·00	65

1938 (14 Dec). *Voortrekker Centenary Memorial. Nos. 76/9 of South Africa optd as T* 11.
105	½d. + ½d. blue and green..	..	8·00	15·00	1·75
106	1d. + 1d. blue and carmine	..	18·00	8·00	1·00
107	1½d. + 1½d. chocolate & blue-green	22·00	20·00	2·75
108	3d. + 3d. bright blue	..	42·00	50·00	6·50
105/8	..	*Set of 4*	80·00	85·00	11·00

1938 (14 Dec). *Voortrekker Commemoration. Nos. 80/1 of South Africa optd as T* 11.
109	1d. blue and carmine	..	..	10·00	14·00	1·50
	a. Three bolts in wheel rim		..	40·00		
110	1½d. greenish blue and brown	..	12·00	16·00	1·75

1939 (17 July). *250th Anniv of Landing of Huguenots in South Africa and Huguenot Commemoration Fund. Nos. 82/4 of South Africa optd as T* 11.
111	½d. + ½d. brown and green	..	12·00	12·00	1·10
112	1d. + 1d. green and carmine	..	15·00	12·00	1·25
113	1½d. + 1½d. blue-green and purple ..	22·00	12·00	1·25
111/13	..	..	*Set of 3*	45·00	32·00	3·25

SWA   SWA   SWA   S W A
  (29)   (30)   (31)   (32)

1941 (1 Oct)–43. *War Effort. Nos. 88/96 of South Africa optd with T* 29 *or* 30 (3d. *and* 1s.). (a) *Inscr alternately.*
114	½d. green (1.12.41)	..	..	75	2·75	15
	a. Blue-green (1942)	..	..	65	2·00	15
115	1d. carmine (1.11.41)	..	..	55	2·25	15
	a. "Stain" on uniform	..	..	7·00		

116	1½d. myrtle-green (21.1.42)		..	55	2·25	15
117	3d. blue	..	..	..	22·00	17·00	1·00
	a. Cigarette flaw ..		..	60·00		
118	4d. orange-brown ..		..	6·50	12·00	1·00
	a. Red-brown	..	..	18·00	24·00	3·00
119	6d. red-orange	..	..	2·50	3·25	50
120	1s. 3d. olive-brown (15.1.43)	..	11·00	14·00	1·25

(b) *Inscr bilingually*

					Un single single	Us single
121	2d. violet	..	..	..	50	40
122	1s. brown (17.11.41)	..	..	60	40
114/22		*Set of 7 pairs and 2 singles*	40·00	48·00	

1943–44. *War Effort (reduced sizes). Nos. 97/104 of South Africa, optd with T* 29 (1½d. *and* 1s., *No.* 130), *or T* 31 (*others*).

(a) *Inscr alternately*

				Un unit	Us unit	Us single
123	½d. blue-green (T) ..	..	..	40	3·00	10
	a. Green ..	..		3·75	4·25	15
	b. Greenish blue ..		..	3·75	4·25	10
124	1d. carmine-red (T)		..	1·25	3·00	10
	a. Bright carmine		..	2·25	4·00	10
125	1½d. red-brown (P) ..		..	45	60	10
126	2d. violet (P)	..	..	5·50	3·50	10
	a. Reddish violet ..		..	6·50	3·75	10
	b. Apostrophe flaw		..	20·00		
127	3d. blue (T)	..	..	3·25	14·00	45
128	6d. red-orange (P) ..		..	5·50	2·75	30
	a. Opt inverted ..		..	£425		

(b) *Inscr bilingually*

129	4d. slate-green (T)	..	..	2·00	15·00	45
	a. Opt inverted ..		..	£450	£300	50·00
130	1s. brown (opt T 29) (P)	..	11·00	23·00	2·00
	a. Opt inverted ..		..	£425	£300	
	b. Opt T 31 (1944)	..	..	4·00	5·00	30
	c. Opt T 31 inverted	..	£375	£275	40·00
	d. "Bursting shell"	..	..	30·00		
123/30b	..	..	*Set of 8*	20·00	42·00	1·75

The "units" referred to above consist of pairs (P) or triplets (T).
No. 128 exists with another type of opt as Type **31**, but with broader "s", narrower "w" and more space between the letters.

1945. *Victory. Nos. 108/10 of South Africa optd with T* 30.
131	1d. brown and carmine	..	..	25	50	10
	a. Opt inverted	..	..	£225	£250	
132	2d. slate-blue and violet	..	30	55	10
133	3d. deep blue and blue	..	..	1·25	90	10
131/3	..	..	..	*Set of 3*	1·60	1·75	20

1947 (17 Feb). *Royal Visit. Nos. 111/13 of South Africa optd as T* 31, *but* 8½ × 2 mm.
134	1d. black and carmine	..	..	10	10	10
135	2d. violet ..	..	..	..	10	20	10
	a. "Bird" on "2"	..	..	6·00		
136	3d. blue	..	..	..	15	20	10
134/6	..	..	..	*Set of 3*	30	45	15

1948 (26 Apr). *Royal Silver Wedding. No. 125 of South Africa, optd as T* 31, *but* 4 × 2 mm.
137	3d. blue and silver ..	..	..	1·50	35	10

1949 (1 Oct). *75th Anniv of U.P.U. Nos. 128/30 of South Africa optd as T* 30, *but* 13 × 4 mm.
138	½d. blue-green	..	..	..	1·00	2·00	25
139	1½d. brown-red	..	..	..	1·00	1·00	15
140	3d. bright blue	..	..	..	1·50	1·50	25
	a. Serif on "C"	..	..	22·00		
	b. "Lake" in East Africa ..	..	27·00		
138/40	..	..	..	*Set of 3*	3·25	4·00	60

1949 (1 Dec). *Inauguration of Voortrekker Monument, Pretoria. Nos. 131/3 of South Africa optd with T 32.*

								Un single	*Us* single
141	1d. magenta..	..	..	..	..	..	..	10	10
142	1½d. blue-green	..	..	..	..		..	10	10
143	3d. blue	..	..	..	..	..		15	25
141/3 ..	..	..	..	..		*Set of 3*		30	30

1952 (14 Mar). *Tercentenary of Landing of Van Riebeeck. Nos. 136/40 of South Africa optd as T 30, but 8 × 3½ mm (1d., 4½d.) or 11 × 4 mm (others).*

144	½d. brown-purple and olive-grey	..	..	10	50
145	1d. deep blue-green ..	..	..	10	10
146	2d. deep violet	..	..	50	10
147	4½d. blue	..	..	30	2·75
148	1s. brown	..	..	1·25	20
144/8 ..	..	..	*Set of 5*	2·00	3·25

OFFICIAL STAMPS

OFFICIAL   OFFISIEEL

(O 11)   (O 12)

1938 (1 July). *English stamp optd with Type O 11 and Afrikaans with Type O 12 in red.*

O17	27	1½d. purple-brown	..	..	24·00	45·00	6·00

OFFICIAL   OFFISIEEL

(O 13)   (O 14)

1945–50. *English stamp optd with Type O 13, and Afrikaans stamp with Type O 14 in red.*

O18	12	½d. black and emerald ..	..	13·00	27·00	5·00
O19	13	1d. indigo and scarlet (1950)	..	4·25	16·00	3·25
		a. Opt double ..	..	..	£425	
O20	27	1½d. purple-brown	..	..	45·00	40·00	6·50
O21	14	2d. blue and brown (1947?)	..	£450	£600	£100
O22	17	6d. blue and brown	..	..	13·00	45·00	7·00
O18/20, O22		..	..	*Set of 4*	65·00	£110	20·00

OFFICIAL   OFFISIEEL

(O 15)   (O 16)

1951 (16 Nov)–**52.** *English stamp optd with Type O 15 and Afrikaans stamp with Type O 16, in red.*

O23	12	½d. black and emerald (1952) ..	12·00	20·00	4·50
O24	13	1d. indigo and scarlet ..	..	4·00	13·00	1·75
		a. Opts transposed	..	..	70·00	£100
O25	27	1½d. purple-brown	..	..	24·00	24·00	5·00
		a. Opts transposed	..	..	70·00	80·00
O26	14	2d. blue and brown	..	..	1·50	16·00	3·50
		a. Opts transposed	..	..	45·00	£100
O27	17	6d. blue and brown	..	..	2·75	38·00	7·50
		a. Opts transposed	..	..	22·00	£110
O23/7		..	*Set of 5*	40·00	£100	20·00

The above errors refer to stamps with the English overprint on Afrikaans stamp and *vice versa*.

Sudan

10 milliemes = 1 piastre; 100 piastres = 1 Sudanese pound

ANGLO-EGYPTIAN CONDOMINIUM

2 Arab Postman

6   **7**

1927–41. *W* **7.** *Chalk-surfaced paper.* P 14.

37	**6**	1 m. black and orange	..	..	60	10
		a. Ordinary paper (1941)	..	..	70	10
38		2 m. orange and chocolate	..	..	50	10
		a. Ordinary paper (1941)	..	..	1·50	10
39		3 m. mauve and green	..	..	40	10
		a. Ordinary paper (1941)	..	..	2·25	30
40		4 m. green and chocolate	..	..	40	10
		a. Ordinary paper (1941)	..	..	3·00	30
		aw. Wmk inverted	..	..	75·00	
41		5 m. olive-brown and black	..	..	30	10
		a. Ordinary paper (1941)	..	..	2·50	10
42		10 m. carmine and black	..	..	1·25	10
		a. Ordinary paper (1941)	..	..	3·00	10
43		15 m. bright blue and chestnut	..	..	80	10
		a. Ordinary paper (1941)	..	..	1·25	10
44	**2**	2 p. purple and orange-yellow	..	..	1·00	10
		a. Ordinary paper (1941)	..	..	3·50	10
44b		3 p. red-brown and blue (1.1.40)	..	..	2·75	10
		ba. Ordinary paper (1941)	..	..	16·00	10
44c		4 p. ultramarine and black (2.11.36)	..	..	3·50	10
45		5 p. chestnut and green	..	..	1·00	10
		a. Ordinary paper (1941)	..	..	3·75	40
45b		6 p. greenish blue and black (2.11.36)		4·75	40
		ba. Ordinary paper (1941)	..	..	27·00	1·25
45c		8 p. emerald and black (2.11.36)	..	..	5·50	2·25
		ca. Ordinary paper (1941)	..	..	27·00	3·50
46		10 p. black and reddish purple	..	..	2·25	10
		a. Ordinary paper. *Black and bright mauve* (1941)		8·00	70
46b		20 p. pale blue and blue (17.10.35)	..	..	2·25	10
		ba. Ordinary paper (1941)	..	..	3·50	10
37/46b		..		*Set of 15*	25·00	3·00

The ordinary paper of this issue is thick, smooth and opaque and was a wartime substitute for chalk-surfaced paper.

For similar stamps, but with different Arabic inscriptions, see Nos. 96/111.

10 Statue of Gen. Gordon    **(16)**

1931 (1 Sept)–**37.** *Air. Recess.* W **7** (*sideways**). P 14.

49b	**10**	3 m. green and sepia (1.1.33)	..	..	2·50	5·50
50		5 m. black and green	..		1·00	10
51		10 m. black and carmine	..	..	1·00	20
52		15 m. red-brown and sepia	..	..	40	10
		aw. Wmk top of G to right	..			
		b. Perf 11½×12½ (1937)	..	..	4·50	10
53		2 p. black and orange	..	..	30	10
		a. Perf 11½×12½ (1937)	..	..	4·50	15·00
53b		2½ p. magenta and blue (1.1.33)	..	..	3·50	10
		c. Perf 11½×12½ (1936)	..	..	3·00	10
		ca. Aniline magenta and blue	..	7·50	3·25
		cx. Wmk reversed	..	..		
		cy. Wmk top of G to right reversed		
54		3 p. black and grey	..	..	60	15
		a. Perf 11½×12½ (1937)	..	..	85	35
55		3½ p. black and violet	..	..	1·50	80
		a. Perf 11½×12½ (1937)	..	..	2·50	10·00
56		4½ p. red-brown and grey	..	..	10·00	15·00
57		5 p. black and ultramarine	..	..	1·00	30
		a. Perf 11½×12½ (1937)	..	..	3·75	35
57b		7½ p. green and emerald (17.10.35)	..	9·00	4·50
		by. Wmk top of G to right reversed		
		e. Perf 11½×12½ (1937)	..	..	4·00	10·00
57d		10 p. brown and greenish blue (17.10.35)	8·50	1·00
		e. Perf 11½×12½ (1937)	..	..	4·00	17·00
		ey. Wmk top of G to right reversed		
49b/57d		..	..	..	*Set of 12 (p 14)*	35·00	24·00
52b/7e		..	..	*Set of 8 (p 11½×12½)*	24·00	45·00

*The normal sideways watermark shows the top of the G pointing left *as seen from the back of the stamp.*

1938 (1 July). *Air. Nos.* 53c, 55, 57b *and* 57d *surch as T* **16.**

74	**10**	5 m. on 2½ p. mag & bl (p 11½×12½)	3·50	10
		w. Wmk top of G to right	..		
		x. Wmk reversed		
75		3 p. on 3½ p. black and violet (p 14)	35·00	48·00
		a. Perf 11½×12½	..	..	£425	£550
76		3 p. on 7½ p. green and emerald (p 14)	7·00	6·50
		ax. Wmk reversed		
		ay. Wmk top of G to right reversed	50·00	
		b. Perf 11½×12½	..	..	£425	£550
77		5 p. on 10 p. brown & greenish bl (p 14)	1·75	4·75
		a. Perf 11½×12½	..	..	£425	£550
74/7				*Set of 4*	42·00	55·00

A 5 p. on 2½ p., perf 11½×12½, exists either mint or cancelled from a trial printing (*Price* £350 *unused*).

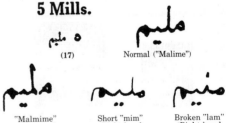

5 Mills.

(17)   Normal ("Malime")

"Malmime"   Short "mim"   Broken "lam"
(Left-hand   (Right-hand   (Right-hand
pane R. 5/1)   pane R. 3/1)   pane R. 6/2)

5 M

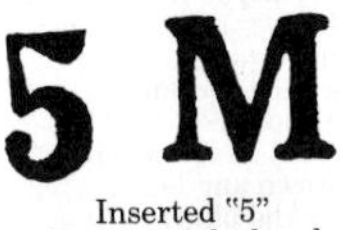

Inserted "5"
(Bottom right-hand
pane R. 4/5)

1940 (25 Feb). *No.* 42 *surch with T* **17** *by McCorquodale (Sudan) Ltd, Khartoum.*

78	**6**	5 m. on 10 m. carmine and black . .	. .	. .	50	30
		a. "Malmime" . .	. .	. .	45·00	50·00
		b. Two dots omitted (Right-hand pane R. 8/6) . .	. .	. .	45·00	50·00
		c. Short "mim" . .	. .	. .	45·00	50·00
		d. Broken "lam" . .	. .	. .	45·00	50·00
		e. Inserted "5" . .	. .	. .	£130	

$4\frac{1}{2}$
Piastres

$4\frac{1}{2}$
PIASTRES

(18)

قرش ٤ ١/٢

(19)

1940–1. *Nos.* 41 *and* 45c *surch as T* **18** *or* **19** *at Khartoum.*

79	**6**	4½ p. on 5 m. olive-brown & blk (9.2.41) . .	48·00	3·75
80	**2**	4½ p. on 8 p. emerald and black (12.12.40)	38·00	9·00

20 Tuti Island, R. Nile, near Khartoum

21 Tuti Island, R. Nile near Khartoum

(Des Miss H. M. Hebbert. Litho Security Printing Press, Nasik, India)

1941 (25 Mar–10 Aug). *P* 14 × 13½ (*T* **20**) *or P* 13½ × 14 (*T* **21**).

81	**20**	1 m. slate and orange (10.8) . .	. .	. .	1·00	3·50
82		2 m. orange and chocolate (10.8) . .	. .	. .	1·00	3·50
83		3 m. mauve and green (10.8) . .	. .	. .	1·00	20
84		4 m. green and chocolate (10.8) . .	. .	. .	80	50
85		5 m. olive-brown and black (10.8)	. .	. .	30	10
86		10 m. carmine and black (10.8) . .	. .	. .	7·00	1·75
87		15 m. bright blue and chestnut	. .	. .	70	10
88	**21**	2 p. purple and orange-yellow (10.8)	. .	. .	3·50	60
89		3 p. red-brown and blue . .	. .	. .	70	10
90		4 p. ultramarine and black	. .	. .	90	10
91		5 p. chestnut and green (10.8)	. .	. .	4·50	8·50
92		6 p. greenish blue and black (10.8)	. .	18·00	40
93		8 p. emerald and black (10.8) . .	. .	14·00	45·
94		10 p. slate and purple (10.8)	. .	. .	50·00	75
95		20 p. pale blue and blue (10.8)	. .	. .	50·00	29·00
81/95	. .		. .	. .	*Set of* 15	£140	45·00

24   **25**

1948 (1 Oct). *Golden Jubilee of "Camel Postman" design. Chalk-surfaced paper. Typo. W* **7**. *P* 13.

112	**24**	2 p. black and light blue	. .	. .	20	10

1948 (23 Dec). *Opening of Legislative Assembly, Chalk-surfaced paper. Typo. W* **7**. *P* 13.

113	**25**	10 m. rose-red and black . .	. .	30	10
114		5 p. brown-orange and deep green	. .	50	70

26 Blue Nile Bridge, Khartoum

(Des Col. W. L. Atkinson (2½ p., 6 p.), G. R. Wilson (3 p.), others from photographs. Recess)

1950 (1 July). *Air. T* **26** *and similar horiz designs. W* **7**. *P* 12.

115		2 p. black and blue-green . .	. .	. .	4·50	90
116		2½ p. light blue and red-orange	. .	. .	75	1·00
117		3 p. reddish purple and blue	. .	. .	3·00	60
118		3½ p. purple-brown and yellow-brown	. .	1·25	1·50
119		4 p. brown and light blue . .	. .	. .	1·00	2·00
120		4½ p. black and ultramarine . .	. .	. .	2·50	3·50
		a. Black and steel-blue	. .	. .	5·50	5·50
121		6 p. black and carmine . .	. .	. .	1·00	2·50
122		20 p. black and purple	. .	. .	1·75	4·50
115/122			. .	*Set of* 8	14·00	16·00

Designs:—2½ p. Kassala Jebel; 3 p. Sagia (water wheel); 3½ p. Port Sudan; 4 p. Gordon Memorial College; 4½ p. *Gordon Pasha* (Nile mail boat); 6 p. Suakin; 20 p. G.P.O., Khartoum.

34 Ibex

35 Cotton Picking

103	**23**	2 p. purple and orange-yellow	. .	. .	6·50	1·50
104		3 p. red-brown and deep blue . .	. .	6·00	20
105		4 p. ultramarine and black	. .	. .	4·00	1·75
106		5 p. brown-orange and deep green	. .	4·00	1·75
107		6 p. greenish blue and black . .	. .	4·50	3·00
108		8 p. bluish green and black	. .	. .	4·50	3·00
109		10 p. black and mauve . .	. .	. .	11·00	3·25
		a. Chalk-surfaced paper (June)	. .	25·00	4·25
110		20 p. pale blue and deep blue . .	. .	4·50	30
		a. Perf 13. Chalk-surfaced paper (June) . .	. .	. .	48·00	£130
111		50 p. carmine and ultramarine . .	. .	6·50	2·00
96/111		. .	. .	. .	*Set of* 16	60·00	26·00

A single used example is known of No. 101a.

For similar stamps, but with different Arabic inscriptions, see Nos. 37/46b.

1948 (1 Jan–June). *Arabic inscriptions below camel altered. Typo. W* **7**. *Ordinary paper* (8, 10, 20 p.) *or chalk-surfaced paper* (others). *P* 14.

96	**22**	1 m. black and orange . .	. .	. .	35	3·25
97		2 m. orange and chocolate	. .	. .	80	3·75
98		3 m. mauve and green . .	. .	. .	30	3·25
99		4 m. deep green and chocolate	. .	. .	30	10
100		5 m. olive-brown and black	. .	. .	5·00	1·75
101		10 m. rose-red and black	. .	. .	5·00	10
		a. Centre inverted	. .	. .	†	
102		15 m. ultramarine and chestnut	. .	4·50	10

22   **23**

(Des Col. W. L. Atkinson (1 m., 2 m., 4 m., 5 m., 10 m., 3 p., 3½ p., 20 p.), Col. E. A. Stanton (50 p.). Typo)

1951 (1 Sept)–**62?** *Designs as T* **34/5***. Chalk-surfaced paper.* W 7. P 14 (*milleme values*) *or* 13 (*piastre values*).

123	1 m. black and orange			70	1·25
124	2 m. black and bright blue			1·50	50
125	3 m. black and green			5·00	2·25
126	4 m. black and yellow-green			1·00	2·50
127	5 m. light and purple			1·50	10
	a. *Black and reddish purple* (1962?)			4·50	40
128	10 m. black and pale blue			20	10
129	15 m. black and chestnut			3·00	10
	a. *Black and brown-orange* (1962?)			3·25	10
130	2 p. deep blue and pale blue			20	10
	a. *Deep blue and very pale blue* (1962?)			3·00	10
131	3 p. brown and dull ultramarine			5·00	10
	a. *Brown and deep blue* (1962?)			7·50	90
132	3½ p. bright green and red-brown			1·25	10
	a. *Light emerald and red-brown* (1962?)			2·75	10
133	4 p. ultramarine and black			60	10
	a. *Deep blue and black* (1962?)			5·50	10
134	5 p. orange-brown and yellow-green			30	10
135	6 p. blue and black			6·50	5·00
	a. *Deep blue and black* (1962?)			14·00	5·50
136	8 p. blue and brown			11·00	2·25
	a. *Deep blue and brown* (1962?)			14·00	2·00
137	10 p. black and green			1·25	10
138	20 p. blue-green and black			4·50	1·25
139	50 p. carmine and black			12·00	1·25
123/39			*Set of* 17	50·00	12·00

Designs: *Vert as T* **34**—2 m. Whale-headed Stork; 3 m. Giraffe; 4 m. Baggara girl; 5 m. Shilluk warrior; 10 m. Hadendowa; 15 m. Policeman. *Horiz as T* **35**—3 p. Ambatch reed canoe; 3½ p. Nuba wrestlers; 4 p. Weaving; 5 p. Saluka farming; 6 p. Gum tapping; 8 p. Darfur chief; 10 p. Stack Laboratory; 20 p. Nile Lechwe. *Vert as T* **35**—50 p. Camel postman.

POSTAGE DUE STAMPS

D 2 Gunboat *Zafir*

1948 (1 Jan). *Arabic inscriptions at foot altered. Chalk-surfaced paper.* Typo. W 7. P 14.

D12	D 2	2 m. black and brown-orange		1·00	30·00
D13		4 m. brown and green		2·00	26·00
D14		10 m. green and mauve		18·00	18·00
D15		20 m. ultramarine and carmine		18·00	32·00
D12/15			*Set of* 4	35·00	95·00

The 10 and 20 m. were reissued in 1980 on Sudan arms watermarked paper.

OFFICIAL STAMPS

S.G. **S.G.** **S.G.**

(O 3) (O 4) (O 4a)

1936 (19 Sept)–**46**. *Nos.* 37a, 38a, 39/43 *optd with Type* O **3**, *and* 44, 44ba, 44c, 45, 45ba, 45ca, 46 *and* 46ba *with Type* O **4**. W 7. P 14.

O32	**6**	1 m. black and orange (22.11.46)		1·60	9·00
		a. Opt double		†	£150
O33		2 m. orange and chocolate (*ordinary paper*) (4.45)		50	3·25
		a. Chalk-surfaced paper		—	70·00
O34		3 m. mauve and green (*chalk-surfaced paper*) (1.37)		2·50	10
O35		4 m. grn & choc (*chalk-surfaced paper*)		3·00	2·50
O36		5 m. olive-brown and black (*chalk-surfaced paper*) (3.40)		1·00	10
		a. Ordinary paper		16·00	40
O37		10 m. carmine and black (*chalk-surfaced paper*) (6.46)		70	10
O38		15 m. bright blue and chestnut (*chalk-surfaced paper*) (21.6.37)		6·00	20
		a. Ordinary paper		32·00	1·75

O39	**2**	2 p. purple & orange-yellow (*chalk-surfaced paper*) (4.37)		11·00	10
		a. Ordinary paper		28·00	2·50
O39b		3 p. red-brown and blue (4.46)		5·50	1·75
O39c		4 p. ultramarine and black (*chalk-surfaced paper*) (4.46)		23·00	3·25
		ca. Ordinary paper		48·00	4·00
O40		5 p. chestnut and green (*chalk-surfaced paper*)		14·00	10
		a. Ordinary paper		48·00	4·50
O40b		6 p. greenish blue and black (4.46)		7·00	6·50
O40c		8 p. emerald and black (4.46)		5·00	24·00
O41		10 p. black and reddish purple (*chalk-surfaced paper*) (10.37)		25·00	7·50
		a. Ordinary paper. *Black and bright mauve* (1941)		40·00	2·75
O42		20 p. pale blue and blue (6.46)		24·00	19·00
O32/42			*Set of* 15	£110	65·00

1948 (1 Jan). *Nos.* 96/102 *optd with Type* O **3**, *and* 103/111 *with Type* O **4**.

O43	**22**	1 m. black and orange		30	3·25
O44		2 m. orange and chocolate		1·25	10
O45		3 m. mauve and green		2·50	5·00
O46		4 m. deep green and chocolate		2·50	2·75
O47		5 m. olive-brown and black		2·50	10
O48		10 m. rose-red and black		2·25	90
O49		15 m. ultramarine and chestnut		2·50	10
O50	**23**	2 p. purple and orange-yellow		2·50	10
O51		3 p. red-brown and deep blue		2·50	10
O52		4 p. ultramarine and black		2·50	10
		a. Perf 13 (optd Type O 4a)		13·00	15·00
O53		5 p. brown-orange and deep green		3·00	10
O54		6 p. greenish blue and black		2·25	10
O55		8 p. bluish green and black		2·25	2·25
O56		10 p. black and mauve		3·50	20
O57		20 p. pale blue and deep blue		4·00	25
O58		50 p. carmine and ultramarine		55·00	45·00
O43/58			*Set of* 16	80·00	55·00

1950 (1 July). *Air. Optd with Type* O **4a**.

O59	2 p. black and blue-green (R.)		14·00	3·00
O60	2½ p. light blue and red-orange		1·50	1·75
O61	3 p. reddish purple and blue		80	1·00
O62	3½ p. purple-brown and yellow-brown		80	6·50
O63	4 p. brown and light blue		80	6·50
O64	4½ p. black and ultramarine (R.)		3·75	15·00
	a. *Black and steel-blue*		6·50	15·00
O65	6 p. black and carmine (R.)		1·00	4·25
O66	20 p. black and purple (R.)		5·00	12·00
O59/66		*Set of* 8	25·00	42·00

1951 (1 Sept)–**62?** *Nos.* 123/9 *optd with Type* O **3**, *and* 130/9 *with Type* O **4a**.

O67	1 m. black and orange (R.)		40	3·50
O68	2 m. black and bright blue (R.)		40	60
O69	3 m. black and green (R.)		3·00	14·00
O70	4 m. black and yellow-green (R.)		10	5·00
O71	5 m. black and purple (R.)		10	10
O72	10 m. black and pale blue (R.)		10	10
O73	15 m. black and chestnut (R.)		10	10
O74	2 p. deep blue and pale blue		10	10
	a. Opt inverted		£475	
	b. *Deep blue and very pale blue* (1962?)		75	10
O75	3 p. brown and dull ultramarine		4·50	10
	a. *Brown and deep blue* (1962?)		5·00	1·00
O76	3½ p. bright green and red-brown		25	10
	a. *Light emerald & red-brown* (1962?)		3·00	1·00
O77	4 p. ultramarine and black		30	10
	a. *Deep blue and black* (1962?)		1·50	10
O78	5 p. orange-brown and yellow-green		25	10
O79	6 p. blue and black		30	2·75
	a. *Deep blue and black* (1962?)		6·50	5·50
O80	8 p. blue and brown		45	10
	a. *Deep blue and brown* (1962?)		3·50	1·75
O81	10 p. black and green (R.)		50	10
O81a	10 p. black and green (Blk.) (1958)		13·00	1·50
O82	20 p. blue-green and black		1·25	30
	a. Opt inverted		—	£600
O83	50 p. carmine and black		3·50	1·25
O67/83		*Set of* 18	25·00	26·00

The 5, 10 and 15 m. values were later reissued with a thinner overprint.

Swaziland

12 pence (d) = 1 shilling; 20 shillings = 1 pound

PROTECTORATE

1937 (12 May). *Coronation. As Nos. 118/20 of Jamaica, but ptd by B.W. P* 11×11½.

25	1d. carmine				50	1·25
26	2d. yellow-brown				50	20
27	3d. blue				50	50
25/7				Set of 3	1·40	1·75
25/7 Perf "Specimen"			Set of 3	65·00	

3 King George VI

(Recess D.L.R.)

1938 (1 Apr)–54. *Wmk Mult Script CA. P* 13½×13.

28	**3**	½d. green			1·50	80
		a. Perf 13½×14 (1.43)			20	2·25
		b. Perf 13½×14. *Bronze-green* (2.50)		95	4·00
29		1d. rose-red			1·50	70
		a. Perf 13½×14 (1.43)			80	1·40
30		1½d. light blue			3·75	65
		a. Perf 14 (1941)			2·25	95
		b. Perf 13½×14 (1.43)			30	75
		ba. Printed on the gummed side		£2250	
31		2d. yellow-brown			2·50	85
		a. Perf 13½×14 (1.43)			30	50
32		3d. ultramarine			8·00	1·75
		a. Deep blue (10.38)			12·00	1·75
		b. Perf 13½×14. *Ultramarine* (1.43)		2·25	4·00
		c. Perf 13½×14. *Light ultram* (10.46)	16·00	10·00
		d. Perf 13½×14. *Deep blue* (10.47)	8·50	9·50
33		4d. orange			3·50	95
		a. Perf 13½×14 (1.43)			50	1·40
34		6d. deep magenta			8·00	2·00
		a. Perf 13½×14 (1.43)			3·50	3·50
		b. Perf 13½×14. *Reddish purple (shades)* (7.44)	3·50	1·25
		c. Perf 13½×14. *Claret* (13.10.54)	6·00	3·50
35		1s. brown-olive			8·00	1·50
		a. Perf 13½×14 (1.43)			1·25	65
36		2s. 6d. bright violet			24·00	4·00
		a. Perf 13½×14. *Violet* (1.43)		10·00	2·50
		b. Perf 13½×14. *Reddish violet* (10.47)	10·00	7·00
37		5s. grey			50·00	11·00
		a. Perf 13½×14. *Slate* (1.43)		55·00	50·00
		b. Perf 13½×14. *Grey* (5.44)		24·00	13·00
38		10s. sepia			50·00	5·50
		a. Perf 13½×14 (1.43)			6·50	6·00
28/38a				Set of 11	45·00	24·00
28/38 Perf "Specimen"			Set of 11	£225	

The above perforations vary slightly from stamp to stamp, but the average measurements are respectively: 13.3 × 13.2 comb (13½ × 13), 14.2 line (14) and 13.3 × 13.8 comb (13½ × 14).

Swaziland
(4)

1945 (3 Dec). *Victory. Nos.* 108/10 *of South Africa optd with T* **4**.

				pair	pair single
39	1d. brown and carmine			55	50	10
40	2d. slate-blue and violet		55	50	10
41	3d. deep blue and blue		55	2·00	20
39/41			Set of 3	1·50	2·75	30

1947 (17 Feb). *Royal Visit. As Nos.* 32/5 *of Basutoland.*

				Un	Us
42	1d. scarlet			10	10
43	2d. green			10	10
44	3d. ultramarine			10	10
45	1s. mauve			10	10
42/5			Set of 4	30	30
42/5 Perf "Specimen"		Set of 4	80·00	

1948 (1 Dec). *Royal Silver Wedding. As Nos.* 143/4 *of Jamaica.*

46	1½d. ultramarine			50	10
47	10s. purple-brown			23·00	25·00

1949 (10 Oct). *75th Anniv of U.P.U. As Nos.* 145/8 *of Jamaica.*

48	1½d. blue			20	10
49	3d. deep blue			1·75	90
50	6d. magenta			60	60
51	1s. olive			60	60
48/51			Set of 4	2·75	2·00

POSTAGE DUE STAMPS

D 1

(Typo D.L.R.)

1933 (2 Jan)–57. *Wmk Mult Script CA. P* 14.

D1	D 1	1d. carmine			30	7·50
		a. Chalk-surfaced paper. *Dp carmine* (24.10.51)	20	11·00
		ac. Error. St Edward's Crown, W **9b**	£180	
D2		2d. pale violet			1·75	20·00
		a. Chalk-surfaced paper (22.2.57)	4·75	27·00
		ab. Large "d"		42·00	
D1/2 Perf "Specimen"		Set of 2	42·00	

For illustration of No. D2ab see above No. D1 of Basutoland.

Tonga

12 pence (d) = 1 shilling; 20 shillings = 1 pound

PROTECTORATE

15 Arms

16 Ovava Tree, Kana-Kubolu

18 Prehistoric Trilith at Haamonga

20 Coral

22 Red Shining Parrot

23 View of Vavau Harbour

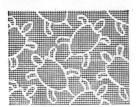

24 Tortoises (*upright*)

26 Queen Salote

29 Queen Salote

(Recess D.L.R.)

1938 (12 Oct). *20th Anniv of Queen Salote's Accession. Tablet at foot dated "1918–1938". W* **24** *(sideways). P* 13½.

71	**29**	1d. black and scarlet	..	..	.. 60 3·00
72		2d. black and purple	..	..	7·00 2·25
73		2½d. black and ultramarine	..	..	7·00 3·00
71/3	..	..	..	*Set of 3*	13·00 7·50
71/3 Perf "Specimen"		..	..	*Set of 3*	70·00

For Silver Jubilee issue in a similar design, see Nos. 83/87.

Dies of 2d.:

Die II

Die III

Normal

Lopped branch (R. 8/5)
(ptgs from 1934 onwards)

Normal

"2½" recut (note lines on "2" and different "½")
(R. 1/1)

(Recess D.L.R.)

1942–49. *Wmk Mult Script CA (sideways on 5s.). P* 14.

74	**15**	½d. yellow-green	..	..	.. 20 2·00
75	**16**	1d. black and scarlet	..	..	.. 1·50 2·00
		a. Lopped branch	..		.. 30·00
76	**26**	2d. black and purple (Die II)	..		.. 3·50 2·00
		a. Die III (4.49)		..	.. 3·75 7·00
77		2½d. bright ultramarine		..	.. 1·25 1·50
		a. Recut "2½"			.. 25·00
78	**18**	3d. black and yellow-green		..	.. 50 2·50
79	**20**	6d. red	..		.. 2·50 2·00
80	**26**	1s. black and red-brown		..	.. 2·50 3·25
		a. Retouched (small) hyphen	..		.. 32·00 38·00
81	**22**	2s. 6d. deep purple (1943)		..	.. 26·00 20·00

82 **23**   5s. black and brown-red (1943)   .. 16·00 42·00
74/82   ..   .. *Set of* 9 48·00 70·00
74/82 Perf "Specimen"   ..   .. *Set of* 9 £170
  In Die III the foot of the "2" is longer than in Die II and
extends towards the right beyond the curve of the loop; the
letters of "PENI-E-UA" are taller and differently shaped.
  Damage to the "2" on R. 4/9 of No. 77 was frequently corrected
by hand-painting.
  For illustration of No. 75a see above No. 38 and of No. 77a see
above No. 55.
  The ½d., 1d., 3d. and 1s. exist perforated from either line or
comb machines. The other values only come line perforated.

UANIMA TA'U 'OE PULE A 'ENE 1/10 1918 -1943

30

(Recess D.L.R.)

1944 (25 Jan). *Silver Jubilee of Queen Salote's Accession. As T* **29**,
but inscr "1918–1943" *at foot, as T* **30**. *Wmk Mult Script CA. P* 14.
83   1d. black and carmine   15   80
84   2d. black and purple   15   80
85   3d. black and green   15   80
86   6d. black and orange   ..   ..   .. 65 1·60
87   1s. black and brown   ..   .. 55 1·60
83/7   ..   .. *Set of* 5 1·50 5·00
83/7 Perf "Specimen"   ..   .. *Set of* 5 75·00

1949 (10 Oct). *75th Anniv of U.P.U. As Nos.* 145/8 *of Jamaica.*
88   2½d. ultramarine   40   60
89   3d. olive ..   .. 1·60 2·75
90   6d. carmine-red   50   50
91   1s. red-brown   50   50
88/91   ..   .. *Set of* 4 2·75 4·00

31 Queen Salote **33**

32 Queen Salote

(Photo Waterlow)

1950 (1 Nov). *Queen Salote's Fiftieth Birthday. Wmk Mult Script
CA. P* 12½.
92 **31** 1d. carmine   ..   .. 40 1·50
93 **32** 5d. green   ..   .. 40 1·75
94 **33** 1s. violet   ..   .. 40 2·00
92/4   ..   .. *Set of* 3 1·10 4·75

34 Map **35** Palace, Nuku'alofa

(Recess Waterlow)

1951 (2 July). *50th Anniv of Treaty of Friendship between Great
Britain and Tonga. T* **34/5** *and similar designs. Wmk Mult Script
CA. P* 12½ (3*d.*), 13 × 13½ (½*d.*), 13½ × 13 (*others*).
95   ½d. green   ..   .. 20 2·25
96   1d. black and carmine   ..   ..   .. 15 2·25
97   2½d. green and brown   ..   ..   .. 30 2·25
98   3d. yellow and bright blue..   ..   .. 1·25 2·25
99   5d. carmine and green   85   70
100   1s. yellow-orange and violet   85   70
95/100   ..   .. *Set of* 6 3·25 9·00
  Designs: *Horiz*—2½d. Beach scene; 5d. Flag; 1s. Arms of Tonga
and G.B. *Vert*—3d. H.M.N.Z.S. *Bellona.*

Transjordan

1000 milliemes = 1 Palestinian pound

BRITISH MANDATE

28   29

(Re-engraved with figures of value at left only. Recess Perkins, Bacon)

1930 (1 June)–**39.** *Wmk Mult Script CA. P* 14.

194b	28	1 m. red-brown (6.2.34)	..	30	1·00
		c. Perf 13½×13 (1939)	..	3·00	3·50
195		2 m. greenish blue	..	30	50
		a. Perf 13½×13. *Bluish grn* (1939)	8·00	2·00
196		3 m. carmine-pink	..	40	70
196a		3 m. green (6.2.34)	..	1·75	85
		b. Perf 13½×13 (1939)	..	13·00	4·25
197		4 m. green	..	60	1·75
197a		4 m. carmine-pink (6.2.34)	..	2·25	90
		b. Perf 13½×13 (1939)	..	50·00	18·00
198		5 m. orange	..	40	40
		a. Coil stamp. Perf 13½×14 (29.2.36)	..	18·00	14·00
		b. Perf 13½×13 (1939)	..	50·00	3·00
199		10 m. scarlet	..	90	15
		a. Perf 13½×13 (1939)	..	80·00	4·25
200		15 m. ultramarine	..	65	20
		a. Coil stamp. Perf 13½×14 (29.2.36)	..	18·00	14·00
		b. Perf 13½×13 (1939)	..	32·00	3·75
201		20 m. olive-green	..	1·25	35
		a. Perf 13½×13 (1939)	..	55·00	12·00
202	29	50 m. purple	..	1·75	1·25
203		90 m. bistre	..	2·50	4·25
204		100 m. blue	..	3·75	4·25
205		200 m. violet	..	8·50	14·00
206		500 m. brown	..	20·00	38·00
207		£P1 slate-grey	..	45·00	80·00
194b/207			*Set of* 16	80·00	£130
194b/207 Perf "Specimen"			*Set of* 16	£170	

For stamps perf 12 see Nos. 230/43, and for T **28** lithographed, perf 13½, see Nos. 222/9.

34

(Litho Survey Dept, Cairo)

1942 (18 May). *T* **28**, *but with Arabic characters above portrait and in top left circle modified as in T* **34**. *No wmk. P* 13½.

222	34	1 m. red-brown	..	80	3·25
223		2 m. green	..	1·50	1·50
224		3 m. yellow-green	..	2·00	2·25
225		4 m. carmine-pink	..	2·00	3·00
226		5 m. yellow-orange	..	3·25	1·00
227		10 m. scarlet	..	3·00	2·75
228		15 m. blue	..	6·00	1·75
229		20 m. olive-green	..	9·00	12·00
222/9			*Set of* 8	24·00	24·00

Forgeries of the above exist on whiter paper with rough perforations.

(Recess Bradbury, Wilkinson)

1943 (1 Jan)–**46.** *Wmk Mult Script CA. P* 12.

230	28	1 m. red-brown	..	20	75
231		2 m. bluish green	..	70	75
232		3 m. green	..	1·75	1·25
233		4 m. carmine-pink	..	1·75	1·25
234		5 m. orange	..	1·25	20
235		10 m. red	..	3·00	1·25
236		15 m. blue	..	3·00	30
237		20 m. olive-green (26.8.46)	..	2·75	1·00
238	29	50 m. purple (26.8.46)	..	3·00	1·00
239		90 m. bistre (26.8.46)	..	4·75	4·00
240		100 m. blue (26.8.46)	..	5·00	1·75
241		200 m. violet (26.8.46)	..	9·00	6·50
242		500 m. brown (26.8.46)	..	13·00	12·00
243		£P1 slate-grey (26.8.46)	..	24·00	22·00
230/43			*Set of* 14	65·00	48·00

Nos. 237/43 were released in London by the Crown Agents in May 1944, but were not put on sale in Transjordan until 26 August 1946.

Printings of the 3, 4, 10, 12, 15 and 20 m. in changed colours were released on 12 May 1947.

POSTAGE DUE STAMPS

D 26   D 35

(Recess Perkins, Bacon)

1929 (1 Apr)–**39.** *Wmk Mult Script CA. P* 14.

D189	D 26	1 m. red-brown	..	60	3·50
		a. Perf 13½×13 (1939)	..	80·00	50·00
D190		2 m. orange-yellow	..	60	4·00
D191		4 m. green	..	90	4·50
D192		10 m. scarlet	..	2·25	4·50
D193		20 m. olive-green	..	6·50	11·00
D194		50 m. blue	..	7·50	17·00
D189/94			*Set of* 6	16·00	40·00
D189/94 Perf "Specimen"			*Set of* 6	65·00	

(Litho Survey Dept, Cairo)

1942 (22 Dec). *Redrawn. Top line of Arabic in taller lettering. No wmk. P* 13½.

D230	D 35	1 m. red-brown	..	1·40	10·00
D231		2 m. orange-yellow	..	8·00	9·00
D232		10 m. scarlet	..	8·50	6·00
D230/2			*Set of* 3	16·00	23·00

Forgeries of the above exist on whiter paper with rough perforations.

(Recess Bradbury, Wilkinson)

1944–49. *Wmk Mult Script CA. P* 12.

D244	D 26	1 m. red-brown	..	15	2·75
D245		2 m. orange-yellow	..	30	3·75
D246		4 m. green	..	55	4·25
D247		10 m. carmine	..	1·10	4·75
D248		20 m. olive-green (1949)	..	25·00	40·00
D244/8			*Set of* 5	25·00	50·00

Trinidad and Tobago

100 cents = 1 West Indian dollar

CROWN COLONY

1937 (12 May). *Coronation. As Nos. 118/20 of Jamaica.*
243	1 c. green		15	10
244	2 c. yellow-brown		35	10
245	8 c. orange		90	1·25
243/5		*Set of 3*	1·25	1·25
243/5 Perf "Specimen"		*Set of 3*	60·00	

37 First Boca   47 King George VI

(Recess B.W.)

1938 (2 May)–**44.** *T* **37** *and similar horiz designs, and T* **47**.
Wmk Mult Script CA (sideways on 1 c. to 60 c.).

(a) P 11½×11
246	1 c. blue and green		55	20
247	2 c. blue and yellow-brown		55	20
248	3 c. black and scarlet		11·00	90
248a	3 c. green and purple-brown (1941)		30	20
	ab. "A" of "CA" missing from wmk			
249	4 c. chocolate		29·00	1·00
249a	4 c. scarlet (1941)		40	70
249b	5 c. magenta (1.5.41)		30	15
250	6 c. sepia and blue		2·25	70
251	8 c. sage-green and vermilion		2·25	85
252	12 c. black and purple		16·00	1·75
	a. Black and slate-purple (1944)		2·50	10
253	24 c. black and olive-green		1·00	10
254	60 c. myrtle-green and carmine		8·50	1·25

(b) T 47. P 12
255	$1.20, blue-green (1.40)		10·00	1·25
256	$4.80, rose-carmine (1.40)		20·00	27·00
246/56		*Set of 14*	75·00	30·00
246/56 exc 249b Perf "Specimen"	*Set of 13*	£190	

Designs:—2 c. Imperial College of Tropical Agriculture; 3 c. Mt Irvine Bay, Tobago; 4 c. Memorial Park; 5 c. G.P.O. and Treasury; 6 c. Discovery of Lake Asphalt; 8 c. Queen's Park, Savannah; 12 c. Town Hall, San Fernando; 24 c. Government House; 60 c. Blue Basin.

1946 (1 Oct). *Victory. As Nos. 141/2 of Jamaica.*
257	3 c. chocolate		10	10
258	6 c. blue		10	90
257/8 Perf "Specimen"		*Set of 2*	48·00	

1948 (22 Nov). *Royal Silver Wedding. As Nos. 143/4 of Jamaica, but* $4.80 *in recess.*
259	3 c. red-brown		10	10
260	$4.80, carmine		18·00	24·00

1949 (10 Oct). *75th Anniv of U.P.U. As Nos. 145/8 of Jamaica.*
261	5 c. bright reddish purple		40	50
262	6 c. deep blue		1·00	65
263	12 c. violet		40	75
264	24 c. olive		40	60
261/4		*Set of 4*	2·00	2·25

1951 (16 Feb). *University College of B.W.I. As Nos. 149/50 of Jamaica.*
265	3 c. green and red-brown		20	60
266	12 c. black and reddish violet		30	60

POSTAGE DUE STAMPS

D 1

1/-   1/-

Row 4   Row 5

The degree of inclination of the stroke on the 1s. value varies for each vertical row of the sheet: Rows 1, 2 and 6 104°, Row 3 108°, Row 4 107° and Row 5 (No. D25a) 100°.

1923–45. *Wmk Mult Script CA. P* 14.
D18	D 1	1d. black		70	1·50
D19		2d. black		1·00	1·50
D20		3d. black (1925)		70	2·25
D21		4d. black (1929)		2·75	17·00
D22		5d. black (1944)		35·00	80·00
D23		6d. black (1945)		42·00	27·00
D24		8d. black (1945)		42·00	£130
D25		1s. black (1945)		60·00	95·00
		a. Upright stroke		£120	£180
D18/25			*Set of 8*	£160	£325
D18/25 Optd/Perf "Specimen"		*Set of 8*	£140	

1947 (1 Sept)–**61.** *Values in cents. Wmk Mult Script CA. Ordinary paper. P* 14.
D26	D 1	2 c. black		1·50	2·25
		a. Chalk-surfaced paper (20.1.53)		20	3·75
		ab. Error. Crown missing. W 9a		70·00	
		ac. Error. St. Edward's Crown. W 9b		25·00	
D27		4 c. black		85	3·00
		a. Chalk-surfaced paper (10.8.55)		2·25	4·50
D28		6 c. black		1·10	6·00
		a. Chalk-surfaced paper (20.1.53)		30	7·50
		ab. Error. Crown missing. W 9a		£180	
		ac. Error. St. Edward's Crown. W 9b		55·00	
D29		8 c. black		1·10	18·00
		a. Chalk-surfaced paper (10.9.58)		35	16·00
D30		10 c. black		1·10	2·75
		a. Chalk-surfaced paper (10.8.55)		3·25	10·00
D31		12 c. black		1·10	15·00
		a. Chalk-surfaced paper (20.1.53)		40	17·00
		ab. Error. Crown missing. W 9a		£225	
		ac. Error. St. Edward's Crown. W 9b		90·00	
D32		16 c. black		2·00	35·00
		a. Chalk-surfaced paper (22.8.61)		8·50	20·00
D33		24 c. black		7·00	7·50
		a. Chalk-surfaced paper (10.8.55)		3·00	30·00
D26/33			*Set of 8*	14·00	80·00
D26/33a			*Set of 8*	16·00	£110
D26/33 Perf "Specimen"		*Set of 8*	£140	

Tristan da Cunha

12 pence (d) = 1 shilling; 20 shillings = 1 pound

DEPENDENCY OF ST. HELENA

During World War II there was little mail from the island as its function as a meteorological station was cloaked by security. Such covers as are known are generally struck with the "tombstone" naval censor mark and postmarked "maritime mail" or have South African postal markings. A few philatelic items from early in the war bearing cachets exist, but this usage was soon stopped by the military commander and the handstamps were put away until peace returned. Covers from the period would be worth from £75 to, at least, £350.

Cachet VIII

C10　**1946** (8 May).　Cachet VIII　..　..　..*from* 85·00

Cachet IX

C11　**1948** (2 Feb).　Cachet IX　..　..　..*from* 45·00

Cachet X

C12　**1948** (29 Feb).　Cachet X　..　..　..*from* 55·00

TRISTAN DA CUNHA

(1)

1952 (1 Jan).　*Nos.* 131, 135a/40 *and* 149/51 *of St. Helena optd with T* **1.**

1	½d. violet ..	..	..	15	1·25
2	1d. black and green	..	..	70	1·25
3	1½d. black and carmine	..	..	70	1·25
4	2d. black and scarlet	..	..	70	1·50
5	3d. grey ..	..	..	1·00	1·25
6	4d. ultramarine	..	..	3·25	2·00
7	6d. light blue	..	..	4·25	2·50
8	8d. olive-green	..	..	3·50	3·50
9	1s. sepia ..	..	..	4·25	2·00
10	2s. 6d. maroon	..	..	17·00	14·00
11	5s. chocolate	..	..	21·00	23·00
12	10s. purple ..	..	..	35·00	38·00
1/12	..	..	.. *Set of* 12	80·00	80·00

Turks and Caicos Islands

12 pence (d) = 1 shilling; 20 shillings = 1 pound

DEPENDENCY OF JAMAICA

1937 (12 May). *Coronation. As Nos.* 118/20 *of Jamaica.*
191	½d. myrtle-green	.. ..	10	10
	a. *Deep green*	.. ..	40·00	
192	2d. grey-black	.. ..	50	40
193	3d. bright blue	.. ..	60	40
191/3 ..	.. .. ..	*Set of* 3	1·00	75
191/3 Perf "Specimen"	.. ..	*Set of* 3	55·00	

46 Raking Salt   **47** Salt Industry

(Recess Waterlow)

1938 (18 June)—**45**. *Wmk Mult Script CA. P* 12½.
194	**46**	¼d. black	.. ..	10	10
195		½d. yellowish green	.. ..	4·00	15
		a. *Deep green* (6.11.44)	..	80	70
196		1d. red-brown ..	..	60	10
197		1½d. scarlet	.. ..	60	15
198		2d. grey ..	.. ..	60	30
199		2½d. yellow-orange	..	4·25	80
		a. *Orange* (6.11.44)	..	2·00	1·50
200		3d. bright blue ..	..	50	30
201		6d. mauve	.. ..	9·50	1·25
201a		6d. sepia (9.2.45)	..	20	20
202		1s. yellow-bistre	..	3·75	7·50
202a		1s. grey-olive (9.2.45)	..	20	20
203	**47**	2s. deep rose-carmine ..	..	42·00	11·00
		a. *Bright rose-carmine* (6.11.44)	..	17·00	16·00
204		5s. yellowish green	..	48·00	13·00
		a. *Deep green* (6.11.44)	..	35·00	20·00
205		10s. bright violet	..	12·00	5·50
194/205		.. .. ..	*Set of* 14	75·00	35·00
194/205 Perf "Specimen"		.. ..	*Set of* 14	£200	

1946 (4 Nov). *Victory. As Nos.* 141/2 *of Jamaica.*
206	2d. black	.. ..	10	10
207	3d. blue	.. .. ..	15	10
206/7 Perf "Specimen"	.. ..	*Set of* 2	55·00	

1948 (13 Sept). *Royal Silver Wedding. As Nos.* 143/4 *of Jamaica.*
208	1d. red-brown	.. .. ..	15	10
209	10s. mauve	.. .. ..	7·00	11·00

50 Badge of the Islands   **53** Queen Victoria and
King George VI

(Recess Waterlow)

1948 (14 Dec). *Centenary of Separation from Bahamas. T* **50, 53**
and similar designs. Wmk Mult Script CA. P 12½.
210	**50**	½d. blue-green ..	..	70	15
211		2d. carmine	..	1·25	15
212	—	3d. blue ..	..	1·50	15
213	—	6d. violet	..	50	30
214	**53**	2s. black and bright blue	..	75	65
215		5s. black and green	..	90	2·75
216		10s. black and brown	..	90	3·25
210/16		.. .. ..	*Set of* 7	5·75	6·75

Designs: *Horiz*—3d. Flag of Turks and Caicos Islands; 6d. Map of islands.

1949 (10 Oct). *75th Anniv of U.P.U. As Nos.* 145/8 *of Jamaica.*
217	2½d. red-orange	.. ..	30	55
218	3d. deep blue	.. ..	1·75	50
219	6d. brown	.. ..	40	50
220	1s. olive	.. ..	40	35
217/20	.. .. ..	*Set of* 4	2·50	1·75

65 Bulk Salt Loading

66 Dependency's Badge

(Recess Waterlow)

1950 (1 Aug). *T* **65** *and similar horiz designs, and T* **66**. *Wmk Mult Script CA. P* 12½.
221	½d. green ..	.. ..	60	40
222	1d. red-brown	.. ..	50	75
223	1½d. deep carmine	..	90	55
224	2d. red-orange	.. ..	30	40
225	2½d. grey-olive	.. ..	70	50
226	3d. bright blue	.. ..	30	40
227	4d. black and rose ..	..	2·50	70
228	6d. black and blue ..	..	2·00	50
229	1s. black and blue-green	..	80	40
230	1s. 6d. black and scarlet	..	6·50	3·25
231	2s. emerald and ultramarine	..	2·50	3·50
232	5s. blue and black ..	..	16·00	7·50
233	10s. black and violet	..	16·00	17·00
221/33		*Set of* 13	45·00	32·00

Designs:—1d. Salt Cay; 1½d. Caicos mail; 2d. Grand Turk; 2½d. Sponge diving; 3d. South Creek; 4d. Map; 6d. Grand Turk Light; 1s. Government House; 1s. 6d. Cockburn Harbour; 2s. Government Offices; 5s. Loading salt.

Virgin Islands

1937. 12 pence (d) = 1 shilling; 20 shillings = 1 pound
1951. 100 cents = 1 West Indian dollar

CROWN COLONY

1937 (12 May). *Coronation. As Nos. 95/7 of Antigua.*
P 11×11½.

107	1d. carmine	..	..	..	20	1·00
108	1½d. yellow-brown	..	..	..	40	2·50
109	2½d. blue	..	..	..	45	1·00
107/9	..	..	*Set of* 3	95	4·00
107/9 Perf "Specimen"	..	..	*Set of* 3 55·00		

15 King George VI and
Badge of Colony

16 Map

(Photo Harrison)

1938 (1 Aug)–**47**. *Wmk Mult Script CA. Chalk-surfaced paper.*
P 14.

110	**15**	½d. green	..	..	..	2·25	1·75
		a. Ordinary paper (10.43)	..		30	90
111		1d. scarlet	..	..	..	2·75	1·25
		a. Ordinary paper (10.43)	..		30	60
112		1½d. red-brown ..	..	..	4·00	4·50
		a. Ordinary paper (10.43)	..		65	95
		w. Wmk inverted	..	..		† £1000
113		2d. grey	..	..	..	4·25	1·75
		a. Ordinary paper (10.43)	..		40	90
114		2½d. ultramarine	..	..	3·50	1·25
		a. Ordinary paper (10.43)	..		60	2·00
115		3d. orange	..	..	..	5·50	70
		a. Ordinary paper (10.43)	..		40	80
116		6d. mauve	..	..	..	4·00	90
		a. Ordinary paper (10.43)	..		1·50	80
117		1s. olive-brown	..	..	9·00	2·75
		a. Ordinary paper (8.42)	..		1·50	70
118		2s. 6d. sepia ..	..	..	24·00	4·50
		a. Ordinary paper (8.42)	..		14·00	3·00
119		5s. carmine	..	..	..	45·00	5·50
		a. Ordinary paper (8.42)	..		13·00	4·00
120		10s. blue (1.12 47)	..	..	7·00	8·00
121		£1 black (1.12.47)	..	..	11·00	20·00
110/21		..	..	*Set of* 12	45·00	38·00
110/21 Perf "Specimen"	..		*Set of* 12 £225		

The ordinary paper, used as a substitute for the chalk-surfaced for printings between 1942 and 1945, is thick, smooth and opaque.

1946 (1 Nov). *Victory. As Nos. 110/11 of Antigua.*

122	1½d. lake-brown	..	..	..	10	10
123	3d. orange ..	..	..	..	10	10
122/3 Perf "Specimen"	..	..	*Set of* 2 55·00		

1949 (3 Jan). *Royal Silver Wedding. As Nos. 112/13 of Antigua.*

124	2½d. ultramarine	..	..	..	10	10
125	£1 black	..	..	..	12·00	15·00

1949 (10 Oct). *75th Anniv of U.P.U. As Nos. 114/17 of Antigua.*

126	2½d. ultramarine	..	..	..	30	45
127	3d. orange	..	..	..	80	2·00
128	6d. magenta ..	..	..	..	50	40
129	1s. olive	..	..	..	50	40
126/9	..	..	..	*Set of* 4	1·90	3·00

(New Currency. 100 cents = 1 B.W.I. dollar)

1951. *Inauguration of B.W.I. University College. As Nos. 118/19 of Antigua.*

130	3 c. black and brown-red (10.4) ..	..	40	80
131	12 c. black and reddish violet (16.2)	..	60	80

(Recess Waterlow)

1951 (2 Apr). *Restoration of Legislative Council. Wmk Mult Script CA. P* 14½ x 14.

132	**16**	6 c. orange	..	..	..	20	90
133		12 c. purple	..	..	..	20	50
134		24 c. olive..	..	..	..	20	50
135		$1.20 carmine ..	..	..	45	90
132/5	..	..	..	..	*Set of* 4	95	2·50

17 Sombrero
Lighthouse

18 Map of Jost Van Dyke

(Recess D.L.R.)

1952 (15 Apr). *T* **17/18** *and similar designs. Wmk Mult Script CA. P* 12½ x 13 *(vert) or* 13 × 12½ *(horiz).*

136	1 c. black	..	..	..	60	90
137	2 c. deep green	..	..	..	35	30
138	3 c. black and brown	..	..	50	80
139	4 c. carmine-red	..	..	..	35	90
140	5 c. claret and black	..	..	1·25	50
141	8 c. bright blue	..	..	..	35	1·00
142	12 c. dull violet	..	..	..	45	1·40
143	24 c. deep brown	..	..	..	35	30
144	60 c. yellow-green and blue ..	..	..	2·50	11·00
145	$1.20, black and bright blue	..	..	3·75	12·00
146	$2.40, yellowish green and red-brown	..	10·00	14·00
147	$4.80, bright blue and carmine	..	..	11·00	14·00
136/47	..	..	..	*Set of* 12	27·00	50·00

Designs: *Horiz*—3 c. Sheep industry; 4 c. Map of Anegada; 5 c. Cattle industry; 8 c. Map of Virgin Gorda; 12 c. Map of Tortola; 60 c. Dead Man's Chest; $1.20, Sir Francis Drake Channel; $2.40, Road Town; $4.80, Map of Virgin Islands. *Vert*—24 c. Badge of the Presidency.

Zanzibar

100 cents = 1 East Africa shilling

PROTECTORATE

37 *Sham Alam*
(Sultan's dhow)

8TH JUNE 1946
(38)

1944 (20 Nov). *Bicentenary of Al Busaid Dynasty. Recess. Wmk Mult Script CA. P 14.*

327	**37**	10 c. ultramarine		60	1·75
328		20 c. red		60	2·25
329		50 c. blue-green		60	30
330		1 s. dull purple		60	50
327/30			*Set of* 4	2·25	4·25
327/30 Perf "Specimen"			*Set of* 4	70·00	

1946 (11 Nov). *Victory. Nos. 311 and 315 optd with T 38.*

331	**33**	10 c. black (R.)	20	20
332		30 c. ultramarine (R.)	20	40
331/2 Perf "Specimen"		*Set of* 2	45·00	

1949 (10 Jan). *Royal Silver Wedding. As Nos. 143/4 of Jamaica.*

333	20 c. orange	30	1·25
334	10 s. brown	17·00	28·00

1949 (10 Oct). *75th Anniv of U.P.U. As Nos. 145/8 of Jamaica.*

335	20 c. red-orange		40	2·00
336	30 c. deep blue		1·40	80
337	50 c. magenta		1·50	2·00
338	1 s. blue-green		1·50	3·00
335/8		*Set of* 4	4·25	7·00

POSTAGE DUE STAMPS

D 3

(Typo D.L.R.)

1936 (1 Jan)–**62**. *Wmk Mult Script CA. P 14.*

D25	**D 3**	5 c. violet		2·50	6·50
		a. Chalk-surfaced paper (18.7.56)		30	13·00
D26		10 c. scarlet		2·50	2·75
		a. Chalk-surfaced paper (6.3.62)		30	5·50
D27		20 c. green		1·75	4·25
		a. Chalk-surfaced paper (6.3.62)		30	13·00
D28		30 c. brown		6·00	15·00
		a. Chalk-surfaced paper (18.7.56)		30	10·00
D29		40 c. ultramarine		6·00	22·00
		a. Chalk-surfaced paper (18.7.56)		40	22·00
D30		1 s. grey		6·00	26·00
		a. Chalk-surfaced paper (18.7.56)		1·00	17·00
D25/30			*Set of* 6	22·00	70·00
D25a/30a			*Set of* 6	2·40	70·00
D25/30 Perf "Specimen"			*Set of* 6	60·00	

Set Prices for British Commonwealth Omnibus Issues

1937 CORONATION

Country	Cat. Nos.	Stamps
Great Britain	461	1
Aden	13/15	3
Antigua	95/7	3
Ascension	35/7	3
Australia		
Nauru	44/7	4
New Guinea	208/11	4
Papua	154/7	4
Bahamas	146/8	3
Barbados	245/7	3
Basutoland	15/17	3
Bechuanaland	115/17	3
Bermuda	107/9	3
British Guiana	305/7	3
British Honduras	147/9	3
British Solomon Is.	57/9	3
Canada	356	1
Cayman Islands	112/14	3
Ceylon	383/5	3
Cyprus	148/50	3
Dominica	96/8	3
Falkland Islands	143/5	3
Fiji	246/8	3
Gambia	147/9	3
Gibraltar	118/20	3
Gilbert and Ellice Is.	40/2	3
Gold Coast	117/19	3
Grenada	149/51	3
Hong Kong	137/9	3
Jamaica	118/20	3
Kenya, Uganda and Tanganyika	128/30	3
Leeward Islands	92/4	3
Malaya—Straits Settlements	275/7	3
Malta	214/16	3
Mauritius	249/51	3
Montserrat	98/100	3
Morocco Agencies		
Spanish Currency	164	1
French Currency	229	1
Tangier	244	1
Newfoundland	254/6, 257/67	14
New Zealand	599/601	3
Cook Islands	124/6	3
Niue	72/4	3
Nigeria	46/8	3
Northern Rhodesia	22/4	3
Nyasaland	127/9	3
St. Helena	128/30	3
St. Kitts-Nevis	65/7	3
St. Lucia	125/7	3
St. Vincent	146/8	3
Seychelles	132/4	3
Sierra Leone	185/7	3
Somaliland	90/2	3
South Africa	71/5	5 × 2
Southern Rhodesia	36/9	4
South West Africa	97/104	8 × 2
Swaziland	25/7	3
Trinidad and Tobago	243/5	3
Turks & Caicos Is.	191/3	3
Virgin Islands	107/9	3
Total		**202**

Price Un Used

Complete set of 202 stamps £120 £120

1945–46 VICTORY

Country	Cat. Nos.	Stamps
Great Britain	491/2	2
Aden	28/9	2
Seiyun	12/13	2
Shihr and Mukalla	12/13	2
Antigua	110/11	2
Ascension	48/9	2
Australia	213/15	3
Bahamas	176/7	2
Barbados	262/3	2
Basutoland	29/31	3 × 2
Bechuanaland	129/31	3 × 2
Bermuda	123/4	2
British Guiana	320/1	2
British Honduras	162/3	2
British Solomon Is.	73/4	2
Burma	64/7	4
Cayman Islands	127/8	2
Ceylon	400/1	2
Cyprus	164/5	2
Dominica	110/11	2
Falkland Islands	164/5	2
Falkland Islands Dependencies	G17/18	2
Fiji	268/9	2
Gambia	162/3	2
Gibraltar	132/3	2
Gilbert and Ellice Is.	55/6	2
Gold Coast	133/4	2
Grenada	164/5	2
Hong Kong	169/70	2
India	278/81	4
Hyderabad	53	1
Jamaica	141/2	2
Kenya, Uganda and Tanganyika	155/6	2
Leeward Islands	115/16	2
Malta	232/3	2
Mauritius	264/5	2
Montserrat	113/14	2
Morocco Agencies		
Tangier	253/4	2
New Zealand	667/77	11
Cook Islands	146/9	4
Niue	98/101	4
Western Samoa	215/18	4
Nigeria	60/1	2
Northern Rhodesia	46/7	2
Nyasaland	158/9	2
Pakistan		
Bahawalpur	O19	1
Pitcairn Islands	9/10	2
St. Helena	141/2	2
St. Kitts-Nevis	78/9	2
St. Lucia	142/3	2
St. Vincent	160/1	2
Seychelles	150/1	2
Sierra Leone	201/2	2
Somaliland	117/18	2
South Africa	108/10	3 × 2
Southern Rhodesia	64/7	4
South West Africa	131/3	3 × 2
Swaziland	39/41	3 × 2
Trinidad and Tobago	257/8	2
Turks & Caicos Is.	206/7	2
Virgin Islands	122/3	2
Zanzibar	331/2	2
Total		**164**

Complete set of 164 stamps 30·00 30·00

1948 ROYAL SILVER WEDDING

Country	Cat. Nos.	Stamps
Great Britain	493/4	2
Aden	30/1	2
Seiyun	14/15	2
Shihr and Mukalla	14/15	2
Antigua	112/13	2
Ascension	50/1	2
Bahamas	194/5	2
Bahrain	61/2	2
Barbados	265/6	2
Basutoland	36/7	2
Bechuanaland	136/7	2
Bermuda	125/6	2
British Guiana	322/3	2
British Honduras	164/5	2
British Postal Agencies in Eastern Arabia	25/6	2
British Solomon Is.	75/6	2
Cayman Islands	129/30	2
Cyprus	166/7	2
Dominica	112/13	2
Falkland Islands	166/7	2
Falkland Islands Dependencies	G19/20	2
Fiji	270/1	2
Gambia	164/5	2
Gibraltar	134/5	2
Gilbert and Ellice Is.	57/8	2
Gold Coast	147/8	2
Grenada	166/7	2
Hong Kong	171/2	2
Jamaica	143/4	2
Kenya, Uganda and Tanganyika	157/8	2
Kuwait	74/5	2
Leeward Islands	117/18	2
Malaya		
Johore	131/2	2
Kedah	70/1	2
Kelantan	55/6	2
Malacca	1/2	2
Negri Sembilan	40/1	2
Pahang	47/8	2
Penang	1/2	2
Perak	122/3	2
Perlis	1/2	2
Selangor	88/9	2
Trengganu	61/2	2
Malta	249/50	2
Mauritius	270/1	2
Montserrat	115/16	2
Morocco Agencies		
Spanish Currency	176/7	2
Tangier	255/6	2
Nigeria	62/3	2
North Borneo	350/1	2
Northern Rhodesia	48/9	2
Nyasaland	161/2	2
Pitcairn Islands	11/12	2
St. Helena	143/4	2
St. Kitts-Nevis	80/1	2
St. Lucia	144/5	2
St. Vincent	162/3	2
Sarawak	165/6	2
Seychelles	152/3	2
Sierra Leone	203/4	2
Singapore	31/2	2
Somaliland	119/20	2
South Africa	125	1 × 2
South West Africa	137	1 × 2
Swaziland	46/7	2
Trinidad and Tobago	259/60	2
Turks & Caicos Is.	208/9	2
Virgin Islands	124/5	2

Zanzibar	333/4	2

Total		138

Complete set—138 stamps £1600 £1600

1949 75TH ANNIVERSARY OF U.P.U.

Country	Cat. Nos.	Stamps
Great Britain	499/502	4
Aden	32/5	4
Seiyun	16/19	4
Shihr and Mukalla	16/19	4
Antigua	114/17	4
Ascension	52/5	4
Australia	232	1
Bahamas	196/9	4
Bahrain	67/70	4
Barbados	267/70	4
Basutoland	38/41	4
Bechuanaland	138/41	4
Bermuda	130/3	4
British Guiana	324/7	4
British Honduras	172/5	4
British Postal Agencies in Eastern Arabia	31/4	4
British Solomon Is.	77/80	4
Brunei	96/9	4
Cayman Islands	131/4	4
Ceylon	410/12	3
Cyprus	168/71	4
Dominica	114/17	4
Falkland Islands	168/71	4
Falkland Islands Dependencies	G21/4	4
Fiji	272/5	4
Gambia	166/9	4
Gibraltar	136/9	4
Gilbert and Ellice Is.	59/62	4

Gold Coast	149/52	4
Grenada	168/71	4
Hong Kong	173/6	4
India	325/8	4
Jamaica	145/8	4
Kenya, Uganda and Tanganyika	159/62	4
Kuwait	80/3	4
Leeward Islands	119/22	4
Malaya		
Johore	148/51	4
Kedah	72/5	4
Kelantan	57/60	4
Malacca	18/21	4
Negri Sembilan	63/6	4
Pahang	49/52	4
Penang	23/6	4
Perak	124/7	4
Perlis	3/6	4
Selangor	111/14	4
Trengganu	63/6	4
Malta	251/4	4
Mauritius	272/5	4
Montserrat	117/20	4
Morocco Agencies Tangier	276/9	4
New Hebrides	64/7,	
	F77/80	4 + 4
Nigeria	64/7	4
North Borneo	352/5	4
Northern Rhodesia	50/3	4
Nyasaland	163/6	4
Pakistan		
Bahawalpur	43/6,	
	O28/31	4 + 4
Pitcairn Islands	13/16	4
St. Helena	145/8	4
St. Kitts-Nevis	82/5	4
St. Lucia	160/3	4
St. Vincent	178/81	4
Sarawak	167/70	4
Seychelles	154/7	4
Sierra Leone	205/8	4

Singapore	33/6	4
Somaliland	121/4	4
South Africa	128/30	3 × 2
Southern Rhodesia	68/9	2
South West Africa	138/40	3 × 2
Swaziland	48/51	4
Tonga	88/91	4
Trinidad and Tobago	261/4	4
Turks & Caicos Is.	217/20	4
Virgin Islands	126/9	4
Zanzibar	335/8	4

Total		310

Complete set of 310 stamps £325 £325

1951 INAUGURATION OF B.W.I. UNIVERSITY COLLEGE

Country	Cat. Nos.	Stamps
Antigua	118/19	2
Barbados	283/4	2
British Guiana	328/9	2
British Honduras	176/7	2
Dominica	118/19	2
Grenada	185/6	2
Jamaica	149/50	2
Leeward Islands	123/4	2
Montserrat	121/2	2
St. Kitts-Nevis	92/3	2
St. Lucia	164/5	2
St. Vincent	182/3	2
Trinidad and Tobago	265/6	2
Virgin Islands	130/1	2

Total		28

Complete set of 28 stamps 9·50 13·00

Index

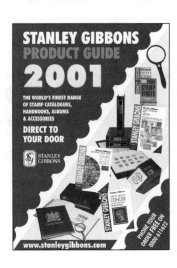

 **STANLEY GIBBONS**
Auctions

100th **ANNIVERSARY**
1901~2001

—— **ESTABLISHED 1901** ——

Searching for the

No.1

Online
Stamp Auctioneers

www.
stanleygibbons
.com

For further information, contact Colin Avery

Stanley Gibbons Auctions Department
399 Strand, London WC2R 0LX
Telephone: +44 (0)20 7836 8444
Facsimile: +44 (0)20 7836 7342
Email: auctions@stanleygibbons.co.uk

Sponsors of the British Youth Stamp Championship

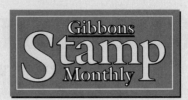

FREE MAIL ORDER LISTINGS

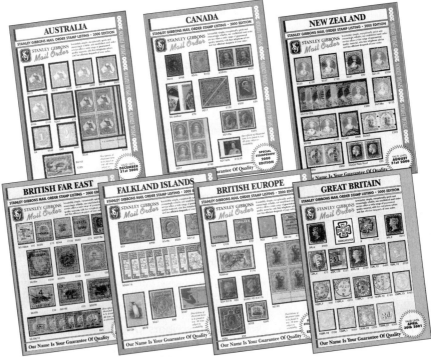

Wants Lists Always Welcome

For your free copies, please telephone
Jonathan Spooner at our London office on 020 7836 8444

STANLEY GIBBONS
Mail Order

Stanley Gibbons Limited
399 Strand, London WC2R 0LX
Tel: +44 (0)207 836 8444 Fax: +44 (0)207 836 7342
e-mail: mailorder@stanleygibbons.co.uk
Internet:www.stanleygibbons.com